WIRING

A

CONTINENT

WIRING
A CONTINENT

The History of
The Telegraph Industry
in the United States

1832 - 1866

Robert Luther Thompson

Princeton, New Jersey
Princeton University Press

1947

TO

M J T

THE study of the emergence of the telegraph industry in the United States is of interest not only for the insight it gives into the development of a particular industry but also for the understanding it provides of the general pattern of industrial development during the 19th century.

The initial stage in the evolution of that pattern may well be termed the era of methodless enthusiasm. In the telegraph field, private industry came to a somewhat retarded realization of the significance of the Morse invention between 1846 and 1850, and the country was hastily webbed with a crude network of wires. Promoters and stockholders had grandiose dreams of the fortunes which would soon be theirs; but ruthless competition, bad management, and poorly constructed lines took their toll. Enthusiasm gave way to disillusionment as company after company failed to make expenses, let alone pay dividends to their luckless stockholders.

Gradually the era of methodless enthusiasm gave way to an era of consolidation. By degrees cooperation supplanted ruinous competition. Some of the companies led by men of vision and determination began to acquire the stock of their bankrupt rivals. Lines were strengthened, service was improved and expanded, and operating costs were reduced. A semblance of order began to manifest itself within the industry. By 1857 the telegraph industry was largely controlled by six powerful companies, each virtually sovereign in its particular geographical area. These companies then gave expression to their determination to monopolize the field by leaguing together to form the Six Nations' Alliance. By the terms of an offensive and defensive treaty, each of the companies, or nations as they termed themselves, was to respect the territorial sovereignty of the others; each was to abide by the rules and regulations jointly formulated for the operation of the industry; and each was to discourage new companies from entering the field.

For a time there were those who looked upon the Six Nations' Alliance as a solution to the industry's ills. At best it proved but a temporary palliative. While paying lip service to the Alliance, each company was suspicious of its associates, and each sought every opportunity to strengthen its position at the expense of its fellows. The Civil War with its attendant political and economic changes afforded one of them—Western Union—just the advantage it needed to triumph over its closest rival, the American Telegraph Company. With the absorption of the United States and the American Telegraph Companies in 1866 the Western Union Telegraph Company emerged as the nation's first great industrial monopoly.

Because of the relative ease and low cost of constructing lines, the telegraph industry was the first in which a single company succeeded in establishing a monopolistic position, but the pattern was to become a familiar one. Steel, petroleum, rubber, utilities, railroads, manufacturing, and other industries were to go through a similar evolution in the years which lay ahead. The story of the rise of Western Union is the story of the irresistible trend towards monopoly inherent in the economic life of the 19th century.

The research upon which this volume is based was begun nearly ten years ago when the author, at the suggestion of Allan Nevins of Columbia University, examined the voluminous O'Rielly collection at the New York Historical Society Library. Further exploration led to the discovery of an extensive body of excellent source material, both printed and manuscript, dealing with the early history of the telegraph industry: the F. O. J. Smith collection at the Maine Historical Society Library in Portland; the Cornell papers in the custody of the Cornell University Library; the Alfred Vail papers in the Smithsonian Institution; the Samuel F. B. Morse and the John D. Caton collections in the Library of Congress, to name but the most outstanding.

With such a wealth of valuable material the author has been content to let the facts speak for themselves. Generalizations and interpretations have been made only where they were deemed essential to a complete understanding of the story.

The author is keenly aware of how much such a work as this is a cooperative undertaking. While he was privileged to weave together the various threads which make up the narrative, his efforts would have been futile had it not been for the splendid cooperation of the many whose contributions made this volume possible. It is doubtful if it would have been carried to completion had it not been for the advice and encouragement of Allan Nevins. He read the manuscript and gave constructive criticism at times when it was needed most. Robert Warren of the Institute for Advanced Study at Princeton,

New Jersey, also gave wise counsel and encouragement. The author is deeply indebted to his wife, Marjorie Jones Thompson, for her invaluable aid as research assistant, typist, and constant critic through the years of preparation of the manuscript.

An expression of gratitude is also due many others who contributed to this work in one capacity or another. For valuable editorial assistance mention must be made of Otho C. Jones, Harold J. Bingham, and Fred C. Cole. The latter in particular read much of the manuscript and made numerous constructive suggestions. Datus C. Smith, Director of the Princeton University Press, and his staff have been helpful and cooperative at every stage of the work.

For help in the gathering of materials the author is indebted to Carleton Mabee for his suggestions on several points connected with the life of Samuel F. B. Morse; to S. R. Kamm for the use of his manuscript, "Thomas A. Scott and the Pennsylvania Railroad"; to Walter Davis and Richard K. Gould for their assistance in making the materials of the Maine Historical Society Library more accessible; to George P. Oslin of the Western Union Telegraph Company, especially for his assistance in providing illustrations for the volume; to the families of Leonard Bacon, Alvah G. Strong, and Harold L. Field of Rochester for making accessible the collections of materials in their possession; and to Bruce McKelvey and Dexter Perkins for their assistance while searching for materials in Rochester. The title for the volume was suggested by the title of an article by James Gamble which appeared in *The Californian Magazine*, Volume III (1881).

No acknowledgment of an author's debt to those who assisted him would be complete without giving wholehearted thanks to those silent partners, the patient and ever helpful librarians. Among the libraries used most extensively were those of Columbia University, the New York Public Library, the New York Historical Society, the Maine Historical Society, Cornell University, the Rochester Historical Society, the Rochester Public Library, the John Crerar Library, Harvard School of Business, Boston Public Library, the Cleveland Public Library, the Library of Congress, the Smithsonian Institution, and the Western Union Library. To the staffs of these libraries, and to the many others whom he is unable to mention individually, the author wishes to acknowledge his gratitude.

ROBERT L. THOMPSON

Washington, D.C.
December 2, 1946

CONTENTS

APPENDICES

$$\{\in \boxed{\text{ILLUSTRATIONS}} \ni\{$$

PLATES

TEXT FIGURES

MAPS

BOOK ONE

BEGINNINGS

1832-1845

CHAPTER I

From Palette to Portrule

1 · — — ·

WHEN the middle-aged and financially unsuccessful American artist, Samuel F. B. Morse, boarded the packet ship *Sully* at Havre, France, for the long return voyage to New York in the autumn of 1832, the United States was still an agricultural commonwealth. The miraculous changes by which the youthful nation was to be transformed into the greatest industrial society the world has ever known were just beginning. The application of steam to the production of useful energy was still in its infancy; most of the little factories which were to be found in the United States continued to depend upon water-power; the steamship, emerging from its experimental stages, was on the way to becoming an important means of transportation; and upon a few of the newly-constructed railways the cars were drawn by clumsy little steam locomotives that were awful to hear and behold, and far from safe or reliable.

In these faint beginnings lay the dawn of a new era in which man, during the brief span of half a century, was to accomplish more towards harnessing the forces of nature than in any similar period since the birth of civilization. Building upon the work of dozens of earnest scientists and seekers-after-the-truth, who over the centuries had slowly and painfully added to man's pitifully inadequate scientific knowledge, a series of practical-minded men now began to apply the newly-discovered forms of energy to old uses, and the old scientific principles to new uses.

One strange new force in particular was to prove revolutionary in transforming our mid-nineteenth century civilization. While this mysterious form of energy men called electricity was not understood, early attempts were made to utilize its amazing qualities. Discovering that electricity would travel along a wire almost instantaneously from one point to another, no matter how widely separated, several men near the close of the eighteenth century attempted to use it for the transmission of information. In these early experiments the frictional electricity employed was fitful and difficult to insulate on account of its high tension, and the results were unsatisfactory.

At the turn of the century the work of the Italian physicists, Galvani and Volta, had led to the introduction of the "voltaic pile" or electric battery, which furnished a continuous and tractable form of electricity. This important discovery brought the telegraph within the realm of practicability. More experiments in the transmission of information were conducted using the new dynamic type of electricity. During the first decade of the new century, Salva of Barcelona and von Soemmering of Munich pioneered in the development of the electrolytic telegraph. This method of telegraphy employed an electric battery to send signals indicated at the receiving end of the circuit by the liberation of bubbles of hydrogen from the liquid into which the electrical impulse was discharged.

Still other advances of the utmost importance were made possible by discoveries in the field of electromagnetism. Two types of electromagnetic telegraph had made their appearance by the 1830's—the needle system and the armature system. The needle system employed the deflections of small magnetic needles, placed at the receiving ends of wires through which an electric current was passed, to indicate the letters of the alphabet. The armature system made use of the passage of an electric current through an electromagnet (a horseshoe-shaped, soft iron bar around which a coil of wire had been wrapped) to attract an iron bar or armature. By means of the movements of this armature, signals could be recorded in graphic form, or by sound, to indicate the different letters of the alphabet.

During the 1820's and 1830's a number of European scientists focused their attention upon the development of the needle telegraph. Ampere in France; Schilling in Russia; Steinheil in Germany; and Davy, and the partners, Cooke and Wheatstone in England, each produced an instrument of considerable interest.

In the United States, meanwhile, some important steps in the development of a magnetic armature telegraph were being taken by the brilliant American scientist, Joseph Henry, who was teaching at the Academy in Albany, New York. Henry constructed and successfully operated a crude electromagnetic signaling apparatus, using a greatly improved electromagnet of his own devising. To make the telegraph practical for commercial use, he realized that some means had to be found for sending the current through miles of wire without its becoming too weak to operate a receiving instrument at the distant end. He solved the problem by substituting a battery of many small cells for the customary battery of one large cell thereby creating a higher voltage and reducing the transmission loss over the wire. Using this "intensity battery," the inventor was able to send his signals over a mile of fine wire with sufficient force to make an armature at the other end strike a bell. His discoveries, made in 1831 —the year before the idea for an electromagnetic telegraph took definite shape in the mind of Morse—provided an invaluable ground-work which made possible the success of Morse's telegraph a few years later.[1]

While Henry's discoveries were fundamental, it was Samuel F. B. Morse, who gave the nation its first practical electromagnetic tele-graph. The early history of the telegraph in the United States is so closely bound up with the life of Morse that the story of the one can scarcely be told without touching upon that of the other.

2 ··—··

SAMUEL FINLEY BREESE MORSE was born in the modest parsonage of the First Congregational Church of Charlestown, Massachusetts, on April 27, 1791. He was the eldest son of the Reverend Jedidiah Morse, a serious young clergyman of keen mind and indomitable spirit. The Reverend Mr. Morse had come to the pulpit two years previously, eager to preach the gospel according to the tenets of Jonathan Edwards, and to champion the cause of orthodoxy in the face of the growing liberalism of the eighteenth century. Despite his active efforts in the service of the church, Jedidiah Morse is remem-bered today, not for his defense of orthodox doctrine, but as the "Father of American Geography." In like fashion his son, Samuel F. B. Morse, although laboring half his life in the cause of American art, takes his place among the immortals, not as a portrait painter, but as the "Father of the Telegraph."

While he was a student at Yale College during the years 1807-1810, Finley, as Samuel F. B. Morse was known by his family and intimates,

1 A detailed picture of the beginnings of electrical and other early methods of com-munication may be found in the following sources, upon which this account is based: Alvin F. Harlow, *Old Wires and New Waves*, 1-75. Carleton Mabee, *The American Leonardo, a Life of Samuel F. B. Morse*, 192-204. James D. Reid, *The Telegraph in America*, 1879 edition, 1-86. Alexander Jones, *Historical Sketch of the Electric Mag-netic Telegraph including its Rise and Progress in the United States*. J. J. Fahie, *His-tory of Electric Telegraphy to 1837*. Alfred Vail, *The American Electro-Magnetic Tele-graph; with Reports of Congress and a Description of all Telegraphs Known, Employ-ing Electricity or Galvanism*. William B. Taylor, *An Historical Sketch of Henry's Contribution to the Electro-Magnetic Telegraph, with an Account of the Origins and Development of Professor Morse's Invention*. "Telegraph" in *Encyclopaedia Britannica*, XXI, 880-891.

came to be increasingly interested in art. In fact, he partially defrayed his expenses by sketching portraits of his classmates. Notwithstanding his predilection for art, Finley also enjoyed the science laboratory. Dr. Benjamin Silliman's lectures on chemistry and galvanic electricity, as well as the absorbing experiments of Dr. Jeremiah T. Day, were especially commented upon in his correspondence with his family. "Mr. Day's lectures are very interesting; they are upon electricity; he has given us some very interesting experiments, the whole class taking hold of hands form the circuit of communication and we receive the shock apparently at the same moment."[2] Here were sown seeds which were to lie dormant for many years before coming to fruition as Morse's electromagnetic recording telegraph.

In the early nineteenth century the study of electricity was merely an absorbing academic pursuit which afforded no means of livelihood. It was therefore natural that Morse, who had decided gifts as an artist, should turn to that field as his vocation. Four years of liberal arts work at Yale were succeeded by four years of art study abroad under Washington Allston and Benjamin West, two of the foremost American artists of the day.

The eager young artist, returning from Europe in 1814 for his American debut, little realized what years of struggle and privation lay ahead. Filled with hope and ambition, Samuel F. B. Morse, painter of historical and allegorical subjects, opened a studio in Boston. Despite the favorable comments of critics and connoisseurs, day followed day with no request for his services and at the end of the year the dejected young artist closed his studio and took to the road as an itinerant portrait painter.

To relieve the tedium as well as the poverty of the intervals when he had no work, Morse, in conjunction with his brother Sidney, invented a patent pump. He believed it was superior to any existing force pump; moreover, it was readily adaptable for use by fire-engines. As he wandered through the New England villages, where his family name gave him access to the finest homes, he took commissions not only for portraits but for pumps as well—a fact which suggests the curious intermingling of the scientific and artistic in his capacities.

Persuaded that the South would prove more receptive to his talent than had New England, Morse sailed for Charleston, South Carolina,

[2] Morse to his parents, February 27, 1809, quoted by Samuel I. Prime, *The Life of Samuel F. B. Morse*, 22.

early in 1818. He painted a sufficient number of portraits in Charleston to enable him to marry Lucretia P. Walker of Concord, New Hampshire, in the fall of that year. The story of their brief married life is one of enforced separation and financial struggle.

Life on the road hardly lent itself to the rearing of a family, and after the birth of their first child, Mrs. Morse went to New Haven to make her home with the Reverend Jedidiah Morse. Young Morse, who was innately domestic, anticipated the day when he might once more open a studio and share in the family life which he so keenly missed. His reputation grew steadily, and the realization of his ambition appeared to be not far distant when in 1825 he was commissioned by the City of New York to paint a portrait of that popular and romantic figure, the Marquis de Lafayette, who was then visiting in Washington. While in the midst of this agreeable commission word reached him of the sudden death of his young wife; word which, due to the meager means of communication of the day, did not reach him until twenty-four hours after the funeral.

After the shock and first poignant grief had abated, Morse returned to lodgings in New York where he hoped to find solace in his work. Painting and an active part in the establishment of the National Academy of the Arts of Design filled his days. In the winter of 1827 his evenings were frequently spent at the Columbia Chapel where he listened, fascinated, to a series of lectures on electricity given by James Freeman Dana. Attracted by the interest and intelligence of Morse, Dana shortly began to frequent Morse's studio where the two men talked at length on that inexplicable phenomenon, electricity. Quite unconsciously Morse, the artist, had taken another important step toward becoming Morse, the inventor of the telegraph. At this time, however, the subject of electricity was only an absorbing hobby for him, and in the spring of 1829 he returned to Europe to perfect his painting technique.

Three more years were devoted to study in Europe; then, in the autumn of 1832, Morse prepared to return to the United States where he expected to take up his art work once more. The long homeward voyage on the packet *Sully* marked a definite turning point in his career.[3]

---

[3] This biographical sketch of Morse is based on Prime, *Life*; *Samuel F. B. Morse, His Letters and Journals*, Vols. I and II, ed. Edward L. Morse; Samuel F. B. Morse Papers, 60 vols., Library of Congress.

3 ··· — ·

AMONG the passengers on that historic voyage was Dr. Charles T. Jackson of Boston, a man of considerable learning and wide interests, with whom the artist enjoyed discussing recent developments in the field of science. One evening at the dinner table the conversation chanced upon the subject of electromagnetism. One of the company asked if the flow of electricity was retarded by the length of the wire. Dr. Jackson replied that electricity could pass instantly over any known length of wire, and that its presence could be detected at any part of the line by breaking the circuit.

"If this be so and the presence of electricity can be made visible in any desired part of the circuit," exclaimed Morse, "I see no reason why intelligence might not be instantaneously transmitted by electricity to any distance."[4] The idea obsessed him and he set to work at once to give it definite form. In one of the sketch books that he always carried with him, he hastily made rough drafts and notations as the ideas rushed from his brain. Those sketches became the working plan from which he constructed his first telegraph instruments several years later.[5]

It seems probable that as a result of his studies while a student at Yale and his conversations with James Freeman Dana and other scientists in later life, Morse was more or less acquainted with the rudimentary principles of electricity, electromagnetism, and related sciences. But apparently at the time he began the construction of his telegraph, he knew little of the work already done toward the development of an electromagnetic telegraph by such men as Cooke and Wheatstone in England and Joseph Henry in the United States.[6]

Upon the *Sully's* arrival in New York in the autumn of 1832, Morse disembarked eager to begin work upon the telegraph; but the necessity of supporting himself and his children left little time for experiment and still less money for engaging in the construction of instruments. Furthermore, since there were no manufacturers of electrical appliances, the work had to be slowly and laboriously done by hand.

In 1835 Morse had the good fortune to secure an appointment as professor of the Literature of the Arts of Design in the new University of the City of New York,[7] and took up his lodgings in the University building on Washington Square. Utilizing these quarters, not only

[4] Autobiographical sketch, Morse Papers, xxxvi; Morse, *Letters and Journals*, ii, 5-6.
[5] Mabee, *American Leonardo*, 151.   [6] *Ibid.*, 150.
[7] Known later as New York University.

as a studio and living apartment, but also as a workshop, he succeeded before the close of 1836 in completing his first, crude telegraph apparatus, and in devising a numerical code to represent the letters of the alphabet.[8]

Morse's early apparatus was composed of several elements. The first, a device for receiving messages, consisted of one of the artist's old canvas stretchers nailed against the side of a table with a bar across the middle of the frame to which was attached an electromagnet. Suspended from the top of the frame was a lever which at its center hung near the electromagnet and at its base held a pencil, the point of which rested on a paper-covered roller. The second element, the portrule—a device for the transmission of messages—consisted of a long, horizontal rod with a deep slot on the upper surface. Sawtoothed type were arranged in this slot so as to open and close an electrical circuit according to a definite code-pattern which was recorded at the receiving end in the form of dots or lines as the pencil traveled up and down upon the moving paper-covered roller. Numbers from one to nine were indicated by dots or lines in series. The numerical code thus recorded was readily translated into letters of the alphabet, and they in turn, into words. The outstanding feature of Morse's crude telegraph system was its simplicity.[9]

Morse now took into his confidence his colleague, Professor Leonard D. Gale, who was a teacher of chemistry in the University. Together they labored for many months improving the apparatus and experimenting with it. At Gale's suggestion a battery of many cups, such as had been employed by Professor Joseph Henry in his experiments of 1831, was substituted for the battery of one cup, thereby providing a battery of intensity capable of projecting the electrical impulse to a distance. Another serious defect, pointed out Gale, was the type of electromagnet used. It consisted of a few open turns of wire around the poles of a horseshoe-shaped soft iron core. To give an electromagnet the greatest projectile power, explained Gale, the number of turns would have to be increased from tens to hundreds, as had been described by Professor Henry in his paper published in the *American Journal of Science* in 1831.[10] With the completion of the improved electromagnet and certain other minor changes messages formerly sent forty or fifty feet were now transmitted, first

[8] Autobiographical sketch, Morse Papers, xxxvi.
[9] *Memorial of Samuel Finley Breese Morse*, 15; Prime, *Life*, 298 ff.; Mabee, *American Leonardo*, 152, 183.
[10] Morse, *Letters and Journals*, II, 54-55.

through two hundred feet of wire, then through one thousand feet, and finally through ten miles of wire arranged on reels in Professor Gale's lecture room at New York University.[11]

4 · · · · ─

ON September 2, 1837, a group of professors and friends were invited by Morse to see the improved telegraph in operation. This exhibition, although made with crudely constructed instruments, suggested the practicability of the invention and resulted in the enlistment of another able partner to aid in the further perfection and promotion of his telegraph. That man was Alfred Vail, son of Judge Stephen Vail, proprietor of the prosperous iron and brass works at Speedwell, New Jersey. Young Vail had always taken an active interest in the steam engines and other machines manufactured in his father's foundry. Saturdays and holidays were frequently passed in the shop, where Alfred gained quite a reputation for his inventive skill as well as his proficiency in working with metals. In 1837 while doing graduate work at New York University he heard of Morse's work, and eager to learn more of the unique experiments then in progress, stopped by the professor's laboratory one day.

From that time Vail took a deep interest in Morse's endeavors, and in the fall of 1837, when the feasibility of the telegraph was demonstrated, he determined to associate himself with Morse in its development.[12] According to the agreement entered into on September 23 of that year, Vail agreed to construct and put into successful operation at his own expense the telegraph instruments to be used for the demonstration before a Congressional committee the following January. He further agreed to devote his time and services without charge to the development of the telegraph; in addition, it was understood that any new discoveries and improvements were to become the joint property of the proprietors. As compensation for Vail's services Morse agreed to transfer to him a quarter part of his interests and rights in the new invention in the United States and a provisional half interest in Europe, should Vail go to the expense of obtaining patents in any foreign countries.[13]

[11] Morse to Vail, November 13, 1837, Alfred Vail Papers in Smithsonian Institution.
[12] *Early History of the Electro-Magnetic Telegraph*, ed. J. Cummings Vail (A collection of excerpts from the letters and journals of his father, Alfred Vail), 11.
[13] "Articles of Agreement between S. F. B. Morse and Alfred Vail, dated September 23, 1837," Alfred Vail's Contract Book, Vail Papers. (Hereafter cited as Vail Contract Book.)

So thoroughly was Alfred Vail convinced of the ultimate triumph of the telegraph that he succeeded in imparting some of his enthusiasm to his father and his brother, George,[14] who furnished both money and materials to forward the invention. Thus Morse not only enlisted the skill of a fine workman when Vail became his partner, but he also secured the financial and material aid needed to put the telegraph into shape for public exhibition. In the hands of Alfred Vail the rude apparatus rapidly took on the mechanical finish which Morse had been unable to provide.[15]

Late in September 1837, Morse, having filed a *caveat* for his invention in the United States Patent Office, formally admitted Professor Leonard Gale and Alfred Vail to partnership. The sturdy, improved instruments which had been constructed at the Vail shop were now taken to New York. A group of men to whom they might be of interest were invited to a demonstration at New York University before the instruments were exhibited in Washington, where Morse had high hopes of having his invention accepted by Congress for government use.[16]

5 ———

THE general subject of telegraphy had been brought to the attention of Congress just at this time by a petition from interested parties urging the construction of a visual semaphoric telegraph line from New York to New Orleans.[17] Semaphoric telegraphs had long been in use at Boston, New York, and Baltimore for sending news of the arrival of ships, and it was the construction of such a line of stations that the petitioners to Congress had in view.[18] The House, before

[14] On December 25, 1837, Alfred Vail gave his brother, George, one-half of his quarter interest in the Morse patent. (Vail Contract Book.)

[15] Morse to a friend, quoted by Reid, *Telegraph in America*, 85.

[16] Autobiographical sketch, Morse Papers, XXXVI.

[17] Senate Doc. No. 107, 24 Cong., 2 sess.

[18] The semaphoric telegraph first came into use in the United States about 1800. In this year Jonathan Grout of Belchertown, Massachusetts, proposed and built stations between Boston and Martha's Vineyard to signal the arrival of ships and to send other bits of commercial news. There is some evidence to show that as early as 1807, as a result of trouble between the United States and England, suggestions were made to Jefferson concerning the expediency of establishing a system of telegraphs which would knit the extremes of the Union to the seat of government. In 1812, when the dangers of invasion were threatening our country, Christopher Colles came forward with a similar proposition, namely, the establishment of a national range of semaphoric telegraphs along the coast from Passamaquoddy to New Orleans. Although his ambitious project failed, Colles did construct and operate a line between Sandy Hook and New York City for transmitting shipping news. (Henry O'Rielly,

taking any action, called upon the Secretary of the Treasury to report "upon the propriety of establishing a system of telegraphs for the United States." Accordingly, the Secretary had sent a circular letter to such people as he thought might aid him in preparing his report, requesting the answers to certain questions, and such general information on the subject as they might care to submit.[19]

Among those receiving the Secretary's letter was Professor Morse who wrote an enthusiastic reply in which he described the operation of his telegraph. The merits of his system were such, he said, that the fullest and most precise information could be sent instantaneously between two or more points joined by a wire conductor; furthermore, the news could be sent by day or by night and in fair weather or foul. The apparatus would occupy but four feet, so that it could be placed in any house. A record of the information sent could be made in a permanent manner and retained for future reference. Moreover, the message could be made secret to all save the persons for whom intended. The construction of a telegraph line such as he had in mind would be neither expensive nor difficult. The wire conductor could be made fast to poles, or placed in iron tubes embedded in the ground. Enclosed in lead tubes, it could even be laid across the bed of a river.[20] In a supplemental letter written a few weeks later, Morse informed the Secretary that, assisted by Professor Gale and Alfred Vail, he had been able to send messages through ten miles of wire and obtain perfect markings on the register.[21]

Encouraged by the apparent interest of Congress in telegraphs, Morse took his apparatus to Washington in February 1838, where he gave demonstrations and explanations of its operation to interested Congressmen. The Morse telegraph so impressed the House Committee on Commerce—especially its chairman, F. O. J. Smith of Maine—that an enthusiastic recommendation was made for an appropriation of $30,000 to permit the construction of an experimental telegraph line to test the practicability of Morse's invention. A bill was reported for that purpose,[22] but the panic of 1837, the skepticism

"Christopher Colles and the First Proposal of a Telegraph System in the United States . . . ," *Historical Magazine*, xv, 262-269; William Duane to Jefferson, July 8, 1807, quoted in *Proceedings of the Massachusetts Historical Society*, second series, xx, 1907; *Annals of Congress*, xvii, 10 Cong., 1 sess., 1223-24, 1271).

[19] "Circular to certain Collectors of the Customs, Commanders of Revenue Cutters, and Other Persons," House Report No. 753, 25 Cong., 2 sess.

[20] House Doc. No. 15, 25 Cong., 2 sess., 28-31.

[21] *Ibid.*, 32-33; Morse to Vail, November 13, 1837, Vail Papers.

[22] House Report No. 753, 25 Cong., 2 sess.

of Congress, and the pressure of other business intervened, and no money was appropriated. Morse's visit to Washington was not entirely in vain, however, for it resulted in his securing still another partner—Congressman F. O. J. Smith of Maine.

6 ······

FRANCIS ORMOND JONATHAN SMITH, chairman of the House Committee on Commerce, inherited little more from his father, a tavern keeper in New Hampshire, than a tremendous capacity for work and an unusually facile mind. Realizing the relation between successful business enterprise and a sound knowledge of legal principles, Smith early turned to a study of the law. He gained some reputation as a lawyer in Portland, Maine, and business opportunities began to present themselves. With increasing capital and few scruples to impede him, Smith bade fair to prosper with the economic development of the country. With the skill of a juggler Smith kept his speculations in western lands, railroad schemes, publishing projects, sundry promotional activities, and affairs of the heart all in motion simultaneously, with little conflict and no apparent strain.

Smith sensed something of the vast potentialities inherent in Morse's invention almost immediately. But not until he had received a report favorable to the telegraph from the Secretary of the Franklin Institute did Smith approach Morse and offer to become counsel, publicity man, and promotional agent for his invention. Coming from the quiet background of the parsonage, unschooled in the methods of the market place, and eager for financial assistance, Morse fell a ready prey. He thought he saw in Smith the business acumen so lacking in himself and his scientific partners, Gale and Vail.[23] Smith was accordingly taken into the partnership in March 1838. In addition to acting as counsel for the partners, and attempting to promote their telegraph interests in the United States, Smith agreed to furnish Morse with the necessary funds for a trip to Europe to secure patents for his invention.[24]

[23] This sketch of Smith is based on the 26 vols. of manuscript material in the Smith Collection at the Maine Historical Society Library; Tal. P. Shaffner, *The Telegraph Manual*, 811-816.

[24] According to the new Articles of Agreement entered into by Morse, Vail, Gale, and Smith at this time, Smith was to finance a trip to Europe for himself and Morse, where the two were to seek patents from the governments of England, France, and such other governments as seemed practicable. Smith agreed further to promote the telegraph interests in the United States and serve as counsellor and attorney at law

7 — — ··

AFTER making formal application for a patent in the United States, on April 7, 1838, Morse set out for England accompanied by Smith. In London the preliminary steps were taken to procure a patent, and as part of the routine the Attorney General's sanction was sought. Edward Davy, and the partners, William F. Cooke and Charles Wheatstone, filed immediate objections. They were "equally interested in keeping a third rival out of the field," Davy wrote his father on July 4.[25] About a week later the Attorney General held a hearing on the question. Morse took his apparatus with him to prove to the examiner how utterly different it was from the telegraphs of his English rivals. The Attorney General would not even examine it. He summarily informed Morse that under the existing law no patent could be obtained inasmuch as the London *Mechanic's Magazine* for February 1838 had published an article from Silliman's *American Journal of Science* describing Morse's invention. Although efforts were made for another hearing, the Attorney General would not listen to argument. Having no further recourse but to Parliament, a procedure which would have been long and costly, Morse and Smith abandoned the idea and went to France.[26]

France was as cordial in her reception as England had been cool. A patent was speedily granted, and François Arago, the illustrious director of the Royal Observatory and permanent secretary of the Academy of Sciences, arranged for Morse to demonstrate his invention to the Academy. In a letter to his brother, Morse wrote, "I could see by the expression of face and the exclamations of surprise [*sic*] . . . which were uttered by the members as they crowded around the table that the Telegraph had won their regard." Joseph Gay-

---

for the patentees. Vail and Gale were working on the scientific development of the telegraph; the former attempting to bring the instrument to perfection, the latter attempting to make improvements upon the invention. The expense of securing the American patents was to be borne by Morse and Vail, while the cost of the foreign patents was to be assumed by Smith. Other expenses were to be prorated among the proprietors on the basis of their respective interests in the patent which were divided as follows:

Domestic—Morse 9/16, Smith 4/16, Vail and his brother, George, 2/16, Gale 1/16.
Foreign—Morse 8/16, Smith 5/16, Vail and his brother, George, 2/16, Gale 1/16.
(Copy of an agreement between Morse, Smith, Vail, Gale, dated March 1838, Vail Contract Book; cf. Smith Papers, xxv; George Vail to David Burbank, August 26, 1844, Vail Papers.)

25 Edward Davy to his father, July 4, 1838, quoted by J. J. Fahie, *History of the Electric Telegraph to 1837*, 431.
26 Reid, *Telegraph in America*, 91.

Morse's 1837 Telegraph Instrument
Above: the recorder. Below: the transmitter

Photograph of the Original Message: "What hath God wrought"

Samuel F. B. Morse

Alfred Vail

Leonard D. Gale

Francis O. J. Smith

THE MORSE PATENTEES

Lussac, a famous French scientist, gave it his unqualified approval; and Baron Alexander Humboldt, the great German naturalist, said that Morse's invention was the best of all the systems which had been devised. Arago gave Morse a letter to the director of government telegraphs in France, Alphonse Foy, from whom he had just received a request for information on the best system of telegraph.

The week following the exhibition, Foy called upon Morse, examined his telegraph minutely, and promised to report it as the best he had seen. He further advised the American inventor to see the Minister of Interior, but he explained that the French Government intended trying experiments with the various types of electric telegraph before selecting one for government use.[27]

Days of delay and inactivity followed. Upon eight different occasions over a period of four months Morse attempted to see the Minister of the Interior, but without success.[28] Meanwhile, the weary inventor had turned his attention in another direction. Arrangements were concluded with the St. Germain Railroad to erect a line of telegraph along their road. Morse hoped that the success of such a line might more readily induce the government to buy the patent rights. Moreover, according to French law, his patent would become invalid unless put into actual use within two years of its granting. But before his arrangement with the railroad could be acted upon government permission had to be obtained. Towards the end of February 1839, the French Government decided finally that it was against public policy to permit the development of the telegraph by private parties. The government, for its part, was not yet ready to take action. In spite of the fact that he held a French patent, Morse could do nothing.

Meanwhile, a scheme for the introduction of his system into Russia was also ending in failure. Full arrangements were worked out with the Russian Counselor of State, Baron Alexander de Meyendorff, but Czar Nicholas I refused to sign the contract. Apparently he was fearful that the telegraph would be used by his enemies to carry on subversive activities.[29]

Seeing that it was useless to spend further time and money in Europe, Morse prepared to return once more to his native land where he hoped his invention might receive a more favorable response.

---

[27] Morse to brother Sidney E. Morse, October 1, 1838, Vail Papers.
[28] Morse to Smith, September 29, 1838, Smith Papers, xi.
[29] *Ibid.*, March 2, and August 12, 1839; Morse, *Letters and Journals*, ii, 96-97; Mabee, *American Leonardo*, 225.

8 — · · · ·

AT the time of his return to the United States in March 1839, Morse found that little progress had been made in telegraph affairs during his absence. His patent had not yet been issued, nor had Congress taken further action on the telegraph appropriation. The public was incapable of comprehending the significance of his invention, and willingly confounded it with various current chimerical projects. Time was required to win public support for an invention as revolutionary as the electromagnetic telegraph. Morse's partners, who had expected more ready acceptance of the electrical phenomenon, grew weary of the delay and inertia which seemed to nullify their efforts. One by one, they returned to their previous interests leaving Morse alone to promote his invention.[30]

Confronted by apathy on the part of the government, desertion by his partners, and the embarrassments arising from insufficient funds, Morse, too, might have grown discouraged and abandoned the whole telegraph idea. But being a firm believer in the ultimate triumph of his invention and the son of the redoubtable Jedidiah Morse, he was able to carry on through difficult years. "The reason of . . . [the telegraph's] not being in operation is not the fault of the invention, nor is it my neglect," Morse wrote Vail on September 7, 1840. "My faith is not only unshaken in its eventual adoption throughout the world, but it is confirmed by every new discovery in the science of electricity," concluded Morse.[31]

9 — · · —

IN December 1842, Morse once more journeyed to Washington in a desperate attempt to obtain a government appropriation for his project. Smith did not come on to help him as he had promised; the Vails did not assist him with funds; Gale could not.[32] Wires were strung between two of the committee rooms in the Capitol, and messages were sent back and forth with such success that the Committee on Commerce again reported favorably a bill appropriating $30,000

[30] Morse to Vail, December 18, 1841, Vail Papers; cf. Morse to Smith, December 3, 1841, Smith Papers, XI.

[31] Morse to Vail, September 7, 1840, Vail Papers.

[32] Morse to Smith, January 13, 1843, Smith Papers, XIII; Morse to Vail, February 23, 1843, Vail Papers.

to construct an experimental line between Washington and Baltimore.[33]

At last, late in February, Morse's telegraph bill came before the House. Cave Johnson of Tennessee, quite unaware that he would subsequently become administrator of the United States Telegraph, rose to speak. Since the present Congress was doing so much to encourage science, said Johnson, he did not wish to see the science of mesmerism overlooked. He moved, therefore, that half of the appropriation be given a Mr. Fisk, then exhibiting the wonders of mesmerism, to enable him to continue his experiments.

Houston of Alabama thereupon suggested that the Millerites—a religious sect predicting the second coming of Christ in 1844—should also be included in the benefits of the appropriation.

Stanly of North Carolina then declared that he had no objection to the appropriation for mesmeric experiment, provided the gentleman from Tennessee (Cave Johnson) was the subject.

Cave Johnson promptly replied that he would have no objection provided that the gentleman from North Carolina (Stanly) should be the operator.

After the laughter which greeted this farce had somewhat subsided, Mason of Ohio asked the Chair to rule the amendment out of order since it had been made facetiously.

But Chairman Winthrop of Massachusetts replied that it was not for him to judge of the motives of members in offering amendments. Objection might be raised on the ground that the amendment was not sufficiently analogous in character to the bill under consideration, but in the opinion of the Chair "it would require a scientific analysis to determine how far the magnetism of mesmerism was analogous to that to be employed in telegraphs."[34]

With nearly every cent he owned in the world in his pocket, Morse meanwhile sat alone in the House gallery watching the Twenty-seventh Congress spend itself.

A reporter approached him. "You are anxious," he said.

"I have reason to be," Morse told him, putting his hand to his forehead. ". . . if you knew how important this is to me, you would not wonder. I have spent seven years in perfecting this invention, and all that I had; if it succeeds, I am a made man; if it fails, I am ruined."[35]

[33] House Report No. 17, 27 Cong., 3 sess.
[34] Cong. Globe, 27 Cong., 3 sess., February 23, 1843.
[35] Mabee, *American Leonardo*, 257; Nathan Sargent, *Public Men and Events*, II, 194.

Having exhausted their farce, the House good-naturedly rejected the amendment. Twenty-two members, however, had voted to include mesmerism and Millerism in the appropriation for telegraphic experiment.

Two days later the telegraph bill passed by the narrow margin of 89 to 83. Seventy congressmen failed to vote at all. Not a few of them had left their seats "to avoid the responsibility of spending the public money for a machine they could not understand." Others admitted to Morse that they had voted for his bill in deference to him rather than from confidence in his machine.[36]

As related by Morse and his early biographers, the story of the passage of the bill by the Senate was equally dramatic. According to these sources, the bill was the hundred and twentieth on the calendar on the last evening of the session. There seemed no hope that it could be reached before the hour of adjournment. Morse, who had been in the gallery all day, could stand the strain no longer. He had left to return to his hotel as the lamps were being lighted in the Senate chamber.

In the morning as he was about to have breakfast, a servant informed him that a young lady was calling to see him. It was Annie Ellsworth, the daughter of the Commissioner of Patents. Morse expressed surprise at the early call.

"I have come to congratulate you," she said.

"Indeed, for what?"

"On the passage of your bill."

"Oh, no, my young friend, you are mistaken; I was in the Senate-chamber till after the lamps were lighted, and my senatorial friends assured me there was no chance for me."

"But," she replied, "it is you that are mistaken. Father was there at the adjournment, at midnight, and saw the President put his name to your bill; and I asked father if I might come and tell you, and he gave me leave. Am I the first to tell you?"

Morse could not speak for a moment.

"Yes, Annie," he said at last, "you are the first to inform me; and now I am going to make you a promise: the first dispatch on the completed line from Washington to Baltimore shall be yours."[37]

While this dramatic account appeals to the imagination, later his-

---

[36] Cong. Globe, 27 Cong., 3 sess., February 23, 1843; Mabee, *American Leonardo*, 257-258.

[37] Prime, *Life*, 464-466; *Morse, Letters and Journals*, II, 198-200; Mabee, *American Leonardo*, 259-260.

torians have largely disproved it.[38] The Journal of the Senate shows that the bill was passed on the morning of March 3 and it was signed by President Tyler some hours before the session ended.[39] Moreover, in letters to Smith and Vail dated March 3, Morse had written: "The Senate have just passed my bill without division and without opposition, and it will probably be signed by the President in a few hours."[40]

Whenever it was passed the important thing was that the telegraph bill had been accepted. Morse had won the first battle in the struggle to give the nation a practical electromagnetic telegraph.

[38] *Ibid.*, 260; Harlow, *Old Wires and New Waves*, 86; John B. McMaster, *History of the People of the United States*, VII, 129.

[39] Senate Journal, 27 Cong., 3 sess., 278, 295.

[40] Morse to Smith, March 3, 1843, Smith Papers, XI; Morse to Vail, March 3, 1843, Vail Papers.

The Telegraph on Trial

1 · — — ·

WITH the $30,000 Congressional appropriation at his disposal, Morse turned eagerly to the fulfillment of his dream.[1] Once the practicability and efficacy of the telegraph had been demonstrated to the American public, he felt sure that it would receive an enthusiastic welcome and produce a virtual revolution in the field of communication.[2] At the very outset, Morse made one serious error which almost resulted in the failure of the whole experiment. Instead of placing the conducting wires on poles erected at regular intervals—the cheapest and easiest method—he decided to follow the plan first adopted in England of laying the conductors beneath the ground in pipes. He began at once to make the necessary arrangements.[3]

As scientific assistants he employed his partner, Gale, and Professor James C. Fisher, who had been associated with Morse in some of his experiments. Alfred Vail was placed in charge of making the necessary instruments and the purchase of materials, and Smith was given the contract for laying the new line. Smith lost no time in pointing out to Morse that, inasmuch as the government was furnishing the funds, the cable-laying contract should be increased beyond the amount they had tentatively agreed upon earlier. He magnanimously offered to divide the resulting construction profits with his partner. Morse, anxious only for the success of the enterprise, viewed his partner's business methods with troubled eyes and vehemently denounced the suggestion.[4]

It was agreed that the work of laying the line should proceed as rapidly as possible. Smith, in an effort to equip himself for his part of the undertaking, was down on hands and knees on the floor of his newspaper office one day in July attempting to demonstrate to a willing but unimaginative mechanic what he needed in the way of a plow to lay the cable. He was interrupted by the appearance in

[1] "An Act to test the practicability of establishing a system of electro-magnetic telegraphs in the United States," U.S. Statutes at Large, v, 618-619.
[2] House Doc. No. 15, 25 Cong., 2 sess., 28-31.
[3] Morse to Secretary of Treasury, J. C. Spencer, March 10, 1843, cited by Prime, Life, 474-475.
[4] Morse to Smith, May 17, 1843, Smith Papers, XI; Ibid., May 22, 1843.

the doorway of a lanky individual whom Smith introduced as Ezra Cornell. Cornell had made the acquaintance of editor Smith on a previous occasion when he had visited the office of the *Maine Farmer* in an attempt to get some favorable publicity for the patent plow which he was promoting in the state. So agreeable had been their first meeting that he had stopped on his next trip to Maine to renew his acquaintance with the editor of the farm journal. His immediate grasp of the technical problem presented to him was evidence that Cornell was no novice in applied mechanics. From the time he had left home as a lad of eighteen, the rise of Ezra Cornell had been steady. As carpenter, mechanic, and business manager he had made an adequate living for himself and his family. The big flour and plaster mill near Ithaca, New York, with which he had been associated for twelve years, had prospered; and Cornell, a partner in that prosperity, had risen from millwright to general manager. In 1841 the mill had changed hands and Cornell's services were no longer required. Cornell had become interested in an improved plow and had purchased the patent rights for the states of Maine and Georgia, where he was attempting to promote its sale. But this was an occupation engaged in through necessity rather than choice; and as eagerly as a diverted stream finds once more its natural bed, Cornell joined the perspiring pair on the floor, where he sketched under their admiring eyes a machine which he claimed would dig the trench, lay the cable, and cover it, in one process. Impressed by Cornell's ready discernment, Smith hired him to carry out the trenching contract.[5]

2 ··—··

AFTER some deliberation, Morse had determined to lay the experimental line between Baltimore and Washington. Tentative permission had been obtained from the Baltimore & Ohio Railroad to use its right of way provided it could be done "without injury to the road and without embarrassment to the operations of the company." The agreement also provided that Morse would concede to the company the use of the telegraph upon the road without expense, and reserve

[5] This sketch of Ezra Cornell's life is based primarily on autobiographical fragments, letters, and other papers found in the Cornell Manuscript Collection at the Cornell University Library, and, *True and Firm; Biography of Ezra Cornell* (1884) published anonymously by his son, Alonzo B. Cornell.

to the company the right of discontinuing its use, if it should in any manner prove injurious.[6]

Although Morse and his associates were granted permission to erect a line of telegraph along the Baltimore & Ohio right of way, the attitude of the railroad company was frankly one of suspicion. Neither Morse nor the railroad officials seem to have recognized the natural affinity of telegraph and railroad. In England, France, and most of the other European countries the development of the telegraph and the railroads was closely associated from the beginning, but in the United States nearly a decade was to pass before they joined forces to their mutual benefit.[7]

By October 1843, all the necessary preliminaries had been arranged, and the telegraph promoters were ready to undertake the actual construction of the line. By means of his ingenious trenching machine, Cornell was soon laying half a mile to a mile of cable a day. While he was responsible for the laying of the cable, the joining of the ends and testing of the line were under the supervision of Morse's scientific assistants.[8] By December the cable had been laid from the railroad station in Baltimore to Relay, Maryland, about eight or nine miles distant. Tests had by this time confirmed the growing suspicion that the faulty insulation of the wires in the cable was serious enough to require that the work be halted.[9]

Professor Morse called Cornell aside and asked him if he could contrive to stop the work for a few days in such a way that the newspapers would not know that it had been interrupted intentionally. Morse explained that he wished to make some experiments before any more cable was laid.[10] Cornell had already done some testing of the line on his own initiative, and was well aware of its condition. By way of reply he grasped the handles of his plow, and signaled the mule drivers to proceed. Watching his opportunity, he shattered his plow against a point of rock.[11]

Long and painful consultations were followed by discouraging ex-

<hr>

[6] Edw. Hungerford, *The Story of the Baltimore & Ohio Railroad, 1827-1927*, I, 281-282; Morse to Smith, April 11, 1843, Smith Papers, XIII.

[7] For a detailed discussion of early railroad and telegraph relations in the United States see Chapter XIII.

[8] Cornell, *True and Firm*, 77-81.

[9] Cornell to Prime, April 28, 1873, Morse Papers, XLVII.

[10] Prime, *Life*, 478; Cornell, *True and Firm*, 84.

[11] Cornell to Prime, April 28, 1873, Morse Papers, XLVII.

periments. It was a dark hour, for between one-half and two-thirds of the government appropriation had been spent on a line which was practically worthless. Professor Fisher, whose duty it had been to test the wires after insertion into the lead pipes, was dismissed. Gale resigned. Smith, on the other hand, despite the absolute futility of proceeding, demanded that Morse abide by the construction contract. Regarding the whole enterprise as a failure, he proposed to reimburse himself for expenditures made in promoting the scheme by insisting on his legal rights under the contract. He threatened to sue Morse for the money still due him.

Even in the face of these conditions, Morse refused to give up. After much thought and consultation he decided to place the wires upon poles erected at regular intervals. In the meantime, Ezra Cornell had been appointed Morse's mechanical assistant at a yearly salary of $1,000. A basement room in the Patent Office was put at his disposal, and he spent the winter months removing the wires from the cables.[12]

With the coming of spring outdoor work was resumed, but this time the wires were strung on poles. One of the most serious problems which confronted the builders was that of insulating the wires where they were fastened to the poles so that undue leakage would not again bring failure. Both Vail and Cornell submitted plans. Finally, upon the advice of Professor Joseph Henry, Morse decided in favor of Cornell's insulator, composed of two glass plates between which the wire was placed after being well wrapped with cloth saturated with gum shellac. These insulators were shortly replaced by the more satisfactory bureau-knob pattern, also of Cornell's devising.[13]

By the middle of April, six miles of the line extended from Washington to Bladensburg; and by May 1, to within fifteen miles of Baltimore. On that day the Whig National Convention met at that city and nominated Henry Clay for the presidency by acclamation. News of the nomination was rushed via the railroad to the end of the telegraph line, where it was transmitted to the telegraph office that had been set up temporarily in the basement of the Capitol. Telegraphic news of Clay's nomination had been in circulation throughout Congress for a full hour and a half before the train from Baltimore arrived with a confirmation of it. When news of the nomination of

12 Cornell to his wife, Mary Ann, and children, Dec. 24, 1843, Cornell Papers.
13 Morse to Cornell, March 18, 1844; Cornell to Morse, March 29, 1844; Morse to Vail, May 1, 2, and 14, 1844; and Morse to brother Sidney, May 7, 1844, Morse Papers, XVII.

Theodore Frelinghuysen as vice-president arrived in the same manner, even the skeptics had to admit the success of the telegraph.[14]

The line was now pushed steadily forward, so that early in May the railroad depot on Pratt Street, Baltimore, was joined with the Supreme Court chamber in Washington which was to serve as telegraph office for the official opening of the line. On the twenty-fourth of May 1844, in the Supreme Court chamber at Washington, before many of the most distinguished officers of the government and a number of his friends, Morse quietly seated himself at the telegraph key.

"Dot, dash—dash—space—dot, dot dot, dot—space—dot, dash—
    space—dash . . . ."

Along the forty odd miles of wire that separated him from his partner, Vail, in Baltimore, sped that famous message:

"What hath God wrought!"[15]

No longer was the telegraph a theory; it was a fact. No less important than the profound change which was even then being wrought in the field of transportation by the railroad was the far-reaching effect which the introduction and rapid extension of the telegraph was to have upon the economic and social development of the United States.

3 · · · — ·

THE newly completed telegraph line was given an additional opportunity to prove its utility, when, on May 27, the Democratic National Convention assembled in Baltimore to select its candidates for the coming election. Morse and Vail had carefully prepared for the transmission of news from the Convention to the Supreme Court chamber in Washington. Martin Van Buren appeared to be the likely candidate to receive his party's nomination, but after an exciting struggle, the two-thirds rule was adopted by the Convention. Van Buren, failing to receive the required number, was dropped in favor of a "dark horse," James K. Polk of Tennessee. Having rejected Van Buren for the presidency, the Convention hoped to placate the Van Buren forces by nominating his friend, Silas Wright, for the vice-presidency. Wright, United States Senator

14 *Philadelphia Public Ledger*, April 12, May 7, 1844; *National Intelligencer*, May 8, 1844, quoted by John B. McMaster, in *History of the People of the United States*, VII, 130.
15 Morse to brother Sidney, May 31, 1844, Morse Papers, XVII; cf. entry May 25, 1844, in "Journal of the Magnetic Telegraph between Washington and Baltimore," kept by Alfred Vail from May 25 to September 27, 1844, Vail Papers.

from the State of New York, was in the Capitol at the time of his nomination. Vail at once communicated the news to Morse by telegraph, and the latter in turn notified Wright. A short time later the Convention was astonished to receive a telegraphic message from Wright respectfully declining the nomination. Some doubted the authority of the evidence before them, while others utterly disbelieved the fact that communication could have been established with Washington and an answer returned in the few minutes that had elapsed since the nomination had been made. Consequently, the Convention was adjourned to await the report of a committee sent to the Capitol to wait upon Senator Wright.[16]

The following morning, however, the committee report confirmed the information contained in the previous day's telegraphic dispatch. There followed an interesting conference. At Baltimore a committee, determined to make one more effort to secure Wright's consent, met with Vail in the little telegraph office there; in Washington Senator Wright and Professor Morse stood by ready to answer such communications as were received. The committee in Baltimore sent a message urging Wright to reconsider and accept the nomination. A number of confidential messages were then sent back and forth along the line, and a short time later the committee announced to the Convention that Wright was inflexible. Another candidate, George M. Dallas of Pennsylvania, was chosen.[17]

4 · · · · —

THE public in good American fashion flocked to see the latest wonder of the age. Hundreds begged and pleaded to be allowed merely to look at the instrument. They declared that "they would not say a word or stir and didn't care whether they understood or not, only they wanted to say they had seen it."[18] While hundreds of people were eager to see the wonderful new invention in operation, relatively few cared to make use of its services. To test the accuracy of the instruments, as well as to occupy their time, the operators in Washington and Baltimore promoted chess games by telegraph between outstanding players in the respective cities.[19] The idea had just begun to attract

16 *Ibid.*, entry of May 28, 1844.

17 *Ibid.*, entry of May 29, 1844; *National Intelligencer*, May 30, 1844, cited by McMaster, *History of the People of the United States*, VII, 131.

18 Vail to Morse, June 3, 1844, Morse Papers, XVII.

19 O. S. Wood to Cornell, December 5, 1844, Cornell Papers; Vail, *The Electro-Magnetic Telegraph*, 63.

the public interest when a confidential note from operator Rogers of Baltimore to Vail in Washington warned, "We are making an unfavorable impression on the religious part of the community and . . . if we continue we will be injured more than helped. . . . I think Congressional news is as much as your fingers or mine can manage for the present." Moreover, if telegraphic chess continued, Rogers cautioned, "after session hours we will have to play for all the members who are chess players and get ourselves into a *nice business*." He suggested discontinuing the chess games unless the telegraph was to derive some revenue from them.[20]

The instruments used on this first practical electromagnetic recording telegraph line had undergone considerable improvement and change in the seven years that had elapsed since Morse had shown his first crude instruments to Gale in the studio at New York University. The clumsy old portrules which had been used for sending the signals to the distant station had been replaced by the simple Morse key, or "correspondent." The facile dot-and-dash alphabet had supplanted the inadequate numerical system of signals. The pencil, and later the pen which had served to record the early signals, had given place to a steel stylus. Passing immediately over a groove, it left clear-cut indentations on the paper as dots and dashes. In fact, under the skillful hands of Alfred Vail all of the instruments had been simplified, and improved.

One of the most important of all the discoveries later to be associated with the development of a great nation-wide telegraph system was the relay. In 1837 Morse had shown Gale how a current that had become feeble as a result of having traveled through many miles of wire could be reinforced or renewed by means of an ingenious device which came to be called a relay, or repeater. By the introduction of the relay into a circuit a feeble current might be reinforced sufficiently to operate the recorder with ease; or it could be used to renew the strength of the current and send it speeding on its way for another hundred miles without further help from human hands.[21] By means of the relay as successfully applied on the forty-mile experimental line between Baltimore and Washington, telegraphing could be employed to transmit messages throughout the entire United States.

20 Henry J. Rogers to Vail, December 5, 1844, Vail Papers.
21 Prime, *Life*, 295-296, 302-303; Morse, *Letters and Journals*, II, 42.

5 ———

ON June 3, 1844, Morse officially notified the Secretary of the Treasury *ad interim*, McClintock Young, that the experimental telegraph line between Washington and Baltimore was completed. He proudly pointed out some of the various ways in which the new invention had already proved both its practicability and utility. The proceedings of the Democratic National Convention at Baltimore had been transmitted to Washington where they were announced to the hundreds assembled in front of the terminus at the Capitol. A family living in Washington, hearing that a member had died in Baltimore, entreated Morse to find out if it were true, and in ten minutes received the welcome reply that the rumor was entirely without foundation. A Baltimore merchant telegraphed to the Bank of Washington to ascertain whether a check drawn by one of its depositors was good, and in a few minutes had the answer.[22] Political, social, and economic interests had all been served by the telegraph in the first month of its operation. The immense value of a national communications system was at least foreshadowed here.

At the same time Morse addressed a memorial to Congress pointing out that the telegraph, with its great potentialities for good or evil, should be controlled by the government rather than by private individuals or associations. He expressed the willingness of the proprietors to transfer to the United States Government the exclusive use and control of the telegraph from Washington, D.C., to New York City, if Congress would provide for the construction of a line of telegraph upon either of the following terms: (1) Congress should buy outright all rights to the line, in which case the Government should construct it at its own expense and under its own direction; or (2) the Government might contract with the proprietors to construct the line, which should be delivered into the charge of the Government along with all rights belonging to the proprietors as each successive section of ten miles should be completed, "for the sum of .... dollars."[23]

[22] Report of Morse to Secretary of Treasury *ad interim*, McClintock Young, June 3, 1844, House Doc. No. 270, 28 Cong., 1 sess.

[23] Morse's "Memorial to the Congress of the United States," June 3, 1844, quoted in full by Prime, *Life*, 507-509. It should be noted that no mention was made of any specific price for which Morse and his associates would sell their rights to the government. Concerning this point the *New York Evening Post*, June 10, 1844 writes, "He [Morse] proposes to sell out to the government the right to the invention for the route from Washington to New York for a sum which the Committee on Com-

The House Committee on Commerce introduced a bill for the extension of Morse's telegraph from Baltimore to New York, but the session of Congress closed without any action having been taken upon it.[24]

6 ......

FOLLOWING the adjournment of Congress in the summer of 1844, the proprietors—especially Smith, who with the success of the experimental line had once more begun to take an interest in the telegraph—determined to seek the aid of private capital. It was with some reluctance that Morse consented to such a course of action. He continued to have great hopes that the government could be persuaded to purchase the patent rights. He would agree to grant contracts to private parties only on the condition that the contracts contain a clause making it possible for the government to buy any lines so constructed at cost plus a 20 per cent profit.[25]

Enlisting private capital proved difficult. In July a Philadelphia promoter, J. Reese Fry, seemed willing to organize a company to build a line of telegraph from that city to New York, but when the patentees insisted upon reserving to themselves the rights on the way lines, Fry and his Philadelphia associates lost interest.[26] All through an uncertain summer and fall, another promoter, David Burbank, was trying to interest capital in the new invention. With his friend Smith, he proposed to purchase the patent rights of Morse, Vail, and Gale for the entire United States. Morse, who wished to go to Europe to push the sale of his patent rights there, offered his share, amounting to 9/16, for $110,000 cash.[27] Vail, convinced that the government should control the telegraph in the interests of all the people,[28] at first refused to name any price for his 1/8 interest; then, being pressed, he named a sum twice as large as that which Morse had asked for his

merce . . . may decide to be just and reasonable." See also, *Philadelphia Public Ledger*, June 13, 1844, and *New York Journal of Commerce*, June 13, 1844.

24 Cong. Globe, 28 Cong., 1 sess., 648.

25 Morse to brother Sidney, January 18, 1845, *et seq.*, Morse Papers, XXIX.

26 Morse to Smith, July 10, 1844, Smith Papers, XI; Morse to Smith, July 17, 1844, *et seq.*, Morse Papers, XVIII.

27 Morse to Smith, July 10, 1844 and Burbank to Smith, July 17, 1844, *et seq.*, Smith Papers, XVIII; Morse to Burbank, July 1, 1844, *et seq.*, Morse Papers, XVIII.

28 Copy of letter, Vail to Henry Clay, August [?] 1844; Henry Clay to Vail, September 10, 1844, Vail Papers.

holdings.[29] Seeing that he was getting nowhere, Burbank grew discouraged. None of his many telegraph schemes ever got beyond the "paper stage."

In October of this year, Ezra Cornell was employed by Smith to show the wonders of telegraphy to the people of Boston in hope of obtaining funds for the construction of a line of telegraph from that city to New York.[30] From a room in School Street wires were strung over the roof of the City Hall to Sudbury Street. When the Boston public proved unappreciative, it was decided to transfer the exhibition to New York in the belief that its business men would surely finance the project.[31]

The City of New York, however, at first refused to allow even the construction of an experimental line, asserting that the wires across the housetops might attract lightning. It was only after payment of a fee of $50 to the distinguished scientist, Dr. Silliman, who vouched for the harmlessness of the wires, that Cornell and his brother-in-law, Orrin S. Wood, were allowed to stretch a line for a mile or so along Broadway. A charge of one shilling was made to see the telegraph in operation, but New Yorkers showed so little interest that it was not possible to pay expenses.[32] Notwithstanding the favorable press notices and the active efforts of Fry, Burbank, Smith, and others to raise money for telegraph lines, the immediate and tangible result of these exhibitions in two of the great seaboard cities was exactly nothing.[33]

7 — — · ·

In December 1844 Morse, urged on by Alfred Vail, appealed again to Congress to accept control of this mighty new instrument of communication before it was too late. He pointed out that while the little experimental line had proved the practicability of the telegraph, it had not given the government a fair conception of the great utility of a more extensive system linking some of the nation's great business centers. Again he cited numerous examples of how even the tiny line from Baltimore to Washington had served a variety of purposes.

29 Burbank to Smith, July 17, 1844; *Ibid.*, September 3, 1844, Smith Papers, xviii.
30 Smith to Cornell, September 5, 1844, Smith Papers, xviii; Cornell to H. L. Ellsworth, November 23, 1844, quoted by Reid, *Telegraph in America*, 353.
31 Cornell, *True and Firm*, 93.
32 *Ibid.*, 94 ff.
33 *New York Herald*, March 29, 1845, quoted by Frederic Hudson, *Journalism in the United States from 1690-1872*, 599.

Upon one occasion the Baltimore & Ohio Railroad had made use of it to give the right of way to a special express from Baltimore which was bearing important dispatches for the President and the Cabinet. Upon another, an offender against the law was arrested as he stepped from the cars at Baltimore, the Washington police having telegraphed a description of the man and a request for his arrest. When Congress was in session its proceedings were regularly published in the Baltimore morning and evening papers. Innumerable private messages both social and business were transmitted daily. Another advantage not to be overlooked by the government was the mighty aid which a well-developed system of telegraphs would be to the national defense. The banker, the merchant, the business man, the general public, the government, and the army all stood to gain by the development of this new communications service.

Nor did the adroit Morse stop there. He also attempted to anticipate objections that might arise in the minds of the legislators. Fear that the exposed posts and wires might be tampered with frequently, or even destroyed by vandals, had proved groundless. Doubts as to the ability of the telegraph to send messages fast enough to be practical were also without foundation, for in a recent experiment sufficient news had been transmitted in thirty minutes to fill nearly a whole column in the *Baltimore Patriot*—faster, in fact, than the reporters in Baltimore could transcribe it. Finally, in regard to the cost of maintenance, a system of telegraphs linking the important cities of the country could, by the application of a reasonable tariff, be made not only self-supporting, but actually the source of a handsome revenue.

Morse declared that the proprietors of the telegraph were willing to sell all their rights to the government for a fair consideration, but no definite sum was named. In conclusion he hinted at what would happen if Congress failed to act. "For myself, I should prefer that the Government should possess the invention, although the pecuniary interests of the proprietors induce them to lean towards arrangements with private companies."[34]

The press in general agreed with Morse that the telegraph should not be left to the exploitation of individuals. Of the leading publishers who took up their pens on the question, none was more active than William Swain of the *Philadelphia Public Ledger*. Less than a

[34] Letter from Secretary of Treasury to House of Representatives, December 17, 1844, transmitting a letter from Professor Morse relative to the Magnetic Telegraph, House Executive Doc., No. 24, 28 Cong., 2 sess., 1-9.

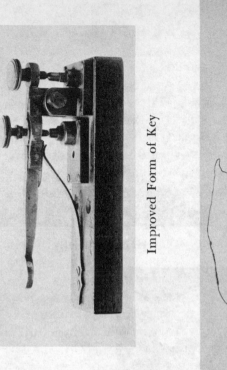

Improved Form of Key

Morse Telegraph Register, 1844

First Form of Key

Early Relay

MORSE TELEGRAPH INSTRUMENTS, 1843-1846

Theodore S. Faxton

Henry O'Rielly

Amos Kendall

John J. Speed

Ezra Cornell

EARLY TELEGRAPH PROMOTERS AND BUILDERS

month after the completion of the experimental line he was urging that "the Government . . . possess itself at once with this triumph of American genius, and give to every city throughout the Union the advantages which may be derived from it."[35] Frequent editorials which followed testified to his profound feeling in the matter. James Gordon Bennett, though somewhat less articulate on the subject, felt that by the very nature of the invention the "Government must be impelled to take hold of it" and develop it as a part of the postal service.[36]

But the aid of Congress was sought in vain. Although the friends of the telegraph did everything in their power to push through a bill for its extension, the opposition was able to prevent any action.[37] The most that its proponents could get was an amendment to the Civil and Diplomatic Appropriation Act granting $8,000 for defraying the expenses of the existing line from Washington to Baltimore, and transferring it from the Treasury Department to the direction and superintendence of the Postmaster General.[38] The golden opportunity for the development of the telegraph as a government monopoly passed, and as Morse had warned, he and the other proprietors of the patent necessarily turned to private capital in earnest.

8 — · · · ·

THE incoming Postmaster General, Cave Johnson, who two years earlier as Congressman from Tennessee had ridiculed the telegraph, now proceeded to establish a tariff of one cent on every four characters transmitted, and on April 1, 1845, the government line which had hitherto been operated without charge, was opened for public business. Alfred Vail was appointed as the operator at Washington and Henry J. Rogers became the operator at Baltimore.[39]

During the first four days the total receipts amounted to one cent. That was obtained from an office-seeker who had dropped into the Washington office to see the operation of the telegraph. A free exhibition was refused. When the visitor explained that he had only a twenty dollar bill and one cent, Vail offered to give him one cent's worth of telegraphy if he liked. To this offer the office-seeker grudg-

---

[35] *Philadelphia Public Ledger*, June 20, 1844.
[36] *New York Herald*, May 12, 1845.
[37] Cong. Globe, 28 Cong., 2 sess., 328, 341, 366-367; House Report No. 187, 28 Cong., 2 sess.
[38] U.S. Stat. at Large, v, 757.   [39] Sen. Doc. No. 1, 29 Cong., 1 sess., 891-892.

ingly assented, whereupon Washington asked Baltimore, "4," which meant in code, "What time is it?" Baltimore immediately replied, "1," which meant one o'clock. The amount of the operation was one character each way, making two in all, which at the rate of four for a cent amounted to a half a cent. The customer laid down his cent, but was told that half a cent would suffice, if he could produce the change. Magnanimously declining the offer, the visitor went on his way.

Such was the income of the Washington office for the first four days of April 1845. On the fifth, twelve and one-half cents was received. The sixth was the Sabbath. On the seventh, the receipts ran up to sixty cents; on the eighth, to one dollar and thirty-two cents; and on the ninth, to one dollar and four cents. "It is worthy of remark," declared Vail, commenting on the perversity of human nature, "that more business was done by the merchants after the tariff was laid than when the service was gratuitous."[40]

At the end of the first three months of operation on a revenue producing basis, receipts had amounted to $193.56, while total expenditures, including a charge of $680.15 incurred before the charge of regular tariffs had commenced, were $1,859.05. The second quarter ending September 30, 1845, showed only slight improvement with the receipts of $219.88, and expenses of $1,425.12.[41]

Postmaster General Johnson in his annual report submitted on December 1, 1845, discussed the situation carefully. He pointed out that the proprietors of the Morse patent had already negotiated with private interests for the establishment of telegraph lines to connect the principal cities of the Union, and that their success would surely diminish the revenues of the Post Office Department.

"It becomes, then," said Postmaster General Johnson, "a question of great importance, how far the government will allow individuals to divide with it the business of transmitting intelligence—an important duty confided to it by the Constitution, necessarily and properly exclusive? [sic] Or will it purchase the telegraph, and conduct its operations for the benefit of the public?"

While the operation of the telegraph between Washington and Baltimore had not satisfied Johnson that its revenues could be made equal to its expenditures under any feasible rate of tariffs, he was firmly convinced that the government should control it. Its importance to the public, explained the Postmaster General, was not

40 Diary of Alfred Vail, quoted by Prime, *Life*, 499 ff.
41 Report of Postmaster General, Ex. Doc. No. 2, 29 Cong., 1 sess., 860.

based upon any probable income that could be derived from it, but from its function "as an agent vastly superior to any other ever devised by the genius of man for the diffusion of intelligence." In this role it would have a decisive influence upon commercial transactions and be of inestimable value to the government in time of war. "The use of an instrument so powerful for good or evil," concluded the Post-master General, "cannot with safety to the people be left in the hands of private individuals uncontrolled by law."[42]

While the Postmaster General, having based his revenue estimates on the results obtained from the forty mile line between Washington and Baltimore, was very much in error in regard to the possible returns to be derived from a nation-wide business, he was, neverthe-less, keenly aware of the vast potentialities of the new invention and favored government ownership, or some sort of government control. Congress, not the Postmaster General, must bear the re-sponsibility for the government's failure to take decisive action at this critical juncture.[43] After making a further appropriation of $4,000 to maintain the line from Washington to Baltimore, Congress author-ized the Postmaster General to lease the line to any person who would keep it in operation for its earnings, or to sell it under the direction of the President of the United States.[44] The recommendations of the Postmaster General were ignored, and instead of bringing the tele-graph under closer governmental control, Congress proceeded to cast off such control as did exist.

9 — · · —

IN his annual report for 1846, Johnson made a last urgent appeal for careful consideration of the telegraph question. "It is the settled conviction of the undersigned," he wrote, "that the public interest, as well as the safety of the citizen, requires the government should get the exclusive control of it [the telegraph], by purchase, or that its use should be subjected to the restraint of law."[45] He pointed out that privately-owned telegraph lines were now in operation between New York and Boston, Buffalo, Philadelphia, Baltimore, and Wash-

---

[42] *Ibid.*, 861.

[43] Previous writers have emphasized the failure of Postmaster General Johnson to realize the significance of the telegraph and have blamed him for governmental inaction. See Prime, *Life*, 510 ff.; Reid, *Telegraph in America*, 108.

[44] U.S. Stat. at Large, IX, 19.

[45] Ex. Doc. No. 4, 29 Cong., 2 sess., 689.

ington; that others were in contemplation from Washington, south; and from Buffalo, west; and that in a few years telegraph lines would undoubtedly extend to all the principal cities of the Union. He warned of the irreparable damage which might result if this private enterprise were allowed to proceed unchecked. Feeling as he did, Johnson had addressed a letter to the owners of the patent rights to find out what it would cost if Congress were inclined to make the purchase. The owners had replied that, while they were willing to dispose of all their rights to the government for a fair consideration, they were unwilling to enter into any negotiation upon the subject without authority first given by Congress.[46] The government, now busily engaged in prosecuting the war with Mexico, could not be bothered with anything so trivial as the telegraph, so Johnson's appeal was ignored.

Despairing of any further action on the part of the government, in December 1846, the Postmaster General proceeded to lease the pioneer Baltimore-Washington line to Vail and Rogers. According to the agreement, they were to keep up the line at their own expense and without any charge for their personal services other than the proceeds of the telegraph.[47] The following spring the line was leased to one of the recently-formed private telegraph organizations, the Magnetic Telegraph Company, and it was soon absorbed as part of that concern's telegraph system.[48] Thus, the telegraph question passed out of the hands of Congress not to return again for many years.

[46] *Ibid.*, 688-689. The statement is made in numerous books dealing with this period of telegraph history that the telegraph patent was offered to the government for $100,000, which it foolishly refused; Prime, *Life*, 510-511; Cornell, *True and Firm*, 92; Albert W. Smith, *Ezra Cornell, a Character Study*, 44; Morse, *Letters and Journals*, II, 446; Reid, *The Telegraph in America*, 108-112. Official government records indicated in the preceding footnotes give no such evidence. In all cases definite figures are avoided. In the Congressional Globe, 28 Cong., 2 sess., 366, a plan was proposed for building a line from Baltimore to New York not to exceed in cost $461 a mile for a line of six wires, the total cost of which would have been about $100,000; Morse, *Letters and Journals*, II, 235, quotes a letter written by Morse to David Burbank on July 1, 1844, in which he offered to sell his share of the patent for $110,000 in cash. Just what complete control of the telegraph would have cost in 1844 or 1845 was never clearly determined since the government did not evidence any great desire to purchase it.

[47] Contract between Postmaster General Cave Johnson and Alfred Vail and Henry J. Rogers, Assistant Superintendents, U.S. Electromagnetic Telegraph, November 16, 1846, Vail Papers.

[48] Order of the Post Office Department, April 13, 1847, leasing U.S. Electromagnetic Telegraph to the Magnetic Telegraph Company, in J. C. Vail, *Letters and Journals of Alfred Vail*, 21-22.

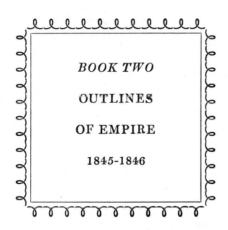

BOOK TWO

OUTLINES

OF EMPIRE

1845-1846

CHAPTER III

Thrust to the South

1 ·—·

WHETHER Congress might have taken a more sympathetic interest in the development of the telegraph, in the spring of 1845, had not such problems of manifest destiny as the "Reoccupation of Oregon" and the "Reannexation of Texas" absorbed its attention, cannot be determined. The proprietors of the Morse patent, for their part, were weary with the uncertainties of government patronage and turned to private enterprise in earnest. Morse realized his inadequacy for coping with the intricate business arrangements which would have to be made. He wisely chose as his representative, therefore, a man who seemed well-fitted for this type of work. That man was Amos Kendall, an earnest individual of fifty-six, who, having already made a name for himself as a journalist and a member of Jackson's Cabinet, was now seeking another field in which to engage an active mind.

Kendall had left his New England home and come to Washington to seek his fortune more than three decades earlier. A Dartmouth diploma, evidence to show that he had read law with a reputable attorney, and seventeen dollars were the young man's only assets. While awaiting a propitious moment for establishing himself in the legal profession, he accepted a position as tutor in the home of Henry Clay near Lexington, Kentucky, in the year 1814. Kendall had hoped his new situation would give him opportunity to discuss the social and political problems of the day with his employer, but Clay unfortunately was absent most of the time.

Kendall shortly left the academic backwater in which he found himself, and opened a law office in the village of Georgetown, Kentucky. The law, for Amos Kendall, was a profession which had been arrived at through a process of elimination; it was not that he liked law so much, but that he disliked medicine and surgery so much more, and felt himself unqualified to go into the ministry as his family had wished. An early interest in writing induced him, when the occasion arose, to accept a partnership in the local Georgetown paper. His vigorous pen in the course of time won for him a reputation, not only as a journalist, but also as a humanitarian.

In 1829 while Kendall was editor of the *Frankfort Argus,* Andrew Jackson sent for him and made him a member of his political family in Washington. Close contact served to deepen Jackson's respect for the editor of the *Argus;* and when Postmaster General Barry resigned in 1835, Amos Kendall was named to succeed him. Kendall's love of order and his executive ability were given ample opportunity to assert themselves. When he resigned in 1840, he had reorganized the Department's finances and relieved it from the harassing debt in which he had found it.

Having completed the task of bringing order out of chaos in the Post Office Department, and not being in the most robust health, Kendall had retired from the Cabinet in the hope that he might manage his farm and complete a long deferred biography of Andrew Jackson. He had amassed little capital during his active life, however, and when in the next five years financial troubles arose, his modest means were not sufficient to extricate him. This financial embarrassment had prompted him in 1845 to form a partnership with his nephew, John E. Kendall, in a general agency for the prosecution of claims against the government.

In the course of his activities at the Capital, he had met the discouraged Samuel F. B. Morse, weary with waiting for Congressional action which he despaired of ever coming. Kendall had intimated to Morse that should the bill for the extension of the telegraph fail, he would like to discuss the situation further with him.[1] Morse approached Kendall, therefore, following the failure of Congress to act, and after careful consideration that gentleman became agent for three-fourths of the Morse patent interest in the United States by contract dated March 10, 1845.[2] Kendall's executive ability, legal training, and unquestionable integrity, satisfied Morse that he had placed his telegraph interests in able hands.[3]

While Kendall thus became the agent for three-fourths of the patent right, it is a highly significant fact that the remaining one-

[1] Kendall to Morse, February 25, 1845, first of a long series of letters between these men which ultimately led to the appointment of Kendall as Morse's business agent on March 10, 1845, Morse Papers, xix.

[2] According to the terms of the agreement, Kendall was to get 10 percent on any sum which the proprietors might receive from the U.S. Government or any other purchaser. If Morse's interest of 9/16 should be sold for over $100,000, Kendall would receive 50 percent of all over that amount. (Copy of agreement of Morse and Vail with Kendall, March 10, 1845, in Vail Contract Book.)

[3] This biographical sketch of Kendall is based on his *Autobiography,* edited by his son-in-law, William Stickney; also the article on Kendall in *Dictionary of American Biography,* x, 325-327.

fourth was retained by Smith, whose consent would be required for any conveyance of patent rights. Smith warned that his cooperation in any plans for the future development of the telegraph would be withheld unless his claims against his co-patentees were satisfied.[4] Kendall was confident, however, that a satisfactory working basis could be reached with Smith through compromise and by arrangements that would be to their mutual interest.

2 ··—··

KENDALL's experience as Postmaster General had given him a thorough familiarity with the main commercial routes of the country. He proposed, therefore, to interest private capital in the construction of trunk telegraph lines along these routes, and then to build the numerous side or feeder lines necessary to serve the entire country. After money had been raised, lines built, and companies organized, stock was to be issued to those taking part in the enterprise. In most instances 50 percent of all stock issued was to be turned over to the patentees in return for conveyance of patent rights to the respective companies. Through this controlling stock interest Kendall expected to maintain that degree of unity among the individual companies which he believed to be essential to the efficient working of a nation-wide system of telegraphs.[5]

With New York as a hub he visualized great arteries radiating to the south, to the north, and to the west. He set to work energetically to find groups of men willing to finance the construction of the main lines. When his first attempts to secure capital for operation on a large scale failed, he himself assumed responsibility for a line from New York to Washington; while John J. Haley, a relative of Smith, ultimately undertook the building of a section from Washington to New Orleans. In the North, Smith agreed to connect New York City with Boston. And in New York State a contract was signed with the stage owner, John J. Butterfield of Utica, for the construction of a line from Buffalo via Albany to Springfield, Massachusetts—a terminus which was changed to New York City before actual building got under way. In the West, Henry O'Rielly[6] of Rochester was granted a

---

[4] Smith to Kendall, March 10, 1845, Smith Papers, XI.

[5] Series of letters Kendall to Morse, March-August, 1845, Morse Papers, XX.

[6] While the family spelling of the name was "O'Reilly," Henry preferred the form "O'Rielly," and adopted that spelling in later life. For the sake of clarity "O'Rielly" will be used consistently throughout this book.

contract for a line from the seaboard to the Mississippi and the Great Lakes.

While Kendall was working earnestly for the development of the telegraph by private enterprise, he strongly favored the sale of the patent rights to the government. Provisions had been made in every contract for the purchase of the lines at cost-plus premiums ranging from 20 to 100 percent, should Congress take steps to secure the invention prior to March 4, 1847.[7] Kendall's business associate, Smith, on the other hand, was not of like opinion. He had made up his mind that he would never again be a party to any application to the government to purchase the telegraph. "If this Government sees fit to adopt measures for its [the telegraph's] purchase, I shall meet it as I would all other purchasers," he wrote Kendall on August 6, 1845, "and if I could do as well by selling, as by holding on, I would sell—otherwise not." In fact, Smith freely stated that he should be reluctant to see the telegraph fall into government hands when the patentees could make so much more by private management.[8]

Kendall tried to reconcile their differing points of view. Smith was right in believing their primary object was money and not philanthropy, he replied. And yet should the telegraph be sold to the government at a fair price, the patentees would realize at once a comfortable wealth and be spared the years of struggle and uncertainty which private promotion would entail. It seemed to Kendall that this would be the best solution of all. Still, if something were not done by Congress at its next session, then he agreed to go along with Smith in making arrangements with private capital, and without any reservation. In conclusion, Kendall set forth the policy of appeasement which so greatly influenced his early dealings with Smith. "Whatever we do we must concert out plans and go on together," he wrote. "It is only by harmony in action that we can do anything, and to preserve it we must make concessions where we cannot agree in opinion."[9]

7 O'Rielly Contract, June 13, 1845 (Cost plus 20 percent); Articles of Agreement and Association of the Magnetic Telegraph Company, May 15, 1845 (Cost plus 100 percent or market value of stock); Articles of Association of the New York, Albany & Buffalo Telegraph Company, September 25, 1845 (Cost plus 50 percent); Articles of Association of the New York & Boston Magnetic Telegraph Association, October 22, 1845 (Cost plus 50 percent); Articles of Association of the Washington & New Orleans Telegraph Company, November 2, 1846 (Cost plus 20 percent).

8 Smith to Kendall, August 6, 1845, Smith Papers, XI.

9 Kendall to Smith, August 12, 1845, Smith Papers, XI.

3 · · · — ·

By the autumn of 1845 telegraph builders were constructing lines on virtually all of the important routes.[10] Kendall set out to organize a company of his own to build the New York-Washington line, following his failure in getting a group of New York capitalists to undertake the project on satisfactory terms. Several weeks of strenuous canvassing were not at all encouraging. Kendall became convinced that it would be best to build between New York and Philadelphia first, and to limit the request for capital to $15,000, the amount required to complete this section. He hoped that the success of the New York-Philadelphia line would induce capital to provide means for the extension of the telegraph to Baltimore and Washington.[11] Fifteen thousand dollars was a modest sum to ask of eastern capitalists even in 1845; but as one of the great speculators of that time, Jacob Little, declared, an investment in the telegraph was too great a gamble for him.

Finally William W. Corcoran of Washington, prominent financier of the banking house of Corcoran & Riggs, opened the subscription list with a pledge of $1,000. The largest subscription, and the only one for more than $1,000, was that of Smith for $2,750—which he failed to pay at the time it was needed, thereby obliging Kendall to make use of his own private funds to insure completion of the line. Funds were at last raised through the numerous small subscriptions of friends of the patentees and of interested men of limited means. The original list of subscribers was as follows:[12]

Corcoran & Riggs	$1,000	Amos Kendall	500
Benjamin B. French	1,000	Ezra Cornell	500
Eliphalet Case	1,000	Daniel Gold	1,000
Charles Monroe	1,000	Simon Brown	500
Peter G. Washington	200	A. J. Glossbrenner	500
John J. Haley	500	John M. Brodhead	$1,000
John E. Kendall	300	Charles G. Page	500
James A. McLaughlin	350	George Templeman	200

10 The seaboard line from Washington to New Orleans was delayed in building until November 1846.

11 Series of letters between Kendall and Smith, May-August, 1845, Smith Papers, XI; also Kendall to Morse, August 5, 1845, Morse Papers, xx.

12 "Minutes of the Meetings of the Stockholders and Board of Directors of the Magnetic Telegraph Company," November 7, 1845, in a bound volume of pamphlets entitled: *Articles of Association and Charter from the State of Maryland of the Magnetic Telegraph Company, together with the Office Regulations and the Minutes of the Meetings of Stockholders and Board of Directors.* (This work will be cited subsequently as Minutes of the Meetings of the Magnetic Telegraph Company.)

Henry J. Rogers	100	Keller & Greenough	500
J. W. Murphy	100	J. C. Brodhead	500
A. W. Paine	500	T. L. and A. T. Smith	200
F. O. J. Smith	2,750	A. Thomas Smith	100
J. Black	200		
			$15,000

On May 15, 1845, carefully drawn and specific Articles of Association were adopted and the Magnetic Telegraph Company, the first telegraph company in the United States, came into being.[13] Among other things the Articles provided that "for fifty dollars paid in by subscribers . . . a certificate for one share of one hundred dollars" should be issued.[14] Therefore, the original subscription of $15,000 required an issue of $30,000 in stock to the subscribers. The patentees were to receive an additional $30,000, or half the capital, in return for the right to use the Morse system on a line from New York to Philadelphia. In other words, the value of the line was estimated at four times its cost, so that an actual outlay of $15,000 was to be represented by a capitalization of $60,000. W. W. Corcoran and B. B. French were made trustees to hold the patent right and property until final organization was effected.[15]

4 · · · · —

THE building program was under the direction of Amos Kendall.[16] As his assistants in the field he chose Ezra Cornell and Dr. A. C. Goell. Cornell was placed in charge of work on the section from Somerville to Newark, New Jersey, while Dr. Goell was to supervise construction of the Philadelphia section. From the Merchants' Exchange in Philadelphia the line was to follow the ordinary wagon road to Newark by way of Norristown, Doylestown, and Somerville. This circuitous route was necessitated by Kendall's inability to make satisfactory arrangements with the railroads for the use of their rights of way. Construction contracts provided for conductors of unannealed

[13] The Articles of Association of the Magnetic Telegraph Company so influenced the administration of subsequent pioneer companies that they have been given in full in Appendix 1.

[14] Articles of Association of the Magnetic Telegraph Company, May 15, 1845.

[15] Minutes of the Meetings of the Magnetic Telegraph Company, November 7, 1845.

[16] Amos Kendall and F. O. J. Smith had been made joint contractors in the original agreement with the trustees. Smith resigned, however, in protest against the trustees' refusal to accept wire and other telegraph materials that he had on hand as part payment for his subscription pledge of $2,750. (Minutes of the Meetings of the Stockholders and Board of Directors of the Magnetic Telegraph Company, November 7, 1845.)

copper wire, poles set two hundred feet apart, and insulators of the glass bureau-knob pattern.[17] Work was pushed vigorously throughout the fall and winter of 1845-46. As a result of the unceasing efforts of Kendall the line from Philadelphia to Newark, New Jersey, was completed on January 20. But New York City, the ultimate goal, could not be reached until some practical method could be found for spanning the Hudson River.[18]

Upon the completion of the line the stockholders met in New York for final organization in accordance with the provisions of the Articles of Association which the company had adopted the previous May. Kendall's democratic principles found expression in Article 2, which stated that the line should "be opened alike to all men . . . and the first to come shall be first served." No individual was to have the use of the telegraph for more than fifteen minutes at one time when others were waiting. The only exceptions were to be in case of "public emergencies and to promote the arrest of fugitives from justice, and prevent the commission or consummation of crime."[19] So fundamental did its framers consider the principle of impartiality in telegraph operation that they rephrased it in two different sections of the bulky body of rules called "Office Regulations." Among some sixty-six other detailed regulations it was further provided that "the Telegraph Offices . . . should be kept open for business every day from sunrise until 10 o'clock P.M. except the ordinary hours for morning and afternoon services on the Sabbath." Operators were enjoined to observe the strictest decorum towards all customers and to listen to complaints, however unreasonable, with good temper. They were urged to cultivate good feeling with each other, and especially warned that "all angry or impertinent messages sent along the wires from operator to operator . . . were absolutely prohibited, or if sent, must be paid for as other messages not pertaining to the business of the line."[20]

The stockholders chose as their first board of directors, Amos Kendall, Benjamin B. French, A. Sidney Doane, John J. Haley, John W. Norton, Thomas M. Clark, John C. Stearns, William M. Swain,

[17] Kendall to his wife, June 6, 1845, cited in Kendall, *Autobiography*, 529; Kendall to Morse, June 7, 1845, Morse Papers, XX; Kendall to Smith, July 18, 1845, Smith Papers, XI.

[18] Kendall to Smith, June 24, 1845, Smith Papers, XI; B. B. French to Smith, September 6, 1845, Smith Papers, XXVI.

[19] Articles of Association of the Magnetic Telegraph Company, May 15, 1845.

[20] *Ibid.*, November 1846.

and J. R. Trimble. Amos Kendall was made president, while Thomas M. Clark became secretary and Dr. A. Sidney Doane, treasurer. The salary of the president was fixed at $2,250; that of the secretary at $350; while the treasurer was to receive $300 a year. The salaries of employees were correspondingly low. Chief operators were to receive $600, assistant operators $500, clerks $500, and assistant clerks $350 a year.[21]

The line having been carefully tested to make sure it would work, President Kendall had advertisements inserted in all the leading New York and Philadelphia papers, and sent out a circular letter to prospective customers announcing the arrangements and rates for conducting the new communications service between the two cities:

Sir:

The Magnetic Telegraph between New York and Philadelphia via Newark, will be opened to the public on Tuesday, January 27. Messages will be dispatched from the Telegraph Office, No. 10 Wall Street, (basement) New York, at 9, 11 A.M. and 12 o'clock, M. — 3, 4, and 7 P.M. and will be received from Philadelphia via Newark, at 8½, 9½, and 11½ A.M., and 2½, 4½, and 10 P.M. Communications which must all be pre-paid, will be sent in the order they are received.

The following are the rates established for ten words and under:— For the transmission and writing out of every communication, not exceeding ten words, every figure being counted as a word, exclusive of the signature and address, and the direction of the writer, as to the disposition of the communications, from New York to Philadelphia, Twenty-five Cents. For every addition, not exceeding ten words, the same rate of charge as in the first ten.

Yours truly,
Amos Kendall, President.[22]

5 — — —

RECEIPTS of the new line for the first four days were $100. "When you consider," wrote Treasurer Doane to Smith, "that we anticipate the mails by only a few hours, are obliged to send to Newark, can only send a few times daily, that business is extremely dull, that editors do nothing for us, and we have not yet the confidence of the public and that on 2 of the 4 days we have been delayed and lost business in Philadelphia through mismanagement—when you consider all these

---

[21] Minutes of the Meetings of the Magnetic Telegraph Company, January 21-August 13, 1846.

[22] O'Rielly Manuscript Collection, II. The O'Rielly Collection in the New York Historical Society Library contains about 100 vols. of manuscript and printed material.

things you will see we are all well satisfied with results so far. In one month we shall be doing a $50 business a day."[23]

Morse was even more optimistic. "Telegraph matters are looking very well," he wrote to his brother, Sidney. "We are operating between Newark and Philadelphia and the point is decided that the stock *is a dividend paying stock*; the stockholders are in good spirits and prepared to push forward. We are troubled with the river and that is the reason we cannot communicate direct to New York, but hope to be able in a few weeks."[24]

The Hudson was the great stumbling block of the enterprise. No practical means could be found to cross the river to New York City. Balloons, pigeons, submarine cables, water circuits, masts of wood and iron, piers in the bed of the river, anchored ships, and other means were tried with little success.[25] As early as the autumn of 1845, Ezra Cornell had attempted to lay a cable across the Hudson from Fort Lee, New Jersey, to the New York shore. A cotton-covered copper wire was saturated with pitch, placed in a lead pipe, and embedded in the river. Just as Cornell was ready to test his cable he had the unhappy experience of having it brought up on the anchor of a ship. In the process the cable was broken in two and lost.[26]

Having failed to cross the Hudson with their "lightning," Cornell and his associates sought other means for expediting the service. A line was strung from Newark to Fort Lee on the Jersey side of the Hudson River. Messages received at Fort Lee were then taken across the river by boat at regular intervals, and telegraphed to New York City from an office which was opened on the upper end of Manhattan in the home of John J. Audubon, the naturalist. This arrangement was meant to be only a temporary one while the company was awaiting the completion of a second cable by Cornell.[27] When that and other attempts to lay a cable beneath the Hudson had failed, the Magnetic Telegraph resorted once more to its earlier practice of sending messages from Newark to Jersey City by railroad and thence by ferryboat to New York. At the same time plans were made for the immediate construction of a telegraph line to connect Newark with Jersey City.[28] With the completion of the line to Jersey City a small

[23] Doane to Smith, February 1, 1846, Smith Papers, XIX.
[24] Morse to brother Sidney, January 30, 1846, Morse Papers, XXI.
[25] *National Telegraph Review*, July 1853, 111.
[26] *Baltimore American*, October 30, 1845.
[27] Minutes of the Meetings of the Magnetic Telegraph Company, January 22, 1846.
[28] *Ibid.*, January 23, 1846.

room over the ferry house was made into a telegraph office and messengers were dispatched at frequent intervals on the ferry boats with messages for delivery in New York City.

Efforts to span the Hudson did not cease with the extension of the line to Jersey City. From time to time attempts were made to cross the river by means of high masts at Fort Lee, and at a more propitious location upstream, five miles below West Point; but the masts proved very impermanent, and they were, therefore, no solution to the problem.[29] Nearly a decade was to pass before the use of a cable insulated with gutta percha was to provide a permanent means for leading the current through bodies of water.

6 ......

FROM the first day of its operation a host of troubles descended upon the pioneer telegraph company. The glass insulators, as they glistened in the sun, made tempting targets for boys and marksmen, and they were destroyed by the dozen. The soft copper wire was highly susceptible to climatic changes; drawn taut by freezing temperatures, it broke in many places. To overcome this difficulty, copper wire was replaced by iron. Although not so good a conductor, it was stronger, less subject to expansion and contraction under varying weather conditions, and therefore much superior for meeting the needs of early telegraphy.[30] Since the company was forced to rely on well-intentioned but inexperienced men to meet and solve its varied problems, it is not surprising that maintenance of uninterrupted service for several days was an event.[31]

On July 7, 1846, the treasurer reported the profits of the New York office for the preceding five months as $293.17, of the Philadelphia office for the preceding three months as $223.50. Total cash receipts since the opening of the line in January had been $4,228.77. He explained that this rather disappointing showing might be partly accounted for by the fact that the line had been out of order on

[29] Kendall to Smith, October 2, 1846, Smith Papers, XI; Morse to Vail, June 10, 1847, Vail Papers; Vail to B. B. French, September 4, 1848, Vail Papers.

[30] "Annual Report to Stockholders of the New York & Boston Magnetic Telegraph Association," September 5, 1848, in: *Articles of Association of the New York and Boston Magnetic Telegraph Association, together with the Office Regulations, and Records of the Meetings of the Trustees, Stockholders and Directors*; De Bow's Review, September 1847.

[31] Reid to O'Rielly, May 12, 1846, O'Rielly Manuscript Collection, II.

account of breaks in the wires thirty-six days, or nearly a quarter of the time that it had been in operation.[32]

Such experiences were enough to discourage the most stout-hearted, but the prudent Magnetic Telegraph board of directors rose to the occasion. Notices were printed declaring that stockholders were not responsible for debts, and operators were told that they must look to office receipts alone for pay.[33]

7 — — · ·

AMONG the first to patronize the telegraph were the lottery men. The numbers telegraphed from Philadelphia were received at the New Jersey terminus of the line and then sent by pigeon to New York, thereby beating the regular telegraph messenger service by many minutes.

Brokers were another group who quickly realized the value of the new invention. As early as March 3, 1846, the *New York Herald* complained that certain parties in New York and Philadelphia were employing the telegraph for speculating in stocks. Since the board of brokers in Philadelphia met much earlier than the board in New York, it was possible for speculators to have the prices of Philadelphia stocks telegraphed to the terminus of the line in New Jersey from which point they could be transmitted by pre-arranged semaphoric signals to accomplices on the New York side of the Hudson.

The best customer of the early telegraph was the press. Before the Magnetic Company's line was even completed the subject of the relations of the telegraph to the press was carefully discussed by the Magnetic board. It was decided that when a communication exceeded 100 words the price on all words exceeding that number should be reduced to one-third the regular price. These rates were open to all editors and publishers alike. A provision allowing the press to maintain charge accounts soon led to trouble. Some of the papers were persuaded only with the utmost difficulty to pay for services rendered and some of the accounts had to be canceled altogether.[34] The papers were not entirely to blame for their reluctance to pay the company, for the services rendered were often of doubtful value because of long delays and errors.[35]

[32] Minutes of the Meetings of the Magnetic Telegraph Company, July 7, 1846.
[33] *Ibid.*, July-August, 1846.
[34] Minutes of the Meetings of the Magnetic Telegraph Company, November 8, 1845-August 12, 1846.
[35] A detailed discussion of early press-telegraph relations will be found in Chapter XIV.

8 — · · · ·

KENDALL had no sooner completed arrangements for the construction of the line from New York to Philadelphia, than he undertook to raise additional funds for its extension to Baltimore and Washington.[36] Capital showed little interest in his proposal. The soundness of the telegraph as an investment remained to be proved. Had not Postmaster General Cave Johnson in his annual report for 1845 expressed doubt that revenues from the government telegraph line could be made to equal expenditures under any rate of tariffs that the public could afford to pay?[37]

Nevertheless, on January 14, 1846, Kendall was able to report to the Magnetic trustees that $10,000 had been subscribed as follows:[38]

Swain, Abell & Simmons, Philadelphia	$3,500
Jos. R. Chandler, Philadelphia	500
George Bush, Wilmington, Del.	200
Mahlon Betts, "	200
Merritt Canby, "	200
Wm. R. Sellers, "	200
J. R. Trimble, "	200
Furman Black, Washington, D.C.	1,000
Henry O'Rielly, New York	4,000
	——————
	$10,000

This list shows that three-fourths of the total had been pledged by two men—Henry O'Rielly and William M. Swain. To the enthusiastic O'Rielly, the success of the telegraph enterprise was more than a mere business matter; it had become a "cause." Determined that it should not fail, O'Rielly employed funds that he had raised for the construction of his own lines into the West to finance the building of the Magnetic line along the seaboard. The other leading subscriber, William Swain of the *Philadelphia Public Ledger*, had been an early convert to the telegraph. That fact, coupled with the increased demand for news as a result of the mounting tension between the United States and Mexico, prompted him to support and work for the new line.

The necessary funds having been secured, Kendall had asked for construction bids. He had hoped to give Smith the contract, in the

---

[36] Minutes of the Meetings of the Magnetic Telegraph Company, November 8, 1845.
[37] O'Rielly to Kendall, December 25, 1845, O'Rielly Manuscript Collection I.
[38] Minutes of the Meetings of the Magnetic Telegraph Company, January 14, 1846.

interest of better relations, but Smith's bid of $20,000 was unsatisfactory.[39] On November 25, 1845, Kendall informed his Yankee associate that a $12,000 bid[40] by Henry O'Rielly had been accepted. He admitted that he did not see how O'Rielly could afford to build the line for such a price.[41]

Apparently no such doubts assailed the energetic Irishman. All during the winter and spring of 1845-46, O'Rielly pushed steadily forward with the construction of the line in spite of numerous annoyances and difficulties. The funds promised by the subscribers were delayed, and in some cases not paid at all.[42] O'Rielly kept urging Kendall to forward money for him to carry on his work. Kendall kept promising that funds would be available in several days.[43] Annoying as these delays must have been, O'Rielly seemed to understand. Along with his admonitions for failure to send the money, went a note of sympathy. "You have found probably, in your efforts for establishing the Telegraph System, more hesitancy and difficulty than you anticipated—more apathy (if nothing else) on the part of business men and capitalists, than any one could well imagine or expect," he wrote to Kendall on Christmas day, 1845. "It will be a memorable fact in telegraphic history, that, vast as are the advantages it promises, scarcely a merchant or capitalist in the great cities of New York, Philadelphia, or Baltimore, could be induced to take a dollar of stock to encourage the noble enterprise!"[44]

Both public and press fretted and criticized the contractor for his slowness in completing the Philadelphia-Baltimore section. Writing in the *Public Ledger*, O'Rielly apologized for the delay in opening the line. Without mentioning the fact that he had been handicapped for want of funds, he explained that early delay had been caused by the refusal of the railroads to grant rights of way on satisfactory terms. He assured his readers that the posts from Philadelphia to Baltimore were erected, and completion of the line only awaited the arrival of additional iron cord, which the factory was unable to manufacture fast enough to meet his needs. The crossing of rivers had also presented a perplexing problem which had not yet been satisfactorily solved. In spite of these difficulties, he assured his public that every

[39] Kendall to Smith, October 26, 1845, Smith Papers, XI.
[40] This amount was later increased to $14,000.
[41] Kendall to Smith, November 25, 1845, Smith Papers, XI.
[42] Series of letters between Kendall and O'Rielly, December 1845-February 1846, O'Rielly Manuscript Collection, I, II.
[43] Kendall to O'Rielly, December 24, 1845, O'Rielly Manuscript Collection I.
[44] O'Rielly to Kendall, December 25, 1845, O'Rielly Manuscript Collection I.

effort was being made to rush the line to completion. News from Washington and the South could then be delivered to the eastern press and the public with all possible dispatch.[45]

Finally on June 5, 1846, the Philadelphia-Baltimore section was completed. After connection had been made with the government line from Baltimore to Washington, messages were sent directly from Washington to Philadelphia. "This is the longest line of electric telegraph ever operated upon, being one hundred and forty miles, and the messages were sent in a space of time imperceptible to the human mind," declared the *National Intelligencer*.[46] A few days later Professor Morse and Alfred Vail, after repeated attempts, were able to communicate directly between Washington and Jersey City, "a distance of no less than 260 miles."[47] The wonderful possibilities of the new invention were now beginning to manifest themselves. Benjamin B. French, politician, speculator, *bon vivant*, and later to become president of the Magnetic Telegraph Company wrote enthusiastically to his brother, Henry Flagg French, of the newest speculation of a speculative age. "The Telegraph is doing wonders—we are now taking hundreds of dollars daily and have a great deal more work than we can do on one wire. We can communicate from here [Washington] to Jersey City in a second, and next week we shall probably communicate with Boston! The Telegraph stock *must be* the best stock in the country—our line will pay for itself in one year."[48]

The shrewd and somewhat parsimonious Magnetic board, after having the Philadelphia-Baltimore line inspected by Alfred Vail, made a number of complaints and refused to pay O'Rielly the amount of his bill. A long and bitter quarrel ensued in which O'Rielly claimed that Kendall had verbally authorized him to make certain changes in the terms of the original contract, while the board declared for a strict adherence to their written agreement. It refused to allow O'Rielly more than the $14,000 called for, subject to a deduction of the amount required to repair all of the original defects of the line.[49] Eager, impatient of restraint, and believing all men to be as sincerely and whole-heartedly interested in advancing the

[45] *Philadelphia Public Ledger*, May 12, 1846.
[46] *National Intelligencer*, June 6, 1846.
[47] *Washington Union*, June 8, 1846.
[48] B. B. French to Henry Flagg French, June 11, 1846, French Papers, II, in Library of Congress.
[49] Series of letters between O'Rielly and officers of the Magnetic Telegraph Company, July-October, 1846, O'Rielly Manuscript Collection, III; Minutes of the Magnetic Telegraph Company, October 7, 1846.

telegraphic cause as he, O'Rielly was badly used by the Magnetic board. The final settlement left the generous contractor with little or no profit for six months of hard labor.

9 — · —

YET another important development which was to affect materially the future of the Magnetic Telegraph Company was the conclusion of a contract in November 1846, for a line of telegraph from Washington southward through Richmond, Petersburg, Raleigh, Charleston, Savannah, and Mobile to New Orleans. Kendall's earlier experience as Postmaster General had led him to believe that a telegraph line through the South would prove the most profitable of any in the country. As Postmaster General, he had operated an express mail between New York and New Orleans to carry letters at triple the regular postage rates. It was a success from the beginning. In spite of heavy operating costs the express mail had yielded a profit of more than $280,000 a year. Based upon the distance between New York and New Orleans this amounted to better than $200 a mile, or more than enough to build a telegraph line of two wires. Kendall estimated that a telegraph line over this route would yield an income three or four times greater than that produced by the express mail. As he saw it, there was no better opportunity in the world "for creating so great a property by so small an expenditure."[50]

The investing public was not so enthusiastic as Kendall about the construction of a line into the South. Promoters seemed disposed to hold back until the New York-Boston and the New York-Philadelphia lines could be completed and the practical results of a long line ascertained.

In view of the war with Mexico, Kendall had hoped that the government would furnish a portion of the funds necessary to build the line, and a bill appropriating money for this purpose was introduced into the Senate. Meeting with stiff opposition, the proposition was withdrawn. "It was attacked by Mr. Calhoun and others on constitutional grounds!" fumed Kendall. "It is not constitutional to use the lightning against Mexico!"[51]

Annoyed but still undaunted Kendall now proposed to Secre-

[50] Kendall to a friend, September 18, 1846, quoted by Reid, *Telegraph in America*, 142.
[51] Kendall to Smith, May 8, 1846, Smith Papers, XI.

tary of War William L. Marcy the construction of a line from Washington to New Orleans as a war measure. Should Congress underwrite the project, the government would be provided with a rapid means of communication for official dispatches. As remuneration for the use of the patent rights on the route, Kendall merely asked that private messages be turned over to the telegraph company for transmission when the wires were not occupied with government business. To allay fear in some quarters that such action would be a first step toward permanent federal participation in the telegraph industry, Kendall agreed to take over the line at cost upon termination of the war, giving the government a lien on the property as security. This plan also failed.[52]

Kendall's next approach was through Postmaster General Cave Johnson. A private express service for transmitting news forty-eight hours in advance of the regular government mails had been put into operation between Montgomery and Mobile, thereby cutting into the revenues of the Post Office Department, and promoting speculation. In a message to the Senate on June 4, 1846, Postmaster General Johnson described the evils which had grown out of the private express and advocated the establishment of a telegraph line between Mobile and Montgomery as the best means for checking them.[53] But Congress was not receptive.

When all attempts to obtain government aid had proved futile, Kendall turned to private enterprise. Dr. Doane, in conjunction with his friend, Smith, offered to construct the line, but they were unwilling to give more than one-fourth of the stock on the first two wires for the patent rights. Although eager to get the line built, Kendall refused to give the patent rights on this important route for less than one-half of the stock.[54] Doane approached Kendall and offered him a liberal share of stock in the line if he would yield. Kendall indignantly refused the bribe, thereby incurring the bitter hostility of the vindictive doctor who proceeded to do all in his power to force Kendall out of the presidency of the Magnetic Telegraph Company.[55]

Still another possible source of aid was the press. In September Kendall approached a number of the leading eastern papers with the

---

[52] *Ibid.*, May 12, 1846; Kendall to O'Rielly, May 28, 1846, O'Rielly Manuscript Collection, II.

[53] Senate Doc. No. 373, 29 Cong., 1 sess.

[54] Kendall to Smith, March 22, 1846, *et seq.*, Smith Papers, XI.

[55] Kendall to Smith, June 8, 1846, *et seq.*, Smith Papers, XI.

suggestion that they finance the building of a telegraph line to New Orleans, in return for which they would be given exclusive war news, financial and commercial reports, and other desired information ahead of all rivals. Other papers were to be allowed to join the proposed syndicate later upon payment of a sum sufficient to retire their share of the original cost of the line. In this way no odious monopoly would be created since it would be possible eventually for all newspaper interests to be placed on an equal footing.[56] Eager as the press was for prompt news, the telegraph was too speculative for the debt-burdened, competitive journals of 1846, and Kendall's project came to nothing.[57]

Finally on November 2, 1846, a contract was signed with John J. Haley, proprietor of a small restaurant in New York City, and a cousin of Smith. According to the agreement, the patentees were to receive one-half of the stock issued on this line, but as a concession to Smith, Kendall agreed that the patentees would share in the construction profits.[58] Although such an agreement was definitely against Kendall's principles, his eagerness to begin construction on this retarded route caused him to accept the contract's distasteful provisions. The Washington & New Orleans Telegraph Company—the corporate name under which the projected line was established—was expected to bring a great volume of southern business pouring into Washington. There it was to be turned over to the Magnetic Telegraph Company to be relayed on to Baltimore, Philadelphia, New York, and the North.[59] But years were to pass before this expectation was to be realized.

10 ·——·—

IN addition to promotional problems, construction difficulties, financial troubles, and scientific ignorance, the Magnetic Telegraph Company was dangerously threatened by the internal dissensions and jealousies which racked it from the start. Ezra Cornell and Alfred Vail, for example, had developed a dislike for one another from their earliest relations. There was constant conflict between them until

56 *Ibid.*, September 28, 1846.

57 For a full discussion of the press and its relation to the telegraph see Chapter XIV.

58 Contract of J. J. Haley with subscribers of the Washington & New Orleans line, November 2, 1846. Vail Contract Book.

59 Prospectus of the Washington & New Orleans Telegraph Company, December 1846.

Cornell left the employ of the Magnetic to engage in telegraphic labors elsewhere.[60]

Even more serious than the numerous personal antagonisms was the bitter rivalry of various groups within the company for control of the management. Ill health, along with the multiplicity of business details, had caused Kendall to neglect somewhat his duties as president. It is not surprising when the scope of his responsibility is considered; in addition to his regular executive duties he was expected to act as general superintendent for the entire line. At length, certain members of the board of directors came to the conclusion that Kendall should be relieved of the active supervision of the line by appointing a superintendent whose salary would be deducted from that of Kendall.[61] The hard-working Scotsman, James D. Reid, whom O'Rielly had first interested in the telegraph, was finally appointed to this position.[62] While Kendall and Reid cooperated fully and worked hard for the best interests of the company, friction between various rival groups headed by Smith and his colleagues, Doane and Rogers, inaugurated a movement to remove Kendall.[63]

11 ·—— · ·——·

WHILE thus torn by dissension within, the Magnetic Telegraph Company was called upon to meet a further danger which threatened from without. Early in July 1845, articles appeared in the New York papers and rumors were circulated concerning a remarkable printing telegraph instrument that was about to make its appearance.[64] The rival telegraph was the invention of Royal E. House of Vermont, who in 1846 applied to the United States Patent Office for a patent on an ingenious printing instrument. The Morse patentees loudly denounced the newcomer as an infringement upon their patent rights, and it was not until 1848 after House had made certain changes in his instrument that he was granted a patent dated from April 18, 1846.[65]

---

60 Vail to Jos. R. Bailey, January 11, 1846; Bailey to Vail, January 14, 1846, Vail Papers.

61 Minutes of the Magnetic Telegraph Company, May 22, 1846; Smith to A. S. Doane, May 8, 1846, Smith Papers, XXVI; Kendall to Smith, May 30, 1846, Smith Papers, XI; *Ibid.*, June 8, 1846.

62 Minutes of the Magnetic Telegraph Company, October 6, 1846.

63 Kendall to Smith, June 8, 1846, Smith Papers, XI; Kendall to Thos. M. Clark, June 7, 1846, Kendall Papers in Library of Congress; Henry Rogers to O'Rielly, July 17, 1846, O'Rielly MS Collection, III.

64 Kendall to Morse, July 12, 1845, Morse Papers, XX.

65 Shaffner, *The Telegraph Manual*, 391; Reid, *The Telegraph in America*, 457; George B. Prescott, *Electricity and the Electric Telegraph*, Sixth edition, 112.

The House instrument, instead of recording messages in the form of dots and dashes that had to be laboriously translated, printed the message directly upon a paper tape in Roman letters. In general, there were two distinct parts to the apparatus—first the composing or transmitting, and second the registering or printing apparatus. Unlike the Morse instrument which made use of the electric current to do most of the work, the House apparatus relied largely upon manual power, air, and a variety of springs and frictions to achieve its results.[66]

In sending a message with the House printing telegraph the transmitting apparatus was set in motion, a signal (one break of the circuit) was given to the distant receiving station, and then with the communication before him the operator commenced to touch in rapid succession those keys on his keyboard which were marked with the consecutive letters of the message to be sent. On hearing the signal, the operator at the receiving station set his printing apparatus in motion and sent back the signal that he was ready. The receiving operator had nothing to do then except to glance occasionally at the strip of paper upon which the message was being printed to see that no false break had occurred to interrupt the synchronization of the sending and receiving instruments. When the printing was finished, he tore off the strip containing the message and placed it in an envelope for delivery.[67]

While the House apparatus was considerably faster than that of Morse—an experienced operator could attain a speed of between 1,800 and 2,600 words per hour[68]—it was not practical for use upon long circuits, since its electrical resistance was too high. In 1846, moreover, the complex House mechanism was found to work very imperfectly upon the rude lines of that day. Several years were to elapse before the "House humbug," as Morse was fond of terming it,[69] was to become an active competitor.[70]

12 ·——···—··

As the hectic year 1846 drew to a close, President Kendall and Superintendent Reid could not present a very inspiring picture of the Magnetic Telegraph Company's progress. Service had been im-

[66] *Ibid.*, 115.   [67] *Ibid.*, 124.   [68] *Ibid.*
[69] Morse to brother Sidney, October 12, 1847, Morse Papers, XXIII.
[70] Morse to Messrs. Livingston and Wells, January 20, 1847; Morse to brother Sidney, January 28, 1847, Morse Papers, XXII. See also *Cincinnati Gazette*, October 4, 6, 1847; Report of the Superintendent of the Census, 1852.

perfect; and repairs and reconstruction had proved exceedingly expensive. Lottery men, bankers, brokers, business men, and the press had nibbled carefully, and as a result the volume of business had been light. On the other hand, the future seemed to offer promise. The telegraph was now firmly established; each month's receipts showed an improvement over those of the preceding month. Writing to Smith six months after the line had been opened for business, Kendall was able to say, "Our line takes in about $600 a week and had we not run in debt the first three months we could now make a good dividend. Our Treasurer thinks our net income now is 5 percent on the stock or 20 percent on the money invested."[71]

By the close of 1846 not only had all talk of purchase of the telegraph by the government subsided, but negotiations were actually under way for the purchase of the government's experimental line by the Magnetic Telegraph Company.[72] Complete withdrawal of the government from the telegraph business was imminent. In December, no satisfactory terms of sale having been agreed upon, Postmaster General Johnson had leased the Baltimore-Washington line to Vail and Rogers to be maintained and operated for its receipts. The following March, they transferred their lease to the Magnetic Telegraph, and a short time later the Baltimore-Washington line was absorbed as part of the Magnetic system.[73] The government's first chapter in telegraph history was thereby brought to a close, and nearly a score of years was to pass before Congress, aroused by the increasingly monopolistic nature of the telegraph industry, was to begin the writing of another.

[71] Kendall to Smith, October 6, 1846, Smith Papers, XI.
[72] Kendall to Morse, July 12, 1846, Morse Papers, XXI; Minutes of the Magnetic Telegraph Company, October 7, 1846.
[73] William Dundas, Chief Clerk P. O. Dept. to Vail and Rogers, April 13, 1847, Vail Papers. The order transferring the lease to the Magnetic Telegraph Company was dated April 12, 1847 to take effect on the 16th.

CHAPTER IV

Invasion of the North

1 ·——·

THE New York and Boston line was ill-fated from the beginning.
Conceived in adversity and reared under a cloud, it became a re-
proach and byword. Even before it came into being, Boston had been
the audience to which Dr. Charles T. Jackson, Morse's companion on
the ship *Sully*,[1] had addressed his charges concerning the fraudulent
nature of the Morse claims. He contended that he, not Morse, was
the real inventor of the telegraph, and he did his utmost to discourage
its acceptance by his fellow citizens.[2] Unfavorable publicity coupled
with Yankee conservatism resulted in the line's receiving virtually no
financial support from the New England metropolis.[3] Important as
were these influences in its formative period, the most blighting cir-
cumstance was the fact that the line was associated with Smith whose
unsavory reputation was known throughout New England.

After two abortive attempts to solicit funds for the construction of
the line—one undertaken by Smith in the summer of 1844,[4] and the
other by George E. Pomeroy a year later[5]—Smith determined to complete the enterprise even if it meant turning to his personal resources.
At his instigation, therefore, Articles of Association for the New York
& Boston Magnetic Telegraph Association were drawn up on October 22, 1845. The line was to follow the Harlem Railroad to the
outskirts of New York City where it was to turn eastward along the
turnpike through Stamford, Norwalk, and Bridgeport to New Haven,
from which point it was to follow the rights of way of the Hartford
& New Haven, the Worcester, and the Western railroads to Boston.
Smith named Crawford Livingston, Benjamin B. Mussey, and James
M. Thompson to act as trustees of the Association until formal organization of the line; and they, in a spirit of *noblesse oblige*, ap-

[1] For earlier reference see Chapter I.

[2] Vail to Smith, January 11, 1839, Smith Papers, XI; Gale to Smith, January 12, 1839,
Smith Papers, XI.

[3] Minutes of the Meeting of the Stockholders of the New York & Boston Magnetic
Telegraph Association, January 7, 1846.

[4] Contract of Patentees with F. O. J. Smith, June 18, 1844, Vail Contract Book. Smith
was also trying to promote the telegraph in Maine at this time. See letters, Josiah Calef
to Smith, July 22, 1844; W. H. Y. Hackett to Smith, July 31, 1844, *et seq.*, Smith Papers,
XVIII.

[5] Kendall to Morse, August 5, 1845, Morse Papers, XX.

pointed him as contractor.[6] Capitalization was optimistically fixed at $120,000. At the agreed rate of $160 a mile for a line of two wires, it was estimated that construction costs would total $40,000. In addition, for every $50 paid in by a subscriber, a certificate for one share of capital stock with a par value of $75 should be issued. Therefore the original subscription of $40,000 required an issue of $60,000 in stock to the subscribers. A like amount of stock was to be issued to Morse, Vail and Smith for the patent rights. In other words, the line was to be capitalized at three times its construction cost of $40,000.[7]

Although the patentees had been assured that the necessary funds would be subscribed within ten days from the date of the Articles of Association, it was the first week in January before the trustees felt able to take action. On January 7, 1846, they told the stockholders that $28,000 of the necessary $40,000 had been subscribed, and therefore they felt justified in accepting formally the construction contract previously agreed to with Smith. Measures were being taken, explained the trustees, to have the remainder of the stock taken in Boston from which no subscription of consequence had been received.[8]

Formal organization of the Association was also effected at this time, and a unanimous ballot was cast for the following officers: A. Sidney Doane, president; James T. Marshall, secretary; and Francis Hall, treasurer. The board of directors was composed of G. W. Bazin of Boston, J. M. Thompson of Springfield, and A. Sidney Doane, J. J. Haley and E. D. Saxton of New York City.[9]

6 Articles of Association of the New York & Boston Magnetic Telegraph Association, October 22, 1845. The incorporation of the New York & Boston Telegraph Association was unique; it may be said to have been done by proxy. While enjoying the full legal protection of the States of Massachusetts and Connecticut, it was never specifically incorporated in either. On April 10, 1846, the State of Massachusetts, by special act of the legislature, incorporated B. B. Mussey, George W. Bazin, and J. M. Thompson (Crawford Livingston having severed all connection with the line) as the "Proprietors of the Electro-Magnetic Telegraph" for the purpose of constructing lines of telegraph under the Morse patent within the state. Varying mainly in the addition of the names of Edward H. Mitchell and Winthrop Atwill to the list of corporators, Connecticut passed a similar act on June 11 of the same year. Subsequently these acts of incorporation of the "Proprietors of the Electro-Magnetic Telegraph" were accepted by the stockholders of the New York & Boston Telegraph Association. The "Proprietors of the Electro-Magnetic Telegraph," in turn, agreed to accept the Articles of Association of the New York & Boston Telegraph Association. (Massachusetts Statutes, Acts and Resolves, 1846; Connecticut Statutes, Public Acts, 1846; Minutes of Meeting of the Stockholders of the New York & Boston Magnetic Telegraph Association, July 13, 1846.)

7 Articles of Association of the New York & Boston Magnetic Telegraph Association, October 22, 1845.

8 Minutes of the Meeting of the Stockholders of the New York & Boston Magnetic Telegraph Association, January 7, 1846.

9 Ibid., January 6, 1846.

2 ··—··

ACTUAL construction of the line proceeded no more smoothly than the collection of funds. Smith's building program was slipshod and careless; activity on all sections of the line was characterized by poor coordination and confusion born of ignorance. Illustrative of the state of affairs is the letter written to Smith by W. Y. Deere, member of a construction gang, in the spring of 1846: "Arrived in Springfield on the 28th. Reported to Mr. Strong [foreman of the Springfield division] that I was ready for work. But neither Mr. Merrill nor Mr. Fairbanks was there and the freight had not arrived and Mr. Strong knew nothing of the tools. The 29th was the same reason for delay. The 30th Mr. Merrill and myself and a man I hired went to work. Took 1/2 day to get glass and staples down to starting point. My man and I had to carry all irons two miles on our backs. Saturday I was out of stock to do with."[10]

Smith's short-sighted labor policy resulted in further delay. Robert Right, foreman of the Hartford section, writing to his Yankee employer on February 15 told him that the men in the Hartford crew were refusing to work for $12 a month. "They are first class workmen and I think you would do well to pay $13 and keep them rather than try to get a new crew out from Boston," he advised.[11] J. E. Strong reported the same situation on the Springfield division: "Those men whom you employed by the month have left on account of the work being too much for the pay."[12]

Even more serious were Smith's pretensions to scientific achievement. He freely stated that too much stress was being put on the matter of insulation. At one time, he regarded it as an entirely unnecessary device.[13] Amos Kendall, on the other hand, so magnified the necessity of perfect insulation that he had every alternate pole cut down along a large section of the Magnetic line to reduce the number of points of contact with the ground.[14] Although Smith somewhat modified his theories before the actual construction of the New York and Boston line was begun, his attempts at insulation were peculiar, to say the least. In a letter to O'Rielly he described his plan. "I put my wires up in both a more useful and, in milder latitudes, cheaper form," he explained. "I use no glass cap, nor cross-

10 W. Y. Deere to Smith [undated—about April 1846], Smith Papers, XIX.
11 Robert Right to Smith, February 15, 1846, *Ibid.*
12 J. E. Strong to Smith, February 4, 1846, *Ibid.*
13 Reid, *Telegraph in America*, 355.   14 *Ibid.*

bar, but only blocks saturated thoroughly with tar and resin, and also a tin cover and saturated cloth."[15]

As work on the New York-Boston line progressed and tests were made, it became apparent that there was a major construction difficulty. Short circuits, improper connections, and a host of other causes were assigned as reasons for the failure of the line, but the chief difficulty was the faulty insulation. "Yesterday I examined 59 posts and found the wires resting on the screws in *74 instances*," wrote foreman Strong of the Springfield division early in April. "They had not the appearance of having been drawn down by the weight of the wire, but were probably left so at the time they were put up. If there were no further difficulty, what I have discovered would be sufficient to account for failure to get the circuit through."[16] Various expedients were tried, but to no avail. Finally even Smith was forced to the reluctant conclusion that the line would have to be entirely reinsulated before it could be made to work satisfactorily. By the end of April wires were coming down and wooden blocks were being replaced by glass knob insulators.[17]

The New England public and the press had observed the halting progress of the line in silence for a time. Then, although they had contributed little to the undertaking, they began to criticize. The New York & Boston Magnetic Telegraph Association was spoken of as "an arrant humbug." On occasions when important news was to be transmitted the vaunted "lightning lines" were found wanting. Under the caustic caption, "Magnetic Telegraph Myth," the *Boston Daily Whig* remarked; "Some weeks ago wires were run in all directions from the Merchants' Exchange over tops of houses, which were said to be the Magnetic Telegraph to Lowell, Worcester, and nobody knows where not. But all the trouble and expense were of no use apparently. The wires now have all been taken down. . . . The unpainted posts remain, it is true, but for how long nobody can tell."[18]

The editor recalled with evident amusement that it had not been so long since a "nicely smooth-tongued gentleman [Smith]" had visited all the newspaper offices in Boston and offered to furnish them with news at $1.00 a line. He had tried hard to convince them that they must subscribe or be eclipsed. "Since he could not bamboozle

---

[15] Smith to O'Rielly, December 1845, quoted by Reid, *Telegraph in America*, 355.
[16] Strong to Smith, April 1, 1846, Smith Papers, XIX; *Ibid.*, April 2, 1846.
[17] J. Foss to Smith, April 21, 1846, *Ibid.*
[18] *Boston Daily Whig*, May 1, 1846.

us maybe he decided to give up the experiment," concluded the editor.[19]

But Smith had not given up; early in June the line reached New York City. In preparation for the grand opening Smith personally connected the instruments in every station on the route. As a result of improper connections New York could not contact her nearest neighbor, New Haven, let alone more remote Boston. Finally on June 27, the line was able to open its doors to the public.[20]

3 ··· — ·

WITH the actual opening of the line on the twenty-seventh of June, it was hoped that much of the public's distrust of it would disappear. Unfortunately the line was cheaply and carelessly built and its operation was uncertain and unsatisfactory from the start. The copper wires had been put up slackly to avoid breaks, and as a result they were constantly becoming crossed. The maintenance of the lines was a nightmare for the inexperienced linesmen. Some one hundred and seventy breaks were reported in a distance of thirty miles after the first storm. So frequent were the interruptions that Smith, reporting on the first four months of business, was obliged to admit that the line had been disabled more than half of the time.[21]

Morse's electro-magnetic telegraph, "the modern wonder," the much heralded "lightning line," which had promised to revolutionize all communication, was making a sorry spectacle of itself along the New England seaboard. Public opinion was rapidly being alienated, and the entire enterprise was becoming unpopular. The patentees could not help but feel grave concern. "You see how F. O. J. Smith gets on with his Boston line!!" Morse exploded to Vail at the end of the summer. "A little less boasting, a little less self confidence, a little more confidence in our experience, would not have been of any harm. Let them work out of their trouble since they will have things their own way."[22]

Kendall was less explosive and more practical. In a letter to Smith dated September 1, 1846, he mentioned the numerous inquiries he had received concerning the Boston line. People were anxious to

[19] *Ibid.*
[20] D. Brooks to O'Rielly, June 21, 1846, O'Rielly Papers, III.
[21] Minutes of Meeting of Board of Directors of the New York & Boston Magnetic Telegraph Association, October 29, 1846.
[22] Morse to Vail, August 29, 1846, Vail Papers.

know when the line would be open. There seemed to be no question but that their respective lines would have a tremendous interchange of business once the New York and Boston line was operating smoothly. "It would be a great matter for us if your line could be got to work well," he urged. "I passed along some 20 miles of it west of New Haven a few days ago and saw the wires in contact with the limbs or leaves of the trees in five or six places." A little work of a remedial nature would be well repaid, suggested Kendall.[23]

After six months of operation the New York & Boston Magnetic line had earned no money. Already its outside structure required extensive repairs and strengthening, and help could not be expected from the public. Of the original $40,000 required to construct the line, only $28,000 had been raised by the sale of stock. After its poor performance the public was not likely to supply additional funds. Under the circumstances Smith had to turn to his personal resources for support. In return he took over complete control and management of the line.[24] While the Yankee promoter had largely shaped its past, there was every reason to feel that he would dominate its future even more completely.

4 · · · · —

HAND in hand with the efforts of Kendall and Smith along the seaboard were those of a group of stage and express men in New York State. They were actively engaged in establishing a line of telegraph from New York City through Albany, Utica, Syracuse, and Rochester to Buffalo, in accordance with the agreement which had been made between John Butterfield and Amos Kendall on May 30, 1845.[25] Articles of Association for the proposed New York, Albany & Buffalo Telegraph Company had been adopted in Utica the following September 25. They provided for a line of two copper wires, insulated with glass knobs, and having no less than twenty-five poles to the mile. At the contract figure of $200 a mile, the construction cost over the 500-mile route would aggregate about $100,000. Inasmuch as the

---

23 Kendall to Smith, September 1, 1846, Smith Papers, XI.

24 Minutes of Meeting of Board of Directors of the New York & Boston Magnetic Telegraph Association, July 14, 1846.

25 Contract between patentees and John Butterfield, May 30, 1845, Vail Contract Book. Butterfield's contract with the patentees granted him the patent right on a line of telegraph from Buffalo to Springfield, Massachusetts. Before actual construction began, however, the terminus was changed to New York City. For earlier reference see Chapter III.

Morse patentees were to receive a like amount for the patent interest, the capitalization of the New York, Albany & Buffalo Company had been fixed at $200,000, divided into 4,000 shares of $50 each. Following a common practice, the trustees of the new company, Theodore Faxton, John Butterfield, Hiram Greenman, Henry Wells, and Crawford Livingston, also became contractors for the building of the line, and the work of construction was soon under way.[26]

To arouse interest in the new enterprise, one of the sub-contractors, Orrin S. Wood, constructed a short line of telegraph from Utica to the nearby fair grounds where the annual fair was in session. In this way, a large number of people from all parts of the state were enabled to see the Morse telegraph in action. As another publicity measure, Wood built a line from Buffalo to Lockport. When it was opened on November 7, 1845, it had the distinction of being the first in America constructed by private enterprise for commercial business.[27] In contrast to the indifferent reception they had received in New York City the previous fall, Wood wrote to his brother-in-law, Ezra Cornell, of the great enthusiasm of the public in this frontier community. The room from which the messages were sent was constantly "jammed full of eager Yankees with their numerous questions."[28]

Meanwhile, an intensive canvass of the state had been made by Faxton and his fellow promoters, and a fair subscription was secured. With the necessary funds assured, construction was commenced. While others contributed to the success of the enterprise, the dynamic force behind the project was Faxton, who over thirty years before had driven the stages along the route which the new wire was to follow.

5 — — —

THEODORE FAXTON's initiative and skill in managing the stage-coach between Albany and Buffalo had attracted the attention of Jason Parker, veteran stage proprietor of Utica. He had brought young Faxton to that town in 1817 and made him superintendent of the lines. Five years later Jason Parker's had become Parker & Company with Theodore S. Faxton as one of the junior partners. It was also at

[26] Articles of Association of the New York, Albany & Buffalo Telegraph Company, September 25, 1845.
[27] Reid, *Telegraph in America*, 302. The line of the Magnetic Telegraph Company between Philadelphia and Newark was under construction, but not yet in operation.
[28] O. S. Wood to Cornell, November 9, 1845, *et seq.*, Cornell Papers.

this time that Faxton had become associated with John Butterfield who had been brought from Albany to drive for Parker & Company. This association of Faxton and Butterfield led to a variety of joint undertakings in subsequent years.

Little by little the railways began to force the stage lines out of business. In New York State the successful Mohawk & Hudson Railroad had commenced operation in August 1831, and from the outset it had carried from two to three hundred passengers daily between Albany and Schenectady. Aware of the impending doom of the stagecoach, Faxton and several of his associates went into the real estate business about 1835. In addition, Faxton, John Butterfield and Hiram Greenman, entered the canal packet trade. Although lacking formal education, this discerning group of stage men, instead of opposing the new forces which were shaping their civilization, wisely identified themselves with them. One successful enterprise led to another—railroad, steamboat, express, western real estate, and telegraph, all came within the scope of their activity, as they adjusted their interests to the expanding life of the nation.

In 1844 Butterfield and Faxton had first seen the telegraph. On one of their frequent trips to Washington in connection with their packet boat business they had observed the construction of the government experimental telegraph line. They watched its progress with interest. On subsequent trips they had visited the telegraph office and had seen the line in operation. As the likelihood of the government's taking over the telegraph became increasingly remote, Butterfield, Faxton, and a group of their Utica associates had decided to introduce the new means of communication into the Mohawk Valley. With this object in view, Butterfield had journeyed to Washington, and on May 30, 1845, he had entered into an agreement with Amos Kendall for the construction of a line of telegraph along the Erie Canal. The contract secured, Butterfield returned to the management of the canal packet business, while Faxton became the chief promoter of their telegraph enterprise.[29]

---

[29] Accurate biographical material on Theodore S. Faxton is difficult to find. This sketch of his life is based primarily on impressions gathered from the scattered correspondence of Faxton found in the various collections of telegraph papers, as well as an obituary notice in the *Utica Morning Herald and Daily Gazette*, December 1, 1881. The writer of this article was a friend of Faxton's and claimed to have secured much of his information through conversations with him.

6 ......

FAXTON's character and temperament were well fitted for the great task which he had undertaken, and under his earnest direction work on the first section of line from Albany to Utica moved forward with dispatch. While building this line a banker friend called out to him one day to inquire if he were crazy.

"No more than you are, nor half as much," came the ready reply.

"Why Faxton," taunted the banker, "you are the last man I would have suspected to have been caught by such a visionary thing as this. Hadn't you better give it up and go home?"

"See here, old fellow, in a year from now you will be in such need of this crazy thing that you will be wanting to commute,"[30] Faxton replied to his tormentor. "Put that in your pipe . . . and smoke it?"[31]

Faxton's prophecy proved true. Within the year the bank applied for commutation rates, and Faxton then had a hearty laugh at his friend who had thought him "telegraph crazy."

Work on the Albany-Utica section progressed so rapidly that Utica journals were publishing news items telegraphed from Albany early in February 1846. All during the spring and summer of this year work went forward on the sections of the line from Utica to Buffalo and from Albany to New York. Faxton was everywhere—complaining, asking questions, and handling the hundreds of annoying details connected with the building of the line, but above all, driving both the workmen and the work relentlessly.[32] The line reached Syracuse on May 1; a month later an office was opened in the basement of Congress Hall, Rochester. Finally on July 3 the Buffalo office was opened in the basement of the Mansion House, one of that city's leading hotels.[33]

Like all the other pioneer lines the New York, Albany & Buffalo had to pass through a trying introductory phase. The magnets furnished by Ezra Cornell were "horrible indeed." The manufacturer blamed the operators, but Cornell's own brother-in-law, Orrin S. Wood, declared that no matter how skillful the operator, he would

[30] Faxton refers here to the granting of special telegraph rates for volume business.
[31] *Utica Morning Herald and Daily Gazette*, December 1, 1881; Reid, *Telegraph in America*, 303.
[32] Theodore S. Faxton to Vail, October 3, 1845, Vail Papers; *Ibid.*, February 16, 1846, *et seq.*; Series of letters T. S. Faxton to E. Cornell, September-December, 1845, *et seq.*, Cornell Papers.
[33] Reid, *Telegraph in America*, 305.

not have been able to use them successfully.[34] Furthermore, the line was too limited in scope to be profitable, and during the early months of its operation receipts were very light.[35] Not enough was earned to pay expenses. Faxton felt certain, however, that completion of the line to New York City was all that was needed to establish the line on a profitable basis.[36]

The New York-Albany link was delayed because of difficulty in procuring sufficient wire, and as a result of having to build the line along the route of the public highway. Ezra Cornell who was in charge of the construction on this section was assisted by Wood.[37] In spite of obstacles this last link in the telegraph line which was to bind New York with Buffalo was nearing completion by the end of August.[38] But some of the work had not been done to suit the exacting Faxton, and he refused to accept the line until all the defects had been remedied. Posts had been badly set, some of the glass caps were broken, the wire in some places was loosely strung, trees and bushes along the route needed trimming, and there was a deficiency in the number of posts per mile. Cornell fumed but proceeded to remedy the defects.[39]

On September 7, 1846, the stockholders of the New York, Albany & Buffalo Telegraph Company met in Utica for final organization. Theodore S. Faxton, John Wilkinson, John Butterfield, Samuel F. B. Morse, Hiram Greenman, Thomas Y. How, Jr., Crawford Livingston, and Asa Sprague were elected directors. Faxton was chosen president and treasurer, while he, Butterfield, and Wilkinson were constituted as an executive committee.[40]

Faxton's nice attention to detail and determination to make the enterprise successful soon won for his company the reputation of being the most dependable and profitable of the pioneer lines.[41] Commenting on the operation of the New York, Albany & Buffalo line, Ezra Cornell wrote on September 10 that receipts for the day had been over $125, although it was only the second day the line had been in operation, and no announcement had as yet been made to the public that it was at work or ready to work. "$80 per day will

34 O. S. Wood to Cornell, July 5, 1846, Cornell Papers; Ibid., July 29, 1846.
35 Ibid., May 20, 1846.
36 T. S. Faxton to Cornell, May 7, 1846, Cornell Papers.
37 Ibid., March 10, 1846; June 22, 1846.
38 Ibid., August 7, 1846.   39 Ibid., August 27, 1846.
40 List of stockholders in New York, Albany & Buffalo Telegraph Company [undated —about April 1847], Morse Papers, LI; Reid, Telegraph in America, 307.
41 Faxton to Cornell, November 3, 1846, Cornell Papers.

pay *all* expenses and 7 percent on all the stock. Receipts will go up to $200 per day. *Mark that*," predicted the enthusiastic Cornell.[42]

Morse was equally optimistic. "Keep this private for reasons I shall tell you when I see you," he cautioned Vail in a letter written a month later. "Our receipts on the Buffalo line for 23 days only (not one month) were $2,960.00 odd dollars; that is at the rate after expenses are all paid, of 14 percent."[43] So favorable were the prospects of the New York, Albany & Buffalo Company that its stock was selling 20 percent above par by the close of the year.[44] Faxton could not restrain a laugh when he heard of the woes of other lines. He was fond of contending that there was "too much science about them for them to work."[45]

7 — — ··

THE New York, Albany & Buffalo line, while undoubtedly the best which had been erected up to this time, had its full share of troubles. In spite of the fact that Faxton had secured the passage of a law by the New York State Legislature to protect telegraph property from vandalism as early as May 13, 1845, considerable destruction occurred.[46] The glass-knob insulators made fine targets, and their destruction and the breaking of wires was so annoying that the company decided to supplement the provisions of the state law by offering a reward of $100 for the apprehension of violators. Another source

[42] Cornell to Speed, September 10, 1846, Morse Papers, XXVI.

[43] Morse to Vail, October 7, 1846, Vail Papers.

[44] Prospectus of the Washington & New Orleans Telegraph Company, November 1846, Cornell Papers. The success attending the operation of this Company was the occasion of a new contract between Kendall and Morse. Their previous agreement dated March 10, 1845, dealt with their respective interests in the event of an outright sale of the patent right. The new contract dated November 7, 1846, defined their respective interests in the telegraph as it was being developed under private enterprise. It was agreed that all of Morse's telegraph stocks should be rated on the basis of their value on January 1, 1848. Any stock earning 7 percent, after deducting ordinary expenses, was to be rated at par; if earning 14 percent then the stock should be rated at a 100 percent advance, and so on pro rata. On any amount up to $100,000, Kendall was to receive a 10 percent commission; but on all amounts over $100,000 he was to share 50-50 with Morse. (Contract between Morse and his agent, Amos Kendall, defining interests of each in stock issued for patent rights, November 7, 1846. Vail Papers.) James D. Reid in *Telegraph in America*, 320, states that Kendall's contract with Morse, along with the allowance given him by Vail for whom he also acted as attorney, gave Kendall the largest interest in the Morse patent.

[45] Wood to Cornell, February 1, 1846, Cornell Papers.

[46] Inasmuch as this measure, entitled "An Act to facilitate the construction of Morse's Electro-Magnetic Telegraph," May 13, 1845, was the first general easement and protective telegraph act in the country and served as a model for similar legislation in other states, it is given in full in Appendix 2.

of difficulty was the constant conflict between "way business" and "through business" for use of the line. The single wire connecting New York with Buffalo was needed most of the time for the transmission of messages between the two great terminal cities much to the annoyance of such "way stations" as Albany, Utica, Syracuse, and Rochester. Because of the slowness and uncertainty of the "way service" people became dissatisfied with it and the company lost much business.[47]

Scarcely had the new line been put into operation before one of those bitter quarrels which were to characterize the relations between the Morse patentees and their licensees broke out. In this instance it concerned the terms on which side lines should be allowed to connect and do business with the prosperous New York, Albany & Buffalo trunk line.[48] In accordance with the terms of the contract by which the patent right had been conveyed to the company, Faxton was required to grant connections to all side lines which the patentees might subsequently build connecting with his main line. The side or "feeder lines" were to pay one-half of the gross revenue received by them on all messages which they turned over to the New York, Albany & Buffalo Company for delivery. Faxton found this arrangement unsatisfactory since it gave his company only a very modest profit. The rather vague wording of the contract made it possible for him to declare that he did not understand it as Kendall did. He announced that his line would continue to connect with and send messages for the side lines, but that in the future, payment on each message would be proportionate to the distance the communication was sent.[49]

Kendall, having granted contracts for the building of side lines on the basis of the earlier and more favorable terms, felt compelled to insist upon his interpretation. Faxton's terms would spell the doom of many of the branch lines. It looked to Kendall like an attempt by Faxton and his associates to depreciate the interest of the Morse patentees in the side lines and "get them for little or nothing."[50]

The fight which followed was not so one-sided as Faxton had expected. Kendall warned that if he could not obtain a satisfactory connection for the side lines from Faxton's company, he would be compelled to run another line through the state for that purpose,

[47] Faxton to Cornell, October 22, 1846, Cornell Papers.
[48] Kendall to Smith, September 21, 1846, Smith Papers, XI.
[49] Minutes of Meeting of Board of Directors of the New York, Albany & Buffalo Telegraph Company, October 21, 1846, Morse Papers, XXI.
[50] Kendall to Smith, October 6, 1846, Smith Papers, XI.

leaving the New York, Albany & Buffalo a "branchless trunk."[51] The dispute was finally settled on October 29. The patentees agreed to convey the patent rights covering all subsequent side lines connecting with the New York, Albany & Buffalo to that company for an issue of $40,000 of its stock. The patentees also agreed to relinquish all claims against the company for the use of the Morse instrument on any additional wires that Faxton and his associates might erect on the main line.[52] Faxton had won a great victory, but the day was not far distant when he would have cause to regret the hard bargain he had driven with Kendall.[53]

8 — · · · ·

CANADA was not slow to take advantage of the communications service offered by the New York, Albany & Buffalo Telegraph Company. European news flashed from New York to Buffalo by telegraph, was relayed on to Lewistown by stage or railroad, and then sent across Lake Ontario to Toronto by steamer. In the autumn of 1846 a group of Toronto business men, visualizing the possibilities of a Canadian telegraph system, organized the Toronto, Hamilton, Niagara & St. Catharine's Electro-Magnetic Telegraph Company. The American contractors, Livingston and Wells, were engaged to build the line, and it was opened for business on December 19.[54] By the close of the year 1846 the telegraph was no longer regarded as a mere novelty; it had become a recognized mode of communication not only in the United States but also in Canada.

[51] *Ibid.*, October 14, 1846.
[52] Copy of settlement of side line controversy between patentees and the New York, Albany & Buffalo Telegraph Company, October 29, 1846, Cornell Papers. Some 300 miles of side lines already under construction or contracted for were exempted from this agreement.
[53] Some years later Ezra Cornell testified that as superintendent of the New York, Albany & Buffalo Telegraph Company at this time, he had heard Faxton admit that he understood the contract as the patentees did, but seeing an opportunity of compelling the patentees to grant the right of putting up a third wire, he had thought that he had better take it. (Cornell to Kendall, July 25, 1849, cited in deposition of Ezra Cornell in the case of Morse *et al.* vs. Smith.)
[54] E. Green, "Canada's First Electric Telegraph," Ontario Historical Society *Papers and Records*, XXIV, 366-72.

CHAPTER V

To the Mississippi and the Lakes

1 · — ·

AT the time that Kendall was pushing a line south from New York to Baltimore, Smith working northward to Boston, and Faxton driving north and west to Albany and Buffalo, that most picturesque of the telegraph pioneers, Henry O'Rielly, was laying his plans for a mighty system which would stretch from the seaboard to the Mississippi and embrace all the territory west of Philadelphia lying between the Ohio River and the Great Lakes. While others were stimulated by the potentialities of the new enterprise with which they were associated, none was more deeply stirred than Henry O'Rielly. The signing of his contract with the patentees symbolized a literal giving of himself to the telegraph, and he eagerly prepared to undertake his great mission. Broad as were its terms, his charter was to prove too confining; vast as were its boundaries, he was to chafe under its limitations. Family, fortune, friends—all were to be sacrificed to the cause which was to exact so much and leave so little to the man who might well be termed the telegraph's most untiring servant.

2 ·· — ··

HENRY O'RIELLY was born in Carrickmacross, County of Ulster, Ireland, February 6, 1806. Ten years later his father, a merchant, had emigrated to New York City where the boy, Henry, soon identified himself with the life of the new country. An apprenticeship on the *Columbian*, a spirited and effective liberal journal, and a position with the *Patriot*, organ of John C. Calhoun and Henry Wheaton, made an impression on the youth which largely dominated his more mature political thinking.

Pioneer, fighter, and confirmed romantic that O'Rielly was, the suggestion of his friend, Luther Tucker, that they proceed to the remote village of Rochester, New York, to organize its first daily paper met with a hearty response. On October 25, 1826, as a result of their combined efforts, the *Rochester Daily Advertiser* was launched. Life in the rugged frontier community stimulated the active mind of O'Rielly and his rise was rapid. Numerous causes enlisted his support. In his early years, among other things, he labored for the re-election of Andrew Jackson, preached the improvement of the Erie Canal, advocated the cause of Irish Independence, worked for the social betterment of Rochester, and wrote innumerable pamphlets on the problems of the day.

Personally ambitious, he ran for the Assembly as a Jacksonian Democrat in 1836 but was unsuccessful. The following year, however, Postmaster General Amos Kendall appointed him head of the Rochester post office. As an assistant he chose a young Scotch immigrant, James D. Reid, who was to become the Sancho Panza of his subsequent quixotic adventures. But the routine of the post office could not satisfy the crusading zeal in O'Rielly's soul, and in 1842 he put aside his routes and schedules to take up the editorial pen of the *Albany Atlas*, a journal advocating state constitutional reform. This was precisely to his liking. So earnestly did he and others plead the cause that a new constitution for the state was drafted in 1846, shortly after O'Rielly had turned to broader undertakings.[1]

Early in June 1845, the editor of the *Atlas* while returning from New York on the Albany night boat met John Butterfield on his way home from Washington with his telegraph contract in his pocket.[2] Being full of the subject, Butterfield welcomed the occasion to discuss his plans with a fellow upstate New Yorker. The conversation so fired the mercurial O'Rielly that no more than two weeks had elapsed before he also had signed a contract with Amos Kendall for a line of telegraph which should stretch from the seaboard to the Mississippi and to the principal towns on the Great Lakes.[3]

3 · · · — ·

FOLLOWING the execution of this important contract on June 13, 1845, O'Rielly returned to Rochester where he was well known and respected, and approached its business men for aid in carrying out his contract. He first contacted Hervey Ely, who thirty years before

[1] The biographical sketch of Henry O'Rielly is based on "Biographical Sketch of Henry O'Rielly" in *Valuable Source Materials of History*, Rochester Historical Society Publication Fund Series, IX; Reid, *Telegraph in America*, 260-261; and to a great extent on the O'Rielly Manuscript Collection in the New York Historical Society. (Reference to O'Rielly Manuscript Materials will hereafter be abbreviated as O'Rielly MS Coll.)

[2] For earlier reference to the Butterfield contract see Chapter IV.

[3] Kendall to Morse, June 7, 1845, Morse Papers, XX. Because of the controversial nature of the O'Rielly contract and the years of litigation which followed as a result, it has been given in full in Appendix 3. For a detailed discussion of this document see Chapter V.

had built the famous "Red Mill," the first flour mill in the Genesee Valley. The Ely family had long been prominent in the economic life of the community, and through decades of milling had been alternately rich and insolvent. As ranking member of this family of "merchant millers" and a pioneer himself, Hervey Ely was well chosen to give sympathetic ear to O'Rielly's request for funds to aid him in the construction of telegraph lines into the West.[4] After careful examination of O'Rielly's contract with the patentees, Hervey Ely became satisfied of its great value. With Ely's endorsement, O'Rielly presented the project to several of their mutual friends, who shortly became associated with him for the purpose of carrying out the contract. They gave corporate expression to their interest by forming the Atlantic, Lake & Mississippi Telegraph Company.[5] In addition to Henry O'Rielly, the signatories to the original compact, signed in Syracuse on August 20, 1845, numbered six—Hervey Ely's two nephews, Elisha D. and Heman B. Ely; the brother attorneys, Samuel L. and Henry R. Selden (related through their mother to the Ely family); and George Dawson and Alvah Strong, editor and proprietor respectively of the *Rochester Daily Democrat*.[6]

These six men pledged a total of $2,800 for O'Rielly's immediate use; moreover, they agreed to supply such additional sums as might be required to build a line of telegraph from Philadelphia to Pittsburgh and Wheeling. For each $50 paid in, the subscriber was to receive a certificate for one share of Atlantic, Lake & Mississippi Telegraph stock, $150 par value. Of the total stock issue the cash subscribers were to receive five-eighths, the Morse patentees two-

[4] Alexander C. Flick, editor, *History of the State of New York*, VI, 232; Edward F. Foreman, editor, *Centennial History of Rochester, New York* (Rochester Historical Society Publication Fund Series), I, 174-178, 234.

[5] H. Ely to Luman Sherwood, December 20, 1849, O'Rielly MS Coll., VI; Alvah Strong, MS Autobiography, 2.

[6] Articles of Association of the Atlantic, Lake & Mississippi Telegraph Company (original document in O'Rielly's hand), O'Rielly MS Coll., I. It may have been that Hervey Ely's funds were largely invested, or that he was going through one of his less affluent periods at this time, for notwithstanding his interest in the telegraph, his name appears in the list of signatories of the Atlantic, Lake & Mississippi Telegraph Company only as "Attorney for Elisha D. Ely." He was, nevertheless, made a director of the company along with Micah Brooks, O'Rielly's father-in-law, George Dawson, Henry O'Rielly, John S. Skinner, Samuel L. Selden, and Henry R. Selden.

At a subsequent time the names of Jonathan A. Child, a former mayor of Rochester, Josiah Snow, and Alexander L. Ely were added to the list of proprietors of the Atlantic, Lake & Mississippi Telegraph Company. (Articles of Association of the Atlantic, Lake & Mississippi Telegraph Company, August 20, 1845, O'Rielly MS Coll., I; Proposed Agreement relative to the Atlantic, Lake & Mississippi Telegraph Company, in handwriting of Hervey Ely [1848?]. O'Rielly MS Coll., VI.)

eighths, and Henry O'Rielly one-eighth.[7] On September 14, 1845, the stockholders of the Atlantic, Lake & Mississippi Telegraph met in Rochester for formal organization. Henry R. Selden was made president, George Dawson, treasurer, and Henry O'Rielly secretary. So that no time would be lost in fulfilling the terms of the O'Rielly contract with the patentees, the newly organized company entered into an agreement with the Irishman for building a line of telegraph to Harrisburg, and $4,200 was pledged for its construction.[8]

Meanwhile, in a series of widely publicized circulars and addresses, O'Rielly proceeded to outline plans for the development of a vast telegraph kingdom stretching from the seaboard to the Mississippi and the Great Lakes. The Atlantic, Lake & Mississippi Telegraph was to divide the territory covered by the O'Rielly contract into sections, and separate companies were to be organized within each. These companies would be independent in property and profits; their only connection with the other sections of the O'Rielly system would be through a representative in a general "Telegraph Association" which O'Rielly and his associates planned to organize. At regularly assembled meetings of this Association representatives of the different companies were to adopt such general and fundamental rules as they might find necessary "for the harmony, unity of action, and common welfare of the various sections" included within the organization.[9]

Patterning their development after the federal system of government, the Atlantic, Lake & Mississippi Telegraph proposed to subdivide its vast domain in the following manner:[10]

SECTION NO.	NAME	ROUTE
1	Atlantic & Ohio Telegraph Company	Philadelphia to Pittsburgh
2	Pittsburgh, Cincinnati & Louisville Telegraph Company	Pittsburgh to Louisville
3	Ohio & Mississippi Telegraph Company	Louisville to St. Louis
4	Ohio, Indiana & Illinois Telegraph Company	Dayton, Ohio, to Toledo, Ohio, and Chicago via Indianapolis (and branches)
5	Lake Erie Telegraph Company	Buffalo to Detroit, and Cleveland to Pittsburgh
6	Illinois & Mississippi Telegraph Company	St. Louis to Chicago (and branches)

7 Articles of Association of the Atlantic, Lake & Mississippi Telegraph Company, O'Rielly MS Coll., I.

8 Minutes of the Meeting of Stockholders of the Atlantic, Lake & Mississippi Telegraph Company, September 14, 1845, O'Rielly MS Coll., I.

9 Circular issued by O'Rielly; Great Central Telegraph Range between the Atlantic and the Mississippi including the Ohio Valley and the Lake Country [September 1845], O'Rielly Telegraph Documents, First Series, I. (Reference to O'Rielly printed materials will hereafter be abbreviated as: O'Rielly Docs.); O'Rielly to Kendall, September 28, 1846, O'Rielly MS Coll., III.

10 Actually only four of these companies were ever designated by their sectional numbers. By the time the Ohio, Indiana & Illinois and the Illinois & Mississippi lines

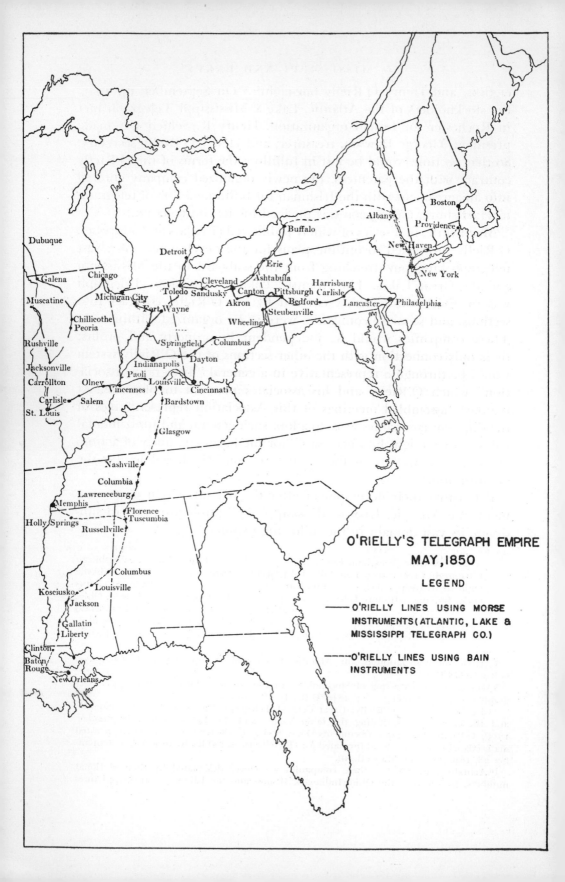

O'RIELLY'S TELEGRAPH EMPIRE
MAY, 1850

LEGEND

—————— O'RIELLY LINES USING MORSE
INSTRUMENTS (ATLANTIC, LAKE &
MISSISSIPPI TELEGRAPH CO.)

- - - - - - O'RIELLY LINES USING BAIN
INSTRUMENTS

In brief, O'Rielly proposed two great trunk lines to the West; one along the shore of Lake Erie from Buffalo to Detroit and ultimately to Chicago; the other from Philadelphia to Pittsburgh and on to St. Louis, largely following the course of the Ohio River. The former was to connect with the projected New York, Albany & Buffalo line at Buffalo, while the latter would make its eastern connections with the Magnetic Telegraph line at Philadelphia. To provide effective communication between the chief centers on the lakes and those along the Ohio River, three north-south junction lines were proposed—one between St. Louis and Chicago, another between Dayton and Toledo, and a third between Pittsburgh and Cleveland. In so far as possible, subscriptions for the construction of each line were to be raised along the route, but should appeals to community interest fail to bring the necessary capital, the members of the parent Atlantic, Lake & Mississippi Telegraph Company were to raise the additional funds. In other words, the Atlantic, Lake & Mississippi Telegraph guaranteed O'Rielly the necessary capital to carry out his contract, and in return, it was to receive at least one-eighth of all the stock issued by the various local companies. It was also understood that the parent company was to have a controlling voice in shaping the general policies for the entire O'Rielly system.[11]

4 · · · · —

THE O'Rielly contract with the patentees was a masterpiece of ambiguity. This famous document, under which the Atlantic, Lake & Mississippi Telegraph now prepared to operate, was to lead to more dissension and prove the source of more litigation than any other single agreement associated with the early lines. For years the controversy growing out of it lay like a malignant growth on the new enterprise, sapping its vitality, and bringing the telegraph into disrepute generally. In its indefinite and rambling style the contract defined the limits of O'Rielly's operations in the following manner:

O'Rielly undertakes on his part, at his own expense, to use his best endeavors to raise capital for the construction of a line of Morse's Electro-

were completed, O'Rielly's affairs had become chaotic and the Atlantic, Lake & Mississippi Telegraph Company was little more than a name.

[11] O'Rielly to Kendall, September 28, 1846, O'Rielly MS Coll., III; H. Ely to Luman Sherwood, December 20, 1849, O'Rielly MS Coll., VI; Circular: Great Central Telegraph Range between the Atlantic and the Mississippi [September 1845], O'Rielly Docs., First Series, I.

Magnetic Telegraph, to connect the great Seaboard Line [Magnetic Tele-graph Company] at Philadelphia, or at such other convenient point on said line as may approach nearer to Harrisburg in Pennsylvania, and from thence through Harrisburg and other immediate towns to Pitts-burgh; and thence through Wheeling and Cincinnati, and such other towns and cities as the said O'Rielly and his associates may elect to St. Louis, and also the principal towns on the Lakes.[12]

At the time of the drafting of this agreement (June 13, 1845) and well into the fall of that year, the route of the Magnetic Telegraph's line from New York to Washington had not yet been determined. Kendall, it may be recalled, had found funds so difficult to get that he had restricted his initial project to the construction of a line from New York to Philadelphia, holding the construction of a second section from Philadelphia to Washington in abeyance.[13] Therefore the "convenient point" on the great seaboard line which might serve as O'Rielly's eastern terminus had not been definitely fixed at the time the Irishman and his associates began their operations. Should Kendall be able to build as he wished, directly along the seaboard via the right of way of the Philadelphia, Wilmington & Baltimore Rail-road, O'Rielly's eastern connection would be Philadelphia. But the difficulty of procuring that right of way had caused Kendall to write that he would probably have to build west from Philadelphia to Lancaster and thence down the Susquehanna Valley to Baltimore, in which case O'Rielly's connection would be Lancaster.[14]

Acting upon this supposition, but without any direct authorization from Kendall, O'Rielly commenced the construction of a line of telegraph from Lancaster to Harrisburg in September 1845. In this way he expected to satisfy that provision of his contract which stipu-lated that "unless the line, from the point of connection with the seaboard route, shall be constructed within six months from date, to Harrisburg . . . this agreement . . . shall be null and void."

5 ———

IF enthusiasm be substituted for experience, it may be said that O'Rielly had a thoroughly competent crew to follow him into the

[12] Contract of June 13, 1845, between the Morse Patentees and Henry O'Rielly, O'Rielly Docs., First Series, I. Complete document given in Appendix 3.

[13] For earlier discussion of this subject see Chapter III.

[14] Kendall to O'Rielly, July 12, 1845, O'Rielly MS Coll., I; *Ibid.*, November 3, 1845; H. Ely to O'Rielly, October 16, 1846, O'Rielly MS Coll., III; Morse *et al.* vs. O'Rielly *et al.* Circuit Court of U.S., 8th Circuit and District of Kentucky, September 12, 1848, Deposition of Henry O'Rielly, August 29, 1848, O'Rielly Docs., Miscellaneous Series, I.

West. Captain John I. Rielly,[15] his brother, and Bernard O'Connor were placed in charge of construction. James D. Reid and Anson Stager, bookkeeper and "devil," respectively, for the *Rochester Daily Democrat*, David Brooks and Henry Hepburn, all had left their jobs to "join up" with the infectious Irishman.

The advent of O'Rielly and his crew caused a sensation along the entire route. To the incredulous and astonished farmers, who regarded railroads an encroachment upon their much loved wagons, the sending of messages through the air "smacked of brimstone and collusion with the world below." When it became known that the lightning itself was to be the agent of transmission, the most extravagant ideas were entertained. "We were looked upon as denizens of another world come to break the quiet and honest industry and sobriety of Pennsylvania," Reid has recorded their reception.[16]

In spite of public hostility the line progressed. It was a primitive affair. Small, unbarked chestnut poles were planted at intervals of two hundred feet along the tracks of the Harrisburg & Lancaster Railroad.[17] A turned black walnut cross-arm resembling a chair rung was inserted through the top of each pole to bear the two wires which were wrapped around either end. "As to insulation," Reid confessed, "it was a long word few of us understood." Alfred Vail's pamphlet on the telegraph was hastily scanned for information. It suggested that cotton cloth be dipped into beeswax and wrapped around the wire where it came into contact with the cross-arm for the best result. The instructions were plain enough; an earnest crew set to work. David Brooks was delegated to purchase the beeswax and contract for cotton cloth. He also superintended the melting process, and thereby "absorbed his first lesson in insulation." The rags were cut up by Henry Hepburn "who didn't take to the business much" and who made his presence felt mainly by making sport with Brooks' wax-pot. "Henry O'Rielly wrote letters and smiled benignantly on the proceedings. Professor Silliman could not have expressed more

15 The various members of the O'Rielly family differed in their ideas as to the proper spelling of the name. Henry O'Rielly, it will be recalled, modified the conventional spelling of "O'Reilly," and he mentions in his letters that Brother John signed himself as "Captain John I. Rielly." There are also letters in the O'Rielly MS Coll. signed "John I. Reilly."

16 Annual Meeting of the Stockholders of the Atlantic & Ohio Telegraph Company, July 1849. Report of Superintendent James D. Reid. This material will be referred to subsequently as Supt's Report, Atlantic & Ohio Telegraph Company, 1849.

17 Contract of B. O'Connor with Henry O'Rielly, October 2, 1845, O'Rielly MS Coll., I.

quiet delight over the scientific aspect of things, than did O'Rielly with his round, rosy face."[18]

In accordance with prevailing scientific opinion the wires were of unannealed copper. Since the idea was general that a curving wire might affect the destination of messages, the wires were drawn taut. "The line looked very trim and handsome," Reid has recorded, "as in the evening of a fine October day we looked at our first day's work. We noticed that some enterprising bees . . . came to our waxed rags, no doubt to replevin on their lost stores." But their opportunity was brief, a heavy rain and a sharp frost soon left the cotton insulation fluttering in the air, and beeswax and cotton soon disappeared.[19]

Thanksgiving day, November 24, saw "four hungry, dirty, unkempt, and unshaven men . . . on the verge of the canal near the railroad depot [in Harrisburg] with an empty reel and wearied hands, hitching the last thread of the mystic line to the post opposite its destined termination."[20] All that remained to put the line into operation were the instruments which Ezra Cornell was manufacturing. At last on December 10, they were received, just three days before the expiration of the time interval in O'Rielly's contract. But they were not Morse instruments. Accompanying them had come a note from Cornell explaining that the enclosed instruments, of his own devising, were an improvement on the Morse relay magnet. Inasmuch as he proposed obtaining a patent upon the improvement, he requested O'Rielly to sign and return an enclosed paper recognizing his rights. O'Rielly denounced the claims of Cornell as unjust to Morse, and promptly returned the instruments to their manufacturer; thereby precluding all possibility of completing his line on schedule.[21] As a result of this delay it was not until the second week in January 1846 that the offices were opened for business.[22]

"The thing is accomplished," Brooks joyously proclaimed to

18 Reid, *Telegraph in America*, 155-156.

19 *Ibid.*, 157.

20 Supt's Report, Atlantic & Ohio Telegraph Company, 1849.

21 *Ibid.*; Cornell to O'Rielly, December 5, 1845, Morse Papers, xx; O'Rielly to Morse, December 23, 1845, *Ibid.*; Faxton to Morse, January 8, 1846, Morse Papers, xxi; Morse to Faxton, January 10, 1846, *Ibid.*; O'Rielly to George Dawson, December 26, 1845, O'Rielly MS Coll., ii; O'Rielly to Cornell, December 31, 1845, *Ibid.*; Cornell to O'Rielly, December 27, 1845, *Ibid.*; Kendall to O'Rielly, December 29, 1845, *Ibid.*; O'Rielly to Cornell, December 30, 1845, O'Rielly MS Coll., i.

22 Supt's Report, Atlantic & Ohio Telegraph Company, 1849; cf. Reid, *Telegraph in America*, 158. Reid's statements in regard to the opening of the Lancaster-Harrisburg line are not in accord, but since the former was written within three years of the event, and the latter, forty-three years later, greater weight has been given to the first statement. (Correspondence also confirms it, *vide* footnotes 23 and 24.)

O'Rielly on the eighth. "We have communicated with Reid by tele-graph this forenoon."[23] And Hepburn, commenting upon the occa-sion, observed, "The section of the 'Atlantic, Lake & Mississippi Telegraph' between Lancaster and Harrisburg is in the full tide of successful operation. There is nothing new here except the 'Tele-graph' which is all the 'go.' "[24]

The following day the offices were opened to the public. "And now we sighed for business," wrote Reid, mindful of the operators' mount-ing board bills. "When the first visitor came in, looking cautiously before him, we felt that the age of gold had come." How kindly he was received may well be imagined. Others followed to whom solici-tous operators delivered learned lectures on electricity, making a good deal of the word "polarity" which sounded well and inspired evident respect. Still nobody proposed to send a message. Seeing this, and their need being great, Reid proposed to do as they had done at Wash-ington—send the names of visitors to and fro for six cents apiece. Slight as were the returns from their first day of operation, Reid optimistically recalled that the receipts of the government experi-mental line upon its first day of public use had been only one cent; while "Harrisburg, brighter than Washington, saw the clear visage of a dime, and sober Lancaster gloried in the possession of a fip."[25]

It was two or three days before anyone offered to send a message. No one seemed willing to be "the first fool." Even after a practical demonstration, business was slight. "The receipts of the week up to last night were $4.50," Brooks reported from the Lancaster office at the close of the first week in February.[26] J. N. Lindsey of the Harris-burg office reported a total of $8.50 for the same interval.[27] Nor did the situation improve. Making his report to O'Rielly two months later Brooks admitted that the receipts of the previous week had been very small—but $2.50—while Lindsey's had been about twice that amount. And then by way of explanation he concluded, "It [the line] was in operation only four days. This forenoon there has been more than a usual call for business, but it's 'no go.' "[28]

Less than two months after the opening of the line it was practically worthless. "The wires along the line has [sic] stretched very much, in

[23] D. Brooks to O'Rielly, January 7, 1846, O'Rielly MS Coll., II.
[24] Hepburn to O'Rielly, January 8, 1846, *Ibid.*
[25] Supt's Report, Atlantic & Ohio Telegraph Company, 1849.
[26] D. Brooks to O'Rielly, February 6, 1846, O'Rielly MS Coll., II.
[27] J. N. Lindsey to O'Rielly, February 7, 1846, *Ibid.*
[28] D. Brooks to O'Rielly, April 20, 1846, *Ibid.*

some places it may be reached from the fence," Lindsey wrote O'Rielly in mid-February. "I thought as we were to have a new line soon, it was scarcely necessary to meddle with them; but if you think it is, I will fix them."[29]

Breaks were such a common occurrence that Brooks went to the Lancaster office every morning at 4:30 A.M. to test for current. Frequently finding none, he shouldered a bundle of copper wire and started out in the gray of dawn to find the difficulty. When it was in operation, the early morning train, puffing its labored way through the Conewago Hills to Harrisburg at the rate of seven or eight miles an hour, made an admirable conveyance from which the telegraph operator might examine his ailing line.[30] Under such adverse conditions successful operation of the line was impossible. After three months of futile effort business was suspended, and the copper wire was taken down and sold to pay the operators' debts.

6 · · · · · ·

O'RIELLY would probably have speedily rehabilitated his Lancaster-Harrisburg line and pushed it on to Philadelphia during the spring and summer of 1846, had it not been for several unusual circumstances. In November 1845, as O'Rielly's own line was nearing completion, Kendall had asked for construction bids on the Philadelphia-Baltimore section of the Magnetic line, even though the route had not been fixed or the subscription list filled. O'Rielly's bid being considerably below the others, the construction contract had been awarded him on November 18, and he had set to work immediately to take care of the preliminaries necessary to building.[31] Before the expiration of a month he had arranged with the Philadelphia, Wilmington & Baltimore Railroad for passage of the line along its right of way.[32] Kendall was pleased by the arrangement, since it gave the Magnetic the direct and most desirable right of way into the South.[33] Henry O'Rielly, working in the interests of the telegraph enterprise as a whole, felt gratified also, even though it left a gap of seventy miles

29 J. N. Lindsey to O'Rielly, February 8, 1846, *Ibid.*

30 William B. Wilson, "The Early Telegraph," Lancaster County Historical Society *Historical Papers and Addresses*, I, Lancaster, Pa., 1897.

31 Kendall to O'Rielly, November 18, 1845, O'Rielly MS Coll., I.

32 Morse *et al.* vs. O'Rielly *et al.* Circuit Court of U.S., 8th Circuit and District of Kentucky, September 12, 1848, Deposition of Henry O'Rielly, August 29, 1848, O'Rielly Docs., Miscellaneous Series I.

33 *Ibid.*

between the easternmost part of his line at Lancaster and the projected Magnetic line at Philadelphia.

In his usual optimistic manner, O'Rielly had told Kendall that he
would be able to work on his own western line and the Philadelphia-
Baltimore section of the Magnetic line simultaneously. He confidently predicted that his line would be extended to Philadelphia by
January 1, while the Magnetic line to Baltimore would be completed
by the middle of that month.[34] As was frequently the case, O'Rielly's
enthusiasm had caused him to minimize difficulties. In addition to
the delay occasioned through negotiating for the route of the Baltimore line, progress was further retarded through lack of funds and
insufficient supplies. Eager to please Kendall, and never dreaming
that those whom he sought to aid would hold him to a narrow interpretation of the terms of his contract, O'Rielly delayed the rehabilitation of his own western line so that he might give his undivided
attention to pushing the Magnetic Company's line on to Baltimore.[35]

The Magnetic line was not completed until June 1846, notwithstanding O'Rielly's earnest efforts. His own line did not succeed in
linking Harrisburg with Philadelphia until September—nine months
after the point of connection with the seaboard route had been
definitely fixed at the Quaker City by O'Rielly himself. These circumstances were to provide the pretext for an unfortunate attack on
the O'Rielly contract the following autumn.

7 — — · ·

TELEGRAPH lines in the blue-print stage in the spring of 1845 had
begun to materialize by the spring of 1846. The Magnetic line from
New York to Philadelphia had been completed in January, and
O'Rielly had extended it to Baltimore by the first week in June.
Before the close of the month Smith had announced the establishment
of telegraphic communication between New York and Boston. Early
September witnessed the completion of Faxton's New York, Albany
& Buffalo line, followed several months later by the opening of
O'Rielly's Atlantic & Ohio line from Philadelphia to Pittsburgh.

Equally as striking as the increase in wire miles during the year
was the change in attitude toward the telegraph. While few of the
early lines were immediately profitable, their operation, irregular
as it was, imparted an impulse to the public mind. "Every day adds to

34 O'Rielly to Kendall, November 17, 1845, Smith Papers, xxv.
35 Ibid. For earlier discussion of the building of the Baltimore line see Chapter III.

my conviction of the importance of this method of communication and of its ultimate value," H. R. Selden wrote to O'Rielly in June 1846. "I . . . presume confidence is now so fixed that capitalists will be willing to hazard something upon it."[36] That the telegraph was rapidly emerging from the highly speculative category in which investors had originally placed it was suggested by Jonathan Child to O'Rielly in a letter dated October 5. "Since the Telegraph has been completed from New York to Buffalo and the public has begun to use it, the character and the value of the stock has greatly improved so that the stockholders are not ashamed to admit they have an interest in it," he wrote in optimistic vein.[37]

Among those fully aware of the changing status of the telegraph was F. O. J. Smith. Along with others he began to see that O'Rielly had "laid the foundation for a fortune,"[38] and he set out to find a means of participating more fully in it. O'Rielly's contract stipulated that "unless the line from the point of connection with the seaboard route shall be constructed within six months from date [June 13, 1845] to Harrisburg, and capital provided for its extension to Pittsburgh . . . then this agreement . . . shall be null and void. . . ." A thorough canvass of the situation revealed that upon the expiration of the first six months' interval (December 13, 1845), O'Rielly had only forty miles of wire strung between Harrisburg and Lancaster leaving a distance of seventy miles separating the latter city from Philadelphia, the projected terminus of the Magnetic Company's seaboard line. Moreover, even the forty-mile section which had been completed was not put into operation until the first week in January.

The circumstances surrounding O'Rielly's failure to meet the exact terms of his contract were extenuating. There was no question as to the Rochester contractor's good faith. Delay in the opening of the Lancaster-Harrisburg line had been occasioned by his desire to protect the patentees from the pretensions of Cornell in regard to the manufacture of telegraph instruments.[39] Furthermore, O'Rielly's failure to connect with the Magnetic Company's seaboard line at Philadelphia was also due to his having put the welfare of the patentees ahead of his own personal interests. According to the Magnetic's original plan its line was to pass through Lancaster. As a

[36] H. R. Selden to O'Rielly, June 21, 1846, O'Rielly MS Coll., III; cf. H. R. Selden to O'Rielly, March 25, 1846, O'Rielly MS Coll., II.

[37] Jonathan Child to O'Rielly, October 5, 1846, O'Rielly MS Coll., III.

[38] Ely to O'Rielly, October 6, 1846, Ibid.; Samuel L. Selden to O'Rielly, August 28, 1846, Ibid.; cf. "Progress of the Telegraph," Cincinnati Enquirer, September 24, 1846.

[39] For earlier discussion of this subject see Chapter v.

favor to the Magnetic management and to the patentees O'Rielly had managed to get permission from the Philadelphia, Wilmington & Baltimore Railroad to run the telegraph along its right of way, thereby changing the route of the line so that it passed through Philadelphia.[40] Under the circumstances the patentees could hardly in good faith censure O'Rielly for failure to meet the terms of his contract with them.

Considerations of good faith bore little weight with F. O. J. Smith. Here was just the sort of technicality he could turn to his advantage. Moreover, his letter file revealed that before the close of the year 1845 he had mentioned to Kendall that the O'Rielly contract was technically void.[41] Being a shrewd lawyer Smith knew that an attempt to abrogate the O'Rielly contract would entail months of expensive litigation. If, therefore, O'Rielly could be persuaded to make certain modifications in the terms of his original contract, Smith could achieve his purpose without resort to the courts. In July 1846, Smith's brother-in-law, Eliphalet Case, former Cincinnati newspaper editor, approached O'Rielly with an offer to aid him in financing and constructing a line of telegraph from Pittsburgh to Cincinnati. "We can easily form a company here [Cincinnati] and raise $50,000 to build a line of Telegraph to Pittsburgh . . . if we can manage our own affairs," Case wrote him in the course of negotiations.[42]

O'Rielly, with his plans already carefully laid for a chain of local telegraph companies democratically governed by representatives from various towns along the route, was loath to see control center in any one city. The good sense of disinterested friends of the telegraph, explained the promoter, would see the propriety of not attempting to concentrate control of the company in Cincinnati, since the line would link various important places—each of which would gladly furnish their portion of the capital for its construction. For this reason, O'Rielly did not warm to Case's proposals.[43]

8 — · · · ·

WHEN the negotiations of the next two months failed to bring the desired result, Smith grew impatient, and on October 2, he abandoned

---

[40] For earlier discussion of this subject see Chapter v.
[41] Kendall to Smith, October 6, 1846, Smith Papers, XI.
[42] E. Case to O'Rielly, August 24, 1846, O'Rielly MS Coll., III; *Ibid.*, September 3, 1846; *Ibid.*, September 24, 1846, *et seq.*
[43] O'Rielly to Kendall, September 30, 1846, O'Rielly MS Coll., III.

all subtleties. "On referring to your contract respecting the Telegraph in the West," he wrote O'Rielly, "you will perceive it has long since expired by its limitations. I hope, however, you have the section to Harrisburg so nearly completed, as to have that section disposed of under your contract. Its retardation has greatly delayed the progress farther west."[44] The design was unmistakable. Smith, with magnanimous gesture, was going to concede to O'Rielly the right to organize the line from Philadelphia to Harrisburg, even though he had defaulted on his contract. All the rest of the territory covered by that agreement was to revert to the patentees for redistribution. Now that the feasibility of the invention had been proved, the extensive and potentially wealthy O'Rielly kingdom, with the exception of one tiny principality, was to be reapportioned.

O'Rielly's wrath and indignation at this summary dismissal knew no bounds, even though he was not entirely unprepared for such action. Kendall, alarmed at the dangerous turn of affairs, had sought to mediate from the moment Smith's design had become evident. Early in September he had cautioned O'Rielly that Smith was referring quite pointedly to the fact that the O'Rielly contract had expired. For his part, Kendall declared, he should be unwilling to enforce the forfeiture of right unless it became absolutely necessary to promote the interest of his principals. At the same time, he urged O'Rielly to appease Smith by accepting the Case proposal.[45] Following O'Rielly's refusal to yield, Kendall subsequently cautioned, "Neither you nor I can get along with our enterprise without consulting to some extent the views of Mr. Smith. Never intending to take advantage of a failure to meet the time limited in your contract, I had not examined it minutely; but now I would ask, whether your line was, in fact, constructed from the connecting point to Harrisburg within six months from its date or from the time that point was finally fixed at Philadelphia? I ask the question, not for my own satisfaction, but to fix your attention on that point and to say that if you treat Mr. Smith as not entitled to be consulted by you it is not difficult to foresee how this matter is to end."[46]

Simultaneously he was urging Smith to a course of moderation. On October 6, Kendall wrote Smith describing the current progress of the retarded Atlantic & Ohio line and predicting its early completion.

[44] Smith to O'Rielly, October 2, 1846, *Ibid.*
[45] Kendall to O'Rielly, September 2, 1846, F. O. J. Smith Letters in the New York Public Library; also in O'Rielly MS Coll., III.
[46] Kendall to O'Rielly, October 15, 1846, O'Rielly MS Coll., III.

Hugh Downing, acting president of the company, and O'Rielly had both assured him, Kendall told his co-proprietor, that although they had the means to carry the line on to Louisville, in the interest of harmony within the telegraph family, they would visit Cincinnati in a few days and "make satisfactory arrangements with Mr. Case and his friends."[47]

The really knotty problem was the attitude which the patentees should adopt towards the original agreement with O'Rielly. Kendall reminded Smith that inasmuch as no official notice had been given O'Rielly of the abrogation of his contract, it remained in full force. He urged his troublesome colleague to meet him in Philadelphia since the problem was too involved and too urgent to attempt a settlement by correspondence. "If we manage with prudence and act in concert, the revenues of a nation are within our reach," concluded Kendall, reaffirming the business philosophy he had vainly urged on Smith from their earliest relations. "If we are divided in counsel or raise the public against us, we jeopardize everything and shall live in constant turmoil."[48]

How long and how effectively Kendall might have shielded O'Rielly against Smith had not new developments caused him to lose confidence in the Rochester promoter is debatable. Unfortunately for O'Rielly a situation arose which caused Kendall to abandon him. By the middle of October, Kendall had become convinced that acceptance of the Smith point of view would be in the best interests of his principals.[49] The impetuous Irishman, in somewhat unorthodox fashion, had issued a few stock certificates on his line without consulting either his associates or the patentees. Even more disturbing to Kendall was the fact that O'Rielly could not see the error of his ways. With almost childlike frankness he told Kendall that certificates had been given to no more than seven persons—editors whose defense of the telegraph cause generally could be no better requited than by a stock gratuity. Was Kendall so rigid in viewpoint as not to see that such a minor infraction, if indeed it was an infraction, was more than offset by the good-will created and the favorable publicity given the entire enterprise? No general issue of stock had been made, nor would it be, until completion of the line and transfer of the patent right according to the agreement. Kendall could judge, therefore,

47 Kendall to Smith, October 6, 1846, Smith Papers, XI. 48 *Ibid.*
49 Kendall to Smith, October 14, 1846, O'Rielly Docs., Legal Series, XI, Correspondence 1846-47. Kendall to O'Rielly, October 24, 1846, O'Rielly MS Coll., IV.

whether there had been anything not dictated by good faith in O'Rielly's proceedings.[50]

Kendall did not view matters in this light. He considered the act a bold assumption of authority, and its author hardly the one to be entrusted with a broad contract for the West. "I said to you as I felt," he reproved O'Rielly, "that I was unwilling to take advantage of a forfeiture of your contract if any existed, as long as you were endeavoring to comply with it in good faith. But how can I excuse myself to my principals if I tolerate such assumption as this?

"Mr. Smith writes that he considers your entire contract forfeited and will not renew it beyond the Ohio River. I hoped he would think better of it, but what is to be expected when he hears that you have organized and issued certificates of stock without his knowledge?"[51]

Distrust of O'Rielly's casual business methods, determination to harmonize patentee policy, and the discord with Faxton over side lines which occupied much of his time,[52] shortly prompted Kendall to desert the Irishman. "As you turn over Faxton & Co. to me, I believe I must turn over O'Rielly & Co. to you," he wrote to his partner on October 15.[53]

Action was not long in coming. In a joint letter to O'Reilly dated November 4, 1846, Kendall and Smith declared that because of irregularities of organization and failure to meet the time limit set forth in his contract, the O'Rielly contract was "absolutely null and void."[54]

9 — ·· —

IF Kendall and Smith thought their declaration would bring about a quick capitulation, they little knew O'Rielly and the group with

50 O'Rielly to Kendall, October 13, 1846, O'Rielly MS Coll., III.

51 Kendall to O'Rielly, October 12, 1846, *Ibid.*; Kendall to O'Rielly, October 24, 1846, O'Rielly MS Coll., IV; also series of letters between O'Rielly and Kendall during October-November 1846, Smith Papers, XI.

52 For discussion of the side line controversy between the New York, Albany & Buffalo Telegraph Company and Amos Kendall see Chapter IV.

53 Kendall to Smith, October 15, 1846, Smith Papers, XI.

54 Kendall and Smith to O'Rielly, November 4, 1846, *et seq.*, O'Rielly MS Coll., IV. (This volume is full of the O'Rielly controversy.) While specific information regarding the relation between the Atlantic, Lake & Mississippi Telegraph and the patentees is difficult to find, apparently it was not the intention of the company to assume the contractual obligations of the six individual companies within its system, unless the individual companies should default. Under the plan of organization the parent company was placed in an extra-contractual relationship with the patentees whose business dealings would be with the individual operating companies comprising the system. In this case, for example, it was the Atlantic & Ohio Telegraph Company, or unit one of the range, which was responsible for issuing one-quarter of its capital stock to the patentees

which he was associated. They held staunchly to the validity of their contract. At the same time they expressed their willingness to arbitrate rather than undertake a "bitter and protracted warfare which could yield neither profit nor pleasure to either party."[55] Speaking for the group three days after notice of nullification, Hervey Ely told Kendall they were of the opinion that their rights under the contract remained unimpaired and he believed the Morse patentees after careful consideration would be forced to accept this view.[56] Nevertheless, to avoid conflict a committee had been appointed to negotiate with the patentees for the sale of the patent interest in the territory embraced by the O'Rielly contract. Among other proposals they offered to accept Kendall's suggestion that they pay for the patent right by building a portion of the retarded southern (Washington-New Orleans) line.[57] They also proposed to settle with the patentees for the privilege of using Morse instruments on the Atlantic & Ohio (Philadelphia-Pittsburgh) line on the basis of one-third instead of one-fourth of the whole stock as provided for originally by the O'Rielly contract. Finally, the question of O'Rielly's rights under the contract would be submitted to the arbitration of three disinterested persons.[58]

But all negotiations were fruitless. Kendall, it will be recalled, had referred the matter to Smith for settlement; and to one whose greed increased in proportion to the mounting telegraph receipts, peace proposals made dull reading. June would have found Smith willing to settle for an increased wedge of O'Rielly's telegraph pie; December found him satisfied with nothing short of the whole thing.[59]

While its diplomats were reporting little success at the conference table, the Atlantic, Lake & Mississippi Telegraph was pressing its advantage of priority in the field. A whirlwind program was launched to build two great trunk lines into the West (one by way of the Great

and, in return, receiving the conveyance of the patent right for its section of line. Formal organization of the Atlantic & Ohio did not come until March 1847, at which time the company attempted to fulfill its obligation. By this time misunderstanding and doubt had already estranged Kendall from O'Rielly, and no stock transfer was ever made.

55 Selden to Kendall, December 29, 1846, *et seq.*, O'Rielly MS Coll., IV; Committee of Atlantic, Lake & Mississippi Telegraph Company to Kendall, December 21, 1846, in Circular: "To the Public," O'Rielly Docs., Legal Series, I.

56 H. Ely to Kendall, November 7, 1846, *Ibid.*   57 *Ibid.*

58 Ely to O'Rielly, December 26, 1846, *et seq.*, O'Rielly MS Coll., IV; Kendall to Smith, November 12, 1846, *et seq.*, Smith Papers, XI.

59 O'Rielly to Selden, October 27, 1846, O'Rielly MS Coll., IV; O'Rielly to E. Cromwell, December 24, 1846, *Ibid.*; H. Rogers to O'Rielly, October 23, 1846, *Ibid.*; H. R. Selden to O'Rielly, October 31, 1846, *Ibid.*

Lakes, the other by way of the Ohio River) before the opposition could get properly organized. While O'Rielly with his accustomed vigor was pushing the Atlantic & Ohio line on to Pittsburgh, his agents appeared in the Ohio River towns to preach the coming of the great promoter, and to offer the people stock in his "lightning lines."[60] To the north, and paralleling this activity, Heman B. Ely opened the subscription books of the Lake Erie Telegraph Company, Section 5 of the Atlantic, Lake & Mississippi Telegraph system.[61] The Lake Erie Company proposed to construct a T-shaped line of telegraph from Buffalo to Detroit and from Cleveland to Pittsburgh at which latter point it would join O'Rielly's trunk line to the West.[62]

Excitement and indignation characterized the breathless activity of the Rochester group. As part of their program Judge Samuel L. Selden took steps to free O'Rielly and his associates from their dependence on the Morse patent. Aid and encouragement were given to Royal E. House of Vermont who was laboring to perfect his printing telegraph system.[63] Of less consequence were negotiations entered into with Charles B. Moss of Philadelphia who claimed to have an invention on the point of completion which would supersede all other telegraphs.[64] Should the Rochester group find a system of telegraphing the equal of, or superior to, Morse's, and secure the patent rights for it, Smith and Kendall might prove more amenable to reason.

"Come what will," Henry Selden wrote his brother on the eve of hostilities, "Mr. Kendall must be taught that we are not to be made use of, like cattle, to launch his ship, and when it is fairly on the wave, to be cast off at his imperial pleasure."[65] If peace could not be had, it was evident that the Rochester promoters were prepared to give the patentees a fight they would long remember.

Meanwhile Smith had taken to the field. A month prior to giving

---

60 Ely to O'Rielly, October 5, 1846, O'Rielly MS Coll., III; *Ibid.*, October 6, 1846; *Ibid.*, October 12, 1846.

61 H. Hepburn to O'Rielly, August 31, 1846, O'Rielly MS Coll., III; H. Ely to O'Rielly, September 3, 1846, *Ibid.*; H. Ely to O'Rielly, September 5, 1846, *Ibid.*

62 Circular: "Lake Erie Telegraph Company" [undated—probably fall of 1846], O'Rielly MS Coll., V.

63 Ely to O'Rielly, November 14, 1846, O'Rielly MS Coll., IV; H. R. Selden to S. L. Selden, November 16, 1846, *Ibid.*; Ely to O'Rielly and S. L. Selden, November 23, 1846, *et seq.*, *Ibid.*; Ely to O'Rielly, January 23, 1847, O'Rielly MS Coll., V; S. L. Selden to O'Rielly, January 27, 1847, *et seq.*, *Ibid.* For fuller detail on the House telegraph see Chapter III.

64 C. B. Moss to O'Rielly, October 17, 1846, *et seq.*, O'Rielly MS Coll., III.

65 H. R. Selden to S. L. Selden, November 16, 1846, O'Rielly MS Coll., IV; cf. H. R. Selden to O'Rielly, January 1, 1847, *Ibid.*; Ely to O'Rielly, October 27, 1846, *Ibid.*

O'Rielly formal notice of nullification, the Yankee intriguer had contracted with the expressmen, Livingston and Wells, for the construction of a telegraph artery from Buffalo to Milwaukee; two weeks later, they in turn subcontracted with John J. Speed, Jr., for the Detroit-Milwaukee section of the proposed line.[66] The Erie & Michigan Telegraph Company, as the corporators of the new line designated their concern, agreed to issue one-half of its total stock to the patentees for the privilege of using Morse instruments on its line.

While the Erie & Michigan Telegraph Company was contesting with the O'Rielly forces along the Great Lakes, another Smith-inspired concern was established to wrest the Ohio Valley region from the opposition. On December 21, control of the Morse patent rights for the Ohio Valley was granted to Smith's brother-in-law, Eliphalet Case, and several associates, and the Western Telegraph Company was organized to develop the telegraph in that area.[67]

In conjunction with these activities the Smith forces launched a series of bitter press attacks against O'Rielly and his associates. "The patentees publicly disavow all acts of H. O'Rielly and all other persons, in building or operating telegraph lines under their appointments," stated a notice in the *Philadelphia Pennsylvanian* on December 12. It was only right that the public be warned against these "pirates." Operators and manufacturers of Morse instruments were told that they had better look to their interests, lest they be found guilty of breaking the patent law through association with O'Rielly. Legitimate telegraph companies were advised to refuse connection with the piratical lines.

The real reason for the patentees' attempt to repudiate the O'Rielly contract, the Rochester forces countered in reply, was the fact that they were accorded only a quarter interest in lines built under its terms, while later contracts granted them a half interest.[68] Although the Rochester group had worked earnestly for peace, there was every indication at the close of 1846 that a bitter and protracted war of attrition with the Smith forces would ensue.

[66] Contract of Patentees with Crawford Livingston and Henry Wells, October 3, 1846, Smith Papers, xi; Ely to S. L. Selden, November 12, 1846, O'Rielly MS Coll., iv; Ely to O'Rielly, November 14, 1846, *Ibid.*; Samuel F. B. Morse vs. Francis O. J. Smith, in the Superior Court of State of New York for the City and County of New York, Deposition of John J. Speed, O'Rielly Docs., Legal Series, x.

[67] Deed of Trust, and Articles of Association of the Western Telegraph Company, O'Rielly Docs., First Series, i.

[68] A Philadelphia daily paper [?], December 12, 1846, Smith's Telegraph Scrapbook, Smith Papers.

10 · — — · —

No survey of telegraph developments during the years 1845-46 would be complete without mention, at least, of the work of dozens of petty promoters who labored to fill in the interstices of the telegraph web. The main trunk lines were hardly begun before myriads of branches were projected from them in all directions to meet the growing demands of outlying communities for more rapid means of communication.

One of the most colorful of these lesser promoters, and illustrative of them all, was Samuel Colt, a wide-awake Yankee business man who was shortly to become the great arms manufacturer. Colt had met Morse in Washington in the early forties where each was lobbying for government aid to promote his special interest—Colt, the submarine battery, to be used in national defense. Despairing of a federal appropriation, Colt had turned to the infant telegraph industry for a livelihood, and shortly established himself as manufacturer and jobber of telegraph wire. Association with the new enterprise served but to confirm Colt's belief in its ultimate success; whereupon in 1845 he organized the New York & Offing Telegraph Association in conjunction with William Robinson, a bookdealer on lower Broadway.[69]

The New York & Offing proposed to erect a line "from New York City to any point or points on the shores of Long Island and New Jersey,"[70] in order to give a ship-to-shore telegraph service to its patrons. Newsboats were to meet and board incoming vessels and report immediately all important intelligence to the telegraph office where for a fee of $12 a year subscribers might peruse the latest telegraphic bulletins before the news reached the general public.[71] Messages might also be telegraphed to Coney Island and put aboard incoming ships as they approached the harbor.

The fact that Colt supplied the wire for the company and received $50 a mile royalty for its use undoubtedly whetted his promotional zeal, and shortly he was organizing a similar service for Boston—the Boston & Offing Telegraph Association. The outbreak of the Mexican War halted Colt's telegraphic ventures rather abruptly. A government order for 1,000 Colt revolvers made possible the reestablishment of his arms manufacturing business, and that occupation soon demanded

[69] Jack Rohan, *Yankee Arms Maker, Samuel Colt*, 131.
[70] Prospectus of the New York & Offing Telegraph Association, May 20, 1846, O'Rielly MS Coll., III.
[71] *Ibid.*

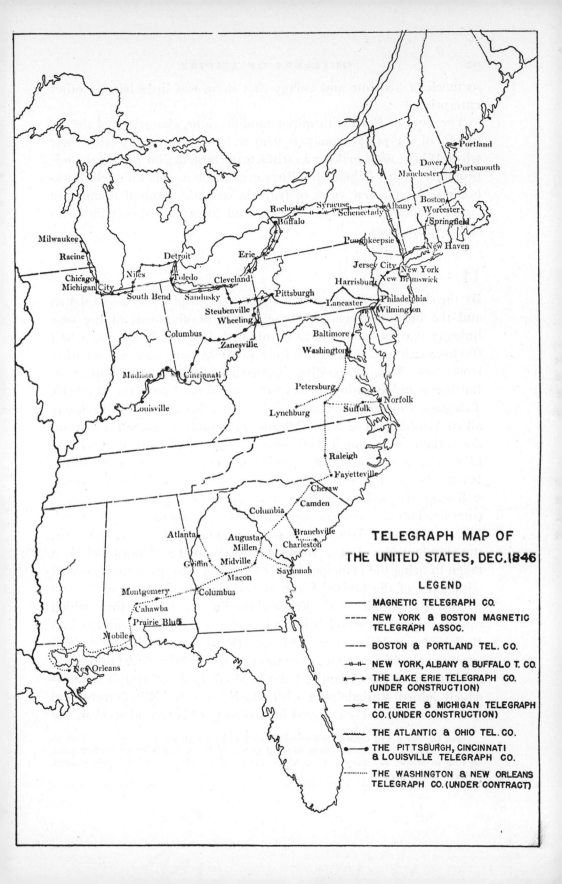

TELEGRAPH MAP OF
THE UNITED STATES, DEC. 1846

LEGEND

——————— MAGNETIC TELEGRAPH CO.

- - - - - NEW YORK & BOSTON MAGNETIC
TELEGRAPH ASSOC.

– – – BOSTON & PORTLAND TEL. CO.

-II-II- NEW YORK, ALBANY & BUFFALO T. CO.

-*-*-* THE LAKE ERIE TELEGRAPH CO.
(UNDER CONSTRUCTION)

-o-o-o- THE ERIE & MICHIGAN TELEGRAPH
CO. (UNDER CONSTRUCTION)

vvvvvv THE ATLANTIC & OHIO TEL. CO.

•—•—• THE PITTSBURGH, CINCINNATI
& LOUISVILLE TELEGRAPH CO.

········· THE WASHINGTON & NEW ORLEANS
TELEGRAPH CO. (UNDER CONTRACT)

so much of his time and energy that there was little left for other enterprise.[72]

The story of Colt, with minor modifications, characterized the activities of the petty promoters who webbed the country with their wires. While often making a satisfactory construction profit for their promoters, few of these side lines ever made a cent for their stockholders. After a few years of fruitless struggle, most of them were either abandoned, or sold for debt and incorporated as tributaries of the trunk lines.

11 · — — · · — — ·

By the close of 1846 telegraphic outlines of empire had taken shape, and the initial pioneering phase in the development of the new industry may be said to have terminated. In a brief year and a half the foundations had been laid for a vast telegraph network radiating from New York. Extending southward through Philadelphia to Baltimore and Washington was to be found the line of the Magnetic Telegraph Company; and arrangements had been made by the closely allied Washington & New Orleans Telegraph to extend a line on down the coast through Richmond, Charleston, Savannah, and Mobile to New Orleans. Reaching northward through New Haven, Hartford, and Springfield to Boston was the line of the New York & Boston Magnetic Telegraph Association; and plans were already completed for the construction of a line to link Boston with Portland, Maine. Following the course of the Hudson and Mohawk Rivers was the excellent New York, Albany & Buffalo line; and steps had been taken to bring the principal cities of Canada into telegraphic contact with those of the United States at Buffalo. Pushing westward from Buffalo were the rival Lake Erie and the Erie & Michigan lines, which upon completion would bring a vast flow of business pouring into Buffalo from Milwaukee, Chicago, Detroit, and Cleveland. Still another valuable western artery was O'Rielly's Atlantic & Ohio line—section one of the Atlantic, Lake & Mississippi Telegraph system—which joined Philadelphia with Harrisburg and Pittsburgh; and O'Rielly was actively engaged in promoting his second section, the

[72] For further detail regarding Samuel Colt's relations with the telegraph see: Colt to Vail, October 19, 1845, Vail Papers; Kendall to Smith, December 5, 1845, Smith Papers, xi; Colt to Morse, February 3, 1846, Morse Papers, xxi; Colt to O'Rielly, July 7, 1846, O'Rielly MS Coll., iii.

Pittsburgh, Cincinnati & Louisville line, which he confidently predicted would be in operation within six months.

Turning from the building to the operation of the lines, it may be said that while such technical problems as insulation, conductors, and cables, had been a cause of concern to pioneer promoters, the most serious threat to the future success of the new industry was the internal dissension and jealousy within the Morse telegraphic family. Arbitrary administration, the rupture with O'Rielly, and the growing rift between Kendall and Smith (not to mention lesser intrigues) were rapidly bringing the telegraph into disrepute. The public made little attempt to differentiate among the various holders of the patent rights, and "Morse men" and "Morse methods" generally came to share the opprobrium. This situation served as a stimulus to the introduction of rival House and Bain telegraphs in the years just ahead.

"If we are divided in counsel or raise the public against us we jeopardize everything and shall live in constant turmoil," Kendall had futilely warned Smith in the fall of 1846, in an effort to stem the tide of internal dissension which he feared would submerge his principals.[72] Had he known the events of the next decade, he could not have predicted developments more accurately.

Although the Morse interests were thus confronted by grave dangers, and no company had been able to pay a dividend up to this time, the principle of electrical communication was now generally accepted. There could no longer be any doubt that the telegraph had come to stay.

[72] Kendall to Smith, October 6, 1846, Smith Papers, XI.

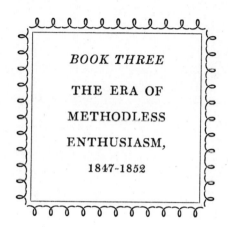

BOOK THREE

THE ERA OF
METHODLESS
ENTHUSIASM,
1847-1852

CHAPTER VI

The Divisional Contracts of June 1847

1 · — — ·

THE interest which attached to the telegraph after 1846 was by no means peculiar to that industry; it was a natural accompaniment of the general movement of expansion which had come about when America, following the War of 1812, had "turned her back on the Atlantic" and given her attention to the virgin continent awaiting development. The road and canal building mania of the 1830's and 1840's was supplanted by a feverish cycle of railroad construction, which was shortly competing with the telegraph for funds. Whereas in 1845-1846 the new means of communication was going through a struggling probation, in the years 1847-1852 it was accorded full public approval. With boundless enthusiasm, but with little knowledge of telegraph construction, dozens of promoters now entered the communications field to exploit the eagerness of all sections of the country for the telegraph. In common with other empire builders of the age, these impetuous promoters had little time to look ahead and plan. Throughout the country, people were clamoring for telegraph lines. A random network of unsound lines, therefore, shortly bore evidence of the zeal with which the telegraph promoters sought to satisfy the public demand.

So unbridled a construction program as that which occupied the telegraph industry during the next few years, could have but one conclusion—a bitter struggle for survival among the numerous small companies. Rival lines contended fiercely for business over every important route. Both the House printing telegraph and a newcomer, the Bain chemical telegraph, contested the right of the Morse patentees to monopolize the telegraph business. A host of pirates, respecting no patent and using all, hastily erected lines. Dozens of lawsuits were commenced. Telegraph fortunes rose to dizzy heights only to collapse. A close examination of the fateful years 1847-1852 must be made to understand the struggle, reveal the rivalries, and suggest the confusion of this mad era of methodless enthusiasm.

2 ··—··

PITTSBURGH put away its tools, wherever possible, on the morning of December 26, 1846. The wonder-working wire from the East had at last reached that thriving river community, and an excited, half-believing crowd gathered around the "Pittsburgh Telegraphery" to witness the telegraph's operation. With the first click of the curious apparatus conversation ceased. A puzzled but respectful silence fell over the group. The first message ever to be telegraphed across the Alleghenies was being sent. It was a war dispatch from Adjutant General G. W. Bowman to the President of the United States, James K. Polk: "The Second Pennsylvania Regiment will be organized and ready to leave Pittsburgh [for the Mexican War] by January 6th."

Local editors were then invited to exchange greetings with the Philadelphia press. Thus was launched the Atlantic & Ohio Telegraph Company, section one of the Atlantic, Lake & Mississippi Range, with the ceremony befitting so auspicious an occasion.[1]

With the announcement that "suitable spaces, railed in against intrusion . . . had been provided for the use of Editors and other persons having business with the Telegraph; another for Ladies; another for Spectators," the new office formally opened its doors to the public on January 1, 1847.[2] While O'Rielly might complain that during the early months of the new line's operation, the spectators outnumbered the customers, the new telegraph line was a financial success from the beginning. The commercial interests of Pittsburgh were too closely linked with the Atlantic seaboard to overlook any reasonable means for facilitating intercourse.

Early in March the Rochester promoters, acting as though the validity of the O'Rielly contract had never been questioned, proceeded to capitalize the Atlantic & Ohio Telegraph at $300,000.[3] In

1 [Henry O'Rielly], "Material for Telegraph History," *Historical Magazine*, January 1867, XI, 22-24; O'Rielly to Directors of the Atlantic & Ohio Telegraph Company, December 28, 1846, O'Rielly Docs., First Series, I.

2 Circular: "Atlantic & Ohio Telegraph Regulations," January 1847, O'Rielly MS Coll., IV.

3 The first officers of the Atlantic & Ohio Telegraph Company were: Hugh Downing, president; John B. Trevor, treasurer; Henry O'Rielly, secretary; and James D. Reid, superintendent. These men were retained in office until July 4, 1848, at which time they were replaced by the following officers who were to play a prominent part in the company's later history: James K. Moorhead, president; William McKee, secretary and treasurer; and James D. Reid, superintendent.

Due to delays the Atlantic & Ohio Telegraph Company was not formally incorporated until March 24, 1849, when a special act of the Pennsylvania State Legislature was passed. Under the terms of that act the company was capitalized at $300,000 divided

accordance with the terms of the O'Rielly contract the company offered the Morse patentees a quarter of the capital stock for the privilege of using the Morse system on its line.[4] The patentees' refusal of the proposal was not well received by the public who listened with sympathetic interest to O'Rielly's plans for pushing a line on to St. Louis.

3 · · · — ·

THE inauguration of business by the Atlantic & Ohio Telegraph Company was the occasion awaited by O'Rielly's adversaries. Attempts at reconciliation between the rival interests having failed,[5] the opening of section one of the Atlantic, Lake & Mississippi system constituted a challenge to the patentees. Kendall now had a basis for legal action against O'Rielly, and within the week he filed a motion for injunction against him in the Circuit Court of Pennsylvania.

At the same time Smith's henchman, Eliphalet Case, as has already been noted, was proceeding with the organization of an opposition line.[6] On January 16, 1847, he constituted John C. Wright, L. Worthington, George S. Coe, and Abel C. Thomas—all prominent citizens of Cincinnati—a board of trustees to hold the patent right vested in him. Judge John C. Wright, who was recognized for his legal talents and qualities of leadership, was chosen chairman of the board. With the establishment of this board its members became associated with Case in the effort to develop the telegraph industry in the Ohio Valley, under the corporate title, Western Telegraph Company.[7]

Little more than a month after the support of the Cincinnati trustees had been enlisted, Kendall's motion for a special injunction

into 6,000 shares of $50 each. For each $50 paid in, three shares of stock were issued to the subscriber. (Proceedings of the Meeting of Stockholders of the Atlantic & Ohio Telegraph Company, July 4, 1848, O'Rielly Docs., Miscell. Series, III; Morse vs. Smith, Superior Court of State of New York for the City and County of New York, Deposition of James D. Reid, O'Rielly Docs., Legal Series, XI; Pennsylvania Laws, 1849.)

[4] O'Rielly to Morse patentees, February 1, 1847, O'Rielly MS Coll., IV.

[5] For earlier discussion of this subject see Chapter V.

[6] Morse et al. vs. O'Rielly, Circuit Court, Eastern District of Pennsylvania, September 1847; C. B. Moss to O'Rielly, December 27, 1846, O'Rielly MS Coll., IV; H. Ely to Judge Selden, January 1, 1847, et seq., Ibid.; H. Ely to Judge Selden, January 21, 1847, O'Rielly MS Coll., V. Letters for January 1847, full of the dispute with Morse patentees, O'Rielly MS Coll., V. For an earlier discussion of this subject see Chapter V.

[7] Morse vs. Smith, Superior Court of State of New York for the City and County of New York, Complaint and Index of E. Fitch Smith, December 12, 1851, O'Rielly Docs., Legal Series, IX.

was denied, and the O'Rielly contract was broadly sustained.[8] To make matters worse, early in March wide publicity was being given the organization of the Atlantic & Ohio Telegraph Company. Eager as the Cincinnati trustees had been to get a telegraphic connection for their city, they ceased their efforts following the judicial decision upholding the O'Rielly contract. It was folly, they contended, to attempt promotion in the face of impending litigation and uncertainty. At the instigation of Judge Wright, therefore, O'Rielly was invited to Cincinnati and compromise terms were readily outlined. The rights of the Atlantic & Ohio Company on the main trunk line from Philadelphia to Pittsburgh were to be recognized, and it was agreed that O'Rielly should continue the line to Columbus, Ohio. The Cincinnati trustees were to build from Columbus to Louisville, from which point O'Rielly was to carry the line on to St. Louis. To the north the Irishman was to construct a junction line from Columbus to Cleveland, while to the south, the Cincinnati trustees would undertake to connect Louisville with New Orleans. These proposals were then sent to the patentees for their approval.[9]

The compromise pleased neither Kendall nor Smith.[10] Kendall's main grievance, as presented to the court in February and steadfastly thereafter, was that O'Rielly had undertaken "to mar the whole plan of the Western telegraph by severing it into many companies" instead of developing it under one powerful organization. Kendall's case was a poor one since no mention had been made of such a plan either in the notice of nullification sent to O'Rielly the previous autumn, or in the correspondence preceding it.[11] Smith's chief cause for dissatisfaction was the meagerness of his interest under the contract. Neither of these objections was met and the proposed settlement failed.[12]

Rejection of a second compromise offer three months later was ruinous to the rapidly declining reputation of the patentees. Kendall's fear that they had "no alternative but to submit" or lose the West,

[8] Morse vs. O'Rielly, Circuit Court, Eastern District of Pennsylvania, February 18, 1847, O'Rielly MS Coll., v; H. R. Selden to O'Rielly, February 19, 1847, et seq., Ibid.

[9] Proposed compromise with Cincinnati trustees in O'Rielly's handwriting, March 1847, O'Rielly MS Coll., v; Kendall to Smith, March 26, 1847, Correspondence, O'Rielly Docs., Legal Series, XI; Morse vs. O'Rielly, Circuit Court of Kentucky, Statement of Henry O'Rielly, August 29, 1848, O'Rielly Docs., Miscell. Series, I.

[10] Morse vs. Smith, Superior Court of State of New York for the City and County of New York, Affidavit of Amos Kendall, 1852, O'Rielly Docs., Legal Series, IX.

[11] Kendall to Smith, March 26, 1847, Correspondence, O'Rielly Docs., Legal Series, XI.

[12] Smith to Kendall, May 19, 1847, Ibid.

proved well-founded. Public opinion and the press now came out overwhelmingly in favor of O'Rielly in the bitter dispute. Even the Cincinnati trustees, notwithstanding the efforts of Case to hold them in line, repudiated their principals; and by refusing either to act or to relinquish their contract, effectively checked for the time being all patentee effort in the Ohio Valley. The inability of the patentees to obtain an injunction, their continued refusal to compromise, and their repudiation by the very group established by them to supersede O'Rielly, made a poor impression upon the public. The general feeling was that the nullification of the O'Rielly contract had been prompted by a desire on the part of the patentees to obtain a larger share of the stock on the lines into the West than had been provided for by the original agreement.[13]

In order to clarify the situation, Kendall urged Smith to go to Cincinnati for a talk with Judge Wright.[14] But Smith did not care to represent the patentees in so involved a controversy. He refused to undertake a settlement, unless he were permitted to purchase the entire patentee interest in the territory covered by the O'Rielly contract.[15]

4 · · · · —

KENDALL had previously discussed with Morse the possibility of some division of the patentee interest, and was pleased to enter into any conversation which might result in freeing his principals from further responsibility for Smith's actions. Accordingly he met his co-proprietor in New York, and on June 22, 1847, the two men signed a series of contracts, dividing the patentee interest between them.[16] In the first of these agreements Morse and Vail, in exchange for their interest in the patent right and in all construction profits on a line of telegraph between Philadelphia and St. Louis, were to receive six thirty-seconds of the total stock issue on the Philadelphia-Pittsburgh section and nine thirty-seconds on the Pittsburgh-St. Louis section. The second agreement, contingent on the first, provided for a division of interest on the other trunk lines. Kendall's principals

13 Kendall to Smith, June 9 and July 14, 1847, *Ibid.*; J. C. Wright to O'Rielly, April 29, 1847, O'Rielly MS Coll., v; Morse vs. O'Rielly, Circuit Court of Kentucky, Statement of Henry O'Rielly, August 29, 1848, O'Rielly Docs., Miscell. Series, I.
14 Kendall to Smith, May 16, 1847, Correspondence, O'Rielly Docs., Legal Series, XI.
15 Smith to Kendall, May 19, 1847, *et seq.*, *Ibid.*
16 Morse to Vail, March 10, 1847, Vail Papers; Kendall to Smith, May 10, 1847, Smith Papers, XI.

were to relinquish all claim to stock in the Great Lakes line (Erie &
Michigan Telegraph) and the projected Ohio Valley line which was
to link Philadelphia with St. Louis; in return Smith agreed to waive
all claim to stock in the great southern line from Washington to New
Orleans (Washington & New Orleans Telegraph).[17] The third agreement pertained to side lines only on all unsold routes in the country.
With reference to the side lines Kendall and Smith agreed that, for the
more effective management of their joint interests, Smith should be
the sole agent for the Morse patent in New England, New York, Wisconsin, Michigan, and those parts of Ohio, Indiana, and Illinois
lying north of the proposed Pittsburgh-St. Louis line;[18] while Kendall
should be accorded a like privilege for the remainder of the country.
Still a fourth agreement placed the O'Rielly controversy entirely in
the hands of Smith. By its terms Smith was (1) to settle the dispute
"amicably or judicially, as soon as may be," and (2) to secure Morse
and Vail against all claims that might be brought against them by
the O'Rielly companies.[19]

Briefly, it may be said that the "Divisional Contracts" of June 22,
1847, constituted a bill of divorce between the antagonistic Morse
patentee interests. Smith became virtually sovereign over telegraph
affairs in New England, New York, and the Old Northwest, while
Kendall assumed control over the remainder of the Union. Apart
from conferring on certain matters of mutual concern at given intervals, the two parties could go their separate ways.

5 ———

HAMPERED no longer by his burdensome partners, Smith was now
free to promote the telegraph enterprise in the territories turned over
to him without any danger of interference. Personal considerations
soon fixed him in his determination to delay settlement of the
O'Rielly controversy. His interest in the patent being only a quarter
of the whole, any agreement would chiefly benefit Morse and Vail.
His plans would be better served by attempting to destroy O'Rielly

[17] For reasons which will be made clear in the subsequent narrative, many provisions of these divisional contracts were never carried out, or they proved to be subject
to differences of interpretation and a cause for further trouble.

[18] This line was to pass through Wheeling, Columbus, Cincinnati, and Louisville,
from which point it was to be extended on to St. Louis by any route Smith should
select.

[19] Agreements of F. O. J. Smith with his partners, Morse and Vail, June 22, 1847,
Smith Papers, Telegraph Pamphlets, II; also in O'Rielly Docs., First Series, I.

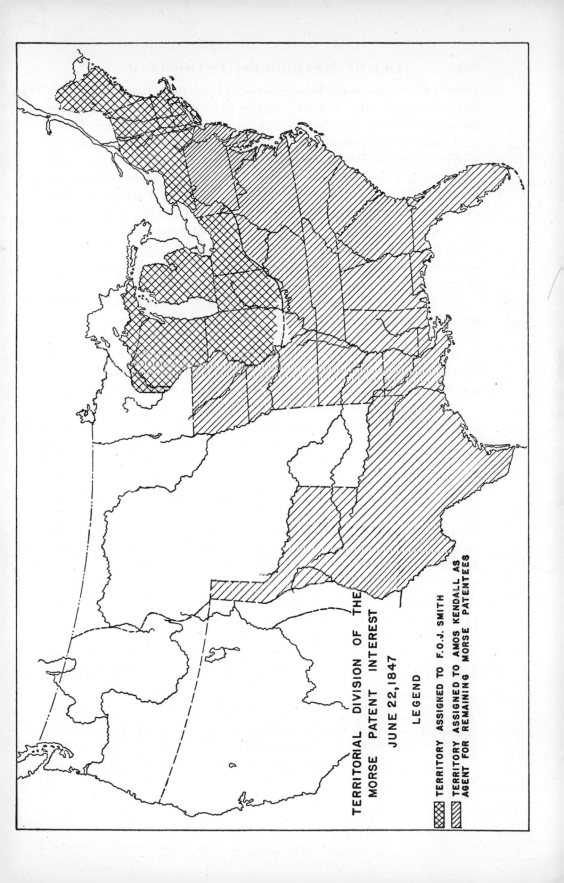

TERRITORIAL DIVISION OF THE
MORSE PATENT INTEREST
JUNE 22, 1847

LEGEND

▨ TERRITORY ASSIGNED TO F.O.J. SMITH

▨ TERRITORY ASSIGNED TO AMOS KENDALL AS
AGENT FOR REMAINING MORSE PATENTEES

and the Rochester group by opposition, rather than to establish them through compromise. While assuring Kendall of his earnest desire for reconciliation, therefore, Smith procrastinated and evaded.

Meanwhile, he quietly matured his own building plans, visualizing a great trunk line along the Ohio Valley from Pittsburgh westward to Cincinnati. There it would branch, one section going on westward to St. Louis, another southward to New Orleans, and others reaching out to important centers in the Ohio and Mississippi Valleys. Any plan that Smith might make for this region, of course, was contingent upon his obtaining a reconveyance of the patent rights for the area from the Cincinnati trustees to whom they had been given in January 1847.[20]

Smith found that Judge Wright and his Cincinnati associates were unwilling to retire quietly from the field. Judge Wright, acting for the group, offered Smith two alternatives. They would build as soon as the O'Rielly dispute had been successfully arbitrated; or they would reconvey the title upon receipt of funds to reimburse them for the embarrassments which the Case contract had caused them.[21]

Smith was furious. He was not accustomed to having the puppets created by his hand turn upon him and draw the strings for him to dance. To have to pay Wright one cent, declared Smith, would be "like paying the man that filches your property while in your employ."[22] Prompt action was imperative, however, since O'Rielly was taking advantage of Smith's embarrassment to push steadily down the Ohio with his line. Consumed with anger, Smith journeyed to Cincinnati in October 1847, to meet his betrayer "face to face," and to see if he could not put down the mutiny. Compromise was hard for Smith at best, and it was especially difficult when he held the weaker side of a question. Wright was inflexible; Smith was equally determined. After several days of fruitless discussion the Yankee promoter returned to the East empty-handed.

In the weeks that followed the Cincinnati trustees held their ground. Smith was in the unhappy position of having to choose between making a settlement with them and abandoning the Pitts-

---

20 For earlier discussion see Chapter VI.

21 Morse vs. O'Rielly, Circuit Court of Kentucky, Statement of Henry O'Rielly, August 29, 1848, O'Rielly Docs., Miscell. Series, I; Kendall to Smith, August 30, 1847, Correspondence, O'Rielly Docs., Legal Series, XI; *Ibid.*, September 2, 1847; *Ibid.*, September 12, 1847; Kendall to Smith, July 31, 1847, Smith Papers, XI; *Ibid.*, August 10, 1847.

22 Smith to Kendall, September 8, 1847, Correspondence, O'Rielly Docs., Legal Series, XI.

burgh-Cincinnati-New Orleans project altogether. Less than two months after his previous visit Smith was back in Cincinnati for another attempt at a settlement. Perhaps it was the tone of his letter a week before his departure in December 1847, which prompted Kendall to accompany him: "Wright is one of the most unmeasured rascals that is yet unhung, in my judgment—a janus-faced scorpion. I would not consent to pay him a farthing to save me from anything short of endless punishment."[23]

Such sentiments were hardly those of an individual bent on reconciliation, and Kendall foresaw grave danger to the patentee interest if matters in the West were stalemated longer. The second negotiation, therefore, found Kendall at the conference table. After hours of heated discussion Kendall, seeing that negotiations were about to fail, made a payment of $500 in recognition of the patentees' debt, and in return Judge Wright and his associates dissolved the trusteeship. By thus putting an end to this organization, Kendall believed that he had not only cleared the way for the Pittsburgh-Cincinnati-New Orleans line, but that he had also removed every obstacle in the way of Smith's taking legal proceedings against O'Rielly.[24]

23 Smith to Kendall, November 17, 1847, *Ibid.*
24 Release of Case, Wright, Worthington and others to F. O. J. Smith, Vail Contract Book; John I. Reilly to Henry O'Rielly, December 11, 1847, O'Rielly MS Coll., xv; Morse vs. Smith, Superior Court of the State of New York for the City and County of New York, Deposition of A. Kendall, January 10, 1857, O'Rielly Docs., Legal Series, xi.

$$\big\{ \boxed{\text{CHAPTER VII}} \big\}$$

Battle for the Lakes

1 ·——·

REFLECTION had convinced Smith that the old Northwest territory was one of the most promising areas in the country for telegraphic exploitation. By skillful use of the vast power with which he had been entrusted, he hoped to carve out a telegraph empire there, and lay the foundations for a personal fortune. Carefully he weighed his position and made his plans. The divisional contracts by which Kendall had sought to appease him had given Smith control of Michigan, Wisconsin, and most of Ohio, Indiana, and Illinois—a vast and potentially wealthy territory. All future building in that area would be determined by him. Moreover, he would control the Erie & Michigan Telegraph Company, the great trunk line already under construction along the Great Lakes, which would ultimately link Buffalo with Cleveland, Detroit, Chicago, and Milwaukee. From this promising nucleus, development might proceed in either of two ways. Smith could establish a second main artery along the Ohio Valley from Pittsburgh to St. Louis, and then make use of a series of cross lines to knit the extremes of his empire together. Or if he preferred, he could attain the same objective by dropping "feeder" lines from the Erie & Michigan trunk line down into the commercial centers of the Ohio Valley. Smith decided upon the latter plan. Feeder lines were offered the right to the use of Morse instruments for a modest cash payment—sometimes as low as $10 a mile—in exchange for pledges of exclusive connection with the parent line. Proceeds from the sale of the patent rights on these side lines, of which Smith would receive but a quarter part, might well be sacrificed to build up the Erie and Michigan line in which he now controlled the entire patentee interest.[1]

Smith's ambition grew with more mature reflection. Subsequently he determined that the business of the Erie & Michigan Telegraph line and its tributaries must, in some way, be given access to the seaboard over a line controlled by him. Under the existing arrangement the business flowing over his wires from Cleveland, Chicago, Milwaukee, and the other commercial centers of the West would have

---

[1] For an earlier discussion of this subject see Chapter VI.

to be turned over at Buffalo to the New York, Albany & Buffalo Company for transmission to New York. The idea of sharing the profits from his western business with others was unpleasant. Although Smith was well aware that all the trunk lines contemplated by Kendall had already been established, and that the right to construct additional lines as set forth in the divisional contracts of June 1847, pertained only to side lines,[2] he nevertheless made plans to run a line (the New York & Erie Telegraph Company) from New York City across the state by an extreme southerly route to reach Lake Erie at Dunkirk. Such a line would not only give him direct contact with New York City, but it would also serve as a link between his eastern (New York & Boston) and his western (Erie & Michigan) systems, giving him an unbroken artery from the New England seaboard to the Mississippi. Details could wait; the grand design was there. Smith now sought able lieutenants to help him effect it.

Ezra Cornell and John J. Speed had already been caught in the mad scramble of telegraph construction. The fever, which was rapidly spreading even to the remote sections of the country, had got into their blood early. Cornell had participated in the building of Morse's first experimental line and had subsequently built a section for the Magnetic Telegraph Company. In the summer of 1847 he was engaged in constructing hundreds of miles of line in New York State and Canada. The same summer found Speed building the western end of the Erie & Michigan line, but he too had been interested in the telegraph for some years. As a young man of thirty-three, having sold the prosperous family farm in upper New York State for a handsome sum, he had set himself up as a merchant in Ithaca. Much of his leisure time in the 1840's, however, was spent in experimenting with both visual and electric telegraphs. The introduction of the Morse machine occurred before his inventions were brought to fruition. Through his acquaintance with Cornell he had become interested in telegraph construction in 1846. Under the circumstances Smith had little trouble in interesting the two contractors in his great undertaking. On July 13, 1847, Ezra Cornell and John J. Speed became Smith's agents for the Morse patent in the Northwest, and his partners in promoting a grand combination of lines for their mutual benefit.[3]

---

[2] *Ibid.*

[3] Morse vs. Smith, Superior Court of the State of New York for the City and County of New York, Deposition of A. Kendall, January 10, 1857, O'Rielly Docs., Legal Series, XI; *Ithaca Daily Chronicle*, July 19, 1847, Cornell Papers; Speed to E. Cornell, July 25,

For the next month Smith went through the motions of negotiating a compromise with O'Rielly, but it was mere pretense. In this way he hoped to divert the Irishman and gain time in which to mature his own plans. When all was in readiness he revealed his true position. In a vigorous letter to Cornell on August 15 Smith gave the signal for an "all out attack" on O'Rielly and his confederates:

I don't want to be humbugged anymore. Out with the plan of our campaign. Show that our Lake lines are to be the great receptacles of the Western intercourse with the Atlantic, and that the connecting lines are open to the people of the West, almost without money and without price, to accomplish this end.

Our course is simple, plain, straight forward, and only requires energy. You, Speed, Livingston and Wells and associates, have enough of this if set at work. Let the law, in the meantime, commence its slow work between the parties.

Whenever you can get money enough raised to get a line up, start it, and Patentees will not hurry for their part, and your share of benefits shall be made satisfactory. I want no pusillanimous, or doubting movement made—but, dash on with all the battery and thunder and lightning you all can command.

Time saved is everything now. The West are as yet possessed of the proposals . . . and views of the O'Rielly interest only. Give them ours in good earnest, and do, as well as *say*. We will determine whether we or the other party make the best lightning. Again I urge you, don't hesitate—go ahead—and open your fire everywhere—set all the West in a light blaze with your proposals, and keep boldly in view the cheapness of the lines offered and the magnificence of the main arteries.

F. O. J. Smith.

P.S. Write Speed, as I write you—and push him forward—delays are ruinous.[4]

2 ··—··

WHILE Smith's campaign was aimed primarily at the O'Rielly lines, its possible consequences to his co-patentees were important also. Under guise of crushing O'Rielly, the business of the Irishman's Philadelphia-St. Louis line, in which the patentees held a potential interest, was to be diverted to the Erie & Michigan line, in which they had relinquished their interest. Then, after O'Rielly had been

---

1847, *et seq.*, Cornell Papers; Smith to Kendall, August 15, 1847, *et seq.*, Correspondence, O'Rielly Docs., Legal Series, XI.

[4] Morse vs. Smith, Superior Court of State of New York for the City and County of New York, Deposition of E. Cornell, O'Rielly Docs., Legal Series, XI.

brought to terms through ruinous competition, Smith proposed to pay his partners in depreciated stock of the O'Rielly lines. To the east, the proposed line from Dunkirk to New York City, in which the patentees were to hold no stock,[5] was designed to draw business from the New York, Albany & Buffalo line, in which they held a large amount of stock, and the one that up to this time, had been their most profitable investment. To build up those great arteries in which he held the complete patent interest, Smith proposed to reduce the cost of tributary lines, in which he would have but a quarter interest, to a figure "so low as to allow every Western village to avail itself of the Telegraph." While O'Rielly might be "brought to a pause" by this program, the patentees would also suffer heavy losses. So far as they were concerned, the Smith remedy would be worse than the O'Rielly disease.[6]

3 · · · — ·

THE contest for the Great Lakes area might well serve as an epitome of the era of methodless enthusiasm. Along the four hundred mile front with business for no more than one company, two rival telegraph concerns stretched their eager but impoverished lines. Endless litigation and inefficient operation, coupled with the ills of competition, sapped the vitality of both lines from the beginning, and brought telegraphy generally into disfavor. In this instance the adversaries called themselves the Lake Erie and the Erie & Michigan Telegraph Companies, but the counterpart of their story is to be found again and again in the history of communications companies prior to the era of consolidation.

In the struggle for control of the Great Lakes region the advantage of priority lay with the Lake Erie Telegraph Company. Heman B. Ely, contractor, had opened the subscription books in the fall of 1846 with the announcement that the proposed line would form section 5 of O'Rielly's Atlantic, Lake & Mississippi Telegraph system. Progress

---

[5] Patentee policy regarding compensation for the use of Morse instruments by the telegraph companies was to take payment in stock on main arteries, and to take a small cash payment on all side lines. At the time of the divisional contracts Kendall had already made arrangements for all the main arteries, and subsequent building was supposed to be confined to side or secondary lines. The Dunkirk and New York City line, although obviously intended by Smith as a main artery to the seaboard, was classified by him as a secondary line, and payment to the patentees was to be made at the rate of $37.50 per mile. The new line was clearly an infringement on the patentees' contract with the New York, Albany & Buffalo Telegraph Company.

[6] Kendall to Smith, August 23, 1847, Correspondence, O'Rielly Docs., Legal Series, XI.

on the T-shaped Lake Erie Telegraph line from Buffalo to Detroit and from Cleveland to Pittsburgh had been fairly satisfactory until the Erie & Michigan Telegraph Company under the direction of Speed and Cornell had entered the field. To arrest the action of their rival, Ely and his Rochester associates launched an effective program of propaganda and public enlightenment. While Ely's propaganda campaign was successful in checking Speed and Cornell, their vigorous counterattacks prevented him from filling his subscription lists, and stopped collection on many previous pledges.[7] Pamphlets, public addresses, and press notices—often in rather broad English—were presented by both parties in rapid succession. Ely warned that O'Rielly held the sole authority to build along the Great Lakes and expressed concern that some citizens stood to lose their money through misrepresentation. O'Rielly, who was determined to give all possible aid to his northern confederate, loosed a series of spirited broadsides against the "Morse Patentees and Patent Right Peddlers." Speed and Cornell countered with assertions of their legality and cautioned against the piratical nature of the O'Rielly group.[8]

After listening to both sides, the public became convinced that an investment in either project would be unwise as long as the Morse patent controversy remained unsettled. Each company had succeeded in blocking its opponent, but in so doing had crippled itself. Speed, whose sense of humor never forsook him, summarized the situation in a letter to Cornell, "If we cannot get the rocks, it is some satisfaction to know that *he* [Ely] is in the same fix."[9]

In this crisis Ely had turned hopefully to the members of the Atlantic, Lake & Mississippi Telegraph Company for aid, but little was forthcoming. All through the fall of 1847 and the spring of 1848 business remained unsettled due to the Mexican War. Money was scarce and the Rochester group, though disposed to give Ely financial aid, were frequently in need of assistance themselves. Ely wrote O'Rielly that he had seen their friends at Rochester and though they were willing, they could not possibly do much. He did not expect

7 Ely to Luman Sherwood, December 20, 1849, O'Rielly MS Coll., VI.

8 Livingston and Wells to Smith, August 21, 1847, Smith Papers, XII; [Chicago daily paper]. Open Letter H. B. Ely entitled, "To Whom It May Concern," August 27, 1847, Tillotson's Scrapbook, Cornell University Library; *Sandusky City Daily Mirror*, August 12, 1847, *Ibid.*; Circular: [H. B. Ely] Atlantic, Lake & Mississippi Range, September 1847, O'Rielly Papers in Rochester Historical Society Library; *Democratic Expounder*, Marshall, Michigan, September 10, 1847, Smith Papers, XXV.

9 Speed to Cornell, March 15, 1848, Cornell Papers.

North American Hotel, Lancaster, Pa., as it appeared in 1846 when the first
commercial telegraph office was opened in it

Regulations Governing the Operation of O'Rielly's
Lancaster-Harrisburg Line, 1846

House's Printing Telegraph Instrument

more than $2,000 or $3,000 from them, which would enable him to pay for posts and complete the work between Buffalo and Cleveland.[10]

Suffering from like circumstances himself, O'Rielly had gradually shifted his financing from Rochester to Pittsburgh. Here Joshua Hanna of the banking house of Hussey, Hanna & Company had watched O'Rielly's progress with interest. When the Irishman's Rochester associates proved unable to meet his ever-increasing financial demands, therefore, O'Rielly had turned to Hanna for funds, and ultimately for assistance in the handling of his entire business interests. Largely through money and credit provided by Joshua Hanna, O'Rielly was enabled to press forward with his line and at the same time to give material aid to Ely on Lake Erie.[11]

"To your *substantial* assistance thus far am I indebted for accomplishing what has been done along the Lake," Ely wrote in recognition of his obligation to O'Rielly. "In the face of the tremendous opposition that has been raised I do not know how I should have got along without it."[12]

4 .... —

SMITH and his lieutenants were finding their situation no more enviable. If anything, the plight of the Erie & Michigan promoters was worse. The winter of 1847-1848 was one of the darkest in Erie & Michigan history. The O'Rielly forces had fought Livingston and Wells to a standstill on the Buffalo-Detroit section, and in September they had willingly relinquished their contract to Speed and Cornell. Those harassed promoters had made some progress on the Detroit-Chicago section, but the work was constantly delayed for want of funds and by petty annoyances. Wire stored in warehouses could not be obtained until the charges were paid. Contractors refused to deliver more poles until they received the money for those already delivered. Employees complained of the irregularity and meagerness of the pay. But there was little that Cornell and Speed could do to

[10] Ely to O'Rielly, December 7, 1847, *et seq.*, O'Rielly MS Coll., xv; Ely to O'Rielly, February 18, 1848, O'Rielly MS Coll., February 1848; *Ibid.*, January 17, 1848, O'Rielly MS Coll., vi.

[11] O'Rielly to H. R. Selden, July 10, 1847, O'Rielly MS Coll., xii.

[12] Ely to O'Rielly, October 24, 1847, O'Rielly MS Coll., xiv; *Ibid.*, September 27, 1847, O'Rielly MS Coll., xiii; H. Downing to O'Rielly, December 11, 1847, *et seq.*, O'Rielly MS Coll., xv.

relieve the situation. In consequence of the O'Rielly difficulty, many subscriptions to the line could not be collected.[13]

In the midst of all their difficulties Speed suffered a severe leg injury which confined him to his bed for weeks.[14] In his gloom he wrote to Cornell on December 12 describing the gravity of the situation: "The mate may say to the captain what it would be the height of imprudence to repeat to the passengers, and what had better be kept from the crew. I may consequently say to you, what I would not like to have other subscribers know. . . . We are so far from shore—there is such a tremendous blow—and the vessel so shattered, that I do not believe that we can make the port. To drop all similies [*sic*]— I do not see how it is possible for us to finish this line to Detroit this winter."[15]

With improving health came a return of fighting spirit and a determination to carry on. "Smith must give us a lift," Speed wrote his partner two weeks later. "His credit is good, if he has no money, and he must aid you with the use of it. I will move to Detroit if you and Smith think it best. I will do anything that can be done; but as to getting much money before we get this line done, I can't. No one can. It is impossible."[16]

Failure to obtain the badly needed funds cannot be attributed to lack of effort on Speed's part. Statements of agents along the route bear evidence to the ingenuity and determination with which Speed tried to promote his line. In an appeal to local pride the hard-working promoter promised that any village subscribing at least $2,000 should have its own telegraph station. Residents of South Bend, Indiana, were guaranteed 7 percent on their investment for five years if they would agree to turn over to Speed all their dividends during that period. Speed's agent there, an enterprising young newspaperman named Schuyler Colfax,[17] reported that the sales talk had helped to obtain subscriptions. The rival village of Niles, Michigan, had to report its inability to raise more than $1,500 despite Speed's promise "to put them on the main line and merely run a branch line to South Bend," if they raised their quota. The Niles agent was forced to

13 E. Cornell to Morse, January 3, 1848, Morse Papers, XXIII.
14 Livingston and Wells to Smith, August 29, 1847, Smith Papers, XIII; Speed to Cornell, March 15, 1848, Cornell Papers; D. T. Tillotson to Speed and Cornell, August 15, 1847, *Ibid.*; Speed to Cornell, December 4, 1847, *et seq., Ibid.*
15 Speed to Cornell, December 12, 1847, *Ibid.*
16 Speed to Cornell, December 30, 1847, *et seq., Ibid.*
17 Later to become Vice-President of the United States under Ulysses S. Grant.

explain regretfully that the $4,000 to $6,000 recently pledged for a railroad through the village had divested the community of speculative capital.[18]

Commenting on his efforts several years later, Speed declared that scarcely a dollar had been collected on any line without his going with the contractor to every town on it and having a personal interview with the leading men in each place to satisfy them they were safe in paying money to any one representing the Morse interest.[19]

5 ———

SPEED's closing of a contract with Jeptha H. Wade in the summer of 1847 for the construction of that section of the Erie & Michigan line lying between Detroit and Jackson, Michigan, introduced into telegraph history a man destined to leave his mark on the development of the industry. Up to this point in his life Wade, now in his mid-thirties, had failed to find himself. Born of humble parentage in Seneca County, New York, on August 11, 1811, Jeptha had early gone to work in a brickyard. Numerous activities as removed from one another as carpentry and portrait painting followed in rapid succession; yet they all had a common denominator—in each occupation Wade worked with his hands. The years of adolescence and young manhood were largely given over to developing his mechanical skill while neglecting a latent ability to deal with people.

Much as Morse had once wandered through the New England villages taking commissions for portraits, the 1840's found Wade adrift on the Ohio and Mississippi earning his way with his brush from one river town to the next. Since Wade was not robust, winters were generally spent in the milder southern climes with a return in the spring to the bracing air of Michigan. Hoping to improve his health, Wade decided to abandon painting for some less confining occupation. The year 1847 found him seeking other employment.

It was at this point that he had met Speed, discussed the Erie & Michigan project with him, and agreed to build a line of telegraph along the Michigan Central Railroad from Detroit to Jackson, Michigan. With such tools as seemed necessary, a tent to accommodate his men, a cook, a hand car, and a horse, Wade made his telegraph

---

[18] Schuyler Colfax to Speed, April 3, 1847, Cornell Papers; C. Dana to J. J. Speed, April 12, 1847, *Ibid.*

[19] Morse vs. Smith, Superior Court of State of New York for the City and County of New York, Deposition of J. J. Speed, O'Rielly Docs., Legal Series, x.

début. He was not long in winning the confidence of his men and the respect of his business associates. It was soon generally conceded that any work under Wade's direction would be well done. Realizing the possibilities of the telegraph, he had set to work to acquaint himself with all the information then available on the subject. Nor did he limit himself to a purely academic interest. In a year's time he could not only operate but make any of the instruments used in the business.

Upon completion of the line to Jackson, Wade was assigned that section of the line from Detroit eastward—one of the regions where rivalry with O'Rielly was hottest. Less than fifty miles out of Detroit he had intercepted the opposition line building west under O'Rielly's son-in-law, Donald Mann. Not knowing exactly what to expect, Wade had prepared for the worst. While the rival construction gangs might have proved pugnacious with proper encouragement, neither contractor seemed disposed to violence. "I find the agent, Mr. Mann, with the appearance of a gentleman," Wade wrote to Speed. "I trust he and I will get along side by side without any difficulty and leave our *superiors* to settle the difficulty in their own way."[20]

Of more concern was a community of mixed French and Indian blood between Monroe and Toledo who objected strongly to either company's building a line in front of their premises. In their ignorance and superstition they feared the telegraph would burn their buildings, kill their cattle, and blight their crops. There was menacing talk of resort to force should the builders persist in their efforts.[21] Wade's men looked to him for orders. Displaying that tact and understanding of human nature for which he was later to become famous, the contractor went out on a scouting expedition, found out who the "head Devil" was, and made his acquaintance, using plenty of "soft soap" and some whiskey. The half-breed's word was law for the whole neighborhood, and Wade, albeit with grave misgiving, felt obliged to accept a cordial invitation to dinner the next day.

At the appointed hour Wade arrived at the "Big Chief's" house after wading for some distance through mud several inches deep. Although the house had a plank floor, it was not in evidence except where the hogs had failed to step. The main course of the dinner, which consisted of squirrels that were intact except for the skins, was carved and served as if it were bologna sausage. Although Wade found it extremely difficult not to offend his host and hostess by

20 J. H. Wade to Speed, November 8, 1847, Cornell Papers.   21 *Ibid.*

refusing the food, he was able to keep his reactions to himself. At the conclusion his host announced his willingness to do anything and everything he could to aid Wade in his enterprise. He even offered to loan him some money. The threadbare promoter found it hard to refuse this freely proffered and much needed financial aid. Doubting the ultimate wisdom of accepting the Indian's money, he politely explained that all he wanted was for the "Big Chief" to use his influence with his neighbors to convince them that the telegraph would do them no harm. Wade explained also that the line on the east side of the road belonged to the opposition and that his own line was building along the west side.

The next morning the Indian went from house to house along the road and gave each one the same order. "On west side all right, leef 'em be, on east side give 'em hell."[22]

6 ······

Six months of active opposition left its mark on both the Lake Erie and the Erie & Michigan Companies. A week before Christmas 1847, Heman B. Ely reported to O'Rielly that while the Lake line was in operation from Pittsburgh to Cleveland and from there to Erie, Pennsylvania, he lacked $8,000 of having enough to complete the link from Cleveland to Buffalo. The Rochester group had promised to raise the funds to get through to Buffalo, but after a thorough canvass of the situation, Ely's uncle, Hervey Ely, wrote him that it would probably be impossible to do anything before January. On the Cleveland-Detroit section the posts were up but not settled for, and the pole contractors were impatient for their money. Unless funds could be secured from some source, Ely feared that he would have to suspend operations.[23]

Referring to the rival Erie & Michigan line, Ely stated that Speed had made considerable progress between Milwaukee and Chicago, but that the rival line's efforts on the Cleveland-Buffalo section were bogged down by lack of funds. In order to get the posts up before frost they had set only every other one intending to fill in the intermediate spaces later. Their obvious poverty and halting progress caused the public and their own workmen to lose confidence in them.

---

22 The biographical sketch of J. H. Wade is based on a manuscript autobiography in the possession of the Wade family in Cleveland, Ohio.
23 Ely to O'Rielly, December 18, 1847, O'Rielly MS Coll., xv.

"Not a breakfast could they get without paying for it," declared Ely.[24]
A small quantity of wire stored in Buffalo which Speed was intending to put up west of Detroit had just been attached. This, explained
Ely, was undoubtedly the result of an undercurrent he had set in
motion "to repay the scamps for their annoyance in having . . . [his]
poles in Pennsylvania attached."[25]

As a result of this bitter contest along the Lakes it was March
1848, before Ely had his line in operation throughout its entire
length from Buffalo to Detroit and from Cleveland to Pittsburgh.[26]
Handbills announcing its opening were distributed along the route.
The terms upon which the new company proposed to do business
reflected well the weaknesses of limited operations and the chaotic
condition of the industry at this period:

ATLANTIC, LAKE & MISSISSIPPI TELEGRAPH

SECTION 5

LINE EXTENDING FROM BUFFALO TO DETROIT, AND FROM CLEVELAND

TO PITTSBURGH

UNDER THE MANAGEMENT OF

THE LAKE ERIE TELEGRAPH COMPANY

1. Correspondents must write out message legibly, with address in full.
2. Despatches must be prepaid.
3. When directed to places beyond range of telegraph communication,
   they will be written out and mailed at the last station.
4. All communications delivered in towns and cities without extra
   charge, provided they give address or occupation of person addressed.
5. Despatches forwarded on other lines must be at the risk of those who
   send them, though correspondents may depend on their reaching their
   destination promptly if such lines are at the time in working order.
6. In case of interruption despatches will be mailed from the place where
   communication is broken.
7. The above tariffs will obtain until further notice. [Tariff schedule
   was given at top of each telegraph blank]

---

[24] *Ibid.*

[25] *Ibid.*

[26] The Lake Erie Telegraph Company had been organized provisionally in Rochester,
New York, in March 1847. The capital stock was fixed at $177,600, which was to be
divided into shares of $50 each. Subscribers were to receive $50 in stock for each $50
paid in. (Circular: The Lake Erie Telegraph Company, March 1847, in the O'Rielly
MS Coll., v.)

Formal organization was not effected until July 6, 1848, at which time Joseph
Weatherby was made president, Heman B. Ely, secretary, and Joshua Hanna, treasurer.
(Stock certificate—Lake Erie Telegraph Company made out in the name of Henry R.
Selden, January 30, 1849, Bacon Papers.)

8. This line connects with all others throughout the United States and the British Provinces—the Line from New York to Boston excepted.[27] The rate of charges, for transmission of messages to places on other lines, will be found at the different offices.

9. Offices open every day, Sundays excepted.

H. B. ELY, Sec'y.[28]

Smith lost no time in taking action against the company. In the Circuit Court of New York he entered suit to restrain it from proceeding under the O'Rielly contract, and in the Circuit Court of Ohio for infringement of the patent right, but neither suit was successful. New York refused to grant an injunction, while the Ohio case was permitted to drag on from term to term without being brought to trial.[29]

Smith's Erie & Michigan line, meanwhile, could point to the completion of its Milwaukee-Chicago section on January 15 as its only offset to the O'Rielly company's grand opening. The Erie & Michigan had to postpone inauguration of its full service until October, and not until the first week of January 1849 was direct contact established between Chicago and Buffalo.[30]

For some months after completion of the rival lake lines business was light and neither company could make expenses. As the volume

[27] As part of his plan to crush O'Rielly, Smith had issued an order in September 1847, forbidding his New York & Boston line to receive dispatches "for or from" any point on the lines constructed by O'Rielly. (O'Rielly to Morse, September 18, 1847, Morse Papers, xxv.)

[28] Circular: Atlantic, Lake & Mississippi Telegraph, Section 5 . . . under the management of the Lake Erie Telegraph Company, January 1, 1848, Vail Papers.

[29] Smith to Kendall, August 27, 1847, et seq., Correspondence, O'Rielly Docs., Legal Series, xi; Smith vs. Selden, Circuit Court of New York, October 1849; Smith vs. H. B. Ely, Circuit Court of Ohio, November 1849.

[30] A. B. Cornell to Ezra Cornell, January 7, 1849, Cornell Papers; Smith to Kendall, February 8, 1848, Correspondence, O'Rielly Docs., Legal Series, xi.

The sources of information concerning the corporate development of the Erie & Michigan Telegraph Company were inadequate. What detail could be found is given below. Formal organization of the company took place during the winter of 1848-1849 at which time John J. Speed, Jr., was made president, and D. T. Tillotson, secretary. The company was capitalized on the basis of $250 per mile of wire. On the 812 wire miles, representing the real property of the Erie & Michigan, total capitalization amounted to $203,000. Of this amount Smith was to receive one half, or $101,500 (812 miles at $125 per mile) as his share of the profits of construction, making in all a total of $125,860 (812 miles at $155 per mile), or 62 percent of the total stock. This agreement would have left only $77,140 to be divided between all the other stockholders and the contractors, Cornell and Speed. As subsequent events will show, the stock for the patent right was never actually issued to Smith since he was unable to restrain O'Rielly in the use of the Morse instruments on the rival Lake Erie line. (Morse vs. Smith, Superior Court of the State of New York for the City and County of New York, in deposition of John J. Speed, December 1856; Ibid., deposition of Amos Kendall, January 10, 1857, in O'Rielly Docs., Legal Series, xi.)

of business increased, competition became more bitter. Tariffs were lowered, and as a result neither company could make a reasonable profit. In his report for the month of January 1849, almost a year after the Lake Erie had begun operation, Superintendent James D. Reid showed receipts of only $1,500 with expenses of $1,200.[31] The situation on the Erie & Michigan was little different. Superintendent D. T. Tillotson's letter to D. S. F. How, operator at Kalamazoo, reflects the penurious condition of the company. "I see that our company furnish a bed and washing, bedding, etc. at your station," he wrote. "That is a saving to you, probably of $30 per annum, which should be considered, otherwise we had better sell it as it is a poor kind of asset to pay dividends with. . . . Your salary should not exceed $200 [per annum]. Many offices with as much or more business, in the east, are kept up for $100."[32]

Ezra Cornell's young son, Alonzo B. Cornell, a lad of sixteen employed as an operator in the Buffalo office, relates the story of the dismal failure of the Erie & Michigan line to give public satisfaction. Fallen wires, broken insulators, ignorant operators, improper insulation, and public complaints made young Cornell's life miserable. An occasional ray of light pierced the gloom. Writing to his father on July 15, 1848, he was fairly optimistic: "We are fast gaining the confidence of the Buffalo public over our enemies [Lake Erie], and I think although our line is so very bad, we do business much more prompt."[33]

Several weeks later the line was not working. Young Cornell explained that on the line near Buffalo four-fifths of the glass insulators had been broken and that leaves touching the wires grounded them in wet weather. "If we could do it right our business would double immediately," asserted the young telegrapher.[34]

7 — — · ·

WHILE methods of operation improved slightly in the early 1850's, the financial position of the Lake Erie and the Erie & Michigan Telegraph Companies grew worse. Both lines suffered keenly from competition; both were burdened with construction debts; and both

---

[31] F. O. J. Smith to William H. Seward, January 5, 1849, *Ibid.*; Reid, *Telegraph in America*, 258.
[32] *Ibid.*
[33] A. B. Cornell to Ezra Cornell, July 15, 1848, Cornell Papers.
[34] *Ibid.*, August 17, 1848.

were confronted with maintenance difficulties. Neither company earned sufficient revenues to do more than meet current expenses.

The situation of the Lake lines was desperate, but it was little different from that of the majority of the pioneer lines. The average company was dangerously near bankruptcy. Aware of the crisis within the industry, a number of far-seeing individuals urged a grand combination of lines, but the time was not ripe. Nearly a decade was to elapse before competition gave way to consolidation, and the telegraph industry emerged from the era of methodless enthusiasm into one of order and prosperity.

CHAPTER VIII

Battle for the Ohio Valley

1 · — — ·

IMPORTANT as was the contest on Lake Erie, the main conflict was in the Ohio Valley where O'Rielly pressed his promotional and building campaign with unflagging energy. For five months after the completion of the Atlantic & Ohio line from Philadelphia to Pittsburgh the O'Rielly forces were immobilized pending the outcome of protracted negotiations with the patentees. These negotiations having come to nothing, June 1 found O'Rielly once more pressing westward from Pittsburgh along the National Road through Zanesville, Columbus, and Dayton to Cincinnati and Louisville. Delay had but intensified his determination to carry on, and in the remaining months of the year he was resolved to reach the Mississippi at all costs.[1]

Public subscription to the line, however, did not begin to keep pace with the building program which O'Rielly had outlined for himself. Once again the bogey of patent controversy stood astride his path. The business men of Cincinnati, Louisville, and St. Louis hailed him onward, but too frequently their enthusiasm spent itself with their cheers. Scarcely six weeks after construction was under way lack of funds threatened to suspend further operations. This threat prompted O'Rielly to pledge all of his Atlantic & Ohio stock to Joshua Hanna of the Pittsburgh banking house of Hussey, Hanna & Company "to idemnify for money that might be wanted for the enterprise till confidence could be . . . established by the progress of the work."[2]

With the extension of the line westward drafts on Hussey, Hanna & Company became more frequent; and indebtedness to the Pittsburgh manufacturers, Livingston & Roggen, grew. O'Rielly was not disturbed. Knowing little of the intricacies of finance, he assumed that his agent, Hanna, could arrange for the necessary credit to finance the work. O'Rielly's concern was to carry the line on to Cincinnati

---

[1] O'Rielly to Isaac Butts, June 23, 1847, O'Rielly MS Coll., XII.
[2] O'Rielly to H. R. Selden, July 10, 1847, Selden Papers in possession of Leonard Bacon family of Rochester, New York; O'Rielly to Ely, July 10, 1847, O'Rielly MS Coll., XII.

and Louisville by himself, if necessary, "just to teach Smith and Kendall a lesson."[3]

The close of August 1847 brought O'Rielly the satisfaction of opening his line to Cincinnati, an event made doubly satisfying by the fact that Heman B. Ely was able to open the Pittsburgh-Cleveland branch of the Lake Erie line within the same week.[4] Pittsburgh, Cincinnati, and Cleveland were thus brought into telegraph communication, but the celebrating was left to the public. The tireless promoter was already pressing forward to Louisville in the hope of stealing a march on Smith's forces, which were inactive as a result of the Yankee's impasse with the Cincinnati trustees.[5]

Smith, it may be recalled, could neither bring legal action against O'Rielly nor build over the route so long as the patent right for it was vested in the Cincinnati trustees. Nevertheless, there remained still another means of halting his rival. On September 4, his New York & Boston Telegraph Association ruled that in the future it would not receive messages "from or for any line of Telegraph not established under the Titles Patent of Samuel F. B. Morse." All "legitimate" Morse lines were urged to establish similar non-intercourse acts. Several of them did so.[6]

The non-intercourse acts, far from discouraging O'Rielly, merely increased his determination to carry on. Within two weeks he had completed the Pittsburgh, Cincinnati & Louisville line, section two of the Atlantic, Lake & Mississippi range.[7] From Louisville, on Sep-

---

[3] *Ibid.*

[4] *Cincinnati Gazette*, August 21, 1847, O'Rielly Docs., First Series, I; *Cincinnati Daily Atlas*, August 28, [1847], *Ibid.*; Circular: "Atlantic, Lake & Mississippi Telegraph Range —Its Backers," August 1847, Morse Papers, XXIII; Sandusky [daily newspaper], August 20, 1847, Tillotson Scrapbook in Cornell University Library.

[5] For a detailed account of the controversy of Smith with the Cincinnati trustees see Chapter VI.

[6] Minutes of the Meeting of the Stockholders of the New York & Boston Telegraph Association, September 4, 1847, Smith Telegraph Documents in F. O. J. Smith Collection at the Maine Historical Society. (Reference to Smith printed materials will hereafter be abbreviated as: Smith Docs.); O'Rielly to Morse, September 18, 1847, Morse Papers, XXIII.

[7] The Pittsburgh, Cincinnati & Louisville Telegraph Company was formally incorporated under the general telegraph law of Indiana, February 18, 1848. The company was capitalized at $138,000 which was divided into 2,760 shares of $50 each. James C. Hall was the first president; Joshua Hanna, treasurer; and James D. Reid, superintendent. President Hall served for a single year only, when he was succeeded by General James K. Moorhead of Pittsburgh who was already the president of the Atlantic & Ohio Telegraph Company. (Proceedings of Convention of Delegates from Stockholders of the Pittsburgh, Cincinnati & Louisville Telegraph Company, Columbus, Ohio, June 6-7, 1849, O'Rielly Docs., Miscell. Series, III; Morse vs. Smith, Superior Court of State of New York for the City and County of New York, Deposition of James D. Reid, December 1856, O'Rielly Docs., Legal Series, XI.)

tember 22, he telegraphed the eminent scientist, Joseph Henry, a message which might well have given the patentees cause for uneasiness: " '*House's Lightning Letter Printer*' this day opened the Cincinnati & Louisville Line—one hundred and forty miles."[8]

The message was significant, not alone for the threat it held to the Morse invention, but as suggestive of the thought maturing in O'Rielly's active brain. The O'Rielly lines must be free from domination by the Morse patentees. They must reach out to every important commercial point in the country, and together comprise a complete and independent telegraph system. No longer must he be held within the narrow confines of his original contract. His operations must be unrestricted by geographic boundaries or restraining patents. Furthermore there must be no delay; speed was of the essence of success.

2 ··—··

SOARING thought heightened by the plaudits of the people, and a determination to keep the initiative in the struggle with his rivals, may explain O'Rielly's seeming loss of equilibrium in the autumn of 1847. Up to this time his building program had borne some relation to his ability to finance it. Now caution and sound business were abandoned. Having completed the line to Louisville, additional lines were projected in all directions from that point. To the south a crew was dispatched to build to New Orleans (People's Telegraph Company); to the northwest the necessary preliminaries were undertaken for a line to Chicago and Toledo (Ohio, Indiana & Illinois Telegraph); to the west O'Rielly, himself, undertook to carry a line on to St. Louis (Ohio & Mississippi Telegraph). O'Rielly believed that extended operation without a moment's delay was necessary, if he was to achieve telegraphic self-sufficiency and triumph over his adversaries.

Without waiting for the subscription lists to be filled agents were hurried westward from Louisville toward St. Louis to obtain poles for the Ohio & Mississippi Telegraph—section three of the great O'Rielly range. As the fragile line with its perishable oak posts— frequently with the bark unremoved—progressed across southern Indiana, it was received by the public with satisfaction. O'Rielly, with his drive and enthusiasm, bidding defiance to all obstacles had captured the heart of the West.[9]

8 Telegram: O'Rielly to Prof. Joseph Henry, September 22, 1847, *Ibid.*
9 Fred L. King to A. Vail, May 14, 1849, Vail Papers; Reid, *Telegraph in America,* 220.

His friends back in the East, however, felt less joy over his apparent successes. Aware of the unsure financial foundation on which he built, they were fearful of the result of so unrestrained a program.[10] His banker, Joshua Hanna, cautioned him against undertaking construction of any line until the money for it had been subscribed. He urged O'Rielly to raise his subscriptions, get 10 percent paid in, and then begin building—not otherwise.[11] Samuel Selden, Hervey Ely, men whose judgment was worthy of respect, also urged a less spectacular but more certain course.

Listen as O'Rielly might, and agree as he did to their counsels of moderation, he was unable to check himself. The fever ran high in his blood. December 1 found him in Vincennes; ten days later he had reached the Mississippi, and within the week the Ohio & Mississippi Telegraph opened its doors to the public.[12]

St. Louis, on the outer rim of civilization at this time, was jubilant. Earlier in the same month some of her citizens had been discussing the great and lasting benefits which would flow from the construction of a railroad from the Mississippi to unite with lines which were already pushing westward from the Atlantic seaboard. Here was an enterprise—already brought to fruition—which would enable business men to speak to their correspondents in Boston or New York and get a response *"in the same hour."* O'Rielly's accomplishment, announced the *Daily Union*, "marked a new era in the history of St. Louis."[13] The *Daily Republican* pointed out that a merchant could no longer "depend upon the slow progress of Mr. Cave John-

[10] S. L. Selden to O'Rielly, October 20, 1847, O'Rielly MS Coll., xiv; cf. S. L. Selden to O'Rielly, May 26, 1847, O'Rielly MS Coll., v.

[11] Joshua Hanna to O'Rielly, October 20, 1847, O'Rielly MS Coll., xiv.

[12] H. Ely to O'Rielly, December 1, 1847, O'Rielly MS Coll., xv; *Niles National Register*, December 25, 1847; *St. Louis Daily Union*, December 21, 1847, O'Rielly Docs., First Series, I.

The Ohio & Mississippi Telegraph Company was formally incorporated by special act of the General Assembly of the State of Indiana on February 14, 1848, with an authorized capitalization of $200,000 which was to be divided into shares of $50 each. James D. Reid, who served as first superintendent of the company, states that at a meeting for formal organization on March 21, 1848, stock to the amount of $90,000 was issued—a statement which was confirmed by other officers of that organization. Officers of the company were: Abner T. Ellis of Vincennes, Indiana, president; John Ross of St. Louis, Missouri, secretary; Sanford J. Smith of St. Louis, Missouri, treasurer; and James D. Reid of Rochester, New York, superintendent. (Indiana Statutes, 1847-1848; Morse vs. Smith, Superior Court of the State of New York for the City and County of New York, Deposition of G. R. McGunnegle, secretary of the Ohio & Mississippi Telegraph Company, November 1856, in O'Rielly Docs., Legal Series, xi; *Ibid.*, Deposition of James D. Reid; cf. Reid, *Telegraph in America*, 222; Case to Smith, February 14, 1848, Morse Papers, xxiv.)

[13] *St. Louis Daily Union*, December 21, 1847, O'Rielly Docs., First Series, I.

son's mail, because his neighbor . . . would outstrip him by using the lightning line."[14] Enthusiasm was general.

The occasion was of too great significance to let pass without a celebration. A public dinner attended by the representative men of the city was given in honor of the "telegraph king"—Henry O'Rielly. In an invitation both enthusiastic and sincere they recognized his achievement:

The citizens of St. Louis congratulate you on the success of your vast undertaking, in connecting with "links of lightning" the Atlantic, the Lakes and the Mississippi. Appreciating the energy, enthusiasm and untiring industry which have enabled you, despite all obstacles, to accomplish so grand and almost inconceivable an enterprise, and regarding the event as of too vast interest to pass without proper recognition, they especially solicit that you will accept a public dinner to be given at the Planters' House, in this city, on Thursday next, the 23d inst., that at the festive board they may interchange with you and each other, the sentiments which the occasion naturally inspires.

With sentiments of the highest esteem and respect, we are,

Your obedient servants,[15]

Sensitive, public-spirited, not a little vain, such tribute was more to O'Rielly than fine gold. Where another, less impulsive, might have halted his advance to consolidate his position, O'Rielly was carried on to new endeavors. Although work was not yet completed on his original range, and he had just launched a line to New Orleans, he now made plans to build across Missouri to Fort Leavenworth, and even offered to dash on to the Pacific within a year if Congress would give him adequate military protection.

3 · · · — ·

MEANWHILE, back along the route, work undertaken earlier on the fourth unit (Ohio, Indiana & Illinois Telegraph Company) of the O'Rielly system had come to a virtual standstill. This line, it may be recalled, was designed to connect O'Rielly's Lake Erie line with his trunk lines in the Ohio Valley region. Projected from Dayton on his Pittsburgh, Cincinnati & Louisville line, it was to run northwest across Indiana by way of Lafayette to Chicago. From there it was to turn back eastward to connect with his Lake Erie line at Toledo. With rapidly growing populations suggesting the future importance of

[14] *St. Louis Daily Republican,* December 21, 1847, *Ibid.*
[15] Citizens of St. Louis to Henry O'Rielly, December 20, 1847, O'Rielly MS Coll., xv.

the towns springing into life between the Ohio River and the Great Lakes, the line promised eventually to be important and profitable. Like so many of O'Rielly's projects, however, its launching was premature. In addition, it suffered from neglect and lack of leadership.

Two agents had been hastily selected to proceed into the section and undertake construction in the fall of 1847, while O'Rielly was dashing on to the Mississippi. Work had commenced at Chicago in November. Inasmuch as no stock was taken there, the line had been erected as far as Crawfordsville, Indiana, at O'Rielly's own expense. Crawfordsville, Indianapolis, Cambridge, and Richmond were induced to aid in the extension of the line, pledging in the aggregate about $16,000. After the first installment had been collected at Crawfordsville, work on the line was carried forward as far as Indianapolis. Then payments were suddenly suspended.[16]

Disquieting news from the North had begun to filter into Indianapolis and its environs. The telegraph promoters, enjoying the importance and glamour with which their mission invested them, had been "strutting through Hoosier land with high looks and proud stomachs," leaving a trail of unpaid bills from Michigan City to Lafayette. Rumors of their dissipation and ribaldry produced consternation among those who had pledged money for the enterprise. No further funds could be looked for until the dissolute pair was recalled. William J. Delano, who had been serving as a telegraph operator at Dayton, was sent to replace them.[17]

Delano was very unlike his predecessors. Earnest and persevering, a man of unquestioned integrity, he did much to restore confidence in the undertaking. Payments were resumed; by March 1848, poles were erected to Dayton, and the work of wiring was well under way. But just at this time another and more formidable obstacle was placed in Delano's path. Agents of John J. Speed and Ezra Cornell invaded the Wabash and Miami Valleys soliciting funds for feeder lines to the Erie & Michigan system. Their appearance and the inevitable interchange of epithets between the opposing parties

[16] W. J. Delano, Report on the Construction, Condition, and Prospects of the Ohio, Indiana & Illinois Telegraph Company, August 5, 1850, O'Rielly Docs., Miscell. Series, III; Smith to Cornell, March 7, 1848, O'Rielly Docs., Correspondence, Legal Series, X.

[17] Reid, *Telegraph in America*, 250; George W. Olney to O'Rielly, May 18, 1848, O'Rielly MS Coll. (May 1848). Starting with January 1848, the O'Rielly Manuscript Material is no longer collected or catalogued by volume; it is arranged by months—one month to a folder—in an order roughly chronological and catalogued in the form given in this footnote.

brought the whole miserable patent controversy into the open. Once again public confidence was shaken and payments were suspended.[18]

Under such circumstances Delano's advance to the Lakes was a record of "delay, disappointment and difficulty." Commencing in Dayton, the line had been carried as far as Richmond, Indiana, by April 17. Indianapolis, only sixty miles away, was not reached until the middle of May.[19] Eight miles east of Crawfordsville there was further delay when materials which had been ordered two weeks before failed to arrive. "I have nothing to do but wait for your promised letter of instruction and for those two reels of wire and the instruments," Delano wrote O'Rielly on May 23. To relieve his employer of the expense of so many idle hands, Delano dismissed all except five of the construction gang. He hoped that he would be able to rehire them when work was once more resumed.[20]

Progress out of Crawfordsville was even more retarded due to the necessity of remapping the route to Chicago. The line as originally projected ran through Lafayette and the Kankakee swamps to Michigan City, a route which, if followed, would have carried the wire through "110 miles barren of towns and importance and utterly impassable in certain seasons of the year." At Delano's suggestion, therefore, the line was rerouted from Lafayette, through Logansport, and Laporte, notwithstanding the fact that a line of poles was already standing to Chicago, via the Kankakee swamps.[21]

Chicago, center of John J. Speed's activity, refused to subscribe a dollar for the enterprise, while business men in Toledo, having received no dividends on O'Rielly's Lake Erie line, refused to take stock in another telegraph project.[22] Pushing ahead when he had funds and suspending activity when his money was exhausted, Delano was over two and a half years in completing the line. The Lafayette office was finally opened in January 1849; Chicago was reached in February 1850; and Toledo, the final objective, was attained six months later.[23]

[18] Cornell to Hon. H. L. Ellsworth, March 13, 1848, Cornell Papers; Morse vs. Smith, Superior Court of the State of New York for the City and County of New York, Deposition of Ezra Cornell, O'Rielly Docs., Legal Series, x; W. J. Delano, Report on Construction of Ohio, Indiana & Illinois Telegraph Company, August 5, 1850, O'Rielly Docs., Miscell. Series, III.

[19] W. J. Delano to O'Rielly, May 29, 1848, O'Rielly MS Coll. (May 1848); Delano, op. cit.

[20] Delano to O'Rielly, May 16, 1848, O'Rielly MS Coll. (May 1848); Ibid., May 23, 1848, et seq.

[21] Ibid., May 29, 1848.

[22] Delano to O'Rielly, May 31, 1849, O'Rielly MS Coll. (May 1849).

[23] Ibid., February 6, 1849, O'Rielly MS Coll. (February 1849); Delano, op. cit.

Second Floor. Operating Room

Ground Floor. Business Office

CINCINNATI OFFICE OF THE PITTSBURGH, CINCINNATI & LOUISVILLE TELEGRAPH
COMPANY, c. 1850

General View

Close-up of the Recorder

BAIN'S ELECTRO-CHEMICAL TELEGRAPH, C. 1850

As an answer to complaints of subscribers because of the delays in the completion and organization of the line, Delano issued a report on the "Construction, Condition, and Prospects of the Ohio, Indiana & Illinois Telegraph Company," in August 1850. He pointed out that while the difficulties under which the line had been constructed had worked a hardship on many, that no one had suffered more through the delay than Henry O'Rielly. Of the $80,000 construction cost, only $37,000 had been subscribed; the remainder had been furnished by O'Rielly in cash or personal obligations for materials.[24] From the time when the first section of the line had been opened for business in April 1848, to August 1850, when the completed line was finally put into operation—a period of a little over two years—net profits had been $68.62. While this financial report was not impressive, Delano went on to explain that it was largely due to the fact that the line had been in a partially finished state during most of the period. Until February 1850, no two of its important terminals had been connected. Now that the line was completed, Delano hoped that the company's difficulties were at an end, and that an era of prosperity was dawning for the Ohio, Indiana & Illinois Telegraph.[25]

4 . . . . —

THE Illinois & Mississippi Telegraph Company, last of the units comprising the original O'Rielly range, had a history little brighter than that of the Ohio, Indiana & Illinois. Conceived at the height of the promoter's mass production program, it suffered not only from physical ills but also from lack of effective leadership. While O'Rielly was dissipating his energies to the four points of the compass, the Illinois & Mississippi's lines were hastily projected to crisscross the State of Illinois. As planned, the main line was to extend from St. Louis to Chicago via Alton, Jacksonville, Springfield, Peoria, Peru, and Ottawa. Three branches were projected—one from Peru to Dubuque, Iowa, via Dixon and Galena; a second from Jacksonville to Bloomington (Muscatine), Iowa, via Beardstown, Quincy, Keokuk and Burlington; and a third from Quincy to Hannibal. These routes comprised in all just over seven hundred miles of line.[26]

24 Ibid.

25 Ibid. The Ohio, Indiana & Illinois Telegraph Company was capitalized at $240,050, divided into shares of $50 each, making a total stock issue of 4,801 shares. (Reid, Telegraph in America, 252.)

26 Reid, Telegraph in America, 233; J. N. Alvord to J. D. Reid [n.d.–1849], Vail Papers.

The building program was set in motion early in 1848. Construction would probably have proceeded smoothly but for two factors—the business panic of that year, and the fact that O'Rielly was already engaged in building the 900-mile People's Telegraph line to New Orleans without help from the people of the South.[27] Sanford J. Smith, the Irishman's agent in St. Louis, had the unenviable task of finding funds for the People's line and the Illinois & Mississippi line simultaneously.[28]

Smith had not found his position easy. More than once he had regretted the impulse that had led him to leave the telegraph office where he had served as operator to take charge of the affairs of a man so contemptuous of money and so ignorant of finance as Henry O'Rielly. The depression following the Mexican War had made his task still more difficult. In April 1848 he warned O'Rielly of the gravity of their position. It was almost impossible to raise money in St. Louis. Drafts were falling due and there were no funds to pay them. He urged O'Rielly to make "a desperate effort" to obtain two or three thousand dollars in New Orleans. "We have a tremendous load to carry. If we do not look out we shall all get swamped," he cautioned.[29]

In addition to handling financial matters for O'Rielly in the St. Louis district, Sanford J. Smith exercised a supervisory authority over the construction of the Illinois & Mississippi line. But, to his annoyance, he found that work on the northern line often had to be delayed because all available funds were being expended on the southern line. To give only one example, O'Rielly's brother, Captain John, building on the southern route, drew drafts on Smith with a ready hand. Complaining of the Captain's incautious course to O'Rielly on April

27 When in the fall of 1847 O'Rielly had first directed his attention to a line from Louisville to New Orleans, he was clearly acting outside the limits of his contract with the Morse patentees. Under no possible interpretation of it could he use the Morse instrument on this route. He believed, however, that he had a satisfactory substitute in the Columbian instrument, the invention of two telegraphic handy-men who knew little of electrical science and still less of patent law. With this untried instrument, and over so contested a route, O'Rielly did not consider it the part of honor to ask for public support until the line had proved itself. He had told southern investors that only when the People's line had demonstrated its ability to perform satisfactorily would they be invited to share in the profits. Until that time he, alone, would assume all the risks.

For a more detailed discussion of this subject see Chapter IX.

28 E. Case to F. O. J. Smith, March 20, 1848, Smith Papers in Manuscript division of New York Public Library; Morse vs. O'Rielly, Circuit Court of Kentucky, Deposition of Henry O'Rielly, August 29, 1848, O'Rielly Docs., Miscell. Series, I.

29 Sanford J. Smith to O'Rielly, April 8, 1848, O'Rielly MS Coll. (April 1848).

16, the agent wrote: "As far as John is concerned I admire his industry and perseverance in prosecuting his business, but he does not seem to have the remotest idea of general financial matters, and with the recklessness he is going on, would break any one were he as rich as the Bank of England."[30] Meanwhile, work on the northern line was suffering, since most of Smith's time was taken up devising ways and means of meeting the drafts which were maturing almost daily. "You can very easily imagine that it was no easy matter for me to pay $25,000 this month (which is the amount I have had to provide for) and not a dollar to pay it with," wrote Smith.[31] He went on to point out that $55,000 had been pledged in subscriptions on the northern line, to be paid in installments as work progressed; but every place that had subscribed was beginning to get uneasy at the slowness with which the work was proceeding. Under the circumstances the harassed agent strongly advised curtailment of operations in the South for a period and acceleration of those in the North where money would be forthcoming as the work went forward.[32]

But connive as he might, Smith could not stem the rising financial tide. Wire factories stopped shipment of supplies until outstanding bills were paid. Subscribers to stock along the route refused to pay any faster than the work progressed. In July he had been obliged to let a considerable amount of paper "go protest" for nonpayment, and no more money could be raised in St. Louis. He regretted the earlier optimism which had induced him to pay over $60,000 of funds obtained from subscriptions to the Illinois & Mississippi line to meet the liabilities on other sections of the O'Rielly range.[33] Through his attempts to save the entire structure, his own line now suffered. Reflections of its bankrupt credit were apparent all along the route.

Charles G. Oslere, foreman of construction, was taxed to the limit for funds to keep his men moving.[34] On September 22, he wrote O'Rielly from Peru, Illinois, where he had gone to see what relief might be given a construction gang which was "tied up for want of means to go ahead."[35] Punctilious in his personal habits, and completely unschooled in the financial legerdemain of men like Smith and O'Rielly, poor Oslere felt the strain of his difficult position. In one long, troubled sentence he described his dilemma: "I am

30 *Ibid.*, April 16, 1848. 31 *Ibid.* 32 *Ibid.*
33 Sanford J. Smith to O'Rielly, July 25, 1848, O'Rielly MS Coll. (July 1848).
34 C. G. Oslere to O'Rielly, September 12, 1848, O'Rielly MS Coll. (September 1848).
35 *Ibid.*

now doged [sic] every place and in the worst kind of a scrape that I have seen yet but hope to come out O.K. before long on my arrival Bert Brady with 18 men was laid up here without funds to move and in debt some eight hundred dollars and I with three dollars in my pocket can not collect one cent here until line is finished to Chicago had to borrow of friends here five hundred dollars to get men out of this and hope to keep them moving if I can get wire and insulators will finish to Chicago in fifteen days and hope to raise money enough to pay them off and discharge them but it makes me so nervous that I can scarcely write or think about anything will go through with it some how."[36]

Good as his word, Oslere pushed the line to Chicago before the close of October, thereby bringing the main section into operation. Branch lines occupied his attention for the remainder of the autumn, and by the turn of the year the Illinois & Mississippi system was ready for presentation to its stockholders. Formal organization had been planned for February 1849, but it had to be deferred until April due to O'Rielly's preoccupation in the East with the lines he was projecting into New England and with his efforts to assist Alexander Bain in obtaining a patent for his electro-chemical telegraph. Meanwhile the leaderless Illinois & Mississippi, badly in need of organization, marked time.[37]

O'Rielly called upon the stockholders to assemble at Peoria, Illinois, on April 10 for permanent organization. Several days before the appointed meeting Judge John Dean Caton of the Supreme Court of Illinois happened into the circuit court room in Ottawa where a number of the subscribers were in consultation. Upon their request Judge Caton agreed to represent their interests at the convention. In this way Caton, the man who was ultimately to become the savior of the Illinois & Mississippi Telegraph Company, became the presiding officer at its first meeting, although at the time he did not hold a share of stock in the company. So spirited were the proceedings and so engrossing to the Judge, that before the call for adjournment he had purchased several shares of stock and had been named a director of the new organization.[38]

The following day, April 11, the Illinois & Mississippi Telegraph Company was formally organized with a capital stock of $500,000

[36] Ibid., September 22, 1848.
[37] Oslere to O'Rielly, February 11, 1849, O'Rielly MS Coll. (February 1849).
[38] Reid, Telegraph in America, 235.

divided into shares of $50 each. William Hempstead of Galena was made president; William Mitchell of Peoria, secretary; Sanford J. Smith of St. Louis, treasurer; and John B. Perkins of St. Louis, superintendent. A unique provision of the articles of association stipulated that every office operating at a profit was entitled to a director to be elected by the local stockholders; another provided that meetings of the board could be held by telegraph.[39]

A further interesting item of business, characteristic of the generous impulses of its author, was written into the minutes of the meeting on the twelfth. Henry O'Rielly, fearful that the "distances traveled and time consumed by members of the Convention . . . might bear onerously on sundry individuals, . . . desired the privilege of providing measurably for these expenses by requesting the President and Secretary to issue to each member in this Convention three shares of stock out of the amount assigned . . . him [O'Rielly]."[40]

It had long been felt by those who struggled through the trying days of construction that once the line had been organized and put into operation their chief concerns would be at an end. They expected that the Illinois & Mississippi Telegraph Company would immediately do a large and profitable business. Nothing could have been further from the truth. The business was there without question, but the line was unable to do it. With the first spring freshets, poles along the river were inundated three to ten feet. Many were washed away by the current and the drifts of logs and brush pushing against them. James Gamble, operator at Quincy, reported to Oslere on April 18 that he had "not been able to do any business of consequence in the last two months—the line not being in order more than two weeks in that length of time." It had been grounded in the Illinois bottom lands along the Mississippi River for about four weeks, and at the time of writing the masts at Churchville and Beardstown were down.[41]

Equally discouraging reports were received from all along the route. J. J. McEwin, operator at Muscatine, Iowa, informed Judge Caton that the line was the poorest that he had ever seen, and that on an average it was not in order more than twelve days in a month. A perusal of the accounts of the local livery stable, which furnished

39 Proceedings of a Meeting of Proprietors and Stockholders of the Illinois & Mississippi Telegraph Company, April 10-April 12, 1849, O'Rielly MS Coll. (April 1849).
40 Ibid.
41 James Gamble to C. G. Oslere, April 18, 1849, O'Rielly MS Coll. (April 1849); cf. James Gamble to A. Vail, April 20, 1849, Vail Papers.

transportation to telegraph repair crews, revealed how large a patron of that establishment the telegraph office was. Instead of constantly expending small sums on temporary repairs, McEwin urged that enough be spent to put the line in good order. The unhappy operator expressed the opinion that the Illinois & Mississippi would never pay expenses unless it were placed in the hands of a more aggressive management.[42]

Scarcely had the spring floods subsided before an outbreak of cholera swept the Ohio and Mississippi Valleys. St. Louis, nerve center of the western telegraph system, was hard hit. Fred Colburn, making the monthly report from that office in July, gave a graphic account of the utter prostration which every branch of business had encountered from the ravages of the dreaded disease. "Heads of some houses have fallen victims to the epidemic," he wrote, "whilst others have run from the city, leaving their business to take care of itself. Farmers and country-men shun the city as they would a pest-house; and now instead of streets crowded with a busy population, and lined with merchandise, we meet the slow-moving funeral procession. This seems a hard picture, but you would hardly recognize in St. Louis (at the present time) the 'Empress City of the West.' "[43]

But there was nothing in either the cholera scourge or the physical defects of the line, which time and good management could not have overcome. The chief weakness of the Illinois & Mississippi Telegraph Company, the weakness of pioneer lines in general, lay in the absence of leadership—the lack of a man of sufficient capacity and determination to take hold of the faltering line and give it direction. President William Hempstead was only a part time executive. He soon discovered that his time could be spent more profitably as a merchant of Galena than as the president of a bankrupt telegraph company, which could give him neither pay nor prestige. He resigned after six months in office, and was succeeded by Francis Voris of Peoria, a well-intentioned but ineffectual executive. The superintendent, John B. Perkins, was a good worker but entirely "innocent of executive ability," a failing which soon manifested itself in general disorder. In the matter of repairs the line worked or not according to the caprice of the operators. Every office was allowed to purchase its own supplies. No uniform system of bookkeeping was adopted. Each

---

[42] J. J. McEwin to J. D. Caton, October 4, 1849, John Dean Caton Papers in Library of Congress. (Material arranged chronologically in some 30 boxes, covering years 1826-1895).

[43] Fred Colburn to O'Rielly, July 3, 1849, O'Rielly MS Coll. (July 1849).

office reported the amount of its monthly business to Superintendent Perkins in its own individual way.[44] Confusion and lack of order were apparent everywhere.

Reports for the first quarter of 1850 indicated that the company was operating at a deficit of approximately $300 a month.[45] At the annual meeting in April the directors, impatient with the loose management and utterly discreditable manner in which business was being transacted, adopted measures to improve the situation. The president was authorized to become purchasing agent, and an executive committee, of which Caton was a member, was appointed to supervise affairs. The superintendent was dropped with the recommendation that the salary due that officer should be paid "when funds come in." Managers of the Jacksonville and Peru offices were appointed operating superintendents while the secretary of the company was made general inspector. Arrangements were made to replace mast crossings over rivers, which had been a constant source of trouble, with submarine cables of gutta-percha covered wire.[46] All efforts to make the line efficient and serviceable, however, were unavailing. The annual report of stockholders made in April 1851, showed total receipts during the preceding year of $8,263.30 as against total expenditures of $8,160.05.[47]

The Illinois & Mississippi was generally conceded to be a dying concern. Its officers were apathetic, and its stockholders had little hope of recovering anything on their investments. For two years the line was left to drift from bad to worse. By the time of the annual meeting in April 1852, matters were desperate. Poles were falling from rot. Transmission was difficult, even in dry weather, due to numerous imperfectly formed joints in the wire and the great resistance of the inferior magnets with which the line was equipped. In addition the books of the treasurer revealed a deficit of $17,000. Nine of the ten directors who were present proposed concluding the company's corporate existence, and salvaging what they could from the sale of the wire and apparatus.[48]

44 Reid, *Telegraph in America*, 235; J. B. Perkins to O'Rielly, February 24, 1850, O'Rielly MS Coll., XLI.

45 L. Howell to J. D. Caton, March 9, 1850, Caton Papers; *Ibid.*, March 16, 1850; *Ibid.*, April 22, 1850.

46 Reid, *Telegraph in America*, 236.   47 *Ibid.*

48 *Ibid.*, 236-237; J. D. Caton to Board of Trustees of Illinois & Mississippi Canal, May 11, 1850, Caton Papers; J. B. Perkins to J. D. Caton, September 27, 1849, Caton Papers; *Ibid.*, October 10, 1849; L. Howell to J. D. Caton, September 27, 1850, Caton Papers.

It was at this point when ruin seemed inevitable that the Illinois
& Mississippi, more fortunate than its neighbor, the Ohio, Indiana &
Illinois, found a leader in John Dean Caton. Forty years before,
Caton had been born on a modest farm in New York State. In 1833,
a young man barely come of age, he had migrated to Chicago then a
town of some 300 inhabitants, to open his first law office. In 1842 he
had been appointed associate justice of the Supreme Court of Illinois,
a role in which he soon won a reputation for personal integrity and
judicial wisdom. Although Caton's first association with the telegraph was in a legal capacity, he had soon become interested in
the science of telegraphy. He studied it earnestly and even learned
to operate the instruments with reasonable skill. When his fellow
directors proposed abandonment of the line he offered strenuous
objection, declaring his faith in the ultimate triumph of the telegraph as a means of communication. Caton countered their defeatism
by proposing: (1) that the whole line be placed under the absolute
control of a single competent officer with broad discretionary powers;
(2) that assessments be levied on all stock from time to time sufficient to produce a fund with which to put the line in proper working
condition; (3) that all stock on which assessments remained unpaid,
after a suitable interval had elapsed, should be condemned and sold
at public auction, after due notice; and (4) that the company should
be authorized to bid in condemned stock at the amount of the assessment and to cancel it. Caton's associates, happy to find some alternative to liquidation of the company, agreed to all of his proposals
without much discussion. They then proceeded to elect him president at a yearly salary of $500.

Judge Caton realized that special legislation would be required to
carry out a scheme so radical as the assessment of fully paid stock.
Accordingly he drew up a carefully amended charter, and it was
presented and promptly passed by a special meeting of the State
Legislature which, opportunely, happened to be in session. No time
was lost in levying an assessment of $2.50 per share of stock. While a
considerable sum was realized from the assessment, there were many
delinquents. A decree of sale was obtained and a public sale of condemned stock was advertised and carried out. The sales were made at
not less than $2.51 per share. When that amount was not bid, the
stock was taken up by the company and canceled. With the money
obtained from these assessments and sales, and with funds realized

by mortgaging his own personal property, Judge Caton set out to rebuild the rapidly disintegrating line.[49] The next few years were to be trying ones, but under Caton's guidance the Illinois & Mississippi Telegraph Company was ultimately to emerge victorious over all its difficulties.

5 ———

FROM the day when O'Rielly had first headed into the West with the ill-fated Lancaster-Harrisburg line in the autumn of 1845, to the summer of 1850 when the last unit of his original range had been brought to completion—a period of less than five years—over 4,000 miles of line had been built. The six units comprising the Atlantic, Lake & Mississippi system—the Atlantic & Ohio; the Pittsburgh, Cincinnati & Louisville; the Ohio & Mississippi; the Ohio, Indiana & Illinois; the Lake Erie; and the Illinois & Mississippi—had been completed. In addition, lines between Louisville and New Orleans (People's Telegraph), New York and Boston (New York & New England Telegraph) and New York and Buffalo (New York State Telegraph) had been constructed. Moreover, a start had been made west of the Mississippi with a St. Louis-Ft. Leavenworth line.

The financing of these lines had been on a stock subscription basis, with the Atlantic, Lake & Mississippi Telegraph Company pledged to cover deficiencies on the original range. Upon the breakdown of this arrangement O'Rielly tried to establish a self-perpetuating system by using his personal stock in a completed unit as collateral to obtain funds for the next unit. To handle all the financial detail in connection with O'Rielly's building program, agents had been established at key centers—Joshua Hanna at Pittsburgh, James W. Ward at Cincinnati, Richard Woolfolk at Louisville, and Sanford J. Smith at St. Louis. Although the primary concern of each agent was to secure funds to keep the telegraph lines within his territory progressing, there was a constant interchange of drafts and notes between these banking centers as the agents, in their desperate attempts to keep the O'Rielly system solvent, turned to one another for help.

The cost of constructing the lines was at the rate of $150 per mile. Stock to the amount of a second $150 was to be issued for the use of

---

[49] John D. Caton to O'Rielly, February 9, 1850, Caton Papers; Reid, *Telegraph in America*, 237-239.

the invention. Although the O'Rielly contract had called for no more than one-quarter of the total capital stock issue to go to the patentees, O'Rielly—following the principle established by the seaboard lines that "stock issued to the patentees should always be equal in amount to stock issued to the subscribers"[50]—called for one-half. Of this amount one-quarter was to be reserved for the patentees, one-eighth was to go to O'Rielly, and the remaining one-eighth was to be issued to the Atlantic, Lake & Mississippi Telegraph Company.

In the case of the Pittsburgh, Cincinnati & Louisville, the Ohio & Mississippi, the Ohio, Indiana & Illinois, and the Lake Erie Telegraph Companies, stock was issued on a dollar for dollar basis. Capitalization was therefore established on the basis of $300 per mile, fixing the stock issue at twice the cost of construction.[51] The Illinois & Mississippi gave a double stock issue. Each subscriber was to receive $100 in stock for every $50 paid in, thereby establishing its total capitalization on the basis of $600 per mile or at four times the cost of construction.[52] The Atlantic & Ohio gave a triple issue thereby establishing its total capitalization on the basis of $900 per mile or at six times the cost of construction.[53]

The first two lines putting out from the seaboard, the Atlantic & Ohio and the Pittsburgh, Cincinnati & Louisville, were undoubtedly the best. Built at a period when O'Rielly was largely concentrating his energies on one organization at a time, their construction, though

[50] Articles of Association of the Magnetic Telegraph Company, O'Rielly Docs., Miscell. Series, II.

[51] Proceedings of Convention of Delegates from Stockholders of the Pittsburgh, Cincinnati & Louisville Telegraph Company, June 6-7, 1849, Report of the Superintendent, James D. Reid, O'Rielly Docs., Miscell. Series, III; Morse vs. Smith, Superior Court of State of New York for the City and County of New York, Deposition of G. R. McGunnegle, secretary of the Ohio & Mississippi Telegraph Company, November 1856, O'Rielly Docs., Legal Series, XI; cf. Reid, *Telegraph in America*, 222; Delano, Report on the Construction of the Ohio, Indiana & Illinois Telegraph Company, August 5, 1850, O'Rielly Docs., Miscell. Series, III; Circular: The Lake Erie Telegraph Company [March 1847], O'Rielly Docs., Miscell. Series, V; Memorandum in handwriting of H. R. Selden regarding apportionment of stock of Lake Erie Telegraph Company [n.d.], Selden Papers; Stock Certificate of Lake Erie Telegraph Company, January 30, 1849, to H. R. Selden, president of the Atlantic, Lake & Mississippi Telegraph Company, Selden Papers.

[52] Proceedings of a Meeting of Proprietors and Stockholders of the Illinois & Mississippi Telegraph Company, April 10-12, 1849, O'Rielly MS Coll. (April 1849); also Articles of Association of the Illinois & Mississippi Telegraph Company, April 11, 1849, O'Rielly Docs., First Series, II.

[53] Proceedings of the Meeting of the Stockholders of the Atlantic & Ohio Telegraph Company, March 1, 1847, O'Rielly Docs., First Series, I; An Act to Incorporate the Atlantic & Ohio Telegraph Company, *Pennsylvania Statutes: Laws Passed at the Session*, March 24, 1849.

suffering from the general telegraphic ills of the day, was relatively better than that of the others.

Their superior administration was of even greater importance. Recognizing the community of interest in their respective lines, the companies, largely Pittsburgh controlled, sought to harmonize their operations through their administrative officers. In September 1848, James K. Moorhead of Pittsburgh, able chief executive of the Atlantic & Ohio, became president of the Pittsburgh, Cincinnati & Louisville line as well; and James D. Reid, who had served as superintendent for both since their organization, was retained in that capacity. By this means, the lines from Philadelphia to Louisville were operated virtually as a single unit, and their business became large and profitable. The Atlantic & Ohio paid dividends of 18 percent in 1848; while the Pittsburgh, Cincinnati & Louisville, though established almost a year later, paid dividends of 11 percent for the same interval. In general these companies were looked to for quarterly dividends of 3 percent.[54]

The financial statements of the other companies were much less attractive. From the time of their completion to the close of 1852, the Lake Erie, and Ohio & Mississippi Companies had paid a few desultory dividends with funds which were badly needed to defray original construction costs and undertake the work of rehabilitation. The Illinois & Mississippi, and the Ohio, Indiana & Illinois, on the other hand, paid nothing; with the utmost economy the business of their lines barely paid expenses. In the spring of 1852, it may be recalled, the discouraged directors of the Illinois & Mississippi had voted to go out of business, and it had only been the labors of Judge Caton which had saved the company. The situation was equally grave regarding the Ohio, Indiana & Illinois; but with no competent individual to come to its rescue, that line was doomed. In the opening months of 1853 it was leased to Ezra Cornell on behalf of the Erie & Michigan Telegraph Company at a yearly rate of approximately one-half of 1 percent on its capital stock of $240,050, which in itself suggests the worthless character of the line.[55]

That transaction marked the beginning of the formal disruption of the O'Rielly system in the West. Within a year the Lake Erie had

---

[54] Morse vs. Smith, Superior Court of State of New York for the City and County of New York, Deposition of James D. Reid, December 1, 1856, O'Rielly Docs., **Legal Series**, XI.

[55] Reid, *Telegraph in America*, 252.

also fallen by the wayside, followed shortly by the Ohio & Mississippi. The Pittsburgh, Cincinnati & Louisville, the Atlantic & Ohio, and the Illinois & Mississippi Companies maintained their independence for a longer period of time, but handicapped by the limited scope of their operations, each was eventually absorbed by larger, more aggressive organizations during the era of consolidation.

CHAPTER IX

Race to the Crescent City

1 ·—·

LIKE the river whose course they largely followed, lines of telegraph projected in the Ohio Valley inevitably turned south toward New Orleans, entrepôt of the entire Mississippi basin. Western farmers and planters had early found the long river journey south their only practical route to market. Down the Mississippi to the Crescent City they floated their tobacco, corn, hemp, wheat, pork, and lumber for transshipment to the eastern seaboard and the marts of the old world; drawn by the same economic force, the telegraph directed its lines to the great commercial center at the mouth of the Mississippi. Conforming to the conventional pattern of the era of methodless enthusiasm, the opening months of 1848 found not one, but three organizations engaged in a heated race to the Crescent City—one was building via the seaboard, while two others were undertaking construction in the Mississippi Valley.

2 ··—··

THE seaboard line was the first to penetrate the South. Amos Kendall had long regarded that section as a fertile field for the employment of the telegraph, and a line from Washington to New Orleans via the coast had been a part of the original network which he had proposed to meet the nation's needs. Since the practicability of a long line of telegraph was still undetermined at that time, he had encountered difficulty in arranging a suitable contract. Consequently trunk lines in all other sections of the country were under construction before Kendall had finally entered into an agreement with J. J. Haley, in November 1846, to build the Washington & New Orleans line.[1]

According to the terms of the contract, Haley was to receive $150 a mile for a line of single wire or $200 a mile for one of double wire; and in keeping with precedent, the patentees were to receive 50 percent of all stock issued. In addition, Haley, Smith, and Kendall entered into a further agreement concerning construction profits.

---

[1] *New Orleans Picayune*, Janury 22, 1846. For a more detailed discussion of Kendall's difficulty in arranging a contract for the Washington & New Orleans line see Chapter III.

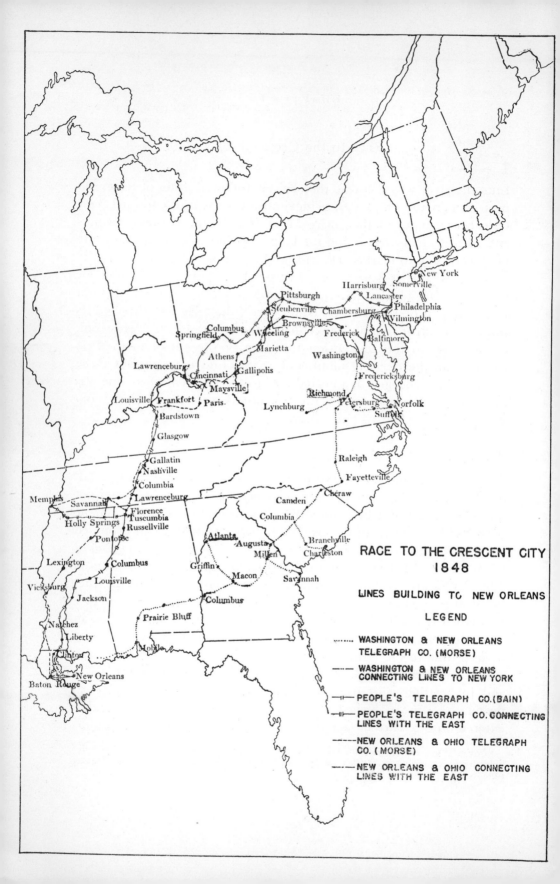

RACE TO THE CRESCENT CITY
1848

LINES BUILDING TO NEW ORLEANS

LEGEND

.... WASHINGTON & NEW ORLEANS
        TELEGRAPH CO. (MORSE)

— · — WASHINGTON & NEW ORLEANS
        CONNECTING LINES TO NEW YORK

—11— PEOPLE'S TELEGRAPH CO. (BAIN)

—11— PEOPLE'S TELEGRAPH CO. CONNECTING
        LINES WITH THE EAST

------ NEW ORLEANS & OHIO TELEGRAPH
        CO. (MORSE)

— · — NEW ORLEANS & OHIO CONNECTING
        LINES WITH THE EAST

Up to this time Kendall had wisely refused to participate in this practice, but eager to promote the retarded building program in the South, he assented to the agreement, a decision which he was later to regret.[2]

Delayed as the Washington & New Orleans Telegraph Company was in getting under way, subscriptions were obtained with ease. The antebellum South was by no means the moneyless section it has sometimes been represented. Funds could be obtained for financing any practicable scheme. The price of cotton had fallen steadily during the decade and many southern people were beginning to look elsewhere for investment. Railroad construction had absorbed considerable capital, but the yield had not been encouraging and investors were chary of further commitments. The telegraph, on the other hand, was now operating successfully between a number of the commercial centers of the North, and although no dividends had yet been made, it seemed to offer long-term prospects for a fair return on money invested.[3]

Early in 1847 William B. Lloyd, acting as a special agent for Amos Kendall, was sent South to solicit subscriptions. On January 14, speaking before the Charleston Chamber of Commerce, he urged support for the proposed line. A committee of seven was appointed to investigate the enterprise and to solicit subscriptions if they found it worthy of support. Similar gatherings were addressed in Savannah and New Orleans, and committees were appointed to inquire into the matter and make recommendations. Other cities along the route took up the question, and by March financial backing seemed assured.[4]

State legislatures proved equally cooperative. North Carolina led the way by passing a special act of incorporation on January 18, 1847, giving the telegraph company power "to set up fixtures along any of the roads or railroads . . . belonging to the state."[5] Two months later the State of Virginia went even further. Its General Assembly declared that the railroads, since they provided right of way for the wires, should have the first privilege of subscribing the necessary capital for their construction. If the railroads failed to respond, the

[2] Reid, *Telegraph in America*, 144.

[3] R. S. Cotterill, "The Telegraph in the South, 1845-1850," *South Atlantic Quarterly*, XVI (April 1917), 149-154.

[4] *Ibid.*

[5] "An Act to incorporate the Washington & New Orleans Telegraph Company," *North Carolina Statutes: Session Laws*, January 18, 1847.

citizens of Virginia were to have the next opportunity. In the event both failed, the State Board of Public Works was to take up the subscription.[6] Within a year legislation designed to encourage the new enterprise had been passed by South Carolina, Georgia, Mississippi, Alabama, and Louisiana.[7]

In so far as possible the telegraph was to go south along railroad rights of way. With the exception of the distance from Raleigh, North Carolina, to Columbia, South Carolina, a continuous line of track extended from Fredericksburg, Virginia, to Atlanta, Georgia, by 1847. The telegraph contractors followed the rails from Fredericksburg through Richmond and Petersburg to Raleigh; from here the route passed across country through Fayetteville, Cheraw, and Camden to Columbia, at which point it once more picked up the railroad to Charleston, and thence to Augusta, Georgia. From Augusta the main line was to follow the railroad to Macon, while a branch line was planned to Savannah. Leaving the railroad at Macon, the telegraph was to proceed westward along the stage road to Montgomery, Alabama, thence down the Alabama River to Mobile, and then on to New Orleans.[8]

Construction moved rapidly forward. The route was divided into sections and work was carried forward on all of them simultaneously. By the last of March 1847, the line was completed from Washington to Alexandria; the posts were set as far as Fredericksburg; and material was on hand for carrying the line on to Petersburg, Virginia. By August 1 all but thirty miles of the posts had been erected on the Mobile-New Orleans section, while those on the Mobile-Montgomery line had been set for more than a hundred miles. Charleston and Columbia were put into communication on December 1, and the first message was sent from Charleston to Petersburg on February 14, 1848. The final link in the telegraph chain connecting the sea-

6 "An Act to facilitate the construction of an electric telegraph line on the great northern and southern mail route," *Virginia Statutes: Acts of the General Assembly*, March 20, 1847.

7 "An Act to incorporate the Washington & New Orleans Magnetic Telegraph Company," *South Carolina Statutes: Acts and Joint Resolutions*, December 17, 1847; "An Act to authorize the construction of the Magnetic Telegraph and providing for the protection of the same," *Georgia Statutes: Acts and Resolutions*, December 29, 1847; "An Act to incorporate the New Orleans & Ohio Telegraph Company" (like powers granted to the Washington & New Orleans Company), *Mississippi Statutes: Laws of the State*, February 10, 1848; "An Act to incorporate the Washington & New Orleans Telegraph Company," *Alabama Statutes: Acts Passed*, March 3, 1848; "An Act to facilitate the construction of the Electric Telegraph and for the protection of the same," *Louisiana Statutes: Acts Passed by the Legislature*, March 10, 1848.

8 Cotterill, *op. cit.*

board cities with New Orleans was not completed, however, until the middle of July.[9]

After formal presentation of the line to the stockholders in September, the Washington & New Orleans Telegraph Company was capitalized at $561,700, divided into 11,234 shares of $50 each. Daniel Griffin of Georgia was chosen president, George Wood[10] of Washington was made secretary, and Amos Kendall became treasurer.[11]

The long-awaited line failed to live up to expectations. It was a source of grief both to its subscribers and to the public. Bad insulation, poor wire, crude transmission—all the difficulties experienced by the shorter lines—were multiplied a hundredfold on the great 1,500-mile route. Contractor Haley may have built the line in good faith, but his primary interest in the project had been the construction profits. Judged even by the low standards of the day the Washington & New Orleans line was inferior.[12]

During its construction and immediately after completion, the wire was flooded with messages. Its inability to give dependable service soon discouraged those who had looked to the telegraph for rapid communication between the commercial centers of the North and the South. When communication was unbroken the volume of business was large, but it was not long before the line's irregular working and bad management was the subject of grave concern not only to its owners but also to the Magnetic Telegraph Company to which it was an important feeder.[13]

Even when the line was working properly, messages often became distorted as they were relayed along the lengthy route. The mystified recipient would call at his local telegraph office hoping that the operator might be able to fathom the unintelligible message. Ultimately the outraged sender would contact the company demanding that it make amends.

So many and so bitter were the complaints that B. B. French, chairman of the board of trustees, addressed an open letter to the operators of the company on June 28, 1848. Much as he hated to do it, the genial French apologized, there had been so many errors of transmission on the southern line that he was conducting an investigation to ascertain at what offices the errors were occurring. As an example

---

[9] *Ibid.*   [10] Morse's private secretary.

[11] Articles of Association of the Washington & New Orleans Telegraph Company together with the minutes of the meetings of the stockholders and board of directors, September 1848, Cornell University Library; also in O'Rielly Docs., Miscell. Series, III.

[12] Reid, *Telegraph in America*, 144.   [13] *Ibid.*, 145.

of the type of carelessness which was causing the public to lose confidence in the telegraph, he traced the distortion of a message between Charleston and New York. The original was relayed from Charleston to Columbia on June 20, 1848:

For Spofford Tileston & Co., N.Y.—Write Brigland, Sons & Jeffrey, Liverpool, Lady Huntley abandoned at sea. Captain at Mobile.

Gourdin Mathieson & Co.

Columbia received the following:

For Messrs. Spofford Tileston & Co., N.Y.—Write Brigland, Sons & Jeffrey, Liverpool, Lady Huntley abandoned at sea, Captain at Mobile.

Gourdin, Mathesson & Co.

The Camden version read:

For Messrs. Spofford Tileston & Co. N.Y.—Write Bigland, Sons & Jeffrey, Liverpool, Lady Huntley Abin died at sea at Mobile.

Jourdan & Co.

The Fayetteville office recorded:

Messrs. Spofford, Tileston & Co., N.Y.—Write Bigland, Sons & Koffrey, Liverpool, Lady Hunnly Abin died at sea near Mobile.

Jourdan, Matthews & Co.

At Petersburg the message read:

For Messrs. Spofford, Tilleson & Co.—Write Bigland, Sons & Koffrey, Liverpool, Lady Hunnly Abin died at sea at Mobile.

Jourdan, Matthews & Co.

Such carelessness, declared French, would have to stop. It was the duty of every operator receiving a message not making sense to call for a repetition. In so far as possible communications were to be sent directly from the office of origin to that of destination, thereby eliminating numerous errors which inevitably crept in where messages had to pass through many hands.[14]

Despite French's importunings, conditions did not improve appreciably, and by the close of its first year of operation the Washington & New Orleans line was rapidly moving along the road to bankruptcy. Nearly half the time the line was not working throughout. Faulty wire, bad insulation, a poorly chosen route—many miles of which passed through the swamp lands of Alabama and Mississippi—

[14] Circular: B. B. French, Chairman of the Board of Trustees of the Washington & New Orleans Telegraph Company, to the operators on the line, May 20, 1848, Vail Papers.

and rapidly mounting debts were ruining the company. Alfred Vail who had labored earnestly for its success wrote President Griffin that unless steps were taken at once to put the entire route into good repair, Washington & New Orleans stock would not be worth $10 per share in nine months.[15]

Serious operating difficulties were not enough. The company was shortly competing for the New York-New Orleans business with another Morse line, the New Orleans & Ohio Telegraph, which early in 1848 had started building southward through the Mississippi Valley.

3 · · · — ·

THE early history of the New Orleans & Ohio Telegraph Company is a record of the dissension, waste, and confusion of an age which eagerly introduced and then promptly brought discredit upon the electric telegraph. To understand the New Orleans & Ohio's complex and disordered background, it should be recalled that following the abrogation of the O'Rielly contract, in the autumn of 1846, the patentees had given Eliphalet Case authority for a line of telegraph from Pittsburgh via the Ohio Valley to New Orleans. At the time they had hoped that O'Rielly could be forced to retire from the field, and that his recently completed Pittsburgh-Philadelphia line (Atlantic & Ohio) could be secured and used to link the proposed Case line with the Atlantic seaboard. But O'Rielly did not retire and Case—even with the assistance of a group of influential Cincinnati business men—was not successful in carrying through his project.[16]

A year later the patentees had met to reorganize their building program. Smith had agreed to build from Pittsburgh to New Orleans by way of Cincinnati, Louisville, Lexington, Nashville, Tuscumbia, and Jackson, under the corporate title of the New Orleans & Ohio Telegraph Company. To supply the eastern link in case they were unsuccessful in securing control of O'Rielly's Atlantic & Ohio line, Kendall had agreed to build from Pittsburgh and Wheeling to Baltimore under the corporate title of the Western Telegraph Company. The inauguration of this program, of course, was contingent upon their obtaining a reconveyance of the patent rights for this route from Case and his associates, the Cincinnati trustees. Such a recon-

---

[15] A. Vail to Daniel Griffin, June 23, 1849, Vail Papers.
[16] For earlier references to Case and the Cincinnati trustees see Chapters V, VI.

veyance had finally been obtained near the close of 1847, but only with great difficulty.[17]

Reflection upon the many problems which would be encountered in constructing nearly 1,500 miles of line over so bitterly contested a route, convinced Smith that such a project was foolhardy. In an area so removed from Boston he would be unable to give the line his personal attention. He had not found in his brother-in-law, Eliphalet Case, the strong generalship needed to carry the enterprise to a successful conclusion. All things considered, Smith decided his efforts could be expended to better advantage elsewhere.

Being in such a frame of mind, it was not surprising that Smith should have refused the request of the corporators of the New Orleans & Ohio Telegraph Company that he visit Nashville in December 1847, to discuss plans for the promotion of their line to New Orleans. But Kendall was eager to see the project succeed. Having been given power of attorney by Smith, he reluctantly journeyed to the Tennessee capital to handle the business.[18] For over ten weeks he remained in the West countering O'Rielly's subversive activity and furthering the enterprise generally. During the course of his sojourn he concluded that if he was to have so great a responsibility in the development of the New Orleans line, there was no reason why he should not also share in the profits. On January 22, 1848, he wrote Smith to this effect.[19]

Smith proved remarkably agreeable. In his reply on February 1 he acceded to all of Kendall's suggestions. Everything was to be on a fifty-fifty basis; both expenses and profits were to be shared equally. Building was to go forward on the basis of popular subscription, in so far as possible; but should this means fail, the builders of the different sections were to draw upon the promoters for such amounts as were required to complete the work.[20]

In their agreement with the New Orleans & Ohio, Smith and Kendall had contracted to build a single-wire line for $150 a mile. To hasten the work of construction, the great 1,500 mile route was divided into five sections. Arrangements were concluded with sub-contractors for each of the sections as follows:[21]

17 For earlier discussion of this subject see Chapter VI.
18 Morse vs. Smith, Superior Court of the State of New York for the City and County of New York, Deposition of A. Kendall, January 10, 1857, O'Rielly Docs., Legal Series, XI.
19 *Ibid.*
20 Smith to Kendall, February 1, 1848, Correspondence, O'Rielly Docs., Legal Series, XI.
21 Kendall to Smith, March 19, 1851, *Ibid.*

SECTION	LOCATION	MILES	CONTRACTOR
1.	Pittsburgh to Wheeling	59	E. D. and E. M. Townsend
2.	Wheeling to Cincinnati and Lexington	401	Eliphalet Case aided by T. C. H. Smith
3.	Lexington to Nashville	273	William Tanner and Taliaferro P. Shaffner
4.	Nashville to Waynesboro	92	H. M. Watterson
5.	Waynesboro to New Orleans	658	John J. Haley and William Lloyd

The subcontractors were to build the line for $75 a mile, an arrangement which left the promoters a like amount to be divided as construction profits.

It became apparent to Kendall, as work progressed, that he could expect little help from Smith on the New Orleans & Ohio project. Smith's interest no longer lay in the South. He had turned his attention to more profitable pursuits elsewhere; and despite his agreement with Kendall, he refused to provide his share of the funds when popular subscriptions failed. Kendall found himself in the unenviable position of carrying the whole burden alone.

4 · · · · —

KENDALL's task of giving direction to the construction of 1,500 miles of telegraph over a difficult route was rendered still more arduous by the activities of his old rival, Henry O'Rielly. The Irishman had organized the People's Telegraph Company with the avowed purpose of building a competing line to New Orleans. The verbal encouragement given him by the people of the West and South, with whom he was exceedingly popular, no doubt influenced his decision, but his bitter feeling toward the patentees was another important factor. Although a series of acts had embittered him, perhaps none had stirred him more deeply than the refusal by a number of the Morse lines to relay messages to or from any of the O'Rielly lines. Within a week after F. O. J. Smith's announcement of the first non-intercourse act, O'Rielly had retaliated by declaring his intention of building to New Orleans.[22]

O'Rielly circulars and handbills were scattered widely. In phrases both determined and denunciatory the Irishman presented his case and outlined his plan of action. His energy and the fury of his

[22] Smith to Kendall, October 5, 1847, O'Rielly Docs., Legal Series, XI.

invective suited the temper of the period. His pluck, social conscious-
ness, and capacity for achievement appealed to the frontier spirit.
It was an enthusiastic audience to which the telegraph king addressed
his remarks concerning the proposed People's Telegraph Company.
The line was to extend from Louisville to New Orleans by way of
Nashville, Tuscumbia, and Jackson. Of the numerous details discussed by O'Rielly two were of outstanding interest and importance.
The first was his statement that he was no longer dependent on the
Morse patent. It was his intention, he explained, to use a new invention, the Columbian telegraph, on his southern line.[23] The second
statement, which evoked widespread approval, was O'Rielly's announcement that no funds would be solicited for the construction of
the line until the Columbian had had an opportunity to prove its
superiority over the Morse instrument by actual operation. While
the exigencies of the case required prompt action, explained O'Rielly,
the enterprise was so hazardous that he preferred "personally en-
countering the contest rather than urging others to take the responsibility."[24]

Such an opponent might well give Kendall cause for alarm. As
Kendall weighed the situation it seemed to him that success or failure
hinged on an unknown factor—the Columbian telegraph of which
O'Rielly wrote so confidently. So far as other factors were concerned
the rival lines were about on even terms. Both followed logical routes
through the commercial centers of the South so that their courses
frequently paralleled one another. If Kendall's sounder financial
position might be considered an offset to O'Rielly's greater popularity, there was little advantage on either side. In final analysis,
therefore, it seemed to Kendall that the situation turned on the mechanical soundness and legality of the Columbian telegraph, for
which much was being claimed and about which nothing was definitely known. Time alone could establish or refute O'Rielly's pretensions. Meanwhile the rival organizations, the New Orleans & Ohio
and the People's Telegraph Company, perfected their plans for the

23 E. F. Barnes to O'Rielly, December 3, 1847, O'Rielly MS Coll., xv; Circular: New
Orleans and Louisville Telegraph, January 1, 1848 (Signed by Charles Doane),
O'Rielly MS Coll. (January 1848); Samuel K. Zook to O'Rielly, December 2, 1847,
O'Rielly MS Coll., xv; T. S. Bell to O'Rielly, January 29, 1848, O'Rielly MS Coll.
(January 1848).
24 Morse vs. O'Rielly, Circuit Court of Kentucky, Deposition of Henry O'Rielly,
August 29, 1848, O'Rielly Docs., Miscell. Series, i; cf. C. G. Oslere to O'Rielly, June 5,
1848, O'Rielly MS Coll. (June 1848).

race to the Crescent City—a contest which was to prove one of the most sensational and strenuous in early telegraph history.

5 ———

WORK on both lines was pushed with energy. Each protagonist so stressed the importance of being first to achieve his goal that rival construction hands were building side by side on the Louisville-Nashville section by the first week in January 1848. It was hoped that no fighting would occur, but it was entirely within the realm of possibility that the men, while nailing the brackets to the poles, might in their enthusiasm strike a few blows for their respective leaders. Should this situation arise, declared Taliaferro P. Shaffner, subcontractor for the New Orleans & Ohio, his men were well armed and he felt reasonably certain that they would do their duty.[25] Professor Morse was greatly upset by this talk of armed conflict. He told Shaffner emphatically that if the law could not protect him he would never sanction the resort to force, no matter how sure he was of being in the right. "No real friend of mine," asserted the aroused inventor, "will allow the shedding of blood to maintain what are considered my rights."[26]

The actual meeting of the opposing forces late in January proved to be more like a relay race than a riot. Shaffner wrote Morse of the amusing encounter. The O'Rielly hands, it seems, got a better start out of Louisville than had his men. Pleased with their forward position, they boasted that the Shaffner hands could never overtake them, a challenge which could not go unanswered. "We were determined to do it," Shaffner wrote. "I had them notified that we were prepared to meet them under any circumstances. We were prepared to have a real 'hug,' but when our hands overtook them they only 'yelled' a little and mine followed and for 15 miles they were side by side and when a man finished his hole he ran with all his might to get ahead, but finally on the 24th, we passed them about 80 miles from here and now we are about 25 miles ahead of them without the loss of a drop of blood, and we shall be able to beat them to Nashville if we can get the wire in time, which is doubtful."[27]

[25] Taliaferro P. Shaffner to Morse, January 9, 1848, Morse Papers, XXIII. Both Shaffner and his acquaintances generally used the abbreviated form, "Tal.," when referring to him. Hereafter, throughout this volume the abbreviated form has been used frequently.
[26] Morse to Shaffner, January 21, 1848, Morse Papers, XXIII.
[27] Shaffner to Morse, January 27, 1848, Morse Papers, XXIII.

While the O'Rielly men might suffer temporary setbacks, they never lost their lead so far as the over-all project was concerned. March found them in Nashville with Shaffner trailing; June found them setting the last posts to New Orleans with promises of wire to follow, while Amos Kendall's subcontractor on the southernmost section had done nothing.[28] The early success of the O'Rielly forces, unfortunately, was more apparent than real; serious troubles were beginning to make themselves felt. Their advance in the future was to be less rapid.

6 ......

MONEY difficulties were O'Rielly's chief obstacle. With hundreds of miles of wire yet to be strung his forces found themselves with no funds. Furthermore, O'Rielly had told the merchants of New Orleans and of other commercial centers along the route that no assistance would be asked of them until the line was operating successfully. Nor did they care to assist while the legality and practicability of the Columbian telegraph remained uncertain. Along the extent of the route public sympathy was with O'Rielly, but no subscriptions were pressed upon him. Meanwhile O'Rielly, trying to carry the line alone, had fallen into serious financial straits.[29]

Up to the time that he reached Louisville in the autumn of 1847, O'Rielly's building program had been sound. Plans for both the Atlantic & Ohio and the Pittsburgh, Cincinnati & Louisville lines had been carefully made and intelligently carried out. It looked as if O'Rielly had laid the foundations of a handsome fortune. Then reason was sacrificed to impulse. Stung into hasty action by the efforts of the Morse patentees to void his contract, he determined to occupy the territory in question as rapidly as possible and thereby forestall any patentee attempt to do so. Nor was his effort to be purely defensive. He would "carry the war into Africa," O'Rielly lines would be strung beside patentee lines as rapidly as he could make the necessary arrangements. Just how they were to be financed or how profitable they might prove were secondary considerations. Lines were projected in all directions with reckless abandon. At the time

---

[28] Morse vs. O'Rielly, Circuit Court of Kentucky, Deposition of Henry O'Rielly, August 29, 1848, O'Rielly Docs., Miscell. Series, 1; Charles Doane to O'Rielly, March 16, 1848, O'Rielly MS Coll. (March 1848).

[29] Chas. Doane to O'Rielly, March 3, 1848, O'Rielly MS Coll. (March 1848); *Ibid.* March 23, 1848, *et seq.*

that the People's line was being built to New Orleans, O'Rielly was also constructing the Ohio, Indiana & Illinois, the Illinois & Mississippi, and the St. Louis & Fort Leavenworth lines. Moreover, plans were being formulated for an invasion of the East. While his telegraph organization was in this greatly overexpanded condition, O'Rielly was caught in the financial disruption which followed the Mexican War.

The agents established at key centers to handle O'Rielly's affairs—James Ward at Cincinnati, Richard Woolfolk at Louisville, Sanford J. Smith at St. Louis, and Charles Doane at New Orleans—worked feverishly to meet maturing drafts.[30] Sanford J. Smith wrote O'Rielly on April 4, 1848, that the preceding week had been more trying to him than any other time since he had become involved in telegraph matters. Business and financial failures on every hand had produced a panic in all the western cities, and it was next to impossible to raise money at any price. Ward had written Smith from Cincinnati in great distress saying he could not raise a dollar there to meet the payments coming due, and that he could not get O'Rielly's acceptances discounted at any rate. Smith had devised ways and means to ease him. Then came Woolfolk with the same story—drafts on him and no way to meet them. Smith also gave him assistance. At this point the hard-pressed St. Louis agent had to look after his own affairs. "Thank God," he declared, "I believe I have passed the crisis without anyone knowing but what I had my pockets full of rocks." In conclusion he urged O'Rielly to press matters in New Orleans and raise every dollar he could and "not be satisfied with their good wishes as that will not pay debts or build lines."[31]

Anxious appeals to the group in Rochester that had first financed O'Rielly brought assurances of a willingness to help but a complete inability to do so. Money was as tight in the Genessee Valley as in other sections of the country. Even Elisha D. Ely, the wealthiest member of the original Atlantic, Lake & Mississippi organization, was unable to meet a draft for $1,000 maturing on June 1.[32] Meanwhile debts mounted and drafts began "to go protest" for nonpayment. There was scarcely a community along the route where the O'Rielly forces did not owe money.

Under these trying circumstances the promoter turned to Joshua

30 S. J. Smith to O'Rielly, February 20, 1848, O'Rielly MS Coll. (February 1848).
31 Ibid., April 4, 1848, O'Rielly MS Coll. (April 1848).
32 H. B. Ely to O'Rielly, June 4, 1848, O'Rielly MS Coll. (June 1848).

Hanna of the Pittsburgh banking house of Hussey & Hanna with a request that the banker take over supervision of the entire enterprise until conditions were stabilized.[33] Hanna, with his business associate, John I. Roggen, countered with the suggestion that a three man committee composed of Roggen, Sanford Smith, and himself, be set up to take complete charge of O'Rielly's financial affairs. Were it not that neighbors and friends had purchased stock and made loans upon his recommendations, Hanna assured O'Rielly that he would never entertain the idea. As it was he felt obligated to protect their interests, and he agreed, therefore, to give the matter his attention despite the constant protestations of his partners that he was devoting too much time to the telegraph. "Altogether," he concluded his lengthy letter, "I have never been in so hot a place—some begging, some scolding and some threatening. Things have come to a crisis. Something must be done or Fog Smith and Kendall will triumph over you yet."[34]

On July 8, 1848, in accordance with Hanna's suggestion, O'Rielly made Joshua Hanna, Sanford Smith, and John I. Roggen his trustees with full power of attorney and right of substitution. The management of all his telegraph interests were turned over to them with the understanding that they would employ all available resources to liquidate his liabilities.[35] The trustees set to work at once to bring financial order out of the chaos. O'Rielly was told that under no circumstances was new work to be commenced.[36] To forestall a number of law suits which threatened, arrangements were made to pay creditors on a pro rata basis as funds became available.[37] The entire O'Rielly program was to be treated as a unit. Resources and materials were to be pooled and apportioned to various lines under construction on a strictly business basis. Those lines most nearly completed were to be given priority.[38]

O'Rielly's commitments were so heavy and his credit so badly strained, that the stabilizing measures of Hanna and his associates could have proved successful only if no further complications had arisen. But the attempt to save the enterprise came too late. The

33 O'Rielly to J. Hanna, June 1, 1848, O'Rielly MS Coll. (June 1848); *Ibid.*, May 18, 1848, O'Rielly MS Coll. (May 1848).
34 J. Hanna to O'Rielly, June 27, 1848, O'Rielly MS Coll. (June 1848).
35 Hanna, Roggen and Smith became O'Rielly's true and lawful Attorneys, July 8, 1848, O'Rielly MS Coll. (July 1848).
36 Joshua Hanna to O'Rielly, June 14, 1848, O'Rielly MS Coll. (June 1848).
37 J. W. Ward to O'Rielly, May 3, 1848, O'Rielly MS Coll. (May 1848).
38 B. O'Connor to O'Rielly, July 30, 1848, O'Rielly MS Coll. (July 1848).

committee had scarcely undertaken its work when a fatal blow fell upon the already tottering O'Rielly structure, and specifically upon the ill-starred People's line. On September 11, 1848, an injunction against the Columbian telegraph was granted to Amos Kendall.[39]

7 — ··

KENDALL had planned his campaign well. He knew that he was no match for O'Rielly in the field. It would have been an uphill fight to turn public support away from the affable Irishman whose efforts throughout his lifetime had been enlisted in the interests of the people. With Kendall's knowledge of government and his legal training, he realized that his approach could be made most effectively through the state legislatures and the courts of law.[40] Accordingly, special acts of incorporation were obtained for the New Orleans & Ohio Telegraph Company in Tennessee, Mississippi, Kentucky, and Ohio.[41] Alabama and Louisiana passed protective legislation and gave the company the right of eminent domain.[42] More subtle was the legislation put through the Tennessee Assembly on January 14, 1848, as a rider to a bill which bore the innocuous title: "An Act to authorize William Hickson of the County of Bledsoe to open a Turnpike Road and for other purposes."[43] Innocent enough on its face, the last sections of the act provided that the owners of any system of telegraphing should have the same right of way in the state as had previously been conferred upon the New Orleans & Ohio Telegraph Company provided such system did not conflict with any private right

[39] Morse vs. O'Rielly, Circuit Court of Kentucky, Injunction granted against Henry O'Rielly for use of the Columbian Telegraph, September 11, 1848, O'Rielly Docs., Appeal to Supreme Court, 1848-50.

[40] A. Kendall to My dear Wife, February 4, 1848, in *Autobiography* of Amos Kendall, 534; Morse vs. O'Rielly, Circuit Court of Kentucky, Deposition of Henry O'Rielly, August 29, 1848, O'Rielly Docs., Miscell. Series, I; Kendall to Smith, February 14, 1848, O'Rielly Docs., Correspondence, Legal Series, XI; *Ibid.*, February 16, 1848.

[41] "An Act to incorporate the New Orleans & Ohio Telegraph Company," *Tennessee Statutes: Acts Passed*, October 18, 1847; *Ibid., Mississippi Statutes: Laws*, February 10, 1848; "An Act to incorporate the New Orleans & Ohio Telegraph Company and the People's Telegraph Company," *Kentucky Statutes: Acts of the General Assembly*, March 1, 1848; "Recognizing the New Orleans & Ohio Telegraph Company as a body corporate and politic within the State of Ohio," *Ohio Statutes: Acts*, March 24, 1849.

[42] "An Act to facilitate the construction of the Electric Telegraph," *Alabama Statutes: Acts Passed*, March 4, 1848; *Ibid., Louisiana Statutes: Acts Passed by the Legislature*, March 10, 1848.

[43] "An Act to authorize William Hickson of the County of Bledsoe, to open a Turnpike Road and for other purposes," *Tennessee Statutes: Public and Private Acts*, January 14, 1848.

secured by government patent. Persons desiring to avail themselves of the privilege were to submit an accurate description of the system under which they proposed to operate to the Board of Internal Improvements. Only after approval by that body would they be allowed to proceed. This clever stratagem raised a bitter outcry from O'Rielly who branded the legislation a mere artifice to establish indirectly what never could be established directly, namely, a Morse monopoly.

Much more devastating was Kendall's attack in the circuit court of Kentucky. Shortly after the Louisville-Nashville section of the People's line had been put into operation, Kendall had brought action against the Columbian telegraph as an infringement of the Morse patents. He contended that the Columbian instrument which had been hastily devised by two telegraphic handy-men, Edmund F. Barnes and Samuel K. Zook, was a mere modification of Morse's. On September 11, 1848, the circuit court upheld his contention and ruled that the instrument could no longer be used within the district of Kentucky.[44]

The action could not have come at a more unfortunate time for O'Rielly. His financial affairs had reached a crisis the previous July, and the committee composed of Hanna, Roggen, and Smith was fighting desperately to keep him from bankruptcy. Even without the injunction it was doubtful whether they could have succeeded; with it, the outlook for O'Rielly was almost hopeless. "The result of the Frankfort suit had prostrated all our expectations," Hanna telegraphed O'Rielly on September 28. "My letters from the South say there is no hope of assistance there. No capitalist will embark where risk or litigation is to follow. I have called our true and only reliable friends together for consultation."[45]

From the South, Charles Doane, agent at New Orleans, reported that the public considered them and their line "used up," and those who had taken a little stock were alarmed, fearing the loss of their investments. "I am looked upon as a visionary fool," he wrote, "who has embarked his all in a precarious speculation . . . and even looked upon in the way of credit with all suspicion—In truth I am literally floored and cannot get on without assistance."[46]

44 Morse vs. O'Rielly, Circuit Court of Kentucky, September 11, 1848, O'Rielly Docs., Appeal to Supreme Court, 1848-50.

45 Telegram: J. Hanna to O'Rielly, September 28, 1848, O'Rielly MS Coll. (September 1848).

46 Chas. Doane to O'Rielly, September 19, 1848, O'Rielly MS Coll. (September 1848).

After recovering somewhat from this blow which momentarily paralyzed their efforts, O'Rielly's associates determined to fight the action. That section of the line which had been completed was to be kept open, not alone for the income, but for its effect on company morale and public opinion. Various means of evading the injunction were devised. Observing the letter but nullifying the spirit of the law, Edmund F. Barnes in the Louisville office put aside the register which was said to infringe Morse and began receiving messages from Nashville by sound. Within a month he was cited for contempt in violating the injunction and made to execute bond to Kendall.[47] Immediately after the proceedings against Barnes had halted him another device was contrived. The People's line was extended from Louisville across the river to Jeffersonville, Indiana, which was not within the scope of the injunction order. From this point the line began to operate once more. Although messages were no longer to be transmitted from Louisville, the company maintained an office in that city where communications for transmission were collected and transferred by regular carriers to Jeffersonville. This attempt was no more successful. Once more the court intervened, and this time there was a finality about the proceedings. On November 15 the marshal was ordered to seize as much of the People's line as might be necessary to prevent its further operation in the district of Kentucky.[48] Having searched in vain for a way to extricate the line, O'Rielly and his associates were obliged to suspend its operation.

8 — · · · ·

THE fate of the People's Telegraph was of vital concern to those member companies of O'Rielly's original Atlantic, Lake & Mississippi system which formed the seaboard-St. Louis connection, notably the Atlantic & Ohio, the Pittsburgh, Cincinnati & Louisville, and the Ohio & Mississippi lines. They, too, were at war with the Morse patent interest and they looked to their southern ally to provide the important connection with New Orleans. With the paralysis of the important Louisville-Nashville section of that line by the injunction against the use of the Columbian instrument, Joshua Hanna came for-

47 Morse vs. O'Rielly, Circuit Court of Kentucky, October 24, 1848, O'Rielly Docs., Legal Series, 1; cf. T. S. Bell to O'Rielly, November 12, 1848, O'Rielly MS Coll. (November 1848).

48 Morse vs. O'Rielly, Circuit Court of Kentucky, November 15, 1848, O'Rielly MS Coll. (October 1848).

ward with a plan for overcoming the difficulty. He suggested that the leaders of the Atlantic & Ohio and the Pittsburgh, Cincinnati & Louisville free themselves of dependence upon the Morse patents by undertaking, as a personal venture, the purchase of the House printing telegraph patent not only for the New Orleans line but for all the lines comprising the O'Rielly range. House machines could then replace Morse machines on all the O'Rielly lines, and the stock and accrued dividends reserved for the Morse patentees on the original lines, in accordance with the terms of the O'Rielly contract, could be apportioned among those who joined with Hanna in the House purchase.[49]

It sounded like a good speculation, but the plan never materialized. Whether satisfactory arrangements could not be made with the holders of the House patent (Samuel L. Selden, Henry R. Selden, and Hugh Downing), whether the House machine was itself adjudged inferior, or whether capitalists found the risk too great cannot be ascertained. The fact remains that after heated discussion of the subject for several months the plan was dropped.

Meanwhile O'Rielly, casting about for a means of liberating his line, had become convinced of the superiority of a new electro-chemical telegraph which had been brought to this country in 1848 by its inventor, Alexander Bain, a Scotch scientist. Bain's telegraph, which had been patented in England a year and a half before, was in many respects similar to the Morse apparatus. The sending of messages was accomplished by a key similar to that of Morse; to get around any objection of patent infringement, Bain substituted for the key a perforated paper ribbon through the holes of which electric impulses intermittently flowed. In the receiving device the electric

---

[49] John S. Roggen to Capt. J. I. Rielly, September 29, 1848, in a folder on which the following is written in O'Rielly's handwriting; "Letter (secret) shadowing forth certain schemes of certain 'Trustees of Henry O'Rielly' for making 'a fine speculation' out of the vast fund of 'Stock and Dividends' which the said O'Rielly had always sacredly reserved to enable him at any time to fulfill his contracts with the Morse patentees. . . ." O'Rielly MS Coll. (June 1848); cf. a folder on which O'Rielly had written: "Light upon the Hanna Conspiracy to plunder the reserved quarter of stock." This folder contains a series of letters: S. D. Morgan to T. S. Bell, n.d. [1848]; T. S. Bell to S. D. Morgan and A. A. Hall; J. I. Rielly to Mr. Roggen; in O'Rielly MS Coll., VI. It was this proposition which later led to the rift between Hanna and O'Rielly. O'Rielly had been no party to the original plan, but when its full purport became known to him, even though the project had already been abandoned, he lost all confidence in Hanna and his associates. In October 1849, at O'Rielly's request, Hanna and Roggen relinquished their trusteeship of his affairs. Sanford J. Smith had withdrawn some time previously. (Legal Paper: Hanna-Roggen Trust Nullified, October 1, 1849, O'Rielly MS Coll., [October 1849]).

current, acting through a fixed metal stylus, produced a series of blue marks upon a paper ribbon by decomposition of the potassium prussiate with which the ribbon had been treated. Bain's apparatus also employed a relay magnet and an alphabet of signs similar to Morse's.[50]

The new telegraph had many features to commend it to the industry. Its operation was simple and rapid. It was said to be twice as fast as House's, three times as fast as Morse's, and eight times as fast as the needle telegraph of Cooke and Wheatstone. It was capable of sending to greater distances without the aid of relays and with a smaller battery than any of its rivals. On the other hand, there were certain disadvantages to the Bain machine. It was frequently troubled by magnetic storms; fumes from the chemically treated paper ribbon were unhealthy; and the fine spiral lines made by the receiving apparatus upon the paper were hard for the operator to read and a strain upon his eyes.[51]

In spite of its shortcomings, O'Rielly had grown increasingly enthusiastic about the Bain apparatus with each passing week. By the autumn of 1848 he was predicting that its introduction would bring about as great a revolution in telegraphing as steam had done in connection with the printing press.[52] On the strength of glowing reports, arrangements were made by O'Rielly and his associates for the American rights to the Bain machine; and O'Rielly undertook to assist the inventor in getting the necessary patents for its use in this country. "All will go well no matter what troubles we may now meet," he wrote to Hanna on the eve of the purchase of the Bain patents in October 1848. Although his affairs were in confusion, and he was on the verge of bankruptcy, he naively concluded, "I tell you I see the way of making more out of the Telegraph System than I have ever yet made. Be of good cheer, my friend . . . I never felt in better courage." Once the Bain instrument was in operation on the People's line, predicted O'Rielly, he would bid defiance to the Morse or any other system of telegraphing.[53]

While there was general discussion of the relative merits of the House, Morse, and Bain instruments at this time, a number of far-seeing leaders warned that there could be no peace and little pros-

50 Shaffner, *The Telegraph Manual*, 269; Harlow, *Old Wires and New Waves*, 143.

51 George B. Prescott, *History, Theory, and Practice of the Electric Telegraph* (4th ed. 1866), 127-134.

52 O'Rielly to H. R. Selden, October 8, 1848, O'Rielly MS Coll. (October 1848).

53 O'Rielly to Hanna, October 1, 1848, *Ibid.*

perity in the industry until the three rival systems were combined.
Negotiations, with this end in view, were set in motion by the representatives of the Atlantic, Lake & Mississippi Telegraph. Henry R.
Selden, president of that organization, presented definite proposals to
O'Rielly. "Now is the time for all concerned to make an arrangement
which will benefit all and put the telegraph business on a footing that
will insure its usefullness [sic] and render it profitable and pleasant
to those concerned in its management," he wrote. "As long as the
rival systems are in different hands there will be continual strife and
controversy. Can they not now *all* be combined?" Selden suggested
that 50 percent of the stock of all lines be divided equally among the
proprietors of the three rival systems in full payment for their patent
rights. The Morse, House, and Bain interests could make more
through their joint efforts, he contended, than any one group could
possibly make through independent action.[54]

Selden had put his finger on a major telegraphic ill, and many concurred in his views; yet attempts to harmonize the rival systems in the
fall of 1848 failed. Personal ambition, suspicion, and greed precluded all possibility of a union of interests at this time. While it was
clear that competition would have to give way to cooperation if the
industry was to prosper, the effort was premature.

9 —··—

ALTHOUGH the seizure of its vital Louisville-Nashville section crippled
the People's Telegraph, that organization continued to struggle
along. As rapidly as funds could be obtained the line was pushed
southward toward New Orleans. But so long as the company was
under the shadow of injunction, money was hard to get. Such meager
help as was obtained came in part from subscriptions for the northern
line (Illinois & Mississippi), and in part from O'Rielly's personal
funds and those of his friends.[55]

The whole line was finished in January 1849, but with the Kentucky section still in the hands of the marshal, it could not operate
over the full extent of the route.[56] Even had this section been free,
it is questionable whether the line could have been made to work

---

[54] H. R. Selden to O'Rielly, November 7, 1848, O'Rielly MS Coll. (November 1848);
cf. H. Ely to O'Rielly, November 6, 1848, *Ibid.*
[55] Chas. Doane to O'Rielly, January 1, 1849, O'Rielly MS Coll. (January 1849).
[56] Henry O'Rielly, Circular: Report and History of the Louisville and New Orleans
Telegraph, November 22, 1849, O'Rielly MS Coll. (November 1849).

throughout its length. Its construction had been too hasty and it was too cheaply done to insure any degree of efficient service. Over great sections of Mississippi there were no poles at all; the wire was borne by brackets nailed to trees. Insulation, likewise, left much to be desired. Instead of being made of glass, the insulators were of glazed earthenware, imperfectly vitrified. The wire soon sawed its way through the thin outer crust of the insulators, leaving the soft pottery cores exposed to the rain which readily soaked into them. Having little chance for evaporation, even in the warmest weather, the insulators became receptacles of moisture, and virtually worthless.[57]

The public soon formed a bad opinion of the line. Investors refused to buy its stock. Farmers, business men, and the press found the mails more reliable and often quicker than the telegraph. Scarcely a day passed that the operators did not have to turn to the steamboat or the mail service to assist them in transmitting dispatches between New Orleans and Nashville.[58] O'Rielly had hoped that the "way-business" would pay for the line's upkeep, while the "through-business" would provide the profits. Conditions being what they were, there was little through-business—in fact, little of any kind. Receipts were not sufficient to keep the line in repair, let alone pay the operators' salaries, or retire any of the numerous debts. "The line is a humbug and I fear it will never be much else," was the hopeless comment of Charles Doane, O'Rielly's agent at New Orleans. "It will apparently take the whole of the diggings of California to keep it up and pay its debts. The community have all lost confidence in it and I cannot wonder."[59]

Meanwhile in Kentucky the inactive Louisville-Nashville section was "going sadly to ruin."[60] Strenuous efforts were made by O'Rielly to free the line from the injunction order. All possible aid was given Bain in procuring his United States patent, but the procedure was long and tiring. It was March 1849 before the court ruled that Bain was no infringement of Morse, and June before O'Rielly obtained the release of his line upon his sworn statement that he intended to substitute the Bain for the Columbian telegraph along the route.[61]

[57] Reid, *Telegraph in America*, 199.
[58] Chas. H. Sheafe [New Orleans operator] to O'Rielly, June 30, 1849, O'Rielly MS Coll. (June 1849); E. L. Witman to O'Rielly, June 24, 1849, *Ibid.*
[59] Doane to O'Rielly, December 20, 1849, O'Rielly MS Coll., VI.
[60] Ira Jones to O'Rielly, February 25, 1849, O'Rielly MS Coll. (February 1849).
[61] Circular: Another Patent Granted to Bain, March 30, 1849, O'Rielly MS Coll. (April 1849); Press Notice in O'Rielly's handwriting: "Kentucky Line Freed from Seizure," June 16, 1849, O'Rielly MS Coll. (June 1849); *Louisville Courier*, June 16,

The deliverance of the Kentucky section of the line from the custody of the court brought satisfaction to O'Rielly but little relief. The line had suffered such great damage while in the possession of the marshal that it actually required more time to repair, or rather to reconstruct it, than had been required to build it originally. Repairs on other sections were necessary, too, due to the inferior nature of the original construction and the depreciation which had occurred during the paralysis of the Kentucky section. If the People's Telegraph was to salvage anything, it would have to carry out a comprehensive and costly job of rehabilitation. With an empty treasury and little likelihood of replenishing it, the company's situation was hopeless.[62]

Typical of the earnest but futile attempts to get the line into working order was Samuel K. Zook's account of rehabilitation efforts in Mississippi. Jacob Campbell, foreman of a crew which had been engaged to repair the lines, had progressed only as far as Jackson when he was halted for lack of funds. He asked aid of Zook who, being powerless to help him, had referred the matter to O'Rielly.

"Jacob Campbell and party are still in camp here. I managed to get them stuff for a tent which they made up themselves. They have a blanket a piece [sic], but no bread nor credit—They have part of a ham & some coffee & sugar left, but their credit has run out where they obtained them.

"In a day or two more, they can begin to practice living on their fat, as they will have nothing to eat. We spent the last money we had in office yesterday repairing the line 35 miles north, where some one had taken a turn in it with a stick & twisted it off for amusement. . . .

"There must be some provision made for setting Jacob's party in motion soon. The requisites are one horse, a camp chest for provisions, ground auger, and other tools, provisions, more blankets & money. The past month has been wasted—utterly thrown away."[63]

Aware of the sacrifice being made by O'Rielly, and influenced by

1849, O'Rielly Docs., First Series, II; Smith to Kendall, June 15, 1849, O'Rielly Docs., Correspondence, Legal Series, XI.

62 S. K. Zook to O'Rielly, July 6, 1849, O'Rielly MS Coll. (July 1849). The manuscript volumes for July and August, 1849, are full of material pertaining to rehabilitation of the People's line. Henry O'Rielly, Circular: Report and History of Louisville and New Orleans Telegraph, November 22, 1849, O'Rielly MS Coll. (November 1849); Rules, Regulations, By-Laws, Charter & Proceedings of the Meeting of Stockholders of the People's Telegraph Company, November 23, 1849, O'Rielly Collection, Rochester Historical Society Library.

63 S. K. Zook to O'Rielly, December 1, 1849, O'Rielly MS Coll., VI.

his indomitable spirit, the operators on the People's line had displayed patience and forbearance. Month after month—often with no salaries—they attempted to keep the fragile line in repair, to adjust complaints of patrons, and to turn aside law suits which threatened. When in the spring of 1849 they began to be ejected from their boarding houses and had no funds to meet their personal needs, unrest developed among them. By summer the disaffection was general. In a letter written to O'Rielly on June 17, 1849, M. Jewell and C. Carroll Butler, operators at Jackson, Mississippi, told O'Rielly of their plight; it might have been the story of almost any operator whether in the main office in Louisville or a remote office in Mississippi.

"We have had promises so long," declared the discouraged operators, "we place no reliance upon them and we conclude we have reached a point where forbearance ceases to be a virtue in consideration of which we submit our designs and intentions to you." They went on to point out that they had had no money of consequence since the office had been first opened and that what they had received had been used to keep the line in repair. Yet receipts had not been sufficient even to do that. For days at a time the line was out of operation for want of repairs. Men sent out to fix it had such limited funds that they were not able to do much. Business people had long since lost confidence in the line and as a result its credit was no longer good. Several creditors had already placed their accounts in the hands of lawyers.

"As far as we are personally concerned," warned the operators, "we have put up with all the inconveniences conceivable since connected with the line, and have done it with as good grace as possible under existing circumstances . . . we have been boarding at the only place, on credit, in town . . . and yesterday we had orders to procure another place.

"Now in consideration of the above facts and statements," concluded the discouraged pair, "we shall, unless our affairs be adjusted, be compelled to close this office and leave town on the first of July, in which case, we shall, of course, take the best measures for the settlement of our matters, and the final security of our claims, these views we are fully determined and forced to execute."[64]

64 M. Jewell and C. Carroll Butler to O'Rielly and Doane, June 17, 1849, O'Rielly MS Coll. (June 1849); cf. E. L. Witman to O'Rielly, June 20, 1849, *Ibid.*; C. M. Humphrey to O'Rielly, December 1, 1849, O'Rielly MS Coll., VI.

The enterprise was bankrupt. The telegraph operators began to salvage what they could from their respective offices, and local sheriffs soon held the keys to many of them.

Against this background of ruin a sad-faced group convened in Louisville on November 23, 1849, to organize the People's Telegraph Company. Capitalization was fixed at $660,000 which was to be divided into 13,200 shares of $50 each. Four shares of stock were issued for each $100 subscribed. All of O'Rielly's prospective stock had, of course, been hypothecated long since to secure the completion of the line, but technically he was the largest stockholder. A glance at the list of principal stockholders will show how completely the People's Telegraph Company had been the undertaking of O'Rielly and his friends: Henry O'Rielly, 3,000 shares; Charles Doane, 2,000 shares; Alexander Bain, 1,980 shares; John I. Rielly, 600 shares; Bernard O'Connor, 300 shares; M. Lefferts, 200 shares; James W. Ward, 180 shares; and Richard H. Woolfolk, 104 shares.[65]

As a fitting climax to the luckless venture, the Mississippi burst through the frail levees on the Louisiana shore in the spring of 1850. Not only was the telegraph wire washed away, but the telegraph office in New Orleans became accessible only by boat. All business was suspended. The penniless proprietors of the company once more congregated in Louisville to determine on a final course of action. Never was an enterprise so apparently broken up and demoralized. A little irregular business on the Louisville-Nashville section alone kept it alive. Just at this time James D. Reid, superintendent of the Atlantic & Ohio and the Pittsburgh, Cincinnati & Louisville lines, came to Louisville on business. Aware of the value of the New Orleans connection to the lines he served, Reid offered to lease the People's line for a term of years at an annual rental of $13,500, or approximately 2 percent on its capitalization of $660,000. This proposition was gratefully accepted by the proprietors of the line and a lease was duly executed. On July 1, 1850, Reid took possession of the People's line which had once been O'Rielly's brightest hope, but had proved to be the grave of his fortune.[66]

[65] Rules, Regulations, By-Laws, Charter & Proceedings of the Meeting of Stockholders of the People's Telegraph Company, November 23, 1849, O'Rielly Collection, Rochester Historical Society Library; also in O'Rielly Docs., First Series, II.
[66] Reid, *Telegraph in America*, 203.

10 · — · —

KENDALL had succeeded in checking O'Rielly on the Mississippi Valley route to New Orleans, but the victory had been dearly won. The measures taken by Kendall to check the opposition had seriously interfered with the progress of his own New Orleans & Ohio line. The Morse patentees were regarded by the public as a group of selfish monopolists, while O'Rielly and his associates were the champions of free enterprise. Attempts to raise money for the New Orleans & Ohio line yielded but meager results. Slowly and painfully the Morse line pushed its way southward, beset by problems on every hand. Even among his own subcontractors Kendall found disaffection and a distressing lack of loyalty. But the story of the New Orleans & Ohio can best be understood by following the different contractors as they struggled to complete the individual sections.

As planned, the easternmost terminus of the New Orleans & Ohio line was to be Pittsburgh, but to secure a connection with the seaboard, Kendall had organized a separate company, the Western Telegraph, to build from Pittsburgh to Baltimore.[67] He had entrusted the construction of this line to E. D. and E. W. Townsend, along with section one of the New Orleans & Ohio, which extended the short distance from Pittsburgh southwest to Wheeling. Through misrepresentations in soliciting subscriptions these dishonest contractors not only defrauded Kendall of $18,000 before they deserted him, but also left more than $3,000 of debts along the Western Telegraph route which Kendall was obliged to make good before he could resume operations in this region.[68]

On section two, Eliphalet Case[69] directed his energies to the construction of a line from Wheeling to Cincinnati and Lexington. Work on this section progressed with relative ease and rapidity, but the line was of inferior construction and could not be relied upon. Six months after its completion section two had deteriorated to the place where it was almost worthless.[70]

Farther south, Taliaferro P. Shaffner and William Tanner had received the contract for section three. Here the race to the Crescent

67 The background of the Western Telegraph Company will be found in Chapter VI and in this Chapter, p. 145.

68 Kendall to Smith, February 12, 1849, O'Rielly Docs., Correspondence, Legal Series, XI; *Ibid.*, February 19, 1849; *Ibid.*, March 17, 1851.

69 For earlier references to Case see Chapters V, VI, and this Chapter, pp. 145-146.

70 Kendall to Smith, March 17, 1851, O'Rielly Docs., Correspondence, Legal Series, XI; Reid, *Telegraph in America*, 202.

City found tangible expression as the forces of Kendall and those of O'Rielly hastily threw up parallel lines along the Lexington-Nashville route.[71] Due to the acute competition in Kentucky and Tennessee, Shaffner and Tanner frequently had to draw on Kendall for funds. Nevertheless, their section was carried to completion; and though frequently out of order, it was the most satisfactory of any along the entire New Orleans & Ohio route.[72]

Section four, extending from Nashville to Waynesboro, Tennessee, had been contracted for by H. M. Watterson. Despite the fact that he had less than one hundred miles of line to erect, Watterson became discouraged by the financial handicaps and took to drinking. When no more than half his task had been completed, he "quit," already in default to Kendall approximately $2,500.[73]

Construction on the fifth and last section was the most difficult of all. For three years Kendall tried to close the 650 mile gap which separated Waynesboro from New Orleans. William B. Lloyd and J. J. Haley had been detailed to this section originally, but their efforts had been abortive. Not only did they fail to accomplish anything, but Lloyd's actions brought disfavor on the entire undertaking. They passed from the scene leaving Kendall an inheritance of bad debts and "bad odor."[74] Kendall's nephew, John E. Kendall, and T. C. H. Smith took over the building operations on this section, and by January 1851 the New Orleans & Ohio line was at last completed to New Orleans.[75]

[71] For the earlier discussion of this subject see this Chapter, pp. 149-150.

[72] Smith to Kendall, February 13, 1848, O'Rielly Docs., Correspondence, Legal Series, XI; *Ibid.*, April 12, 1848; *Ibid.*, April 19, 1848; *Ibid.*, May 19, 1848.

[73] H. M. Watterson to Smith, June 29, 1848, O'Rielly Docs., Correspondence, Legal Series, XI; Kendall to Smith, February 19, 1849, *Ibid.*; *Ibid.*, March 17, 1851.

[74] *Ibid.*

[75] *Ibid.*; Kendall to Morse, January 3, 1850, Morse Papers, XXVII; Morse vs. Smith, Circuit Court of New York for City and County of New York, Deposition of William Tanner, June 18, 1856, O'Rielly Docs., Legal Series, XI.

The New Orleans & Ohio Telegraph Company was incorporated by a special act of the Tennessee State Legislature on October 18, 1847. No exact figures for the capitalization of the company could be found, but a fairly accurate approximation can be given. Kendall gave the actual mileage of the line as 1,483 miles, and Tanner and Shaffner both stated that the line was built on a valuation of $300 per mile. With these figures to work from, the capitalization may be roughly estimated at $450,000, divided into shares of $100 each.

The meeting of the stockholders for final organization following completion of the line was held at the Galt House in Louisville, February 26, 1851. T. C. H. Smith was elected president; F. B. Culver, treasurer; and Charles Carville, secretary. In July 1851, William Tanner became an officer of the company when he succeeded Charles Carville as secretary. (Kendall to Smith, March 17, 1851, O'Rielly Docs., Correspondence, Legal Series, XI; Morse vs. Smith, Circuit Court of New York for City and County of New

In summary, it may be said that of the five contracts entered into by Kendall for building the different sections of the New Orleans & Ohio line, only two were completed in accordance with the terms of the original contracts; and only one of those ever gave any measure of satisfaction.

The subsequent history of the New Orleans & Ohio is the counterpart of that of the hapless People's line. In the case of the O'Rielly company, it will be recalled, bankruptcy had forced it to lease its line to more powerful northern neighbors, little more than a year after its completion. The Kendall company had operated no more than three years when straitened circumstances forced it to lease its line to creditors in Louisville who reorganized it as the New Orleans & Ohio Telegraph Lessees.[76] Kendall had triumphed over O'Rielly, it is true, but in the heat of battle the victor had come to look much like the vanquished.

York, Deposition of Tal. P. Shaffner, September 13, 1853, O'Rielly Docs., Legal Series, VI; *Ibid.*, Deposition of William Tanner: "An Act to Incorporate the New Orleans & Ohio Telegraph Company," *Tennessee Statutes: Acts Passed*, October 18, 1847.)

76 Norvin Green to Morse, July 20, 1855, Morse Papers, xxxv; Kendall, "An Address to the Stockholders of the Washington & New Orleans Telegraph Company," June 2, 1853, Circular in Cornell University Library.

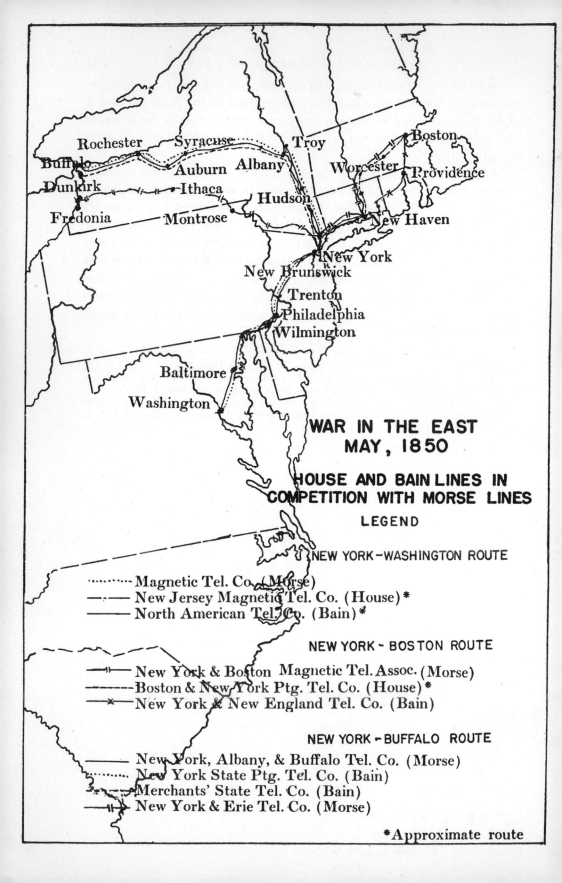

WAR IN THE EAST
MAY, 1850

HOUSE AND BAIN LINES IN
COMPETITION WITH MORSE LINES

LEGEND

NEW YORK–WASHINGTON ROUTE

·········· Magnetic Tel. Co. (Morse)
—·—·— New Jersey Magnetic Tel. Co. (House)*
——— North American Tel. Co. (Bain)*

NEW YORK–BOSTON ROUTE

—I—I— New York & Boston Magnetic Tel. Assoc. (Morse)
———— Boston & New York Ptg. Tel. Co. (House)*
—×—×— New York & New England Tel. Co. (Bain)

NEW YORK–BUFFALO ROUTE

——— New York, Albany, & Buffalo Tel. Co. (Morse)
·········· New York State Ptg. Tel. Co. (Bain)
—·—·— Merchants' State Tel. Co. (Bain)
—I—I— New York & Erie Tel. Co. (Morse)

*Approximate route

CHAPTER X

The War in the East: Patentees vs. Pirates

1 · — — ·

O'RIELLY's announcement in the autumn of 1848 that he would construct a line of telegraph from Boston to New York heralded what might be termed total telegraphic warfare.[1] Should he invade the East, there would remain no section of the country that had not served as a battleground for the rival protagonists. Why O'Rielly should have determined on so rash a course at a time when he was already seriously involved in the South, and still building in the West, may be explained largely in the light of his impetuous and vindictive nature. Deeply angered by his treatment at the hands of the Morse patentees, he was quick to seize the opportunity which the Bain patent gave him for a swift invasion of the East. Apart from personal reasons, he believed that a wisely administered opposition line would be well received by a public hostile to the monopolistic Morse lines along the seaboard.[2] But he was not the first to take to the field. The attack on the Morse companies had been launched the previous year by Hugh Downing, wire manufacturer of Philadelphia and former associate of O'Rielly in his telegraph enterprise.

2 · · — · ·

HUGH DOWNING, it may be recalled, had become interested in the telegraph through his manufacture of wire cord for the O'Rielly lines in Pennsylvania. He had played such an active part in the promoter's early endeavors that he had been made the first president of the Atlantic & Ohio Telegraph Company, section one of the original Atlantic, Lake & Mississippi range. In conjunction with O'Rielly and Samuel L. Selden he had purchased the House patent rights for that line on November 16, 1846, shortly after the Morse patentees had served formal notice of the abrogation of the O'Rielly contract.[3]

---

[1] *New York Journal of Commerce*, October 11, 1848; Circular: New York and New England Telegraph Company, issued by O'Rielly, November 1, 1848, O'Rielly Collection, Rochester Historical Society Library, cxxvi.

[2] *New York Express*, October 19, 1848.

[3] Agreement about House Patent this —— day of —— 1847 (Copy), in which reference to a contract dated November 16, 1846, is made, O'Rielly Docs., First Series, I.

Downing had been carried away by the prevailing enthusiasm for the telegraph enterprise; convinced that there was "millions in it," he and Samuel L. Selden had secured an option on the House patent rights for the entire United States.[4] By the terms of an agreement entered into with Royal E. House, in the fall of 1847, Downing was allotted the patent rights for the states bordering the Atlantic sea-board with the exception of New York; and Selden was awarded like privileges for the Empire State, along with an option for the remainder of the country.[5] O'Rielly had declined to share in the purchase. All his available capital was already pledged for the construction of lines in the West. Moreover, a practical trial of the House instruments on his Cincinnati-Louisville line a short time previously had proved only moderately successful.[6]

O'Rielly's lack of enthusiasm for the House apparatus did not cool Downing's enthusiasm. Proceeding energetically, he organized the New Jersey Magnetic Telegraph Company for the purpose of constructing a line from Philadelphia to New York to serve as unit one of his proposed eastern system.[7] The pioneer Morse line, the Magnetic Telegraph Company, which already occupied the route, viewed with concern the progress of the House wire as it made its way over the turnpike roads from Philadelphia to Fort Lee. Nor were the reports of the superior construction of the line, and its announced intention of building directly into New York City by means of masts over the Hudson River, calculated to allay the fears of the Morse line which had been obliged to stop short on the Jersey shore several years before.[8] "The new company have got their line stretched across the Hudson River by means of a 200 foot mast on the Jersey side and one of 350 feet on the opposite shore," reported the uneasy Magnetic operator at Jersey City to Alfred Vail on March 27, 1848. "Expect it will hurt our line considerable [sic] and some of our operators may be discharged."[9] A month later Downing's New Jersey Telegraph

4 Reid, *Telegraph in America*, 458.

5 Royal E. House to O'Rielly, October 29, 1847, O'Rielly MS Coll., xiv; J. D. Reid to O'Rielly, December 13, 1847, O'Rielly MS Coll., xv. Downing was conceded the privilege of building into New York City, although the House patent rights for the State were vested in Selden.

6 For reference to the first practical trial of House instruments see Chapter viii.

7 Kendall to Smith, August 23, 1847, Correspondence, O'Rielly Docs., Legal Series, xi; Morse to brother Sidney, November 27, 1847, Morse Papers, xxiii; *Niles National Register*, September 25, 1847.

8 For earlier discussion of this subject see Chapter iii.

9 Alfred H. Cummings to brother Alfred [Vail], March 27, 1848, Vail Papers.

Company[10] was opened for business, and stood ready to demonstrate its efficiency against the established Morse Company.

Both public and press desired to see the House line succeed; competition, they believed, would have a salutary influence on the somewhat arrogant Morse company. Typical of the feeling was an editorial which appeared in the *Philadelphia Pennsylvanian* two days after the opening of the House line. Speaking of the relative efficiency of the rival systems as demonstrated in a trial transmission of news for the press, the editor wrote: "Saturday settled the question respecting rival telegraph lines between this city and New York. The old line [Morse] . . . was no where [*sic*]. House's or the *new*, brought over the news, nearly the whole of it, before the old sent a word to anyone. Nearly all the papers issued extras before three o'clock, containing a hurried digest of news brought by the new wire—the first day of its operation." Moreover, concluded the editor, "the operators were obliging and skillful; everyone drawing a contrast between them and the surly, unaccommodating officials who mismanage the old line in this city."[11]

Notwithstanding so promising a start, the House line did not live up to expectations for a number of reasons. Its three-strand cord of unprotected iron wire, although strong and of comparatively low resistance in the beginning, rapidly deteriorated. Its masts over the Hudson, while substantially constructed, were a source of constant trouble. The most serious obstacle to the success of the company, however, lay in its administration. Downing's enthusiasm was no substitute for executive ability. Indiscretion and willfulness caused him to become exceedingly unpopular, especially among the business interests. Unwise interference where he lacked technical knowledge of the problems involved, and his failure to respect the confidential nature of the telegraph business, contributed further to the downfall of the company.[12] The House line, when working, took a fair amount of business on the New York-Philadelphia route, but its service became too erratic to make it a serious competitor of the well

10 The New Jersey Telegraph Company obtained a charter from the legislature of New Jersey under which it was capitalized at $100,000. No further corporate details could be found. (Reid, *Telegraph in America*, 458.)

11 *Philadelphia Pennsylvanian*, May 1, 1848, in F. O. J. Smith's Telegraph Scrapbook, Smith Docs.

12 Reid, *Telegraph in America*, 459.

established Morse line.[13] In fact, it proved useful in shielding the Magnetic Telegraph Company from charges of monopoly.[14]

Of far graver concern to the Magnetic was the appearance of still another rival on the New York-Washington route during the spring of 1849. The North American Telegraph, or "Bain line," as the new-comer was called, was a force to be reckoned with from the beginning. Under the vigorous administration of Zenas Barnum and Henry J. Rogers, the initial link of the new line from Washington to Baltimore was opened in April 1849; within two months it was well on towards Philadelphia with the old line anxiously speculating as to what the interloper could do.[15] "If they get on no better than House, we won't be put to the expense of suing [sic] them at all," Kendall wrote to Morse in a moment of wishful thinking. He concluded in more sober vein, "We should be ready to attack them should they become formidable."[16] No more than six months had elapsed before the Magnetic Telegraph Company, finding competitive efforts insufficient to hold the field against its aggressive adversary,[17] resorted to legal means. In November a bill in equity was filed in the Circuit Court for the eastern district of Pennsylvania charging Alexander Bain with infringing the letters patent granted to Samuel F. B. Morse, and for the next two years another case of patentees vs. pirates dragged its way through the courts.[18]

3 · · · — ·

NOWHERE was the attack on the Morse interests more bitter or more justified than on the New York-Boston route. F. O. J. Smith's line had been badly managed from the start. There was some reason to believe that it was part of a deliberate plan by means of which Smith hoped to gain possession of most of the stock of the New York & Boston Telegraph at depreciated values, and then to use his power to

[13] Alfred H. Cummings to brother Alfred [Vail], May 17, 1848, Vail Papers.
[14] Kendall to Morse, April 13, 1849, Morse Papers, xxv. For the subsequent history of the New Jersey Telegraph Company, see Chapter XVI.
[15] Ibid.; French to Morse, June 6, 1849, Morse Papers, xxvi.
[16] Kendall to Morse, April 13, 1849, Morse Papers, xxv.
[17] The North American Telegraph Company was incorporated by a special act of the Pennsylvania State Legislature, April 10, 1849. The capital stock was fixed at $125,000 divided into shares of $100 each. (Pennsylvania Statutes: Laws, 1849.)
[18] Sworn statement of B. B. French to S. F. B. Morse, November 12, 1849, Morse Papers, xxvii; George H. Hart to Morse, August 9, 1850, et seq., Morse Papers, xxix. For the subsequent history of the North American Telegraph Company, see Chapter XII.

establish a personal monopoly over one of the nation's great communications arteries. He had disregarded the wishes of both the public and the press, and had alienated those who should have been friends of the line.[19] There were few who felt other than satisfaction when, in the fall of 1847, Hugh Downing announced his intention of constructing a House line (Boston & New York Printing Telegraph Company) from New York to Boston, immediately upon the completion of his New York-Philadelphia wire (New Jersey Telegraph Company).

F. O. J. Smith, thoroughly aroused by this threat to his sovereignty in New England, sought to deride his opponent and the patent under which he proposed to operate. In a challenge which received wide publicity, Smith offered to bet $1,000 that his Durham bull weighing over 2,500 pounds could carry a message of 1,000 words from Boston to New York in less time than the House line.[20] Downing, aware of the favorable publicity which he was getting at Smith's expense, made a counter-proposal. If Smith would substitute Morse's instrument in place of his celebrated bull and if he would have the trial made between New York and Philadelphia where each party had a line in operation, then Downing would bet him not $1,000 but $10,000 upon the following conditions: "to wit, $1,000 that he [Smith] cannot transmit by Morse's instruments a message of 1,000 words 60 minutes sooner than I [Downing] can the same message with House's instruments; $1,000 he cannot do it 50 minutes sooner; $1,000 that he cannot do it 40 minutes sooner; $1,000 that he cannot do it 30 minutes sooner; $1,000 that he cannot do it 20 minutes sooner; $1,000 that he cannot do it 10 minutes sooner; $1,000 that he cannot do it on *even time*, and $3,000 that I will do it in less time than he can." Furthermore, concluded Downing, if Smith was really desirous that his bull should figure in as a third competitor, he agreed to "start against both Morse's instruments and the Bull" providing that Smith should ride his Durham.[21]

Hoist on his own petard in the House controversy, Smith observed

---

[19] Morse to brother Sidney, February 24, 1847, Morse Papers, XXII; W. Atwill to Dr. Doane, August 20, [1847], Smith Papers in Manuscript Division of the New York Public Library; *New Haven Palladium* [n.d.], O'Rielly Docs., First Series, II; Alexander Jones, *Historical Sketch of the Electric Telegraph*, 77-78; G. W. Benedict to O'Rielly, January 29, 1849, O'Rielly MS Coll. (January 1849).

[20] Smith to Kendall, October 29, 1847, Correspondence, O'Rielly Docs., Legal Series, XI.

[21] *Boston Evening Transcript*, May 20 [1848]; cf. E. Case to Smith, November 12, 1847, Smith Papers in Manuscript Division of New York Public Library.

a more discreet silence when, in the autumn of 1848, O'Rielly announced his intention of invading New England under the Bain patent.[22] Apart from declaiming against pirate lines in general, Smith did little to advertise the spread of the O'Rielly feud to the East. The press, however—partial to opposition lines in general and to O'Rielly lines in particular—provided the necessary fanfare. "We are gratified to learn that the extortion which has so long been practised on the telegraph line between this city [New York] and Boston is in a fair way to be abated," wrote the *New York Express*. "O'Rielly is a man of the people. Wherever O'Rielly lines are in operation a more liberal system prevails, . . . public sentiment is everywhere in his favor."[23] Joining in the editorial encomiums, the *New York Journal of Commerce* pointed out that O'Rielly's arrangement with Bain would enable him "to work his lines with efficiency and success without infringing any other patent." Therefore, concluded the editor, the public might expect "a healthy competition, a consequent reduction of prices, together with a more civil bearing of some of the telegraph owners and operators towards their customers."[24]

The proposed House and Bain lines were progressing rapidly through New England, in the spring of 1849, to the evident amusement of Cornell and Speed. As Smith's lieutenants in the West, they had so often heard their absentee commandant enunciate the doctrine of invincibility, that the prospect of his having to demonstrate it was most pleasing. "The posts and wires on the House line are up between Providence and Boston, and pushing on towards New York," Cornell wrote Speed. "The Bain line is also going on between New York and Boston so that Smith is likely to have fun enough and I am glad of it. We shall now see what he will do."[25]

---

[22] On the Boston route O'Rielly found himself building not only against his old enemy, F. O. J. Smith, but also against his former associate, Hugh Downing. Up to the fall of 1847, relations between Downing and O'Rielly had been cordial; then a number of circumstances intervened which estranged them and ultimately led to open hostility. O'Rielly's failure to aid Downing financially in the building of the New Jersey Telegraph Company, and the withdrawal of his wire business from Downing's manufactory were especially important. In addition, bills for wire cord supplied to Heman B. Ely on the Lake Erie line at the instigation of O'Rielly had long gone unpaid. As the year 1848 progressed, relations between Downing and O'Rielly had become increasingly strained; and by fall, when O'Rielly started his initial building in the East, the two men had become bitter enemies. (Downing to O'Rielly, October 21, 1847, O'Rielly MS Coll., xiv; *Ibid.*, November 5, 1847, *et seq.*; Downing to O'Rielly, December 11, 1847, O'Rielly MS Coll., xv; *Ibid.*, June 3, 1848, O'Rielly MS Coll. [June 1848]).

[23] *New York Express*, October 19, 1848, from Smith's Telegraph Scrapbook, Smith Docs.

[24] *New York Journal of Commerce*, October 11, 1848, *Ibid.*

[25] Cornell to J. J. Speed, June 4, 1849, Smith Papers, xxvi.

One of Smith's first defensive measures was to seek shelter behind the inviolability of the Morse patent. He contended that the Morse patentees had the sole right to the use of "lightning" for telegraph purposes, and he warned that anyone attempting to operate a line under any other patent was a telegraph pirate and would be dealt with accordingly. "As well say the heirs of Robert Fulton are in justice entitled to a monopoly of all the navigable waters," the *Boston Daily Mail* remarked in derision.[26] In still more contemptuous vein the *Boston Chronotype* observed that Smith was the last man in the world who should complain of piracy "having been guilty of the most unprincipled attempt to appropriate to himself by legal and legislative trickery and conspiracy the common property of mankind."[27]

Holding to his original thesis, Smith explained to his stockholders at the annual meeting on August 1, 1849, that the two opposition lines then building were wholly unauthorized. "The piratical character of each is conceived to be of easy proof," he assured them, "and no motive for their construction is believed to exist on the part of those immediately concerned . . . except a profligate speculation in the price exacted for the construction of these lines.[28] As if the very threat of competition had sufficed to stimulate the service of the New York & Boston line, the superintendent reported a marked improvement in operation and in accuracy of transmission over that of the previous year. One of the principal news reporters in New York had told him that "with all the prejudice existing against . . . the New York & Boston, the reputation of the line was now permanent and stood first on the list of telegraph lines in regard to the manner its business was executed."[29] Just how much of this rebirth was attributable to the added experience and efficiency of the operating staff, and how much to the fact that Smith now owned an overwhelming majority of the stock must remain a matter of conjecture.[30]

Notwithstanding Smith's efforts to halt his rivals, their lines moved steadily forward. The autumn of 1849 found three different lines under three rival patents in operation between New York and

---

[26] *Boston Daily Mail*, March 8, 1849, Smith's Telegraph Scrapbook, Smith Docs.
[27] *Boston Chronotype*, March 7, 1849, *Ibid.*
[28] "Annual Report to the Stockholders of the New York & Boston Magnetic Telegraph Association," August 1, 1849, in *Articles of Association Etc. of the New York & Boston Telegraph Association*, Smith Docs.
[29] *Ibid.*
[30] "Annual Report of the Stockholders of the New York & Boston Magnetic Telegraph Association," September 5, 1848, *Ibid.*; Kendall to Morse, June 18, 1850, Morse Papers, XXIX.

Boston.[31] In addition to Smith's pioneer New York & Boston, or "Morse Line," there was Downing's Boston & New York Printing Telegraph, or "House Line,"[32] and O'Rielly's New York & New England Telegraph, or "Bain Line."[33] The cheaply built and badly administered "House Line" offered slight competition. The "Bain Line," on the other hand, under the able direction of Marshall Lefferts and backed by such substantial capitalists as Edward Cooper and Abram S. Hewitt, was a rival to be feared.[34]

Smith opened hostilities by inaugurating a suicidal rate-war. Prior to the paralleling of his lines by competitors, he had been receiving fifty cents for Boston-New York messages of ten words or less, and three cents for each additional word.[35] Determined to throw his full economic weight into the fray, the pioneer promoter reduced the tariff on his lines to two cents, and then to one cent a word, as the contest grew more heated.[36] In addition, without even waiting to try the strength of the opposition, he filed suit against the Boston & New York Printing Telegraph Company in October,[37] and took similar steps against the New York & New England Telegraph Company in December 1849.[38] Smith was trying to demonstrate the doctrine of invincibility, not only to his curious lieutenants, but to the entire telegraphic world.

4 · · · · · —

THE situation in New York State was little different. Concomitant with the incursions upon the pioneer Morse lines along the seaboard

[31] W. Gibbs to O'Rielly, July 31, 1849, O'Rielly MS Coll. (July 1849); O'Rielly to President and Directors of the New York & New England Telegraph Company, September 29, 1849, O'Rielly MS Coll. (September 1849); M. Lefferts to O'Rielly, October 29, 1849, O'Rielly MS Coll. (October 1849); *New York Herald*, October 1, 1849; *Ibid.*, December 15, 1849.

[32] No figures on capitalization of the Boston & New York Printing Telegraph Company could be found. For the subsequent history of this company, see Chapter XVI.

[33] The New York & New England Telegraph Company was capitalized at $42,300, which was divided into 423 shares of $100 each with the right to increase its capitalization to $200,000. (Copy of Certificate of the Formation of the New York & New England Telegraph Company, April 19, 1849, in Smith Docs.) For the subsequent history of this company see Chapter XII.

[34] Certificate of the Formation of the New York & New England Telegraph Company, April 19, 1849 (Copy in longhand) in *Telegraph Papers, New York and Boston*, Smith Docs.

[35] Rate schedule on New York & Boston telegraph blanks, Smith Papers, II.

[36] Annual Report to Stockholders of the New York & New England Telegraph Company, April 1852, in *Telegraph Papers, New York and Boston*, Smith Docs.

[37] Telegram: Smith to Morse, October 16, 1849, Morse Papers, XXVI; Smith to Kendall, November 18, 1849, Correspondence, O'Rielly Docs., Legal Series, XI.

[38] R. H. Gillett to O'Rielly, December 17, 1849, O'Rielly MS Coll., VI.

came a series of attacks upon the New York, Albany & Buffalo Telegraph Company. Under Theodore Faxton's shrewd direction this
organization had been able to declare a dividend of 3 percent on
the results of its first five months of operation. As the first telegraph
dividend ever earned in the United States, its payment on February 15, 1847, had caused considerable comment.[39] A second disburse-
ment of 4 percent in October of the same year, further emphasized
the practical aspect of electrical communication and drew especial
attention to the profitable New York-Buffalo route.[40] Financial success, coupled with an unpopular administration—for Faxton held
both public and press in utter contempt—offered strong inducement
to rival organizations.[41] Following the established pattern on other
routes, House and Bain lines were shortly contesting the field with
the pioneer Morse line. But in the case of the New York, Albany &
Buffalo the situation was further complicated. In the spring of 1848
a second Morse company had started building from New York City
to a point on Lake Erie just west of Buffalo thereby paralleling the
New York, Albany & Buffalo line.

5 — — —

OF those who had scanned the financial reports of the New York,
Albany & Buffalo Telegraph Company, none had done so with
greater interest than F. O. J. Smith. Under the broad powers given
him as the Morse agent and regional director in New England, New
York, and the old Northwest Territory by the Divisional Contracts
of June 1847, he had set about establishing a vast combination of
lines under his personal control.[42] The Erie & Michigan, main artery
of the proposed system along the Great Lakes, had been informally
organized in 1847; and by the close of that year its line was under
construction between Buffalo and Milwaukee. Moreover, arrangements had been made for hundreds of miles of feeder lines in Ohio,
Illinois, Indiana, Michigan and Wisconsin. With plans in the Northwest well organized, Smith was ready for the next step in his program,

[39] *Niles National Register*, January 16, 1847; Faxton to Morse, February 15, 1847,
Morse Papers, XXII.
[40] Report of the President of the New York, Albany & Buffalo Telegraph Company
to the Stockholders, May 1849, Vail Papers.
[41] Livingston and Wells to Smith, August 21, 1847, Smith Papers; Vail to Kendall,
May 4, 1849, Vail Papers.
[42] For a detailed discussion of Smith's building program in the Northwest, see
Chapter VII.

namely, the establishment of an eastern outlet for his prospective western business.[43] To achieve this purpose, he worked out an ingenious plan for constructing a line from Dunkirk, a town some sixty miles west of Buffalo on the route of the Erie & Michigan line, across southern New York State to New York City.

Authority for the construction of such a line seemed doubtful. At the time that Smith and Kendall had drawn up the Divisional Contracts, it had been understood that the plans for construction of all the main lines had already been arranged. Subsequent grants of power, therefore, were supposed to apply only to the sale of patent rights for subsidiary, or branch lines.[44] A line from New York City to Dunkirk such as Smith contemplated was clearly not a subsidiary line. He believed, however, that legally there was nothing to prevent him from building it as a subsidiary of the Erie & Michigan, and operating it under the Morse patents. He was not concerned with the fact that his line would become a direct competitor of Faxton's New York, Albany & Buffalo system, and thereby constitute a violation of the contract which the patentees had already made with that company.

Accordingly, in February 1848, Smith had entered into an agreement with his associates, Cornell and Speed, to build the New York & Erie line. Operations were to begin at once. Cornell and Speed were to raise subscriptions and construct the new line so as to intersect the Erie & Michigan at Dunkirk. The New York & Erie line, as projected, would largely parallel Faxton's New York, Albany & Buffalo. Passing across the southern part of New York State via Fredonia, Pike, Nunda, Dansville, and Ithaca, to Binghamton, it was to make its way through Montrose and Honesdale in Pennsylvania; and then back across the New York State boundary to Middletown, Goshen, Newburgh, and West Point. There, it was to cross the Hudson and continue to New York City via Peekskill, Ossining, and White Plains. Construction was to be at the rate of $250 a mile for the first wire with an additional $100 a mile for all subsequent wires. Of this amount only $50 a mile in cash was to be paid for the patent right. According to the building contract, the line was to be erected with wire of the best quality, well insulated, and with forty poles to the

---

[43] J. J. Speed to Directors of the New York & Erie Telegraph Company, quoted in a report of Ezra Cornell to the Directors of the New York & Erie Telegraph Company, October 6, 1851, Cornell Papers.

[44] Kendall to Smith, January 18, 1850, Correspondence, O'Rielly Docs., Legal Series, XI.

mile. Since the average line had but twenty-five or thirty poles to the mile, it suggested that the line was to be used as something more than a feeder of the Erie & Michigan system. Of the excess over the actual cost of construction, whether in cash or stock, one half was to go to Smith, while the other half was to be divided between Cornell and Speed.[45]

Kendall was much concerned when news of the New York & Erie project reached him. It was a grave threat to the New York, Albany & Buffalo line, and he immediately questioned the legality of the action.[46] Smith was ready with an answer. Apart from feeling confident of his legal position, he had a statement written by Kendall the year before, suggesting that just such a line should be built. The suggestion had arisen as a result of a quarrel between Kendall and Faxton respecting the rights of side lines that might connect with the New York, Albany & Buffalo.[47] Thoroughly aroused by Faxton's opposition to what he regarded as the best interests of all parties concerned, Kendall had foolishly written Smith: "I have remonstrated, have briefly argued the question . . . have stated that if we cannot obtain from them the connection we are morally bound to furnish and which is necessary to give value to the side lines, we shall be compelled to run another line through the State for that purpose, leaving them a branchless trunk."[48]

It had been a threat which Kendall had no intention of carrying out except as a last desperate resort. He could not afford to jeopardize either his own or Morse's position in the most successful of the early Morse organizations, and a settlement had shortly been arranged. But Smith had not forgotten that letter. He now wrote reminding Kendall of it and expressing a willingness to help him triumph over Faxton. Instead of suspending work on the controversial New York

---

[45] New York & Erie Telegraph Contract, February 28, 1848; signed by Francis O. J. Smith, Ezra Cornell and J. J. Speed, Jr., Cornell Papers.

[46] Morse vs. Smith, Superior Court of New York for City and County of New York, Deposition of Amos Kendall, O'Rielly Docs., Legal Series, xi.

[47] According to the terms of the original agreement between Kendall and Faxton, tributary lines were to have the privilege of connecting with the main line by giving it half their gross revenue on all messages which they turned over to the New York, Albany & Buffalo for delivery. Faxton, feigning a misunderstanding of the arrangement, maintained that the revenues should be divided between the main and the side lines on a pro rata basis for the distance carried. Kendall, having entered into a number of contracts with subsidiary companies on the earlier and more favorable basis, had properly refused to concede to Faxton on this point and a bitter quarrel had developed. For a more detailed discussion of the side line controversy, see Chapter iv.

[48] Kendall to Smith, October 14, 1846, Smith Papers, xi.

& Erie line as Kendall requested, Smith urged Cornell to press forward with the enterprise as rapidly as possible.[49]

6 · · · · · ·

ALTHOUGH Smith, Cornell, and Speed were jointly interested in the construction of the New York & Erie line, Cornell was entrusted with the actual direction of the work. Smith and Speed were occupied elsewhere. Smith was busy trying to cope with the rival companies which had invaded the New York-Boston area, while Speed was concerned with the management of their interests west of Buffalo, especially the Erie & Michigan line.

On March 29, 1849, Cornell received a further extension of power. Smith authorized him to sell the patent right for the side lines connecting with the New York & Erie for cash on the best terms that he could arrange. Cornell needed no further invitation.[50] He proceeded on the theory that it was to the interest of the patentees to sell the patent for all lines as fast as practicable and at whatever price could be obtained. He personally projected the Bridgeport-Bennington, the Troy-Whitehall, and the Auburn-Palmyra lines, to mention but a few.[51] These lines were to be financed by stock subscriptions with 25 percent of each installment allocated for the patent right until the full amount had been paid.[52] Unfortunately, subscriptions did not keep abreast of the promoter's enthusiasm. Both on the New York & Erie and its tributary lines, work was progressing with hardly enough funds to meet construction costs, leaving nothing for the patent right.[53]

So aggressive were Cornell's movements that even Smith, who had once admonished him to "dash on with all the battery and thunder and lightning" he could command,[54] sought to restrain him. Smith complained that Cornell rushed ahead without considering the

[49] Smith to Kendall, January 23, 1850, Correspondence, O'Rielly Docs., Legal Series, XI; Reid, *Telegraph in America*, 290.

[50] Morse vs. Smith, Superior Court of New York for City and County of New York, Deposition of Ezra Cornell, June 30, 1856, O'Rielly Docs., Legal Series, x.

[51] Morse vs. Smith, Deposition of E. Cornell, *op. cit.*; Vail to Kendall, June 2, 1849, Vail Papers; Faxton to Vail, April 30, 1849, Vail Papers.

[52] Agreements of F. O. J. Smith with his partners, Morse and Vail, June 22, 1847, Smith Papers, *Telegraph Pamphlets*, II.

[53] Cornell to Morse, December 2, 1848, Morse Papers, xxv; Morse to Cornell, June 30, 1849, quoted in Morse vs. Smith, Deposition of E. Cornell, *op. cit.*; Cornell to Kendall, August 9, 1849, *Ibid.*

[54] Smith to Cornell, August 15, 1847, *Ibid.*

difficulties in which he involved his superior with Kendall. Smith urged a more conservative course. No further work should be undertaken on the New York & Erie unless Cornell could pay Kendall, and all side lines which could not raise enough money to pay for the patent should be abandoned.[55]

Kendall, for his part, was greatly disturbed by what appeared to be a bold scheme to build up not only a piratical main line, but also numerous subsidiaries at the expense of the legitimate lines and to the detriment of his principals. Hundreds of miles of telegraph were being built in New York State without his knowledge and without the payment of so much as a dollar to the patentees. The use to which these lines were to be put was self-evident; moreover, explanations made by Smith were both vague and unsatisfactory.[56] That individual appeared not to know what operations were going forward in his territory.[57]

Under the circumstances Kendall turned to Cornell and demanded an explanation of his building program. "Satisfy us that you have put a right estimate on your motives and intentions," he urged, "and you will command our highest confidence. If you are to fill the country with lines of Morse's Telegraph and pay nothing for it, in what respect but extravagant professions of fidelity, do you differ from O'Rielly . . . or the host of those you call 'Pirates'?"[58]

With protestations of his loyalty to the Morse patentees, Cornell explained that the building of the New York & Erie line had resulted from the unwarranted conduct of President Theodore S. Faxton of the New York, Albany & Buffalo. Faxton's line, instead of giving its western business to Cornell's Erie & Michigan system at Buffalo, had formed an alliance with O'Rielly's piratical Lake Erie line. Forced to protect itself against the unjustifiable policy of its eastern neighbor, the Erie & Michigan had merely sought the means to command respect through the construction of a connection of its own with the seaboard.[59]

[55] Smith to Cornell, March 13, 1849, *Ibid.*
[56] Kendall to Cornell, June 20, 1849, Smith Papers; Morse vs. Smith, Deposition of Amos Kendall, *op. cit.*; Kendall to Smith, January 18, 1850, Correspondence, O'Rielly Docs., Legal Series, XI; Smith to Kendall, December 16, 1848, *Ibid.*
[57] Kendall to Cornell, August 3, 1849, quoted in Morse vs. Smith, Deposition of E. Cornell, *op. cit.*; Smith to Speed, September 16, 1849, quoted in Morse vs. Smith, Superior Court of New York for the City and County of New York, Deposition of John J. Speed, Jr., December 18, 1856, O'Rielly Docs., Legal Series, X.
[58] Kendall to Cornell, July 19, 1849, Smith Papers.
[59] Cornell to Morse, July 12, 1849, quoted in Deposition of E. Cornell, *op. cit.*

Doubting the sincerity of the explanation, Kendall replied by asking Cornell a few rather pointed questions. First of all, had he not
begun to build the New York & Erie line before Faxton connected
with O'Rielly? Did Faxton not perceive that the New York, Albany
& Buffalo was to be cut off from the eastern business which might
pass over Mr. Smith's Lake line? Had Faxton not good reasons to
believe, therefore, that a connection with the O'Rielly line would
give him more business than a connection with Smith's line? But such
argument was beside the point. Regardless of Faxton's conduct,
pointed out Kendall, the Buffalo-New York business as a result of
solemn contract belonged exclusively to the New York, Albany &
Buffalo Company. Kendall warned Cornell that he exposed himself
to suits and damages whenever he took any part of it.[60]

7 — — · ·

TRYING as the situation was, Cornell was not easily given to dis-
couragement. In spite of the difficulties which beset his path, he had
completed the controversial New York & Erie line by the autumn of
1849. On October 2 the meeting for formal organization was held
in New York City.[61] Smith was unable to be present, but he was well
represented by his partner, Ezra Cornell, and his old friend,
Thomas M. Clark, former treasurer of the Magnetic Telegraph
Company. Writing to Cornell, Smith advised him not to assume the
appearance of supreme control, and yet to direct, if possible, all arrangements; while Clark was instructed to manage so as to be appointed not only director, but, if possible, secretary and treasurer.
Smith visualized the New York & Erie line as the great conduit
"through which western gold would come clinking down to the sea,
and he wanted a reliable man at the hopper." At the same time cash
subscribers were advised to "mortgage their stock at short date, to
the patentees for the cost of the patent, so as to secure its issue."[62]

Following the regular order of business, the company was capitalized at $110,000, which was divided into 2,200 shares of $50 each.[63]

60 Kendall to Cornell, July 9, 1849, Smith Papers; cf. Morse to Kendall, June 2,
1849, Morse Papers, XXVI.

61 New York Herald, October 4, 1849.

62 Reid, Telegraph in America, 291.

63 No exact figures on capitalization could be found. The data given here are from
indirect evidence in: Cornell to Kendall, July 25, 1849, Morse Papers, XXVI; New York &
Erie Telegraph Contract, February 28, 1848, Cornell Papers; E. Cornell to Stockholders of the New York & Erie Telegraph Company, January 16, 1852, Cornell Papers.

Of this amount cash subscribers were to receive $35,000, or less than one-third of the whole stock; the remaining two-thirds was to be apportioned among Smith, Cornell and Speed.[64] Despite Smith's carefully laid plans, arrangements did not work out entirely as he had anticipated. Cornell was made president, and Thomas M. Clark was elected secretary-treasurer, according to plan. But the cash subscribers refused to mortgage their stock to settle the claim of the patentees; and the newly organized company refused to issue any stock to Smith, either for the patent right or for the profits of construction, until he had fulfilled certain conditions. The company denied Smith's right to stock or money until he could convey to it a clear title to the Morse patent rights. So long as the O'Rielly controversy remained unsettled, the New York & Erie stockholders contended that the value of their stock was less than half what it would have been otherwise; therefore the amount due Smith was to be retained until the O'Rielly controversy was settled.[65]

Smith's dream of empire was rudely shattered. The action of the New York & Erie stockholders, and similar action by the Erie & Michigan stockholders, excluded him from any share in the western spoils. Smith had been unwilling to settle the O'Rielly controversy until after his own lines had been erected; he now found himself unable to make a settlement. Indeed, the O'Rielly companies were threatening suit against the Morse patentees for infringement of the O'Rielly contract. Having sown the wind, Smith was to reap the whirlwind. Cornell, Speed, and—to a lesser extent—Wade, were shortly to fall heirs to his domain in the West.[66]

For some time relations between Smith and his lieutenants had been growing increasingly strained. Now, as he saw his telegraph empire in the West slipping from his grasp, he turned to Amos Kendall for aid against his partners. In a tone of humility which immediately made Kendall suspicious, Smith admitted he had no right to build the New York & Erie under the Divisional Contracts of June 1847. He assured Kendall that if he understood the true facts

[64] Deposition of E. Cornell, *op. cit.* Cornell testified that the cost of construction of the New York & Erie was $80 per mile and that its length was 436 miles, making total construction costs of $34,880. Of this amount, he records, he received but $27,000 in cash subscriptions; the remaining $8,000 was presumably supplied by Cornell and Speed.

[65] Morse vs. Smith, Superior Court of New York for the City and County of New York, Deposition of John J. Speed, Jr., December 18, 1856, O'Rielly Docs., Legal Series, x; Francis O. J. Smith vs. Ezra Cornell, Supreme Court of New York for the County of New York, July 1871, O'Rielly MS Coll., VII.

[66] *Ibid.*

he would know his jealousies were unfounded.[67] Despite Kendall's unsympathetic attitude, more than once before the close of 1849 Smith wrote to him for advice as to the steps which ought to be taken against Cornell and the others who had put lines into operation without paying for the patent right.[68] Then in February 1850, Cornell and Speed broke completely with Smith and ceased to be his agents.[69]

The following month the frustrated Smith, having failed in his negotiations with Cornell, presented his grievance to the directors of the New York & Erie. He vigorously protested against the violation of the patentees' rights by the company. He pointed out that the line was to have been constructed "in a particular manner, within a particular time and on specified terms" by Cornell; and that not one of the requirements of the contract had been fulfilled. "The patentees seek not to injure any stockholder," concluded Smith, "but they do insist on a proper compliance with Mr. Cornell's contract and must look to you, as his associates for indemnity against its omission."[70]

No funds for the patent right or for any other purpose were forthcoming. Perhaps there was no desire on the part of the New York & Erie management to reach a settlement. Even if there had been, nothing could have been accomplished, for the New York & Erie was a perpetual failure. In all of Cornell's struggles nothing could compare with the obstacles which continually beset his path in his attempts to establish the New York & Erie on a profitable basis.[71] One

---

[67] Kendall to Morse, November 12, 1849, Morse Papers, XXVII.

[68] Kendall to Cornell, December 13, 1849, Smith Papers; Kendall to Smith, January 18, 1850, Correspondence, O'Rielly Docs., Legal Series, XI.

[69] Morse vs. Smith, Deposition of J. J. Speed, *op. cit.*

[70] Smith to the Associates of the New York & Erie Telegraph Lines and its President and Directors, March 30, 1850, Correspondence, O'Rielly Docs., Legal Series, XI.

In 1857 Smith brought suit against Cornell and Speed for recovery of both patent money and profits of construction on the New York & Erie and the Erie & Michigan lines, as well as on the numerous subsidiary lines which they had built under the general powers he had given them to dispose of the Morse patent rights in Ohio, Indiana, Illinois, and Michigan. These lines, Smith asserted, had been built "without paying to plaintiff or patentees *one single dollar* (beyond $300 paid by their agent, Wade), for all the sales so made and territory so covered."

Long after Cornell, Speed, and Smith were dead, the case still dragged its way through the courts. Ultimately, in 1871, fourteen years after the suit was instituted, Smith's heirs got a judgment against the Cornell estate for $600,000. As the Cornell estate was said to be insolvent, the matter was finally compromised at about one-twelfth of the sum. (Francis O. J. Smith vs. Ezra Cornell, Supreme Court of the State of New York, July 1871, O'Rielly MS Coll., VII. Details concerning the final outcome of the suit in 1881 had been written into the margin of this document in the handwriting of Henry O'Rielly.)

[71] Cornell, *True and Firm*, 101.

of the chief sources of difficulty was faulty insulation. Although it was Cornell who had introduced the glass insulator—the most practical and widely used type of the day—he had equipped the New York & Erie line with an insulator which he had just invented—an insulator filled with brimstone and capped with iron. It proved one of the most unsatisfactory modes of insulation ever employed, and the New York & Erie line did not work properly until the iron caps had been discarded.[72]

From one end of the line to the other there was constant complaint and a general outcry for money. On every side Cornell was approached for money—money for repairs, for operators' salaries, and for equipment and supplies. Claims against the company varied in gravity from the request of an operator that he be reimbursed for the dollar taken from his desk drawer,[73] to the more serious representation of another that he had worked for three months and had not received as much as he had paid out of personal funds for the company.[74]

An unmistakable trend toward bankruptcy was apparent in the correspondence of Ezra Cornell during the grim days of the early 1850's. Less than two years after the opening of the line its service had become so erratic that the humiliated operator at Dansville told Cornell that it was common knowledge in his section that a person could not get an answer as soon by telegraph as he could by mail.[75] The wonder was that the line would work at all. Between New York and Peekskill it was in a disgraceful state of repair. Between Ithaca and Jefferson it took the range of the rail fences and depended upon them for support. Through Pennsylvania the general impression was that the line was abandoned, judging from its bad condition. The majority of its customers had lost confidence in telegraphing and abused the New York & Erie with a will.[76]

A day of reckoning had to come. The defunct line went through bankruptcy proceedings, and on January 15, 1852, was sold to Ezra Cornell and associates for $7,000. As a concession to the former stockholders Cornell issued a circular expressing his willingness

---

[72] Reid, *Telegraph in America*, 356; J. J. Speed to Directors of the New York & Erie Telegraph Company, quoted in a report of E. Cornell to the Directors of the New York & Erie Telegraph Company, October 6, 1851, Cornell Papers.

[73] E. St. John to Directors of the New York & Erie Telegraph Company [September 1849], Cornell Papers.

[74] D. P. Gordon to Cornell, December 22, 1852, Cornell Papers.

[75] C. M. Smith to Cornell, March 12, 1851, Cornell Papers.

[76] L. C. Woodruff to Cornell, July 4, 1851, Cornell Papers.

to give them special consideration if they would join him in rebuilding the line. The capitalization was to be reduced to $55,000, divided into 2,200 shares of $25 each; and former stockholders who wished to retain their corporate rights were asked to pay an assessment of $5.00 a share, and more later, should it be needed, to put the line into first class working order. Having reorganized the company under the corporate title, New York & Western Union Telegraph Company, Cornell set out to establish the line on a paying basis.[77]

8 — . . . .

WHILE Cornell's New York & Erie was proving far less troublesome to the New York, Albany & Buffalo than Faxton had anticipated, other companies had also sprung up to contest the business on this strategic route. In the autumn of 1849, lines were projected under both the Bain and House patents with Henry O'Rielly and Samuel L. Selden as the respective promoters.

A rupture had occurred between O'Rielly and his former friend and associate, Judge Selden, as a result of a misunderstanding between the Rochester group (Atlantic, Lake & Mississippi Telegraph), which had first sponsored O'Rielly, and the Pittsburgh group (Joshua Hanna, John I. Roggen, and others), which had superseded them and had subsequently become his trustees. On the grounds that the Rochester group had failed to live up to the articles of agreement of the Atlantic, Lake & Mississippi Telegraph Company, the Pittsburgh trustees had refused to recognize the Rochester claims for stock in the O'Rielly lines. Although there was no wish on the part of either group to hurt O'Rielly, he was caught between their conflicting views.[78]

Moreover, O'Rielly had permitted his personal affairs to become somewhat confused with those of the companies in which he had an interest. Impatient at delays in his building program, O'Rielly had assumed debts and liabilities for the Lake Erie Telegraph Company, without its express permission, at the time his Rochester allies were

[77] Circular: Cornell to Stockholders of the New York & Erie Telegraph Company, January 16, 1852, Cornell Papers.

[78] H. R. Selden to O'Rielly, March 3, 1849, O'Rielly MS Coll. (March 1849); H. B. Ely to O'Rielly, March 6, 1849, *Ibid.*; Ely to Luman Sherwood, December 20, 1849, O'Rielly MS Coll., VI. The O'Rielly correspondence for the year 1849, and the month of December particularly, is full of the controversy between O'Rielly and his Rochester associates.

building the line in 1847.[79] By the fall of 1849 the Lake Erie's creditors were pressing O'Rielly hard for payment of this debt and even threatening suit. Friends in Rochester had been appealed to in vain. They could not relieve O'Rielly from his crushing debt, they told him, until he had adjusted their claims against him for stock on his lines west of Pittsburgh—claims which the Pittsburgh trustees refused to recognize. O'Rielly suffered keenly as a result of this misunderstanding, and his attitude toward his former Rochester friends grew bitter.[80] When Samuel L. Selden, who had invested heavily in the House invention, announced his intention of building a line of telegraph through New York State along the New York-Albany-Buffalo route in the autumn of 1849, O'Rielly promptly took to the field with the Bain patent.[81]

A heated race up the Hudson and through the Mohawk Valley ensued. The spring of 1850 found Selden completing plans for the formal organization of the New York State Printing Telegraph Company.[82] Simultaneously O'Rielly was concluding arrangements for the organization of the Merchants' State Telegraph Company.[83] Meanwhile the New York, Albany & Buffalo was preparing for a fight. Under the direction of Theodore Faxton, a bold offensive was launched. A resolution of non-intercourse with all lines not operating

[79] Hugh Downing supplied much of the wire for the Lake Erie line. For a reference to the difficulty in which O'Rielly became involved as a result of authorizing Downing to make delivery to the Lake Erie Telegraph Company, see *ante*, footnote 22 of this chapter.

[80] H. R. Selden to O'Rielly, December 25, 1849, *et seq.*, O'Rielly MS Coll., VI.

[81] Ely to O'Rielly, February 3, 1849, O'Rielly MS. Coll. (February 1849); Ely to O'Rielly, April 21, 1849, *et seq.*, O'Rielly MS Coll. (April 1849).

[82] The New York State Printing Telegraph Company was capitalized at $200,000 under the general telegraph law of the State of New York. Its officers were: Levi A. Ward, president; Anson Stager, general superintendent; Charles L. Clarke, secretary, but shortly succeeded by Isaac R. Elwood. The directors were: Isaac Sherman, Lyman A. Spaulding, Harvey Goodrich, Levi A. Ward, Freeman Clarke, Freeman M. Edson, Royal Chamberlain, Samuel L. Selden, James Chappell, Joseph Medbery, Stephen D. Dillaye, William W. Teal. (Reid, *Telegraph in America*, 461.)

[83] L. W. Jerome to O'Rielly, February 1850, O'Rielly MS Coll., XLI; D. Mann to O'Rielly, February 24, 1850, *Ibid.*; D. Mann to O'Rielly, May 16, 1850, *Ibid.*; Circular: New York State Telegraph [Merchants' Line], October 18, 1850, Bacon Papers.

No figures on capitalization of the Merchants' State Telegraph Company could be found. Its officers were: Marshall Lefferts, president; L. W. Jerome, secretary and treasurer. The directors were: William E. Lawrence, R. H. Green, M. Lefferts, Philo T. Ruggles, Samuel Choate, Wilson G. Hunt, R. F. Carman, Peter Cooper, A. C. Downing, A. S. Hewitt, E. R. Jewett, John Hollister, George R. Clarke, Dudley P. Phelps, Charles Wilson, F. A. Hudson, John S. Ide, Joseph Mather, P. Bliss, J. W. Fowler, William Masten. (Circular: New York State Telegraph [Merchants' Line], October 18, 1850, O'Rielly Collection, Library of Rochester Historical Society.)

under the Morse patent was adopted; dividends were suspended; and rates were reduced.[84]

9 — ·· —

As the decade which had witnessed the practical introduction of the telegraph drew to a close, House and Bain lines were to be found in competition with every one of the original Morse lines in the East. Notwithstanding the fact that both the public and the press wished the newcomers well, on no route was a Morse company in danger of being driven out of business. Priority in the field may, in part, explain the strong position of the Morse companies but the chief source of their strength lay in the relative simplicity of the Morse machine as compared with the complex House and Bain instruments. While they worked equally well and in some respects better than the Morse apparatus under ideal conditions, they proved no match for the simple Morse key and sounder on the primitive lines of the day.

[84] Report to Stockholders of the New York, Albany & Buffalo Telegraph Company, January 1, 1851, Vail Papers; Reid, *Telegraph in America*, 310. For later history of this contest, see Chapter XVI.

CHAPTER XI

A House Divided

1 ·−−·

THE methodless enthusiasm which marked the birth of the telegraph industry in the United States reached its peak in the early 1850's. Within the Morse family itself were to be found three rival groups all claiming the exclusive right to use the Morse instruments on the main arteries of the nation. Four Bain and three House companies operating over main routes—to say nothing of the many organizations operating on subsidiary lines—further complicated the situation. All the ills of multiple management and duplicating service were apparent. Inability to fix responsibility for errors in transmission, and high costs when messages passed over the wires of more than one company, made the public reluctant to use the telegraph for long distance communication. Contradictory rules of operation, poorly constructed lines, and inexperienced and inefficient operators contributed to the general dissatisfaction with the service. Under the circumstances telegraph companies were impoverished. Of the twenty-three leading organizations at the opening of the decade, only a few were making substantial profits; a number were barely managing to pay expenses; the majority were sinking deeper into debt each month.

Public confidence was still further alienated by the internal dissension within the telegraph fraternity. Quarrels, lawsuits, and shifting loyalties characterized the relations of its members. Selfish motives often caused promoters to lose sight entirely of the general welfare, and too frequently the public interest was sacrificed to the ambition of one rival to triumph over another. Although there had been some attempt at the concealment of early differences, by the 1850's there could no longer be any doubt that the telegraph industry was, indeed, a house divided against itself.

2 ··−··

THE controversy between the O'Reilly interests and the Morse patentees had been allowed to drag on for years notwithstanding attempts by both sides to negotiate a peace. Morse had informed

Kendall, soon after the outbreak of trouble in 1847, that he was "the more inclined to make every possible allowance for O'Rielly and his associates from the fact that Mr. Smith's design . . . in desiring to set aside their contract was not *morally* right if it was legally so."[1] O'Rielly, Hanna, Moorhead, and Kendall had likewise been disposed to compromise. Even Smith feigned a willingness to arbitrate. On half a dozen occasions negotiations looking toward a settlement had been entered into between the O'Rielly companies and Smith, but he had skillfully blocked all efforts to reach an agreement.[2]

The situation for Morse, Kendall, and Vail had become more and more aggravated as time passed. O'Rielly and his associates, embittered by their fruitless efforts to reach a settlement, had begun a driving attack on the Morse patent in an effort to discredit it. In the fall of 1847 the irate Irishman had offered a prize of $300 for the best essay on "The Progress of Electrical Discovery, with Reference to the Telegraph System." It was his intention, O'Rielly declared, to acquaint the public with the history of the telegraph invention so that people might see how false it was for any man to set himself up as the sole inventor and therefore entitled to a patent of a principal.[3]

Always an effective public relations man, O'Rielly's subtle propaganda began to bear fruit. "My affairs are at this moment gloomy," the distressed Morse had written in the midst of the indignation which O'Rielly had aroused. "My opponents, O'Rielly and Co., by their misrepresentation and perversion have created a hostile feeling throughout the whole West towards me. . . . I am looked upon as an odious monopolizer endeavoring to monoplize the use of one of God's elements, 'electricity,' for my own benefit. . . . The House humbug is held up as a stalking horse to terrify and to invite opposition. . . . Opposition companies are organizing and find no difficulty, it is said, in finding capitalists to help them and to oppose me. . . . What they may effect it is impossible for me to say."[4]

Such a campaign if continued could not fail to injure seriously the Morse patentees. Kendall, therefore, redoubled his efforts to reach an agreement with the O'Reilly interests. Early in 1849, Hanna had implied to Kendall that he was ready to concede to him three-eighths

---

[1] Morse to Amos Kendall, February 16, 1847, Morse Papers, XXII.

[2] F. O. J. Smith to Geo. D. Prentice, December 21, 1847 (open letter in circular form), Vail Papers; Prentice to Morse, February 12, 1848, Morse Papers, XXIV.

[3] *Rochester Whig* [n.d.], an open letter from Henry O'Rielly, dated Cincinnati, September 1, 1847, in Scrapbook of D. T. Tillotson, Cornell Library.

[4] Morse to brother Sidney, November 27, 1847, Morse Papers, XXII.

—instead of the original one-fourth—of all the stock on the lines west of Pittsburgh provided an immediate settlement could be made. Kendall was jubilant for he did not see how Smith could refuse so generous an offer. In confident manner he wrote his co-proprietor of his conversations with Hanna.[5] Smith did not share his partner's elation. In a few brief paragraphs he replied that he was the only one empowered to make a settlement and that Mr. Kendall would do well to look to his own affairs.[6]

By this time Kendall had had adequate proof of the failure of his policy of appeasement. Concession had only led to demands for further concession, and in the end there had been no solution to the trying problem of harmonizing relations with Smith. Kendall now felt that he had no recourse but to the courts.[7]

With the opening of the year 1850 a further factor complicated the relations between Smith and his co-patentees. On the last day of the old year Smith had informed the New York Associated Press that he would no longer transmit dispatches for them over either

[5] Kendall to F. O. J. Smith, January 21, 1849, MS Division, New York Public Library.
[6] Kendall to Smith, March 9, 1849, Smith Papers, XI; Smith to Kendall, March 13, 1849, *Ibid.*
[7] Before instituting legal proceedings against Smith, Kendall made a formal demand on August 27, 1849, that Smith fulfill his obligations to Morse and Vail: "I deem it my duty as the agent of Messrs. Morse and Vail, *to demand of you, as I now do,* the Stocks guaranteed to them in your contract of purchase of the O'Rielly Lines, or *an equivalent therefor in Telegraph Stocks* of equal average value.

"I understand the Stocks provided for on the Lines in question are as follows:

Philadelphia to Pittsburg	$100,000
Pittsburg to Louisville	$172,000
Louisville to St. Louis	$ 95,000
	$367,000

"I also understand that the net earnings of these Lines since they went into operation ...have been as follows, viz:

Philadelphia to Pittsburg	$ 28,000
Pittsburg to Louisville	$ 31,680
Louisville to St. Louis	$ 7,600
	$ 67,280

"When you consider that according to the position assumed by you, Messrs. Morse and Vail have no claims upon the accruing dividends, and that, if your position be right, so long as you procrastinate a judgment, they belong exclusively to you, I think you cannot fail to be satisfied that they do but justice to themselves, in making this demand." (Kendall to Smith, August 27, 1849, Vail Papers.)

For further details regarding the chain of events leading to legal action against Smith see: Kendall to Morse, March 26, 1849, Morse Papers, XXV; Smith to Kendall, August 30, 1849, O'Rielly Docs., Correspondence, Legal Series, XI; Kendall to Vail, March 4, 1850, Vail Papers; Smith to Kendall, March 22, 1850, Smith Papers, II; Kendall to Smith, March 24, 1850, *Ibid.; et passim.*

his Portland or his Boston & New York line. The action had come about as the result of Smith's ambition to establish a foreign news monopoly over the important Halifax-New York route. Controlling the only line between Portland and Boston, he had reasoned that his policy of non-intercourse would very quickly bring the press association to terms. The Associated Press, however, refused to yield to coercion; and beginning in January its press reports were transmitted by telegraph to Portland at which point they were transferred to a locomotive express and carried across the 110 mile gap to Boston where they were turned over to the new Bain company for transmission to New York City. Meanwhile the public suffered as a result of the needless delay in obtaining the news from abroad. With each succeeding day, public displeasure became more manifest; by early spring the press was openly attacking not only Smith but the entire Morse patent interest. Morse companies with which Smith had no association shared in the general condemnation.[8]

On April 12, 1850, Benjamin B. French, president of the Magnetic Telegraph Company, with whom Smith was on the most intimate terms, warned his friend of the short-sightedness of his policy. "Now my dear Smith," he urged, "for God Almighty's sake, and for *my* sake do come to *some* terms with the Patentees and the Press. You are injuring yourself and the whole Morse Telegraphic interest by the course you are now pursuing. . . . When a settlement has been made and all the Morse Telegraph interests *pull one way*, we have before us an enterprise that will beat California and all its gold out and out."[9]

Settlement, however, seemed unlikely. Smith's co-patentees had reached the limit of their endurance. Believing that Smith's utmost hostility would be less harmful than their seeming acquiescence in his manipulations, they announced publicly their opposition to his non-intercourse act and then began preparations for legal proceedings against him. With a great show of bravado Smith retaliated publicly: "Mr. Kendall threatens to sue me, let him sue. I will blow Morse's Patents skyhigh when I open my books. Nobody but myself, Prof. Morse, and the Almighty knows what the facts are."[10]

Kendall began preparations at once for bringing the suit to trial.[11]

[8] The detailed story of Smith's battle with the New York Associated Press may be found in Chapter xiv.

[9] B. B. French to Smith, April 12, 1850, Smith Papers, xx.

[10] Quoted in letter Morse to Smith, March 4, 1850, Smith Papers, xx.

[11] Geo. Wood to Vail, May 5, 1850, Vail Papers.

He sought by injunction to restrain Smith from any further acts as the agent for the Morse Patentees. Countless difficulties now intervened. Kendall became seriously ill.[12] Henry W. Ellsworth, who was chosen to conduct the fight against Smith, proved unworthy and squandered the money paid him without producing any results.[13] When the case finally came before the court late in November 1852, the evidence of Smith's abuse of power was not clearly established and the injunction was denied.[14]

3 · · · — ·

WHILE the triangular Smith-Morse-O'Rielly feud was the focal point in the general dissension which racked the telegraph industry, it was by no means the only conflict. Morse had become involved in a public quarrel with his former friend, Professor Joseph Henry, which was creditable to neither man.[15] Moreover, the deluded Dr. Jackson of Boston was still attempting to prove that he, not Morse, should receive the credit for the conception of the telegraph.[16]

Alfred Vail, ill and assailed by doubts of every kind, began to wonder if Kendall was really working in his best interests. Nurturing the doubt, Smith assured Vail that Kendall's ignorance of the law was appalling, and implied that Vail was being used as a cat's paw to pull Morse's telegraphic chestnuts out of the fire.[17] While no actual rupture occurred, the feeling between Vail, on the one hand, and Kendall and Morse, on the other, ceased to be cordial.[18]

As has already been pointed out, Smith and his former subordi-

[12] Geo. Wood to Morse, June 21, 1850, Morse Papers, XXIX; Morse to Vail, July 25, 1850, *Ibid.*

[13] Kendall to Morse, August 16, 1851, Morse Papers, XXX.

[14] Samuel F. B. Morse and Alfred Vail vs. Francis O. J. Smith, Superior Court of the State of New York, November 20, 1852, Copy of an opinion dissolving the temporary injunction heretofore granted against Smith, in Morse Papers, XXXI; E. Fitch Smith to Morse, November 20 and November 23, 1852, *Ibid.*

[15] "Statement of Professor Henry in Relation to the History of the Electro-Magnetic Telegraph" in *Proceedings of the Board of Regents of the Smithsonian Institution,* 1857; Diary of Alfred Vail, February 18, 1848, Vail Papers; Kendall to Morse, October 20, 1849, Morse Papers, XXVI; Morse to Vail, May 21, 1850, Vail Papers; Vail to Morse, May 24, 1850, *Ibid.*

[16] Amos Kendall, *Morse's Patent. Full Exposure of Dr. Charles T. Jackson's Pretensions to the Invention of the American Electro-Magnetic Telegraph* (1852); Morse to F. O. J. Smith, June 14, 1849, Morse Papers, XXVI; Kendall to Morse, October 20, 1849, *Ibid.*; Smith to Morse, April 24, 1850, Smith Papers.

[17] Smith to Vail, April 30, 1849, Vail Papers.

[18] Smith to Kendall, March 4, 1850, Vail Papers; Vail to E. Alexander, January 11, 1851, *Ibid.*; Kendall to Vail, October 16, 1852, *Ibid.*; *Ibid.*, November 23, 1852; Vail to Kendall, March 11, 1853, *Ibid.*; Kendall to Vail, March 14, 1853, *Ibid.*

nates, Cornell and Speed, had become estranged.[19] Speed's droll letter
to Cornell, in August 1852, reviews the differences which ultimately
led Smith to bring suit against them. "It is apparent that we are to
have trouble with Smith or give him half the stock on our line [Erie
& Michigan] and 30 dollars per mile for profits of construction.
This you very properly say you won't do. Smith now threatens to make
the best terms he can with the Rochester tribe [Lake Erie Telegraph]
and fight us. Well, let him try his hand at that. It only requires a
fight between us and Smith to complete the circuit—the family will
then have had a fight all around."[20]

Smith's intimation that failure to get satisfaction from the Erie &
Michigan would cause him to make terms with its rival, the Rochester-controlled Lake Erie Telegraph Company, was no idle threat.
In fact, his plans for making just such an about-face were already
well advanced. Incredible as it may seem, the closing days of 1851
had brought forth a strange and unholy alliance between F. O. J.
Smith and Henry O'Rielly.[21] It was a relationship born of expediency
rather than choice. Although having small regard for one another,
each party to the arrangement foresaw how the other might serve
him. At the time of entering into the alliance on December 2, 1851,
both signatories were in straitened circumstances. O'Rielly had gone
through bankruptcy earlier in the year,[22] while judgments against
Smith could be purchased for ten cents on the dollar.[23]

The contract which the two promoters drew up in their adversity
made a pretense of settling the interminable O'Rielly controversy.
It provided that Smith was to convey the Morse patent right to the
O'Rielly companies in exchange for a quarter part of the stock and a
like proportion of all the dividends declared to date. Of the amount
so received whether in stock or dividends, Smith was to refund one-
fifth to O'Rielly. In addition, O'Rielly was to waive all claims for
damages against the patentees, and in return, they conceded to him

19 For earlier discussion of this subject see Chapter x.
20 J. J. Speed to E. Cornell, August 21, 1852, Cornell Papers; cf., *Ibid.*, November 1,
1852.
21 "Settlement of certain differences between the Morse patentees [F. O. J. Smith] and
Henry O'Rielly," December 2, 1851, O'Rielly Docs., *Telegraph Pamphlets*; Smith to
Kendall, January 26, 1852, Smith Papers, xi; Kendall to Smith, January 28, 1852, *Ibid.*;
Smith to Kendall, January 29, 1852, *Ibid.*; Kendall to Smith, January 30, 1852, *Ibid.*
22 Donald Mann, Trustee, to Henry R. Selden, March 8, 1851, Bacon Papers; Henry
O'Rielly to Henry R. Selden, April 28, 1851, *Ibid.*; J. J. Speed to E. Cornell, July 25,
1852, Cornell Papers.
23 Morse to Kendall, October 4, 1852, Morse Papers, xxxi; E. W. Chester to Smith,
November 3, 1852, Smith Papers, xxi.

the exclusive right to construct lines of telegraph on the unoccupied routes in the northern portions of Indiana and Illinois, eastern Iowa, Wisconsin, and Michigan.[24] For O'Rielly the contract spelled opportunity—a chance to start anew on the frontier. For Smith it promised some financial relief; moreover, through recognition of the O'Rielly lines as the legitimate Morse lines in the West, it provided him with an opportunity to harass his former lieutenants, Speed and Cornell, on the Great Lakes and his former partner, Kendall, in the Ohio Valley.

The practical results of the Smith-O'Rielly alliance were negative. No one seemed to take their contract seriously. The O'Rielly companies refused to observe its provisions. Their various boards of directors looked upon Smith "with the most utter contempt" and had come to regard his "every movement, a trick." Smith's attempt to inspire the proper respect for his authority through injunction also failed. Nor was he any more successful in obtaining Kendall's cooperation in the plan of settlement. Upon being informed of the nature of the rapprochement, Kendall denounced it as inconsistent with a settlement in the true meaning of the Divisional Contracts. In addition, he warned that Smith would be liable for damages if through any arrangement with the O'Rielly companies, he should injure the Morse lines in the Ohio Valley.[25] Smith, thereupon, contended that he had tried to settle the O'Rielly dispute, but that his co-patentees would not cooperate with him. Under the circumstances Smith declared that he regarded himself as released from further obligation to them.[26]

In the years when unity of action was so essential to the Morse telegraphic interest, family quarrels menaced it from within, while rival House and Bain systems threatened it from without. It was, indeed, a house divided.

[24] "Settlement of certain differences between the Morse patentees [F. O. J. Smith] and Henry O'Rielly," December 2, 1851, O'Rielly Docs., *Telegraph Pamphlets*.

[25] The Western and the New Orleans & Ohio Telegraph Companies.

[26] Morse vs. Smith, *op. cit.*, Affidavit of Amos Kendall, March 1852, O'Rielly Docs., Legal Series, IX; *Ibid.*, Deposition of J. K. Moorhead, August 12, 1856, O'Rielly Docs., Legal Series, XI.

CHAPTER XII

The Trend Toward Consolidation

1 ·—·

As the situation within the telegraph industry had grown more and more desperate, its leaders had become convinced that the only hope for salvation lay in organization, cooperation, and consolidation. Kendall's dream of a closely coordinated series of Morse companies indirectly controlled by the patentees and linking all the important points of the nation had been dissipated by the O'Rielly quarrel, the treachery of F. O. J. Smith, and the entrance of rival House and Bain companies into the field. Almost as ephemeral had been the plan of Henry O'Rielly for a great democratic telegraph association to which all of his companies should send delegates to talk over their common problems and decide matters of general policy. With the first meeting of the General Council of the Atlantic, Lake & Mississippi Telegraph system in New York City on July 16, 1850, it became apparent that the bond which united the member organizations was so feeble as to be ineffectual.[1] With no means for compelling the allegiance of its member companies, the Atlantic, Lake & Mississippi system had rapidly deteriorated.

Less ambitious but much more effective were the working agreements, leases, and consolidations arranged between some of the companies during the early 1850's. In the East, the North American Telegraph, or Bain line, after the defeat of its patent claims at the hands of the Magnetic in November 1851, welcomed the Morse company's reasonable offer of consolidation.[2] As a result, its property, consisting of two wires between New York and Washington, was surrendered to its rival the following January in exchange for an issue of $83,000 of Magnetic stock.[3]

[1] Announcement of a Meeting of the National Telegraph Convention (Circular issued by O'Rielly, June 20, 1850), O'Rielly Collection, Library of the Rochester Historical Society.

[2] French *et al.* vs. Rogers *et al.*, Circuit Court, Eastern District of Pennsylvania, November 3, 1851, 9 Federal Cases, 790-797.

As a result of this defeat of the Bain patent, Bain lines throughout the country were absorbed by their Morse rivals so rapidly that in less than a year not one was to be found in operation.

[3] Reid, *Telegraph in America*, 140. For the early history of the North American Telegraph Company, see Chapter x.

Shortly after this union the receipts of the Magnetic showed an increase of 100 percent. The dividend record of the Magnetic during this period gives an excellent idea of how vigorous the opposition had been. For the four years ending with 1851, dividends had been 6 percent, 9 percent, 2 percent, and 2 percent per annum, respectively. In 1852 dividends jumped to 9 percent while in 1853 and 1854 they were 13 percent per annum, and thereafter, dividends of 12 percent were paid quite regularly.[4]

The defeat of the Bain patent on the New York-Washington route had repercussions elsewhere. Six months after the consolidation of the North American with the Magnetic Telegraph Company, a similar merger of Morse and Bain lines took place on the New York-Boston route. After suitable preliminaries, Smith's New York & Boston Magnetic and the Bain-operated New York & New England agreed to unite in a new organization to be known as the New York & New England Union Telegraph Company. Of the joint capital of $300,000, two-thirds was to be issued to the Morse company and one-third to the Bain interest.[5] Among the other provisions, it was expressly stipulated that F. O. J. Smith was not to have a controlling interest in the new organization.[6] On July 1, 1852, therefore, the New York & New England Union Telegraph Company was organized with Henry M. Schieffelin as president and Levi L. Sadler, Smith's henchman, as treasurer.[7] So successful did the consolidation prove that on October 9, 1852, a dividend of 2 percent was declared from the earnings of the first quarter.[8]

Developments on the New York-Buffalo route were following a similar pattern. Simultaneously with the Morse and Bain consolidation in New England, Faxton's powerful New York, Albany & Buffalo was purchasing the Bain-operated New York State, or Merchants' State Telegraph Company.[9] The sale was effected on June 7, 1852,

4 *Ibid.*

5 Articles of Association of the New York & New England Union Telegraph Company, July 1, 1852, in *Telegraph Papers*, Smith Collection, Library of the Maine Historical Society, Portland, Maine.

6 McKesson to Smith, July 26, 1852, Smith Papers, XXI.

7 Articles of Association of the New York & New England Union Telegraph Company, *op. cit.*

8 New York & New England Union Telegraph Company, Treasurer's Report, September 21, 1852, in *Telegraph Papers*, Smith Collection, Library of the Maine Historical Society. For the early history of the New York & New England Telegraph Company, see Chapter x.

9 For details of organization of the New York State, or Merchants' State Telegraph Company, see Chapter x.

the Morse company agreeing to pay $65,379.20, of which $26,079.20 was to be in cash and the balance in New York, Albany & Buffalo stock at par.[10]

The trend towards consolidation did not stop there. On January 11, 1853, Faxton leased the wires of Cornell's hapless New York & Western Union Telegraph Company for two years at $2,000 per annum.[11] The previous January, it may be recalled, Cornell's line, then operating under the name of the New York & Erie, had gone through bankruptcy, at which time it had been purchased by Cornell for $7,000.[12] Subsequently it had been reorganized and its wires moved to the Erie Railroad right of way, but despite Cornell's best efforts the line could not be made to pay. As a result, Cornell had readily entertained Faxton's proposals—modest as they were—for leasing the line. Faxton, for his part, was interested primarily in removing a competitor from the field. It was no surprise to him to find the New York & Western Union in no condition for service and utterly without revenue. Upon expiration of the lease, therefore, it was not renewed, and the ill-starred New York & Western Union Telegraph Company passed quietly out of existence.[13]

2 ··—··

NOWHERE was the need for consolidation more evident than on the Mississippi Valley route to New Orleans. On this important artery Kendall's New Orleans & Ohio and O'Rielly's People's Telegraph Company had effectively stalemated one another.[14] From the beginning their ill-fated courses had run parallel. The O'Rielly concern, it may be recalled, had gone bankrupt after attempts at rehabilitation had failed in the spring of 1850. At that time, James D. Reid had leased the bankrupt concern in the interests of the connecting O'Rielly lines of which he was superintendent. Not until the autumn

10 Reid, *Telegraph in America*, 310; Office of the New York, Albany & Buffalo Telegraph Company, February 1, 1853 (Circular issued by T. S. Faxton), in Horn's *Old Time Telegraph History* (MS volume), Cornell University Library.

11 *Ibid.*; Lease entered into by the New York, Albany & Buffalo Telegraph Company with the New York & Western Union Telegraph Company, January 6, 1853, Cornell Papers.

12 For the early history of the New York & Erie Telegraph Company, see Chapter x.

13 Reid, *Telegraph in America*, 293-294; Contract of Purchase of the New York & Erie Telegraph Company, December 20, 1851, signed by E. Cornell, D. T. Tillotson, and P. A. Hopkins, Cornell Papers; E. Cornell to Kendall, April 9, 1852, Morse Papers, xxx.

14 The early struggle for control of the Mississippi Valley route to New Orleans is presented in Chapter ix.

of that year did he succeed in establishing contact between New Orleans and New York, by way of the Mississippi Valley. But his efforts to maintain the line on a paying basis failed. With each passing month it went more deeply into debt. Kendall's New Orleans & Ohio, for its part, while making no money and often not even meeting expenses, had the negative distinction of being somewhat less indigent than its rival. Apart from that fact, their situations were similar. Both companies depended largely on their "through" business for support. Both were confronted by the difficult problem of maintaining uninterrupted service over hundreds of miles of unprotected and fragile wire. Neither was able to maintain its through service more than half of the time, and each had operating expenses in excess of $150 a day. All the evils of competition were present to aggravate the technical problems attendant upon the development of the new industry.[15]

By the spring of 1852 both the New Orleans & Ohio and the People's Telegraph Company were threatened with extinction. Under the circumstances the forces working for consolidation proved irresistible. In consequence an agreement was entered into for the joint operation of the two companies for a period of one year from the first of June 1852. The advantages of cooperative effort became readily apparent. Savings in excess of $22,000 were effected in the first six months of joint operation, and by the end of a year, representatives of both companies were ready to translate their tentative business agreement into a permanent union.[16] William Tanner, New Orleans & Ohio president, expressed the general feeling when he informed his stockholders just prior to the merger that operating separately the property of neither party was likely to be of any material value; united, the stock of both would unquestionably be better and might become quite valuable.[17]

To carry out the terms of the consolidation, the People's Telegraph was dissolved, and on May 13, 1853, its property was sold to its former rival, the New Orleans & Ohio. By the terms of the agreement which was to become effective on June 1, the New Orleans & Ohio Telegraph Company agreed to issue to the stockholders of the People's Telegraph an amount of New Orleans & Ohio stock equal

15 Report of the Committee of the Board of Directors to the Stockholders of the People's Telegraph Company, April 6, 1853 (pamphlet), Cornell University Library.
16 *Ibid.*
17 New Orleans & Ohio Telegraph Company, Proceedings of the Stockholders at their Annual Meeting, May 1853 (pamphlet), Cornell University Library.

to $150 a mile over the 957 1/3 miles which comprised the People's line; or upon presentation of nine and one-half shares of People's stock (par value $50 each), the stockholder was to receive one share of stock in the New Orleans & Ohio (par value $100 each). In addition, the New Orleans & Ohio agreed "to assume debts of the People's line to the amount of $40,000 which was to be paid out of net proceeds of the lines of both parties and to be pro rata with a debt of $27,000 owing by the New Orleans & Ohio." William Tanner was made president, George L. Douglass, secretary and treasurer, and James D. Reid, superintendent of the consolidated company.[18]

3 ··· — ·

AMONG the lines leading into the West a similar movement was under way. Everywhere, the leaders in the telegraph business had come to a realization that in consolidation lay their only hope of making their lines generally profitable. Addressing the stockholders of the Cleveland & Cincinnati Telegraph Company on June 28, 1852, President Jeptha H. Wade warned of the critical times through which the industry was passing and stressed the urgency of a sound financial position and the proper business connections if the company was to survive the changes which he believed to be imminent.

Discussing the question of consolidation he declared, "If all the prominent lines were consolidated in one Company, it would add much to the *reliability* of the system, and consequently to the *amount* of business to be done. It would save a large expenditure that is now required to support separate officers for each line in every town and city, and the saving in this item alone, would make a handsome dividend on the whole capital employed in the business. This is but one among many advantages to be derived by such a union—business being better done, with less delay, fewer mistakes, and at less than half the expense. It would soon double, even quadruple in amount, the public would be better served, stockholders better paid, and the Telegraph made to answer in every respect more perfectly the purpose for which it was designed.

"As we are evidently on the eve of a revolution in the business that must materially benefit those Companies that are taken into . . . consolidation on favorable terms, and leave others in a worse position than they now are, it seems to me to be very important that we take

18 *Ibid.*

the course that shall put us in the best possible position to negotiate with other lines."[19]

Wade's analysis of the situation was sound. The telegraph business was on the eve of a revolution which was to increase in intensity until the last vestige of independent organization had been swept away and the industry had emerged as the nation's first great monopoly. The year 1852 merely foreshadowed the future. In the West at this time the movement was apparent only in the efforts of Cornell, Speed, and Wade, successors to F. O. J. Smith, on the one hand, and in the earnest attempts of James D. Reid, *de facto* successor to O'Rielly, on the other, to increase the extent and vitality of the systems under their control.

The obvious need for coordinating the operation of the various O'Rielly units, and the failure of the Atlantic, Lake & Mississippi system to achieve this purpose, had led a number of the companies to appoint Reid as their common superintendent. Reid, Hanna, Moorhead, and some of the other leaders had labored zealously to establish close working alliances among the O'Rielly lines and with contiguous companies. In addition to the mutual exchange of business the Atlantic & Ohio and the Pittsburgh, Cincinnati & Louisville companies employed a common superintendent, occupied the same office in Pittsburgh, adopted the same rules, and elected a number of the same directors.[20] They, in turn, entered into a working alliance with the New Orleans & Ohio in June 1852.[21] The following month the Pittsburgh, Cincinnati & Louisville had instigated an alliance with the Ohio, Indiana & Illinois.[22] A short time later, working agreements were concluded with the Ohio & Mississippi and the Illinois & Mississippi Companies.[23] Moreover, arrangements were entered into with

[19] Meeting of Stockholders of the Cleveland & Cincinnati Telegraph Company, June 1852, O'Rielly Docs., Miscellaneous Series, III.

[20] Meeting of Stockholders of the Pittsburgh, Cincinnati & Louisville Telegraph Company, June 6, 1849, O'Rielly Docs., Miscellaneous Series, III; *Ibid.*, June 2, 1851, Cornell University Library; *National Telegraph Review*, July 1853, Cornell University Library.

[21] New Orleans & Ohio Telegraph Company, Proceedings of the Stockholders at their Annual Meeting, May 1853 (pamphlet), Cornell University Library.

[22] Presentation of the Pittsburgh, Cincinnati & Louisville Telegraph Company to Board of the Ohio, Indiana & Illinois Telegraph Company [1853], O'Rielly Docs., Miscellaneous Series, III.

[23] Articles of Agreement between the Ohio & Mississippi and the Pittsburgh, Cincinnati & Louisville Telegraph Companies, January 1, 1853, O'Rielly Docs., *Telegraph Pamphlets* (The Atlantic & Ohio Telegraph Company authorized their president to sign this agreement on January 6, 1853); J. N. Alvord to J. D. Caton, February 2, 1853, Caton Papers.

a number of other companies for the mutual exchange of business.[24]

James D. Reid strove earnestly to bring more closely together this great, loosely-bound combination of lines, which came to be known as the National Lines system. Time and again he urged upon the boards of the different companies the need for consolidation. The only real safety, declared Reid, lay in monopoly. "You are safe only in absolute control over your whole interests [as] far as your arm can reach, though in doing so your fingers freeze upon an iceberg and your toes burn at the meridian," he had told the Pittsburgh, Cincinnati & Louisville stockholders in his report for 1851.[25] But local jealousies, personal antagonisms, and the ruthless tactics of opposing interests were to prove more than a match for the hard-working but mediocre Reid.[26] One after another the lines composing the system were to slip away until the National Lines system had completely disintegrated.

Cornell, Speed, and Wade worked equally hard to build up their system which centered around the important Erie & Michigan line between Buffalo and Milwaukee.[27] Hundreds of miles of feeder line pledged to exclusive connection with their main line had been built by the promoters. Furthermore, their policy of expansion had led them to buy up numerous bankrupt lines in the Northwest in the hope that once the impoverished lines were incorporated into their system, they would become profitable.[28] It was in keeping with this policy that Cornell had purchased a controlling interest in the Ohio, Indiana & Illinois by buying O'Rielly's stock for $2.50 a share.[29] This transaction marked the beginning of the actual dissolution of the O'Rielly system.[30] O'Rielly's holdings in the stock of this line had been large, and through the purchase Cornell was able to turn the bankrupt organization from its allegiance to Reid's National Lines

24 Meeting of Stockholders of the Pittsburgh, Cincinnati & Louisville Telegraph Company, June 2, 1851, Cornell University Library.

25 *Ibid.*; Reid to Vail, November 25, 1848, Vail Papers.

26 Report of James D. Reid, Superintendent to Board of Directors of the Atlantic & Ohio Telegraph Company in reference to the operation of the Contract of Union of the Lines between Philadelphia and St. Louis, January 1, 1855 (pamphlet), Cornell University Library.

27 Alvord to Caton, February 2, 1853, Caton Papers; Cornell to Speed, March 20, 1853, *et seq.*, Smith Papers, xxvi; T. S. Faxton to Cornell, May 16, 1853, *et seq.*, Cornell Papers. The development of the Cornell, Speed, Wade system is outlined in Chapters VII, x.

28 Cornell to Gardiner, January 30, 1853, Cornell Papers; Gardiner to Cornell, February 4, 1853, *et seq.*, Cornell Papers; Alvord to Caton, July 7, 1853, Caton Papers.

29 For earlier discussion of this subject, see Chapter VIII.

30 Account of Ohio, Indiana & Illinois stock purchased of O'Rielly (Cornell's handwriting), January 30, 1853, Cornell Papers; Cornell to F. O. J. Smith, March 4, 1853, Smith Papers, xxvi; Cornell to J. J. Speed, March 17, 1853, *Ibid.*

system and draw it into the Erie & Michigan orbit.[31] It was but a matter of time until the other O'Rielly units were absorbed by more aggressive organizations.

4 · · · · —

WHILE the leading telegraph companies were groping toward closer cooperation and consolidation, there was born in Rochester, New York, an insignificant little company which was to play a great role in the future of the telegraph industry—the New York & Mississippi Valley Printing Telegraph Company. As early as 1847, Hugh Downing, Judge Samuel L. Selden, and several of their associates had become interested in the promotion of the House printing telegraph throughout the United States.[32] Downing's activities had been confined to the seaboard and New England, where they had resulted in the organization of the New Jersey Magnetic and the Boston & New York Printing Telegraph Company. Samuel L. Selden, Freeman M. Edson, and Royal Chamberlain, having become the exclusive owners of the patent for the State of New York, had organized the New York State Printing Telegraph Company in 1849, and a moderately good line had been constructed linking New York with Buffalo. In the meantime, Selden and Edson had secured the House patent rights for the remainder of the United States. According to the terms of the contract Royal E. House and his partners, William Ballard and John B. Richards, were to receive one-fourth interest in all lines which might be constructed and operated using House instruments.[33]

Selden and Edson, eager to exploit the vast field thus opened to them, set out to organize a company to operate in the territory west of Buffalo. Well-known and respected in the progressive and rapidly growing city of Rochester, Selden turned to its business men for assistance. The support of a number of them was finally enlisted among whom was the aggressive, wide-awake Hiram Sibley; and the New York & Mississippi Valley Printing Telegraph Company was organized on April 1, 1851, to construct a line of telegraph from

31 Reid to Morse, March 11, 1853, Morse Papers, XXXII; Presentation of the Pittsburgh, Cincinnati & Louisville Telegraph Company to Board of the Ohio, Indiana & Illinois Telegraph Company [1853], O'Rielly Docs., Miscellaneous Series, III.

32 For an earlier discussion of this subject, see Chapter X.

33 Trust of House Patent: Article of Agreement entered into on April 18, 1853, between Freeman M. Edson, Samuel L. Selden, Hiram Sibley, Isaac Butts, Francis Morris, Robert W. Russell, Cambridge Livingston and John B. Richards, O'Rielly Docs., Telegraph Pamphlets.

Buffalo to St. Louis.[34] Considering the chaotic conditions which existed in the industry at this time, it is not surprising that Selden, Sibley, and their associates found it difficult to secure the necessary money to carry out their project, and the immediate results were disappointing. In fact, during the first few years of its existence, in spite of the best efforts of its promoters, the New York & Mississippi Valley appeared to be just another telegraph company.

5 — — —

A GENERAL survey of the telegraph scene at the close of 1852 presents an immediate picture of hopeless confusion, but a closer examination shows a clear and unmistakable trend toward consolidation. The New York & New England Union Telegraph Company dominated New England; Kendall's Magnetic controlled the route from New York to Washington, and also largely dominated the policies and business of the Washington & New Orleans extending on southward along the coast to New Orleans; and the New York, Albany & Buffalo, while facing the competition of the Rochester controlled New York State Printing Telegraph Company, gave no signs of relinquishing its leadership on this route to its ambitious rival. The Mississippi Valley route to New Orleans was feebly held by the New Orleans & Ohio and the People's Telegraph Companies, which were on the verge of consolidating. The situation in the West, while still in a state of upheaval, was gradually assuming definite shape. A nucleus of former O'Rielly lines—the Atlantic & Ohio and the Pittsburgh, Cincinnati & Louisville—and several other cooperating lines, all under the superintendency of James D. Reid, constituted the National Lines system. The Erie & Michigan with dozens of small feeder lines extending throughout the whole Northwest, under the direction of Cornell, Speed, and Wade, made up another formidable system in the West. Finally, the New York & Mississippi Valley Printing Telegraph Company under the leadership of Hiram Sibley, while it had made no spectacular progress in the first two years of its existence, had learned much and was now ready to embark upon a program of expansion which was to carry it to fame and fortune as the Western Union Telegraph Company—a title it was shortly to assume.

34 Details concerning the organization of this company are presented in Chapter XVI.

CHAPTER XIII

The Railroad and the Telegraph

1 ·——·

THE introduction of the railroad into the United States parallels so closely the advent of the telegraph that the story of the one cannot be told properly without touching upon that of the other. Four years before Morse even conceived the idea for his telegraph, the Baltimore & Ohio Railroad had begun the construction of a dubious little railway line into the West. Sixteen years later, in the spring of 1844, the telegraph had made its official *début*, significantly enough, on the Baltimore & Ohio right of way. Telegraph leaders had become aware almost at once of the advantages to be derived from constructing their lines along the railroads, but the restrictions with which the Baltimore & Ohio hedged its first telegraph agreement gave evidence that the railroad, far from seeing any value in the telegraph, barely suffered it to build along the railroad right of way.[1] In fact, many less liberal railroads refused to be bothered with electric wires along their roadbeds. Some years were to pass before the natural affinity of wire and rail came to be recognized by the conservative railway managements.

In both railroad and telegraph construction the initial period, which drew to a close about 1850, had been one of methodless enthusiasm. Wires had been strung and rails laid with feverish haste as promoters eagerly sought to be the first to break into virgin territory. Samuel W. McGowan, canvassing for telegraph subscriptions in Canton and Potsdam, New York, in July 1849, informed his principal, Ezra Cornell, that he found every person of any little capital and influence so completely involved in the Boston Railroad that they would not listen to anything in favor of a telegraph line. "The people are Railroad mad," declared McGowan, ". . . and more than one man in this vicinage is bordering on absolute bankruptcy in consequence of the Railroad mania."[2]

Although progress had been made by both the telegraph and the railroad during the 1840's and the great future which lay ahead began

---

[1] For a detailed account of this early agreement between Morse and the Baltimore & Ohio Railroad, see Chapter II.

[2] Samuel W. McGowan to Cornell, July 10, 1849, Cornell Papers.

to be foreshadowed, neither enterprise could be termed an assured success as the decade drew to a close. The telegraph had certainly not won the public confidence, and the railroad was hardly capable of competition with the canals.[3] It was during the next decade—1850 to 1860—when sober consolidation began to bring order out of enthusiastic chaos that the railroad and the telegraph came to be recognized as the indispensable "Siamese twins of commerce."[4] As great railway trunk lines and extended telegraphic systems began to absorb the haphazard pioneer lines which sprawled over the countryside, and order and efficiency began to appear, the attitude of the public became one of approbation and support.

Because of the comparative ease and lower cost of construction, telegraphic development rapidly eclipsed railroad growth during the period. "Lightning lines" reached out to embrace every town and city connected by rail, and then pushed on beyond the railroad frontiers. In most parts of the West the "iron cord" preceded the "iron horse."[5] Hiram Sibley succeeded in pushing a "lightning line" all the way to the Pacific, eight years in advance of the railroad. The telegraph as well as the railroad is entitled to a share of the credit for the prodigious development of the West.

2 ··—··

THAT the telegraph was the natural complement of the railroad had been quickly recognized in Europe, where wires were commonly strung along the railroad rights of way. C. A. Saunders, secretary of the British Great Western Railway Company, testified that Cooke and Wheatstone's telegraph had been brought into actual operation upon the Great Western Railway as early as 1839 and its capabilities severely tested.[6] Shortly thereafter the Yarmouth & Norwich Railway issued a circular explaining at length Cooke's new system of train dispatching by telegraph which the road had adopted in 1844. Through the use of this system the railway officials claimed that they

[3] Henry V. Poor, *Manual of the Railroads of the United States* . . . (1881).

[4] H. D. Estabrook, "The First Train Order by Telegraph" in *Baltimore & Ohio Employees Magazine*, I (July 1913), 27-29.

[5] B. H. Wilson, "In Line With Progress," in *Palimpsest*, VII (August 1926), 256-260; [Cornell] *True and Firm*, 103.

[6] Charles V. Walker (Superintendent of the Southeastern Railway, England). Scrapbook covering period 1847-1876, New York Public Library; cf. J. H. Kennedy, "The American Railroad; its inception, evolution, and results . . . ," *Magazine of Western History*, XI, 176-192.

had been free from accidents arising from trains meeting or overtaking one another, even though the Yarmouth & Norwich was a single track line.[7]

American railroads confronted with similar traffic problems were slow to turn to the telegraph for their solution. Typical was the action of the pioneer Baltimore & Ohio Railroad Company in 1846. Officials of the line were concerned by the growing number of accidents which seemed to be in direct ratio to the increasing volume of traffic. Accidents involving serious damage and in some instances loss of life were of almost daily occurrence. The chief engineer, Samuel Jones, was asked to report on means for improving the efficiency of the road. He reported that the only effective solution was to doubletrack the line, a project hardly feasible in view of the straitened circumstances of the company. Although Morse's experimental telegraph line had been in operation along the Baltimore & Ohio tracks since 1844, no mention of the telegraph was made among Jones' suggestions for improvement. Neither he nor other railroad men, at this time, considered it a possible method of regulating the movement of trains.[8]

On the single-track lines of the day, trains were operated on what was known as a "time interval system." Under this arrangement trains were designated as "superior" and "inferior" according to their class and the direction in which they moved. The Baltimore & Ohio Railroad, for example, gave the right of way over other trains of its class to the train going east, while the Erie Railroad gave priority to the train going west.[9] Inferior trains were required to wait one hour at designated passing points for late superior trains. At the expiration of that time if the superior train had not arrived, the inferior would start a flagman on foot to the next station, the train following slowly ten minutes later. This procedure was continued until the trains met. If the meeting occurred between stations, the train nearest a siding or the train of lesser importance would back up.[10] Sometimes a battle

[7] Walker, op. cit.

[8] Annual Report of the president and directors of the Baltimore & Ohio Railroad to the stockholders, October 7, 1846. New York Public Library.

[9] Both passenger and freight trains were classified (first class, second, etc.), and a first class passenger train would always have priority over a second class train regardless of direction.

[10] [n. a.] "Telegraph and Railroads" Mutual Magazine (Pennsylvania Railroad employees' magazine), XVIII (July 1932), 20; Estabrook, "The First Train Order by Telegraph," Baltimore & Ohio Employees Magazine, I, 27-29.

of fisticuffs between the respective crews settled the controversy.[11] During its early days the Boston & Worcester Railroad maintained a relay of horses at five mile intervals along the route to report the location of retarded trains. By this means the company was able to diminish the possibility of accidents or excessive delay.[12]

Despite the evident need for some system of determining the location of trains along the route, railroaders were reluctant to trust the telegraph for the movement of their trains; nor were they to be blamed entirely. Pioneer telegraphy in the United States left much to be desired in the way of dependability. J. H. Wade recalled his efforts to induce J. W. Brooks, president of the Michigan Central Railroad, to permit him to build along that road's right of way. Brooks at first ridiculed the idea. "Why," exclaimed he, "I had rather have one hand car for keeping my road in repair and handling my trains than all the telegraph lines you can build."

Wade admitted that after a reluctant consent had been obtained and the line built, it "worked with about the same regularity as most of the early lines—which wasn't very regular." Sometimes it aided materially, and at other times, when needed most, it was out of order. It took several years to perfect the telegraph lines to the point where they were worthy of the full confidence of the railroad officials.[13]

3 · · · — ·

THE first train official to realize the potentialities of the telegraph for railroad use in this country seems to have been Charles Minot, superintendent of the New York & Erie Railroad. At least, it was he who first demonstrated the value of the telegraph as a vital agent in the management of railroads, the running of trains, and the insuring of the safety of the passengers. Minot, watching Ezra Cornell construct the luckless New York & Erie Telegraph line in 1849, conceived the idea that this new means of communication could be of practical service to his recently reorganized railroad. Accordingly, he proposed to the directors that a line of telegraph be built paralleling the railroad. They laughed at him and declared it to be an absurd idea. Minot persisted, however, asserting that such a line would pay for itself in one year. The greatest objection the directors raised was

---

[11] Agnes C. Laut, *The Romance of the Rails*, I, 205-207.

[12] B. H. Meyer, C. H. MacGill, *et al.*, eds. *History of Transportation in the United States before 1860*, 3-4.

[13] J. H. Wade, Autobiography (manuscript).

that operators' salaries would more than offset any benefit which might be derived from the line. Minot met their objections by explaining that the various depot masters and clerks could be used as operators at no extra expense to the railroad.[14]

Having finally obtained the requisite authority, Minot proceeded to equip the Erie with a telegraph system. By the latter part of 1850 it had been completed between Piermont, the Erie terminal on the Hudson River, and Goshen, New York. At this time passengers, freight, livestock, mail pouches, and baggage were transferred from the trains at Piermont and brought to the Erie station at the foot of Duane Street in New York City by steamer. Little of the produce in the Piermont warehouse could be loaded, however, before the arrival of the train from the west, because a considerable portion of the deck had to be reserved for an unknown number of livestock. Since the stevedores were laid off between trains, this system of operation resulted in great loss for them as well as unnecessary delay for the passengers.[15]

The operator at Piermont, D. H. Conklin, who had learned telegraphy under Cornell, was aware of the needless waste of time and money which the existing system entailed. One day early in January 1851, therefore, Conklin arranged with the conductor of a stock train to telegraph information regarding his cargo from Goshen. By this means the rivermen were enabled to load their barges, reserving only sufficient space for the number of livestock which would be arriving by train. Instead of the two hours usually consumed in loading after the arrival of the train, thirty minutes sufficed to start the barges on their way down the Hudson. Conklin's ingenious arrangement is believed to have been the first practical application of the telegraph for facilitating railroad work in the United States.[16]

In June 1851, came a still more important application of the telegraph to railroading. One day Superintendent Minot chanced to be aboard the westbound express which was scheduled to meet the eastbound express at Turners (now Harriman), New York. A few minutes elapsed and the belated train still had not arrived. Stepping into the telegraph office at Turners, Minot inquired of the operator

[14] Edward H. Mott, *Between the Ocean and the Lakes: the Story of the Erie*, 415-422; Kennedy, "The American Railroad . . . ," *Magazine of Western History*, XI, 176-192; Amos Kendall to F. O. J. Smith, May 11, 1850, Smith Papers; Charles Minot to Smith, September 8, 1850, *Ibid.*; Smith to Minot, September 13, 1850, *Ibid.*
[15] Mott, *Between the Ocean and the Lakes*, 417-418.
[16] *Ibid.*

at Goshen whether the eastbound train had left his station. Receiving a negative reply, Minot telegraphed Goshen as follows:

> To Agent and Operator at Goshen
> Hold the train for further orders.
> Chas. Minot, Superintendent.

He then wrote this order and handed it to the amazed conductor:

> To Conductor and Engineer, Day Express
> Run to Goshen regardless of opposing train.
> Chas. Minot, Superintendent.

"I took the order," said conductor W. H. Stewart, relating the incident, "showed it to engineer, Isaac Lewis, and told him to go ahead."

The surprised engineer read the order, and handing it back to Stewart exclaimed: "Do you take me for a d - - n fool? I won't run by that thing!"

Stewart reported to the superintendent, who went forward and personally issued the order. But the engineer was unyielding. Minot then climbed aboard the engine and took charge himself. Engineer Lewis jumped off and got in the rear seat of the rear car where he remained, while the superintendent ran the train to Goshen. The eastbound train had not yet reached that station. He telegraphed to Middletown. The train had not arrived there. The westbound train was run on a similar order to Middletown, and from there to Port Jervis, where it entered the yard from the east as the other train came onto it from the west.[17] Although attended with no ceremony and attracting little attention, Minot's experiment was ultimately to lead to a revolution in American railway operation.

The doubt and distrust with which the railroad interest had long regarded the telegraph was not dispelled overnight by this "rash" demonstration. Even on Minot's own line, open revolt broke out among the apprehensive trainmen when an attempt was made to introduce a modified form of electric train dispatching. But the enlightened general superintendent had the courage of his convictions, and orders were issued designating certain division superintendents as train dispatchers with authority to direct the movement of trains under specified conditions. The first train orders were crude and handled with considerable uneasiness; but as time brought con-

17 *Ibid.*, 418-420.

fidence and improved service, the system developed, and reports of its popularity spread to connecting roads which after investigation began similar services.[18] More than a decade was to pass, however, before telegraphic train dispatching attained any general adoption.

The Pennsylvania Railroad in its annual report to the stockholders on January 1, 1852, made its first reference to the telegraph. The report of the superintendent of transportation, H. Haupt, suggests how tentative was the relation of the electric wire to their road at that time. Haupt claimed that despite all precautions which had been taken to equip the engines to meet the rigors of winter, irregularities had occurred from circumstances beyond his control. Such interruptions were to be expected, explained the superintendent, since any delay to a passenger train was necessarily extended throughout the entire extent of the single-track line. This difficulty, he asserted, was "greatly aggravated by the fact that . . . express passenger trains pass over the road in both directions at night, when the telegraph line is not in operation, and when no information can be obtained of the relative positions of trains running in constant expectation of meeting."[19] While the telegraph had been of some value, apparently it had not yet proved itself sufficiently indispensable to warrant the necessary increase in operating costs to maintain day and night service.

When Andrew Carnegie went to work for the road as a clerk and telegraph operator in 1853, he found that no one but the superintendent was permitted to give a train order on any part of the Pennsylvania. It was considered a dangerous expedient to give telegraphic orders, for the whole system of railway management was still in its infancy, and men had not yet been trained for it.[20]

4 · · · · —

GRADUALLY the advocates of a railroad-telegraph alliance began to overcome the opposition of conservative railway managements. In a circular letter dated July 1852, Henry O'Rielly tried to show the many benefits which a railroad might enjoy through the use of telegraphic facilities. "The necessity for increased *safety* in conjunc-

[18] G. C. Kinsman, "The Railway Telegraph," *The Railway Magazine* (April 1897), 349-358.
[19] Annual report of the directors of the Pennsylvania Railroad Company to the stockholders, January 1, 1852.
[20] Andrew Carnegie, *Autobiography*, 67-70.

tion with the increased *speed* in Railroad traveling, as well as the general convenience of transacting business among employees along railroad routes, should turn Public Attention promptly and strongly upon the vast importance of *Telegraphic facilities* in connection with *Railroad operations*," explained O'Rielly. A "well-arranged telegraph for railroad purposes, would, each and every year, render sufficient benefits to counter-balance the whole cost of construction."[21]

By the mid-fifties the enlightenment campaign of O'Rielly, Minot, and others began to bear fruit. Indifference and hostility slowly gave way, and one railroad after another turned to the telegraph for aid. Noting the trend, the *Racine* (Wisconsin) *Advocate* in 1854 declared, "The electro-magnetic telegraph is beginning to be applied . . . to facilitating the operations of railways; securing greater safety by obviating the danger of collision, accidents and so forth."[22]

Notwithstanding the favorable publicity and a growing interest in the telegraph, a reporter for the *London Quarterly Review* in 1854 declared, "The telegraph is rarely seen in America running beside the railway, for what reason we do not know; the consequence, however, is that locomotion in the United States is vastly more dangerous than in England."[23]

Of such common occurrence were railroad accidents in New York, for example, that the legislature felt obliged to set up a commission to investigate the cause and make recommendations for improvement. In connection with the latter objective the New York State engineer, John T. Clark, reported at length on the telegraph system in use on the Erie Railroad in 1855. "The telegraph has been in use on the Erie since 1852," the report began. "It has saved more than it cost every year." An enthusiastic account of the Erie's railway telegraph system then followed. There was an operator, so placed that he had a fair view of the track, at every station on the line, and at the important ones, day and night. He was required to note the exact time of the arrival, departure, or passage of every train, and to transmit this information by telegraph to the proper officer. On each division there was an officer called the train dispatcher, whose duty it was to keep constantly before him a memorandum of the position of every

21 Henry O'Rielly (circular), Railway Telegraph System: for facilitating business and protecting life and property along railroads, July 1852, O'Rielly Docs., First Series, II; cf. O'Rielly to the officers of the Philadelphia, Wilmington & Baltimore Railroad Company, July 1, 1846, O'Rielly MS Coll., III.

22 Quoted in *Shaffner's Telegraph Companion*, I, April 1854.

23 *London Quarterly Review*, XCV (June 1854), 161.

train upon his division, as ascertained by the telegraphic reports from the several stations. The trains were run upon the Erie by printed time-tables and in accordance with carefully drawn regulations. When they became disarranged for any reason the telegraph was used to disentangle and move them forward. When trains upon any part of the Erie were delayed, the fact was immediately communicated to the nearest station, from which point it was telegraphed to every station on the road. Approaching trains were thus warned of the danger and accidents prevented.

When trains had been delayed or their operating schedule deranged, the dispatcher was authorized to move them forward by telegraph according to accepted rules and regulations. Having before him a time schedule, he could ascertain the position of each train at any desired moment with sufficient accuracy to determine the best means of advancing the delayed trains and of regulating the movement of all so as to avoid collision or further entanglement.

If a passenger train was delayed for an hour or more, the freight trains held up by it were moved forward by telegraphic orders. In this way railway service was greatly accelerated and substantial savings were effected in the utilization of rolling stock.[24] New York State engineer Clark's report left little doubt that he regarded the telegraph as absolutely essential in the safe and efficient operation of a railroad.

By 1855 the advantages of a railway telegraph system were becoming too obvious to be ignored by the railroads any longer.[25] In his report to the Erie directors for that year, D. C. McCallum, successor to Charles Minot as superintendent of that road, made an arresting statement. To persuade some of the more prosaic members of his board who regarded the telegraph as an unnecessary expense and a foible of the administration, McCallum declared: "A single track railroad may be rendered more safe and efficient by a proper use of the telegraph than a double track railroad without its aid. . . . It would occupy too much space," he went on, "to allude to all the practical purposes to which the telegraph is applied in working the road; and it may suffice to say that without it, the business could not be conducted with anything like the same degree of economy, safety, regularity, or dispatch."[26]

24 Mott, *Between the Ocean and the Lakes*, 42.
25 Kinsman, "The Railway Telegraph," *The Railway Magazine* (April 1897), 349-358; Wade, Autobiography.
26 Reports of the president and superintendent of the New York & Erie Railroad to the stockholders for the year ending September 30, 1855, 44-50.

McCallum's report spread far beyond the narrow confines of the Erie management. His words were carefully weighed in railroad circles, and leading companies began to see the telegraph in a new light. During the next decade and a half the use of the telegraph became almost universal, and some of the most perplexing problems of railway operation were solved.

By the close of the nineteenth century "every railroad in every country and clime" made manifold use of the telegraph. Its weather reports aided officials in guarding against danger from approaching storms. By giving prompt warning of damage by wind or flood, it prevented disaster in many ways. It moved trains promptly and safely and practically doubled the capacity of every single-track road. It brought the most distant stations and diverse patrons of the company into close relationship with the management, and united the officers and employees of a great railroad system into one compact and well-organized army. It transmitted observatory standard time automatically to every station at the same instant. It gave steady employment to thousands of persons. All this, and much more, was done by the railway telegraph at a cost of less than 3 percent of the total expense of the operation and maintenance of the railway. The railway telegraph had, indeed, come into its own; it had become an absolute necessity for the safe and efficient operation of the railroad.[27]

5 – – –

THE partnership of wire and rail was by no means a one-sided affair. If the telegraph was essential to the efficient operation of the railroad, the reverse was just as true. Telegraph leaders found that lines constructed along railroad rights of way and allied with the railroads by favorable contracts were in such a strong position that rivals could not compete successfully with them. The tremendous advantages to be derived from such an alliance are readily apparent from an examination of several typical contracts.[28] In general, the terms of these early contracts stipulated that:

---

[27] Kinsman, "The Railway Telegraph," *The Railway Magazine*, 353-354; cf. Rhoads, *Telegraphy and Telephony with Railroad Applications*, 311-312.

[28] Contract between the New York & Mississippi Valley Printing Telegraph Company and the Cleveland & Toledo and the Michigan, Southern & Northern Indiana Railroad Companies, February 7, 1854, O'Rielly Docs., Telegraph Pamphlets; Contract between the New York & Mississippi Valley Printing Telegraph Company and the Buffalo & Erie Railroad Company, August 14, 1855, *Ibid.*; Contract between the New York & Mississippi Valley Printing Telegraph Company and the Michigan Central Railroad

1. The telegraph company was to furnish the railroad company with a single wire of proper size and quality, and provide Morse instruments at certain specified stations on the line of their road.

2. The telegraph company was to maintain the main battery for working the wire day and night.

3. The telegraph company was to keep the wire erected for the railroad company in order, except as otherwise provided.

4. All receipts for messages at offices opened on the line of the railroad, by either party, were to belong to the telegraph company.

5. The railroad company was not to send any message free except for its own agents on its own business.

6. At all stations in addition to those named, the railroad company was to supply all machinery and local battery.

7. The railroad company was to instruct its men to watch the line, straighten poles, re-set them when down, mend wires, and report to the telegraph company.

8. The railroad company was to convey and distribute wire and insulators and all other material free, and also furnish a hand-car for stringing wire.

9. The two companies were to reciprocate in the use of wires when those of either were out of order, but the railroad wires were never to be interrupted when sending railroad business.

10. The railroad company was to transport all instruments, material for repairs, all operators, officers and agents of the telegraph company free of charge when on business of the company, and to furnish and distribute the poles when the line had to be renewed, the telegraph company setting and insulating the line.

11. The railroad company was to pay for stringing the railroad wire and insulating it, and for the necessary instruments, at the rate of thirty dollars per mile.

12. The railroad company was not to allow any other telegraph company to build a telegraph line upon its property.

13. Railroad telegraph operators might accept public business at the ordinary tariffs, but should account to the telegraph company for

Company, March 3, 1856, *Ibid.*; Contract between the Western Union Telegraph Company and the Cleveland & Pittsburgh Railroad Company, October —, 1856, *Ibid.* This volume in the O'Rielly collection contains many other early railroad contracts for the years 1857 and 1858. A number of later contracts may be found in the library of the Bureau of Railway Economics, Washington, D.C.

all receipts. No messages, however, were to be accepted or sent so as to interfere with railroad business.[29]

By means of contracts similar in character to the summary form given above, the railroads obtained the use of telegraph lines which were essential to the efficient operation of their roads, while the telegraph companies were assured of protected routes on terms that amounted to a monopoly. Under this arrangement every railroad depot, at a very small cost to the telegraph company, might be used as a telegraph office merely by installing a set of Morse instruments in a convenient corner. The station agent, having learned to operate a Morse key, became the joint employee of the railroad and the telegraph company. He usually had sufficient time to sell tickets, handle baggage, keep up reports, take and send train orders and commercial business, and perform the other multifarious tasks of a station agent. His was an important function in hundreds of small towns throughout the United States. Obviously telegraph lines built along the public highways could not compete with those operating in conjunction with the railroads, and the telegraph companies enjoying railroad contracts were able to force their rivals from the field.[30]

Sibley, Wade, Stager, Caton, and numerous other wide-awake telegraph leaders had early become aware of the tremendous power that a series of favorable railroad contracts could give them. Reporting to the stockholders of the Cleveland & Cincinnati Telegraph Company on January 25, 1854, President Jeptha H. Wade had asserted, "I cannot urge upon you too strong[ly] the importance of rebuilding, in the most permanent manner, the old line, as fast as the resources of the company will permit, and, when suitable arrangements can be made, to get it on to [sic] Railroads."[31] A short time later as an agent of the Western Union Telegraph Company, Wade, along with Anson Stager, entered the field of railroad relationships with striking success. Stager, whose popularity with railroad men gave him ready access to their offices, spent much of his time explain-

[29] Reid, *Telegraph in America*, 480-481; For a specific railroad-telegraph contract, see Chapter XVII.

[30] N. C. Kingsbury, *Who is Getting the Fun Out of it?* An address before the Cleveland Chamber of Commerce, 1913, pamphlet; G. Burford, "The Telegraph Operator," *Rock Island Magazine* (February 1925), 19; Rhoads, *Telegraphy and Telephony with Railroad Applications*, 32-33.

[31] Proceedings of the 5th annual meeting of the stockholders of the Cleveland & Cincinnati Telegraph Company, January 25-26, 1854, O'Rielly Docs., Telegraph Pamphlets.

ing the value of the telegraph in the operation of a railroad. His personality, coupled with a fair comprehension of the problems of railway management, made him admirably suited to act as contact man for the undertaking; while Wade with his discerning eye was equally well adapted to meet with applicants and arrange the terms. So well did the work of the one complement that of the other, that the pair as "canvasser and comptroller" of railroad contracts, performed an invaluable service for Western Union.[32] It was these railroad contracts, entered into during the 1850's and 1860's, which in later years made the position of Western Union almost unassailable.[33]

The negotiating of contracts that would be mutually satisfactory to the managements of the telegraph and the railroad was not easy. Every clause had to be carefully scrutinized to prevent one or the other party from securing some special advantage. In a letter to his business associate, Judge Caton, on January 8, 1860, Hiram Sibley expressed his concern lest under the existing arrangements some of the railroad telegraph lines might become rivals of the regular telegraph companies. By uniting their lines for railroad business they might gradually become so familiar with the telegraph business and so interested in the profits to be derived from the public business, that they might decide to compete with the regular telegraph companies for it. One of the most threatening combinations of this kind, Sibley told Caton, was the Michigan Central and its extension west to St. Joseph. "It has occurred to me," he wrote, "that we ought to make some fair arrangement with you to divert the public business from the Hannibal & St. Joseph line so as to render the enterprise unprofitable to them. As that line is a pioneer in the enterprise, it becomes important to us all that it should not be successful, as it would be a bad example. As you are familiar with the business of that line and quite as likely to appreciate the necessity for some plan to remedy the trouble I apprehend, please think over the suggestion and give us the benefit of your opinion."[34] Some insight into the methods which Sibley proposed to employ to maintain control of the telegraph industry is provided by this frank statement.

[32] Kennedy, "The American Railroad . . . ," *Magazine of Western History*, XI, 185-187.
[33] E. Y. Gallaher, "The Development and Present Composition of the Western Union Telegraph Company," *Telegraph and Telephone Age* (January 1, 1912), 17; D. H. Craig, *Answers to the United States Senate Committee on Education and Labor* (1883), pamphlet; *Remarks of Norvin Green, president, to the board of directors of the Western Union Telegraph Company*, September 13, 1882, pamphlet; Erastus Winan, *A Talk on Telegraphic Topics* [1882], 16.
[34] H. Sibley to J. D. Caton, January 8, 1860, Caton Papers.

In spite of rivalries, difficulties and misunderstandings, the relations between wire and rail were gradually adjusted, and the working alliance between them was extended until the railroad and telegraph systems of the continent had become inextricably bound up with one another. From this fusion there emerged strong and aggressive communication and transportation systems which transformed the life of the nation.

CHAPTER XIV

Rise of the Associated Press

1 · — — ·

MORSE's struggle to introduce his invention had been a long and difficult one, but twice, at critical times for the infant telegraph, circumstances had favored it. The first fortuitous event had been the convening of the Democratic National Convention in Baltimore three days after the formal opening of the government's experimental line; the second was the outbreak of the Mexican War, less than a month prior to the completion of the first commercial wire in the country. The former incident served to prove the practicability of electrical means of communication; the latter virtually forced its adoption by the newspaper press.

On his last day of office, President Tyler had sent a courier to inform Texas that only her consent was necessary to become the twenty-eighth state. Mexico, watching the course of events, informed the United States that the admission of Texas into the Union would be a just cause for war. Attempts to negotiate the outstanding differences with Mexico having failed, on January 13, 1846, President Polk had ordered General Zachary Taylor to take up his position on the Rio Grande del Norte. Four months later, on May 13, 1846, the two nations were at war.[1]

News of hostilities stirred the nation. An aroused populace clamored for details of the sharp battles of Palo Alto and Resaca de la Palma. The press could not satisfy the demand for news from the front. The seat of war was seven days removed from the eastern seaboard by the fastest government mails, thanks to the "blundering incapacity and ridiculous parsimony" of the Post Office Department.[2] Enterprising journalists were challenged to find more rapid means of forwarding their dispatches.

Already engaged in costly, competitive news-gathering exploits, the prospect of even greater distances to cover caused concern. Enormous sums were being spent on pony expresses, special trains, rowboats, and clipper ships. A careful review of the situation convinced editors that some sort of a New York press association was needed. Such a

---

[1] S. E. Morison and H. S. Commager, *The Growth of the American Republic*, I, 483-488.

[2] *New York Herald*, November 27, 1847.

body, allied with the leading presses throughout the North and working in conjunction with the journals of New Orleans and the South, might bring a semblance of order in the hitherto chaotic field of news gathering. Motivated by a mutual desire to overtake the United States mail and outstrip competitors, the *New York Sun* and the *Charleston Courier* joined forces in 1847. Early in that year their respective proprietors, Moses Y. Beach and William S. King, established a pony express over the 150-mile route between Mobile and Montgomery. In this way they hoped to cover the distance in one-third of the time normally taken by the stage coaches.

More ambitious was the "Great Southern Daily Express" running its sixty-odd ponies between New Orleans and New York for the purpose of bringing the news from the South a day or two in advance of the government mails.[3] Most prominent in this grand design were the *Baltimore Sun* (Arunah S. Abell), the *Philadelphia Public Ledger* (William M. Swain), and the *New York Herald* (James Gordon Bennett).

In their efforts to get the news to the public promptly, enterprising journalists from the very outbreak of the war had looked hopefully to the infant telegraph. Horace Greeley introduced *Tribune* readers to a telegraphic column on Tuesday, May 12, 1846, with the arresting caption, "50,000 Volunteers Called For! $10,000,000 to be Raised." Columns headed "Latest Intelligence by Mail" were shortly subordinated to "Latest Intelligence by Magnetic Telegraph" in many of the leading journals. The dispatches were usually brief and as much condensed as possible since the cost was high. At first only a few papers in each city employed the lines to any material extent.[4]

The telegraph, for its part, though willing and even anxious to aid in the rapid transmission of war news could be of little help at the outset. On the day of the formal declaration of war, it could boast of no more than 130 miles of wire; and the battle fronts were some 1,300 miles away. The only telegraph line, besides the experimental line from Baltimore to Washington, was a single wire connecting New York and Philadelphia. Henry O'Rielly was constructing an additional section from Philadelphia to Baltimore but work was seriously hampered for want of funds.[5] The construction of a great southern trunk line to link Washington and New Orleans, although the subject of numerous discussions, had not yet been started. Private

[3] *Ibid.*   [4] Alexander Jones, *Historical Sketch of the Electric Telegraph*, 122.
[5] For a detailed account of the building of this line, see Chapter III.

enterprise, the Government, and the Eastern press had each been looked to for assistance in the building of such a line, but no satisfactory arrangement had been reached.[6] Apart from instructing the chief operator at Washington to make preparations for night work in so far as it might be necessary,[7] there was little that the telegraph managers could do to aid in the rapid transmission of messages from the theater of the war.

James Gordon Bennett, William M. Swain, Horace Greeley, Moses Y. Beach, and other alert publishers were disposed to make what use they could of the fragmentary lines, and asked their immediate extension. A week after the outbreak of war, dispatches were being sent from Washington to Baltimore by telegraph, and thence by special steam and horse express to Wilmington, from which point they were telegraphed to Jersey City.[8]

Three weeks later on June 7, 1846, the *Herald* told with evident satisfaction of "The First Flash of the Lightning Line" from Washington to New York. "The lightning line from Washington to this city is complete," wrote the editor, "and we received the first flash— the first intelligence, at an early hour last evening—eighteen hours in advance of the mail. The completion is of vast importance. It enables us to give in the morning *Herald* the interesting intelligence from the Rio Grande, one whole day in advance of the old dog-trot way of receiving news from the South."[9]

Some progress was being made in the race against time. Telegraph lines in the blueprint stage in the summer of 1846 had become realities by the summer of 1847. New Orleans was now three days nearer New York. Bennett, a most enthusiastic and faithful chronicler of the "wonderwire," surveyed its progress for his *Herald* readers on July 12, 1847. "At the present time there are upwards of seven thousand miles of telegraph in operation, and in the course of construction in the United States and Canada. Lines have recently been constructed extending from Portland . . . to Fredericksburg, and in a week or two . . . [the telegraph] will be in operation as far as Richmond. At the West there is a line in operation to Wheeling, and in a very short time it will extend to Cincinnati. . . . In the month of August there

---

[6] For negotiations preliminary to the building of this line, see Chapter III.

[7] Kendall to C. T. Smith, May 24, 1846, O'Rielly MS Coll., II.

[8] *New York Herald*, May 23, 1846. The Magnetic Telegraph Company's line had been terminated in Jersey City, since no satisfactory means of crossing the Hudson had yet been devised.

[9] *Ibid.*, June 7, 1846.

will be a line completed between Mobile and New Orleans, a distance of one hundred and fifty miles. When that line shall have been completed, we will be within three or four days of the latter city by means of the telegraph and our Southern overland express and will receive news from there four days in advance of the mail. A line between Portland and Halifax is about to be constructed . . . by which the foreign markets can be made known throughout the whole country in a few minutes after the arrival of the English Cunard steamships, and which will bring New York, Boston, and the extreme West and South within nine or ten days of England."[10]

By December 1847, telegraph lines had reached St. Louis; and in the following July, the *New Orleans Picayune* was able to announce: "The telegraph communication between this city and New York, and therefore all the North, is completed by way of Montgomery and Augusta."[11]

With the rapid extension of the wires the press came to depend more and more fully on the telegraph for transmission of its reports. Alexander Jones, pioneer in the field of telegraph reporting, first general agent of the Associated Press, and author of an early book on the electro-magnetic telegraph, wrote that "the utility of the telegraph to the press in forwarding army news was such as, in a measure, to force them into its employment."[12] Frederic Hudson, business manager of the *Herald,* as if in confirmation, subsequently stated, "With the brilliant conflicts on the Rio Grande the Telegraphic Era of the Press really began. What a commencement! What a revolution!"[13]

2 ··—··

BUT eager as telegraph and press were to collaborate with one another, their early relations were not always pleasant. Inexperienced telegraph operators, inadequate facilities, lack of coordination, high costs of early telegraphing, and ruthless competition for telegraphic service among rival papers made the period 1846-1848 one of great confusion and general dissatisfaction on the part of both industries. The press contended it was trying to adapt itself to a telegraph going through an awkward adolescence; the telegraph, for its part, main-

10 *Ibid.,* July 12, 1847.
11 *Niles' National Register,* December 25, 1847; *New Orleans Picayune,* July 19, 1848.
12 Alexander Jones, *Historical Sketch of the Electric Telegraph,* 122.
13 Frederic Hudson, *Journalism in the United States . . . ,* 600.

tained it was having difficulty in serving an industry going through a revolution. Both were correct.

Much of the early confusion resulted from the lack of a system for the collection, transmission, and distribution of news. Was news-gathering and distribution a proper function of the telegraph, the press, or the independent news broker? At different times each sought to perform the duty, and sometimes all attempted it. In the days when the service was trying to popularize itself, news messages had been furnished gratuitously by many telegraph operators. Under this arrangement the operator assumed the role of news reporter.[14] As the demand of editors throughout the nation for telegraphic re-ports grew, operators along the Eastern seaboard, with a Philadelphia or New York morning paper before them, would send the important items to newspapers in the interior where they were received with much satisfaction. By arranging for the transmission of news reports each day during certain hours when commercial business was dull, it was possible to send news reports simultaneously to many stations, all of which were worked together as one grand circuit. Congres-sional reports, for example, could be sent from the office at Washing-ton and received concurrently in Baltimore, Philadelphia, and New York. Intermediate stations merely had to have an operator present to receive the messages. Each journal obtaining the news was charged a moderate weekly fee for the service.[15] President Faxton of the New York, Albany & Buffalo line may have been the instigator of this idea, for as early as July 4, 1845, when his line was only partially completed, he called for a telegraphic conference of the editors located along the route. The editors having assembled in the various tele-graph offices which were in use between Albany and Buffalo, a meet-ing was convened. The desirability of establishing a federation for supplying telegraphic news was discussed telegraphically, and an affirmative decision was reached. The first daily reports to the press of the State of New York were introduced the following January 1.[16]

Operators in important offices, however, could not be expected to collect news for the press in addition to their regular work. This task was shortly assumed by individuals who made telegraph reporting their main concern. Alexander Jones, a journalist, had been among the first to enter the new profession. He had sent his first telegraph

14 B. H. Wilson, "Telegraph Pioneering" in *Palimpsest*, VI, 389.
15 Jones, *Historical Sketch of the Electric Telegraph*, 90-91.
16 Reid, *Telegraph in America*, 307.

news report to the *Washington Union* as early as the autumn of 1846.[17] But the independent telegraph reporter soon found it to his advantage to join forces with other independents, and a year or two after the development of reporting by telegraph, an association of three or four members was organized. This association was soon employing reporters in various important localities to receive and forward news for the press. The newspapers using the service were charged a weekly fee, while the association paid the expenses incurred.[18]

Many journals, although they utilized the association reports for commercial or general news, maintained their own agents to gather news of a more specialized nature. In this field also, combinations were frequently formed to cover some special event. Members of the Philadelphia press, for instance, under the leadership of the *Ledger*, kept a telegraph reporter at Fredericksburg in the spring of 1847, "to collect, compile, and forward the news from the South . . . in accord with the wishes of the publishers of the Philadelphia press, associated for such purposes."[19]

The lot of the men engaged in supplying the papers with news by telegraph was not a happy one. On the uncertain lines of the day their reports came through irregularly and were often so full of errors as to be unintelligible to the irate editors who received them. Not for several months after the opening of the Magnetic Telegraph Company's line could any reliance be placed upon it.[20] The *Herald* had announced its intention of establishing a regular "Telegraphic Report" with the first flash over the Magnetic wires on June 7, 1846. Five days later it reported to its readers that an "accident to the telegraph wires" precluded all possibility of communication. From the twelfth through the fourteenth repairs were presumably in progress, for on the fifteenth the *Herald* announced that contact had been restored. Brief reports appeared for a week followed by another troubled interval. During the Magnetic line's first six months of operation, at least one week in every four was lost as a result of broken wires or faulty insulation.[21]

As the fragmentary lines were extended and gradually came to form a great network over the country, the problem of relaying messages over contiguous lines had to be satisfactorily met. Patrons

[17] Jones, *Historical Sketch of the Electric Telegraph*, 136-137.   [18] *Ibid.*
[19] George H. Hart to J. F. Howe, April 23, 1847, Vail Papers.
[20] Alexander Jones, *Historical Sketch of the Electric Telegraph*, 132.
[21] *New York Herald* files, 1846.

of the telegraph despaired of fixing the responsibility for long distance dispatches on any one of them. Each company was quite willing to lay the blame for errors at the door of its neighbor. Even when the lines of but a single company were involved, messages were frequently lost in transit. The *New Orleans Picayune*, for example, bitterly denounced the service of the Washington & New Orleans Company. Upon numerous occasions, declared the *Picayune*, money was paid in New Orleans for a message to be sent to Washington. The operator willingly took their money, and transmitted the message to Mobile. It might possibly get one step farther toward its destination. "But the despatch is nine times out of ten, lost between the offices, if it is sent on at all, whilst the company pockets the money for the whole service."[22]

Certain other practices increased still further the general confusion. Many pioneer telegraph companies, while giving the press special rates of from one-third to one-half the normal fee on general news reports, charged the ordinary tariff on special messages. Although apparently making some concessions to the press, the relief was not enough, and controversies over telegraphic charges were frequent.[23] To reduce costs and obtain a more economical use of the telegraph for the press, Alexander Jones invented a cipher language by means of which a whole paragraph could be condensed into a single word. Telegraph companies were asked to send such one-word messages as "Caserovingedsable" or "Retackmentativeness." A market report to the *New York Herald* using the shorthand system read: "Buffalo, Nov. 13, P. M. Abbott, None, Annex, Cabman, Accord, Dolphin, Directors, Allay, Apron, Falcon, Fosters, Actuate, Adapt, Mathew."[24] When translated the fourteen words became a full report of sixty words.

The cipher system, while saving greatly in transmission costs, increased the tendency to error on the part of operators for whom the cabilistic messages could have no significance. The *Herald*, profuse in its praise of the system in December, was complaining four months later of communications which were hardly intelligible, occasioned by desire on the part of the telegraph correspondents to condense as much as possible with the view of making telegraph expenses correspondingly small.[25]

[22] *New Orleans Picayune*, August 17, 1848.
[23] Moses Beach & Sons to Thomas M. Clark, December 15, 1847, Smith Papers, II.
[24] *New York Herald*, December 5, 1847.
[25] *Ibid.*, April 23, 1848.

3 · · · — ·

DISTRESSING as were the costs and annoying as was the incompetence
of operators, the most serious obstacle in the path of regular transmission of news for the press was the inadequacy of the lines themselves. Pioneer lines had not the capacity to handle the volume of
press dispatches which poured in at critical times. With only a few
wires at their disposal the operators could not send all the messages
promptly. Most companies, in an attempt to deal impartially with
their patrons, had early accepted the principle of "first come, first
served." But this seemingly fair policy led to all manner of abuses.
Reporters, in their desire to reserve the wire for their particular
dispatches, upon several occasions had had chapters of the Bible
tapped out until they were ready with their news dispatches. Telegraph operators were instructed to begin with Genesis, and on one
occasion the weary operator was well into Leviticus before the press
news was ready for transmission. Sometimes reporters would not
yield the wire until they were certain that no rival could possibly
transmit his report in time for publication the same day. Occasionally, wires were even cut by disappointed reporters who were unable
to get the line. To mitigate such evils and to make the telegraph the
servant of all men, the Magnetic Telegraph Company introduced the
idea of timed transmission. Messages were dispatched in order of
receipt, but no one could hold the wire for more than fifteen minutes.
This plan proved no better. *Herald* reporters rushing to the most
southerly telegraph office during the exciting days of the Mexican
conflict, were apt to find *Sun* reporters close on their heels. Sometimes the *Herald* would be first, and sometimes the *Sun*. Frequently
the messengers of these journals would enter the office together.
Since the exclusive use of the wires could not be given to either, each
was allowed fifteen minutes. Not many lines of news could be transmitted in that brief space of time over poor lines, with miserable
insulation, and inexperienced operators.[26] The result was that no
one was satisfied. Superior enterprise counted for little under a
system which tended to reduce all papers to a common and mediocre
level. Money was spent freely, but little advantage was gained.[27]

Inadequate telegraph facilities coupled with ruinous costs made
union of effort among the newspapers inevitable. Leaders of the
press, painfully aware of the impossible situation, met in the office

[26] Frederic Hudson, *Journalism in the United States*, 610.   [27] *Ibid.*, 611.

of the *Sun* in 1848 to discuss remedial measures.[28] At the conference presided over by Gerard Hallock, representatives of the *Tribune, Herald, Courier & Enquirer, Sun, Express,* and *Journal of Commerce* agreed to unite "for the purpose of collecting and receiving telegraphic and other intelligence" at common cost.[29] To translate their aim into action, two organizations were formed, the Harbor News Association for obtaining the foreign news, and the New York Associated Press for the collection and dissemination of domestic news. For the foreign news one fleet of news boats was to replace the half dozen which normally patrolled New York harbor. Joint effort was to supplant individual initiative in the forwarding of dispatches from Boston and Halifax. The domestic news service was to be under the direction of a general agent in New York City who would be responsible for the management of the office and the direction of the staff.[30]

It had been no part of the original plan of the New York Associated Press to do more than obtain news for its six members.[31] No paper outside the environs of New York City was included in the first agreement. Newspapers in other parts of the country, however, desired to avail themselves of the news services of the new press association. As a result, there emerged shortly a number of subsidiary regional organizations such as the New England Association, the New York State Association, the Western Association, the Southern Association, and others. The organizations taken collectively came to be known finally as the Associated Press.

All the aspiring news vendors did not immediately yield their interests and leave the New York Associated Press in uncontested domination of the news-gathering field. Independent news brokers, disappointed journalists, and greedy telegraph managers, all contested its claims. Those whose livelihood was jeopardized, whose prestige was involved, or who saw an opportunity for profit, were not disposed to capitulate weakly. The New York Associated Press, organized with no more ambitious pretension than to provide its

[28] Victor Rosewater, *History of Cooperative News-Gathering in the United States,* 66. There seems to be considerable controversy concerning the date of the organization of the Associated Press. Rosewater fixes the date as the spring of 1848. Sources that tend to confirm his research are: O'Rielly to H. R. Selden, October 8, 1848, O'Rielly MS Coll. (October 1848); O'Rielly to J. Hanna [November 1848], O'Rielly MS Coll. (November 1848); *Niles' National Register,* September 25, 1847.

[29] Rosewater, *op. cit.,* 62. [30] *Ibid.,* 72.

[31] The *New York Times* upon its establishment in 1851 was taken into the Associated Press as a seventh member.

six founders with telegraphic intelligence, found itself engaged almost immediately in a bitter struggle for news supremacy.

4 · · · · —

THE first adversary of the Associated Press and by far the most engaging was Daniel H. Craig, a man whose calm exterior belied the energy and indomitable will that lay within. Craig was born of humble parents in Rumney, New Hampshire, about 1813.[32] While still a boy of twelve or thirteen he was apprenticed to the office of the *Plymouth* (New Hampshire) *Gazette*. But that journal fell on evil days and the young apprentice was sent to Lancaster, Massachusetts, to complete his indenture in the office of the *Lancaster Gazette*. When barely of age Craig set out for Boston to engage in his chosen profession. Several failures did not break his spirit; each served but to sharpen his determination to succeed and to make him less fastidious about the means employed. Painful experience convinced him that the average man of limited capital might better divert his energies into channels less competitive than journalism. Accordingly, he began training carrier pigeons for the conveyance of commercial and other news. Several years before the introduction of the telegraph he had established a lucrative carrier-pigeon news reporting business between Boston and New York.[33] His reputation for anticipating the regular steamers by several hours attracted speculators and commercial interests. Craig sold his news to anyone who would buy, whether it was Jacob Little or James Gordon Bennett.

The New York Associated Press, having completed its organization in the spring of 1848, took steps to perfect its arrangements for the transmission of foreign news. The steamer *Buena Vista* was chartered to express dispatches from Halifax to Boston, at which point they were to be put on the wire for New York. An agreement was also entered into with F. O. J. Smith on May 15, 1848,[34] by which the Associated Press dispatch was to be given priority on his Boston-New

32 This date is only approximate. In *Answer of Daniel H. Craig to the Interrogatories of the United States Senate Committee on Education and Labor* (1883), he said he was apprenticed to the *Gazette* in 1825. Since the average age for apprenticing was from 12 to 14, it may be assumed that Craig was born sometime between 1811-1813.

33 *Ibid.*

34 Smith to Raymond, May 15, 1848, copy appended to Smith, *An Exposition of the Differences Existing Between the Different Presses and Different Lines of Telegraph, Respecting the Transmission of Foreign News* (1850), 29, pamphlet.

York telegraph line from the moment of its receipt in the telegraph office until its completion.

Upon the arrival of the *Buena Vista* in Boston Harbor, Craig's dark eyes flashed. No one had been able to distance him in getting his reports to New York. He determined that no one should now. Craig need have had no fear of the *Buena Vista*, however; she was ill-starred from the first. On her maiden voyage from Halifax the ship's boiler sprang a leak, and as it could not be stopped nor any head of steam maintained, the vessel was compelled to rely on her sails for the rest of the voyage.[35] So tardy was her arrival that the *Hibernia*, the transatlantic ship whose news she carried, was docking in New York just as the newsboat nosed into Boston.

On a subsequent trip D. H. Craig was among the passengers who boarded the *Buena Vista* at Halifax for Boston. With a packet of papers in one hand and a basket of birds in the other, he retired to his stateroom. As the Massachusetts shore came into sight, Craig's pigeons, heavily freighted with news were released from the port-hole. So well had his strategy worked that even before the press boat landed, the news she bore was being cried in the streets by opposition journals.[36] The retainers of the newsboat soon wearied of its fruitless expense, and the *Buena Vista* was retired.

Craig had won the first skirmish in the fight for news supremacy and, for a moment, was left in undisputed possession of the field. But Craig's domination was not to go unchallenged for long. The relative calm during the fall of 1848 was but the respite in which plans were being laid and forces mobilized for another attack. As the telegraph wire pushed its way steadily toward Halifax, the focal point of news interest constantly changed. By February 1849, the telegraph had reached St. John, New Brunswick, and for the next nine months this northern port was the contact point from which the news brought in from Europe was telegraphed to the commercial centers of Canada and the United States. Craig knew his carrier pigeons could not compete with electricity, nor could he always expect to outsmart the Associated Press as he had in the last encounter. Nevertheless, he laid his plans for securing the latest European news as it was brought weekly to Halifax by the Cunarders. He then proposed to rush it to St. John by means of a pony express between Halifax and Digby, Nova Scotia, a distance of about a

[35] *Philadelphia Public Ledger*, May 30, 1848.
[36] Craig, *Answer to Senate Committee*, 2.

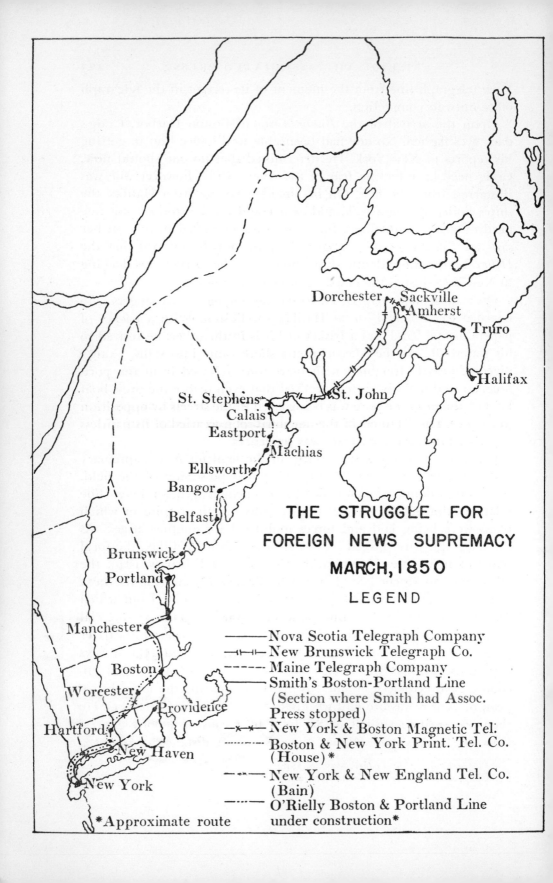

Dorchester Sackville
Amherst
Truro
Halifax

St. Stephens St. John
Calais
Eastport
Machias
Ellsworth
Bangor
Belfast

Brunswick
Portland

Manchester

Boston
Worcester
Providence

Hartford
New Haven

New York

*Approximate route

THE STRUGGLE FOR FOREIGN NEWS SUPREMACY MARCH, 1850

LEGEND

——————— Nova Scotia Telegraph Company
—┼┼┼┼— New Brunswick Telegraph Co.
— — — — Maine Telegraph Company
——————— Smith's Boston-Portland Line
(Section where Smith had Assoc.
Press stopped)
—×—×— New York & Boston Magnetic Tel.
·············· Boston & New York Print. Tel. Co.
(House)*
—·—·—·— New York & New England Tel. Co.
(Bain)
—··—··—·· O'Rielly Boston & Portland Line
under construction*

hundred miles; and thence thirty or forty miles across the Bay of Fundy by steamboat express.[37]

The opposition was no less busy. The Associated Press concluded arrangements with the various lines of telegraph as the wire pushed northward into Canada. L. R. Darrow, superintendent of the New Brunswick Telegraph Company, acting on behalf of the telegraph interests, and Frederic Hudson and H. J. Raymond acting for the Associated Press, entered into an important agreement on February 9, 1849.[38] By its terms the Association was given priority on the wire from the moment its dispatch was received, and in return, it guaranteed the telegraph companies a message of not less than 3,000 words upon the arrival of each steamer at Halifax. F. O. J. Smith, however, would not permit the inclusion of his lines between Portland and Boston in the agreement unless it was amended "to allow the Boston papers to come in by paying their share of expenses."[39] This stipulation, having been accepted by the Associated Press, a compact with Smith was entered into on February 15, 1849.

Smith's defense of the Boston press interests had not been prompted solely by love of fair play and justice. Since the time of his first arrangement with the New York journals, Smith had become aware of the tremendous value of the telegraph to the press. The guaranties made by the Associated Press to anyone who would undertake to push a line on toward Halifax[40] served to confirm his belief that ultimately the great volume of European news would be transmitted by telegraph from Halifax to New York, and that the individual who controlled its transmission and distribution would have a monopoly at once powerful and profitable. Believing such a goal within his reach, Smith quietly laid his plans. In the autumn of 1849 an independent foreign news agency under the management of one John T. Smith of Boston made its appearance. It soon became clear that the newcomer was merely a puppet of F. O. J. Smith.

Meanwhile, the journals of Boston, actuated by motives similar to those of the New York press, had been persuaded to unite in their newsgathering efforts, and arrangements were shortly made with John T. Smith's news agency to forward foreign dispatches to them

[37] *Ibid.*, 3.

[38] Agreement entered into by Hudson and Raymond with Darrow, February 9, 1849, copy appended to Smith, *An Exposition of Differences*, 30-31.

[39] Smith to Raymond and Hudson, February 15, 1849, copy appended to Smith, *An Exposition of Differences*, 32-33.

[40] Jones, *Historical Sketch of the Electric Telegraph*, 140.

from St. John, New Brunswick. Naturally enough, F. O. J. Smith determined that John T. Smith should succeed. Through his control of two of the four lines composing the circuit to St. John, and membership on the board of a third, F. O. J. Smith saw no reason why the Smith news agency should not easily dominate the foreign news field. When he had been approached by the New York Associated Press early in 1849, therefore, and asked to enter into an agreement giving that organization's news reports priority over his lines, he had conditioned his acceptance upon the inclusion of the Boston press in the new arrangement. At the same time, he had urged the Associated Press to appoint John T. Smith as its news agent at St. John. Both of his requests having been acceded to, F. O. J. Smith looked forward confidently to a speedy conquest of the foreign news field.

John T. Smith, joint agent of the New York and Boston presses, was dispatched to Halifax to arrange for rushing news reports from that port to the telegraph office in St. John.[41]

Against such odds it might appear that the independent news reporter, Daniel H. Craig, had little chance. Moreover, on his first trip through St. John on the way to Halifax to perfect his arrangements, Craig had been told by the superintendent of the New Brunswick Telegraph Company that he had better save his money, for under no circumstances would the superintendent permit him to dispatch his news from the telegraph office at St. John until the agent of the Associated Press had forwarded his summary. Whereupon Craig informed the superintendent that he expected to beat all competitors in putting his news on file, and that if he did so and was not given the first use of the wire, he would prevent the superintendent from sending the news to anyone and then prosecute him for damages.[42] So fraught with meaning were Craig's words that upon his arrival from Halifax with the first news summaries, hours ahead of his competitor, the superintendent gave him a cordial reception and put no obstacles in his way. Nor was Craig's early performance a matter of luck. In the months that followed he repeatedly demonstrated his ability to put his news through to its destination ahead of his opponent. The unhappy patrons of John T. Smith were frequently obliged to purchase their news reports from Daniel H. Craig and to pay handsomely for them.

[41] Reid, *Telegraph in America*, 364.
[42] Craig, *Answer to Senate Committee*, 3.

The New York Associated Press at length came to a realization that Craig was the man who could give them news supremacy. Henry J. Raymond of the *Courier & Enquirer* and Frederic Hudson of the *Herald,* acting on behalf of the Associated Press, asked Craig to become European news agent for the Association, a proposition to which he readily agreed.[43] In this way the Association wisely absorbed its most competent rival. He could be held in no other way.[44]

5 — — —

F. O. J. SMITH's grand design had, for the moment, miscarried, but its author was not yet ready to admit defeat. He carefully took the measure of the man who had come between him and his objective and laid a threefold plan for driving Craig from the field. First, he organized a campaign to impugn the character of Craig. Opportunely enough, the leakage of news to New York and the big commercial centers in advance of the press report had occurred with sufficient frequency to make it a subject of controversy. No sooner would a steamer be reported at Halifax, than the wire would be mysteriously broken or cut, and the Associated Press and the public would be kept in ignorance of the latest European news for hours. Brisk activity in the market suggested that the chief outlines of commercial news might have been carried to the city by carrier pigeon or telegraphed in cipher before the line failed.[45] Smith was quick to capitalize on so timely a situation. Had not Craig engaged in carrier pigeon activity previously? And had not his birds served speculative interests in the past? The truth was self-evident. Second, he set to work to drive a wedge between the Boston and New York press allies. If it could be made to appear that he was the champion of the Boston press against the pretensions of the great New York papers, he might further his own ends under a smoke screen of public approval. Third, although controlling the Boston and Portland lines, he determined to bring the Maine Telegraph Company into his orbit. With three of the five links of the New York-Halifax system under his domination, he believed that he could shape telegraph policy to his liking.

[43] *Ibid.*
[44] Reid, *Telegraph in America* (1886), 794-795.
[45] *New York Journal of Commerce* (n.d.), quoted in the *Boston Journal*, September 28, 1849.

6 ······

ON the morning of November 16, 1849, excitement ran high along the Halifax waterfront. Two days previously the town had been connected telegraphically with New York and now the populace crowded about the wharves as the proud steamship *America* eased gracefully into the harbor.[46] The arrival of a Cunarder was always an event of interest in the town, but more importance than usual was attached to this arrival. The rival news agents, D. H. Craig and John T. Smith, each purporting to be the accredited agent of the New York Associated Press had entered the town and the race from ship to telegraph office promised to be highly diverting. Each, in turn, had sought recognition from the Nova Scotian commissioner of the telegraph, Joseph Howe, but that gentleman had informed them that the rule of "first come, first served" would be the policy of the new government-owned line.

Now the rivals were anxiously waiting, each with the fastest horses that could be hired, for the desperate race from the dock to the telegraph office. As the great ship neared her dock, the purser, obviously well paid for his effort, mounted the paddle-box and tossed a parcel of journals directly into the eager arms of Smith. Before Craig had even obtained his reports, Smith was tapping out his news over the single wire leading to New York.

Craig was thoroughly aroused; his reputation and prestige, as well as that of the New York Associated Press of which he was the official representative, were threatened. Speedily he devised a plan. By outbound steamer careful instructions were sent to the Liverpool agent of the Associated Press. On the next crossing the Liverpool agent was to send news summaries and duplicate copies of the latest European journals by special messenger. One parcel was to be tossed to Craig's newsboat five miles below Halifax, and the other thrown to a second newsboat stationed opposite the telegraph office a mile from the wharf. Communication with Europe was not frequent in 1849, however, and it would be a month, or possibly two, before Craig could test his new strategy; meanwhile, Smith went confidently about his task.

A week before the next ship was due, Craig manned his two newsboats and arranged for a fast pony express from a point five miles below the city. He took pains to see that Smith should learn indirectly

---

[46] Reid, *Telegraph in America*, 364.

that Craig was secretly plotting to have news bundles thrown over to special boats as the steamer neared the city.[47]

Another part of Craig's plan was not revealed to Smith. The morning the ship was due, Craig had a fleet runner stationed at the water's edge with a parcel of old papers under his arm. Craig had been careful in making up this dummy parcel the night before to be sure that the dates were concealed, but that a portion of the titles were revealed. As the steamer passed up the harbor, Craig's confederate tossed the bundle of old journals into the water, retrieved them and rushed as fast as his legs would carry him to the telegraph office. With a breathless, "Here is Craig's parcel of European news," he deposited the dripping bundle on the counter and vanished.

Fifteen minutes later Smith panted into the office only to be greeted with a gesture from the operator toward the soggy bundle on the table. "Mr. Craig has beaten you, sir." Thirty minutes later the frustrated agent was steaming out of the harbor on the ship bound for Boston. Meanwhile, Craig, having received his true European news bundle, prepared his report in leisurely fashion and then proceeded to the telegraph office.[48]

7 — — · ·

THERE had long existed a feeling of rivalry between the Boston and New York presses. Necessity had brought about an uneasy alliance between them, but they continued to regard one another with suspicion. The Boston papers feared they might be made subservient to the interests of the big metropolitan papers; and the latter had no intention of giving the advantage to their junior partners. These contentions, "fanned, if not engendered by the jealousies of some of the Morse lines, and especially those under the control of F. O. J. Smith,"[49] had led to a division of the Boston press into two rival camps by November 1849. Of the ten papers comprising the Boston press association, the seven morning journals continued their arrangements with the New York Associated Press; while the three evening journals withdrew and once more entered into an agreement with F. O. J. Smith.

Smith made this event the occasion for addressing the New York Associated Press on the subject of their foreign news agent. He in-

47 *Ibid.*, 363.   48 *Ibid.*, 366.
49 Jones, *Historical Sketch of the Electric Telegraph*, 140.

formed them that Craig would "use the facilities of the Associated Press to prey upon the mercantile community, and that the wires would be cut in the rear of each American market, to which a pigeon would be dispatched."[50] In the interest of the people Smith demanded that another agent be employed. He advised them further that the agreement of the previous February giving Associated Press dispatches priority on his lines was no longer valid since a portion of the Boston press was not represented in the arrangement.

The New York Associated Press, accordingly, dispatched a letter to the superintendents of the various telegraph lines along the New York-Halifax route on the subject of a new agreement.[51] Although the Association refused to take any action against their agent, Craig, until the charges against him had been substantiated, they started an investigation into his activities.

Deeply aroused by the tactics of the enemy, Craig wrote a reckless letter to his rival, John T. Smith, on December 14, 1849:

> Now, sir, you and your friends may say or do or attempt to do whatever you or they please; but there is one *fixed fact* that will always remain, and that is that you will find me *here*—and neither F. O. J. Smith, any portion of the public press, yourself or friends, nor the devil himself, shall ever drive me from any position that I may see fit to assume.
>
> I observe you are much disposed to make capital of the fact that I was formerly engaged in expressing news from Boston for speculative purposes and also that I have now placed my carriers over the telegraph office here.
>
> I intend to make my birds available for procuring foreign news from every steamer that passes within 100 miles of the coast of Nova Scotia. But this is a personal and private enterprise and in the results of which the press and the public will . . . fairly participate, if they choose to pay me a *quid pro quo*; if not, I shall assume it as right to sell my news, as I would a string of onions, i.e., to the highest bidder.[52]

The impetuous note closed with a warning that no communications would be allowed to pass over the line to Boston unless Craig's dispatches—if they were filed first at the telegraph office—were given priority.

50 *New York Tribune*, January 25, 1850.

51 H. J. Raymond, Frederic Hudson and James G. Bennett to the Superintendents of the Telegraph Lines between Halifax and New York, December 29, 1849, appended to Smith, *An Exposition of Differences*, 24-25.

52 D. H. Craig to John T. Smith, December 14, 1849, in Craig, *Review of an Exposition of the Differences Existing between the Different Presses and Different Lines of Telegraph* (1850), 15, pamphlet.

F. O. J. Smith was delighted. Craig had allowed his anger to trap him this time. Had he not admitted that he would sell his news as a "string of onions—to the highest bidder?" This statement would serve Smith as a pretext for refusing the use of his line to the perfidious pigeon trainer, and for bringing the New York Associated Press into a more tractable frame of mind. He need seek no further for a moral issue under which to cloak his own design. Smith, as guardian of the public interest, could now promote his own plan with the approval and sympathy of the community. Reasoning thus, on the last day of December 1849, Smith informed the Associated Press that he now had all the evidence he could ask of "Craig's reckless system of business over the telegraph." Until he totally abandoned the use of carrier pigeons, Smith told the Association, he would refuse to transmit any dispatches from Craig over either the Portland or Boston & New York line.[53]

Translating his threat into action, Smith telegraphed the executive committee of the New York Associated Press upon the arrival of the next ship off Halifax, reminding them that not one word of the news she carried should pass over his lines if sent by Craig.

8 — · · · ·

THE Associated Press did not intend to yield to such coercion. Their investigation of Craig having brought forth insufficient evidence upon which to indict him, they firmly refused to dismiss their agent.[54] Moreover, they took immediate steps to overcome the obstacle put in the way of their news transmission. They could telegraph their dispatches to Portland, as usual; and the House and Bain lines could be utilized between Boston and New York. But on the link from Boston to Portland, Smith was in complete control. Their only re-

[53] Smith to Hudson and Raymond, December 31, 1849, appended to Smith, *An Exposition of Differences*, 35-36.

[54] In December 1849, James Anderson had been caught in the act of cutting the telegraph wire at St. John, New Brunswick, to prevent the foreign news from being received by the press until his employers had first accomplished private purposes (*New York Herald*, December 31, 1849). A charge was made against Craig of his having been engaged with Anderson in cutting the wire. L. R. Darrow, Superintendent of the New Brunswick Telegraph Company, however, informed the Associated Press, in reply to a request from them, that "after careful investigation they had found that Craig had employed Anderson and a Mr. Till, the one to print, the other to carry his daily dispatches to patrons" in St. John. Further than this, Darrow believed Craig had no relations with Anderson and the evidence led him to believe that the press agent was innocent. (Darrow to Hudson and Raymond, January 4, 1850, in Craig, *Review of an Exposition*.)

course was to have a fast locomotive express to cover the 110-mile gap.[55] Such an arrangement, however, would be of little help against an opposition with uninterrupted telegraphic communication between Halifax and New York. Under the circumstances the companies controlling the lines northeast of Portland were appealed to for aid in bringing Smith to terms.

The Maine, New Brunswick, and Nova Scotia Telegraph Companies gave their support to the Associated Press in the controversy. Aside from the fact that they believed Smith's position to be wrong, their existence depended upon the well-being of the Associated Press. If that organization had not guaranteed them a certain volume of business each year, two of the three lines would not have been built; and should that support be withdrawn, the lines would rapidly become unprofitable.[56] The northeastern lines, therefore, granted the Associated Press the priority which it sought, stipulating only that "the news should be publicly placarded on bulletin boards in New York City immediately upon its arrival that the whole community might derive the benefit of it."[57]

Under this new arrangement the luckless John T. Smith, who had so frequently pinned his hopes on his employer's bold assurances, found himself in a worse dilemma than ever. There was now no chance of beating his rival. The field was no longer open for competition; Smith's dispatches were accepted at Halifax, but he was told that they would not be sent until the Associated Press dispatch had gone through. Sometimes Smith's reports were sent on to Portland with instructions to the operator there not to forward them to Boston until after the 3,000 words for the Associated Press had gone through to New York. It was too much to be borne. Whether upon his own volition or at the suggestion of his employer, John T. Smith shortly retired from the field and his agency was taken over by E. S. Dyer.

F. O. J. Smith, distressed at this latest turn of affairs, addressed a bombastic letter to the commissioners of the Nova Scotia Telegraph Company alleging that they were "subverting the salutary laws of telegraphing," and by their policy "practically excluding other public press associations from the advantageous use of the line."[58]

[55] Jones, *Historical Sketch of the Electric Telegraph*, 140.
[56] Proceedings of the Nova Scotia House of Assembly in the *New York Herald*, March 1, 1850; Smith, *An Exposition of Differences*, 20-21.
[57] *New York Herald*, March 1, 1850.
[58] Smith, *An Exposition of Differences*, 43-45.

9 _ · · _

THE grand design, so feasible in theory, was not working out in practice. F. O. J. Smith had failed to drive Craig from the field, and the three Boston evening papers which had severed connections with the Associated Press had become so feeble as to be practically ineffectual by 1850. Smith's efforts to obtain control of the Maine Telegraph line had been no more successful. Kendall had emphatically declined selling his stock in that line or "taking any other step which might strengthen . . . [Smith] in so mischievous a controversy."[59]

Even the public support on which he had counted was conspicuously absent. Merchants were annoyed by the interruption to the regular dispatch of commercial news from abroad. On January 25, 1850, the *Tribune* advised its readers to be on their guard against speculators. "We will endeavor to obtain the news," the paper assured them, "but between us and the news there are 350 miles of telegraph wire over which the press are not permitted to send a message, unless we consent to employ the agents selected for us by the manager of . . . [the Boston-Portland] line."[60] The *Herald* had explained the situation to its readers the previous day. "The N.Y. press employs their own agent, and Mr. Fog Smith wishes to control the agent of the press." Instead of facing issues squarely, however, "he flies off and makes a long story about pigeons and pigeoning, which he attributes to the agent of the press, all his inferences in the matter being humbug and deception."[61] The *Boston Daily Mail* disabused Smith of the idea that he was fooling anyone. "Your objection to Mr. Craig," that editor asserted, "is not that he has used carrier pigeons. That is merely a pretext. He has upset some of your schemes of monopoly."[62] And thus the controversy raged. Smith had raised a storm with the newspapers which would not be easily allayed.[63]

F. O. J. Smith was not big enough to stand in the path of public interest for long. By the spring of 1850, Henry O'Rielly with the whole-hearted support of the press was to be found building a Bain line between Boston and Portland. Upon the completion of the O'Rielly line, declared the *Herald*, "the project of a general monopoly

59 Amos Kendall to Smith, April 2, 1850, Smith Papers, II; cf. Kendall to H. O. Alden, May 2, 1850, Vail Papers.
60 *New York Tribune*, January 25, 1850.
61 *New York Herald*, January 24, 1850.
62 *Boston Daily Mail*, January 26, 1850.
63 Vail to Kendall, January 25, 1850, Vail Papers.

in the brains of Fog Smith will be as completely scattered to the winds as any mist that ever hung over the seaboard."[64]

Despite the inevitable failure of his scheme, the importuning of his friends, and the general disapproval of the public, Smith was obdurate. To his friend in Washington, B. B. French, the former Congressman from Maine wrote that he would neither retreat nor modify his orders. Craig had to be crushed at all costs.[65] And although the futility of his act must have been apparent, Smith now took the final step in his policy of non-intercourse. On March 22, 1850, he announced that not only would all Craig dispatches from Halifax be refused transmission on his lines, but that thereafter no dispatches from New York would be sent beyond Portland.

James Gordon Bennett could not restrain himself. In a satirical editorial on the following day he commented on this latest example of telegraphic absolutism:

Fog Smith is getting into a thicker fog than ever. . . . With the most consummately impudent pretensions . . . [he proceeds] to issue laws and regulations wholly subversive of the rights of the commercial public. His latest edict, to which the manifestoes of eastern potentates are trifles, shows that 'down-Eastern' authority is no joke. Non-intercourse has been announced as the policy to be carried out with the telegraph lines between Portland and Halifax, and in this highly ingenious and diplomatic style. No despatches from New York will be sent beyond Portland by lightning —but, coming into the bureau of the distinguished telegraphic minister will be deposited in the mails for Halifax![66]

The patentees had been strangely quiet all through the bitter press controversy. Kendall, through previous experience, was well aware of the impossibility of reasoning with Smith, and the two men had long since gone their separate ways. But now some action was necessary. The quarter interest held by Smith threatened the whole Morse patent interest. The commercial community was coming to look upon House and Bain as its deliverers from an odious monopoly. Kendall could keep silent no longer.

On April 1, 1850, Kendall wrote Smith reminding him that Morse and Vail owned three-sixteenths of the Portland line. Now it looked as if that property were in imminent danger of being lost. Had they believed Smith to be right in his controversy, explained Kendall, they would have made no complaint; but believing him wrong, both

64 *New York Herald*, March 23, 1850.
65 Smith to B. B. French, May 1, 1850, Smith Papers, xx.
66 *New York Herald*, March 23, 1850.

in principle and in policy, they wished to be relieved from all responsibility for his acts.[67] Morse also wrote Smith that he believed the New Englander's position was untenable and he suggested that he withdraw before it was too late.[68]

The words of Smith's co-patentees fell on deaf ears. He refused to turn back now, even though his course was leading to his undoing. On the morning of June 22, 1850, Smith was greeted by the unpleasant news that the New York Associated Press had established telegraphic communication between Halifax and New York.[69] O'Riclly had bridged the gap between Boston and Portland with his Bain line and Smith's scheme was crushed.

The Associated Press had emerged triumphant in its bitter struggle for news supremacy—a position it was to maintain for nearly a decade before another press association should arise to contest its claim.

[67] Amos Kendall to Smith, April 1, 1850, Smith Papers, XIII.
[68] Morse to Smith, April 8, 1850, Morse Papers, XXVIII.
[69] *New York Herald*, June 22, 1850.

CHAPTER XV

End of an Era

1 ·—·

THE telegraph, virtually unknown in 1832, had been so inextricably woven into the warp and woof of the national fabric two decades later that the Superintendent of the Census in his report for 1852 saw fit to devote twelve pages to the new industry. Here in the United States, the Superintendent pointed out with pride, "the telegraph system is carried to a greater extent than in any other part of the world, and numerous lines now in full operation form a net-work over the length and breadth of the land. They are not confined to the populous regions of the Atlantic coast, but extend far into the interior, climb the sides of the highest mountains, and cross the almost boundless prairies; and in a few years," he confidently predicted, "a continuous communication will be established between the capital of the nation and the shores of the Pacific, as it now exists between the Atlantic, the Great Lakes, and the Gulf of Mexico."[1] With 23,283 miles of wire in operation and 10,000 more under construction, the telegraph was fast becoming the nervous system of the nation.[2] Between 450 and 500 towns and villages had already been brought into communication with one another by this growing telegraph net, and additions were being made almost daily.[3]

While there had been no fewer than sixty-three claimants for different varieties of telegraph between 1820 and 1850, the Morse system—due not so much to its pioneering in the field, as to its ease and simplicity of operation, nominal cost, and ready adaptation to primitive conditions—had rapidly eclipsed other less practical contenders. Of the total miles of wire in operation in 1852, more than 18,000 used the Morse machines, while House and Bain, the only other claimants worthy of mention, totaled but 2,400 and 2,012 miles respectively.[4]

To the men who had labored to get nominal sums for the pioneer

---

1 "Telegraphs," *Report of the Superintendent of the Census*, December 1, 1852, 106-107. This reference will be cited subsequently as *Report of Superintendent of Census* (1852).
2 *Ibid.*, 112-113.
3 Jones, *Historical Sketch of the Electric Telegraph*, 87-90.
4 *Report of Superintendent of Census* (1852), 110-113.

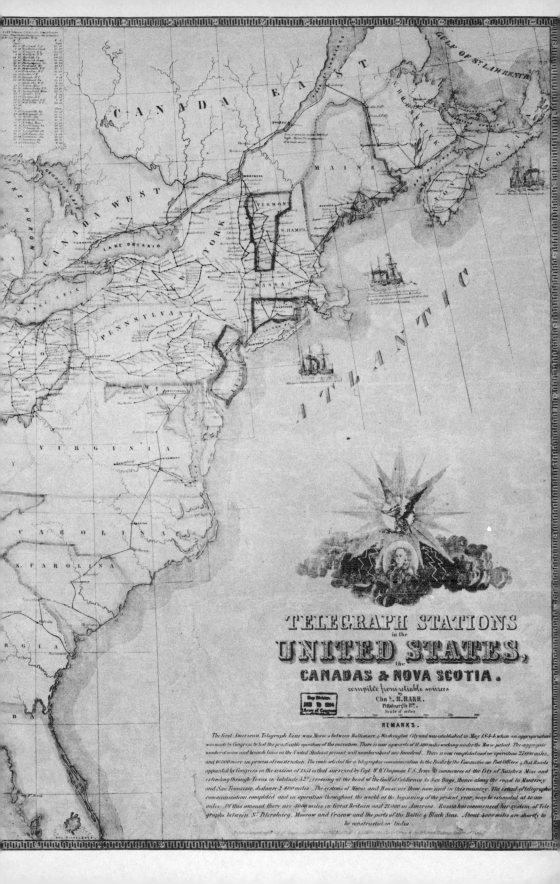

TELEGRAPH STATIONS
in the
UNITED STATES,
the
CANADAS & NOVA SCOTIA.

compiled from reliable sources
by
Chas. B. BARR.
Pittsburgh Pa.
Scale of miles

REMARKS.

The first American Telegraph Line was Morse's between Baltimore & Washington City and was established in May 1844 when an appropriation was made by Congress to test the practicable operation of the invention. There is now upwards of 17,000 miles working under the Morse patent. The aggregate number of main and branch lines in the United States at present will number about one hundred. There is now completed and in operation 27,000 miles, and 10,000 more in process of construction. The route selected for a telegraphic communication to the Pacific by the Committee on Post Offices & Post Roads appointed by Congress in the session of 1851 is that surveyed by Capt. W. H. Chapman U.S. Army. It commences at the City of Natchez Miss and extending through Texas in latitude 32°, crossing at the head of the Gulf of California to San Diego, thence along the coast to Monterey and San Francisco, distance 2,400 miles. The systems of Morse and House are those now used in this country. The extent of telegraphic communication completed and in operation throughout the world at the beginning of the present year, may be estimated at 40,000 miles. Of this amount there are 4000 miles in Great Britain and 22,000 in America. Russia has commenced her system of Telegraphs between St. Petersburg, Moscow and Cracow and the ports of the Baltic & Black Seas. About 4000 miles are shortly to be constructed in India.

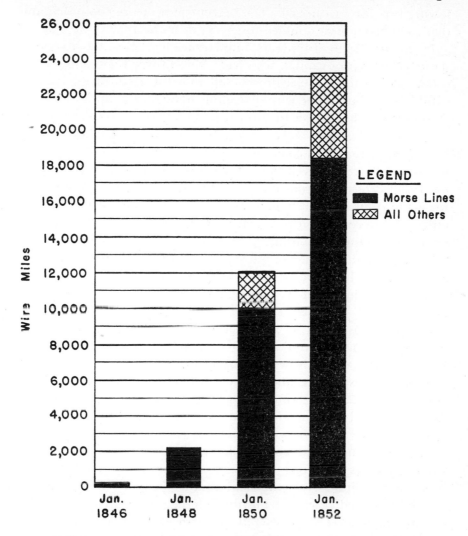

**WIRE MILES OF TELEGRAPH IN OPERATION
IN THE UNITED STATES, 1846–1852**

Source: *Report of the Superintendent of the Census* (1852), 110-113.

commercial lines in 1846, the rapid development of the telegraph industry must have seemed phenomenal. On January 1, 1846, the total wire mileage in the United States had amounted to little more than the 40 miles which stretched between Baltimore and Washington. Two years later it had risen to more than 2,000 miles; the following two years witnessed a 600 percent jump to 12,000 miles; and that total had almost doubled to 23,283 miles by 1852.[5]

In the brief span of six years, indifference had given way to enthusiasm. The men of capital, who had "looked over their immaculate collars at the ticking machinery, and into the faces of the hungry exhibitors and up at the wire struggling among the chimney-pots and then down at the meager furniture and said 'No,' "[6] to the entreaties of Cornell and O. S. Wood for a line from New York to Philadelphia in the fall of 1845, had come to recognize the possibilities of the new invention. By 1852 eleven lines of telegraph were to be found radiating in all directions from the great commercial city of New York.[7] Even the comparatively remote State of Ohio could boast of 3,210 miles of wire controlled by fourteen companies which were eager to serve the needs of the public.[8]

The increasing volume of business carried by the lines was encouraging also. "There are bankers, brokers, etc., in Wall Street that receive and send, on an average, six to ten messages per day, throughout the year," declared Henry O'Rielly.[9] Numerous commercial houses spent as much as $500 per annum for telegraphing while there were a few that would average $1,000.[10] During the year ending November 1852, the New York Associated Press had paid nearly $50,000 for dispatches, about one-third of which was for foreign news. During the same time, the several newspapers composing the Association had paid an additional $14,000 for special and exclusive dispatches.[11]

"Telegraphing, in this country, has reached that point, by its great stretch of wires and great facilities for transmission of communications, as to almost rival the mail in the quantity of matter sent over it," declared Lawrence Turnbull in the preface to his book, *The Electro-Magnetic Telegraph*, published in 1853. Nearly seven hundred messages, exclusive of those for the press, had been sent over the Morse-operated New York, Albany & Buffalo line in a single day, while the Bain line at Boston had sent and received as many as five hundred communications, exclusive of reports for the press. "These

[5] *Ibid.*; Edward Highton, *The Electric Telegraph: Its History and Progress*, 144.

[6] Reid, *Telegraph in America*, 115.

[7] *American Telegraph Magazine*, November 15, 1852, 71-73.

[8] Lawrence Turnbull, "The Telegraph in the United States," *Journal of the Franklin Institute*, LIV (September 1852), 183.

[9] Jones, *Historical Sketch of the Electric Telegraph*, 105.

[10] *Ibid.*, 112.

[11] *National Telegraph Review* (July 1853), 170.

facts," concluded the enthusiastic author, "show how important an agent the magnetic telegraph has become in the transmission of business communications. It is every day coming more into use, and every day adding to its power to be useful."[12]

2 ··—··

ORGANIZATION within the industry, however, had not kept pace with this remarkable expansion program. Rate-making was an enigma. There appeared to be no common basis for determining rate structures on the part of the different companies. The cost of building telegraph lines had varied greatly depending upon the nature of the country through which they passed, the number of streams to be crossed, the price of labor, the quality of the materials used, and the care with which they were constructed. Some flimsy, rapidly-built lines had been erected for as little as $50 or $100 a mile, while other well-constructed lines had cost $200 a mile or more. Under the circumstances, the officers of the different companies established their rates more or less blindly, and would have been hard pressed to explain how they were computed.[13]

The usual charge for transmission was twenty-five cents for ten words or less, sent one hundred miles, but charges for longer distances varied considerably on the different lines. A table submitted by the Superintendent of the Census showing the rates of telegraphic transmission between Washington and some of the principal cities of the nation for messages of ten words or less indicates the variations:[14]

City of Washington to:

PLACE		MILES	RATES
Albany	N.Y.	376	.80
Baltimore	Md.	40	.20
Boston	Mass.	448	.75
Chicago	Ill.	1,238	1.25
Cincinnati	Ohio	578	.70
Detroit	Mich.	970	1.00
Dubuque	Iowa	1,449	1.70
Frankfort	Ky.	669	2.00

[12] Lawrence Turnbull, *The Electro-Magnetic Telegraph with an historical account of its Rise, Progress and Present Condition*, vii-viii; cf., *Report of Superintendent of Census* (1852), 108.

[13] Jones, *Historical Sketch of the Electric Telegraph*, 93, 102, 109, 114, 189-194; *Report of Superintendent of Census* (1852), 109.

[14] *Ibid.*, 109-110.

MAGNETIC TELEGRAPH CO.

RATES OF CHARGES,

Between New-York, New Brunswick, Princeton Trenton, Philadelphia, Wilmington, Havre de Grace, Baltimore and Washington.

For the first 10 Words or under, exclusive of address and direction,

Between NEW-YORK and					
New Brunswick,	10 Cts.	every addit'l Word,	1 Ct.		
Princeton,......15 "	do	do	do	2 "	
Trenton,........20 "	do	do	do	2 "	
Philadelphia,.. 25 "	do	do	do	2 "	
Wilmington,....35 "	do	do	do	3 "	
Havre De Grace,45 "	do	do	do	3 "	
Baltimore,......50 "	do	do	do	4 "	
Washington,....50 "	do	do	do	5 "	

Between NEW BRUNSWICK and

Princeton,......10 Cts.	every addit'l Word	1 Ct.
Trenton.........15 "	do do	do 1 "
Philadelphia,..20 "	do do	do 2 "
Wilmington ....30 "	do do	do 3 "
Havre De Grace,40 "	do do	do 3 "
Baltimore,......50 "	do do	do 4 "
Washington,....50 "	do do	do 5 "

Between PRINCETON and

Trenton, ...10 Cts.	every addit'l Word	1 Ct.
Philadelphia,...15 "	do do	do 1 "
Wilmington,....25 "	do do	do 2 "
Havre de Grace,.35 "	do do	do 3 "
Baltimore,......45 "	do do	do 4 "
Washington,....50 "	do do	do 5 "

Between TRENTON and

Philadelphia, ...10 Cts.	every addit'l Word	1 Ct.
Wilmington,....20 "	do do	do 2 "
Havre de Grace,.30 "	do do	do 3 "
Baltimore.......40 "	do do	do 4 "
Washington,....45 "	do do	do 4 "

Between PHILADELPHIA &

Wilmington,....10 Cts.	every addit'l Word,	1 Ct.
Havre De Grace,20 "	do do	do 2 "
Baltimore,......25 "	do do	do 2 "
Washington,....30 "	do do	do 3 "

Between WILMINGTON and

Havre de Grace,10 Cts.	every addit'l Word	1 Ct.
Baltimore,......20 "	do do	do 2 "
Washington,....25 "	do do	do 2 "

Between HAVRE de GRACE

Baltimore,......10 Cts.	every addit'l Word	1 Ct.
Washington,....20 "	do do	do 2 "

Betw'n BALT. and { Washington,....10 Cts. every addit'l Word 1 Ct.

When a Communication exceeds One Hundred Words, the price on all words exceeding that number, will be reduced One-Third.

Communications destined for any place beyond the termination of this Line will be faithfully written out at the last station, and delivered to the other Lines; but this Company, in no case, hold themselves responsible for the correct transmission or prompt delivery of any message beyond the terminus of their Line.

OCTOBER, 18th, 1847.

PLACE		MILES	RATES
Jackson	Miss.	1,325	2.00
New Orleans	La.	1,408	2.20
New York	N.Y.	232	.50
Pittsburgh	Pa.	307	.45
Portland	Me.	555	.95
St. Louis	Mo.	989	1.20
Springfield	Ill.	851	1.45

These tariffs were subject to change without notice, and competition over a route sometimes resulted in a bitter rate war and fluctuating tariffs. On the New York-Boston route, for example, the contest between F. O. J. Smith's Morse line and the rival Bain company had resulted in a gradual reduction of the customary twenty-five cent rate to ten cents. Then with the union of the lines in July 1852, the old twenty-five cent fee had been promptly restored.[15]

Wages, hours, and conditions of labor varied widely also. A chief operator in a city like New York might get $1,000 to $1,200 a year, while operators in way-stations sometimes received as low as $300.[16] Under the system of "farming out" unprofitable offices which was evolved by some of the hard-pressed lines, the operator might receive even less. By this ingenious plan an operator was placed in charge of an office and received approximately 50 percent of net receipts of the office. Just what this aggregated in some instances was clearly shown in letters written to Ezra Cornell by his operators. Cornell's proposition for "farming out" the office at Litchfield, Connecticut, declared the irate operator, A. L. Lewis, would mean that he would operate the office seven months for a compensation of $5.70½. "I regret that the company is having a bad time of it but the operators cannot make it up. . . . I must have a decent compensation or I cannot remain. When I took hold, talk was about $200 to $250 per year—now it is, say $12 to $25—It won't pay Mr. Cornell."[17]

George Wells, operator at Lenox, Massachusetts, when told by Cornell that his salary was to be one-half the net proceeds of the office, wrote that he was too poor to throw away his time, and he

---

[15] Reid, *Telegraph in America*, 381.

[16] Jones, *Historical Sketch of the Electric Telegraph*, 98-99; O. D. Guston to Cornell, December 9, 1852, Cornell Papers; Contract of J. F. Wallack, operator, with Ezra Cornell, *Ibid.*; numerous other letters and contracts in Cornell Papers; Superintendent's Report on employees, salaries, etc., July 1, 1853, in Certificate of Formation, etc. of the New York & New England Union Telegraph Company, 123, Smith Docs.

[17] A. L. Lewis to Cornell, August 21, 1849, Cornell Papers.

declared his intention of leaving unless a more satisfactory arrangement could be made.[18]

Hours of labor were uniformly long, the average being about fourteen a day. Many times operators were called upon to work overtime and on Sundays to accommodate press dispatches and other special messages. In the larger cities they were paid for overtime, but those employed at the way-stations usually received nothing. Moreover, the operating and battery rooms of the average telegraph office were small, dirty, and poorly ventilated.[19]

Messenger boys were usually paid on the basis of the number of dispatches delivered. In cities like New York, they were given two or three cents for each message delivered below Canal Street or within a radius of a mile from the office. Beyond that, or at night, a charge of twelve and one-half cents was made, and delivery in distant parts of Brooklyn or Williamsburg cost twenty-five cents. The wages of the boys under this plan averaged between two and four dollars a week.[20] In spite of the rather unfavorable conditions of labor within the industry, there were always young men eager to enter the business. While not a very promising career in itself, it served as a stepping stone to respected positions for many, of whom Andrew Carnegie and Thomas A. Edison are outstanding examples.

3 · · · — ·

WRITING of his telegraphic experiences in his *Autobiography* many years later, Andrew Carnegie drew an intimate picture of the business in the early 1850's. The earnest, young Scotch lad's business career began as a messenger for the Pittsburgh office of the Atlantic & Ohio Telegraph Company.

"A messenger boy in those days had many pleasures," relates Carnegie. "There were wholesale fruit stores, where a pocketful of apples was sometimes to be had for the prompt delivery of a message; bakers' and confectioners' shops where sweet cakes were sometimes given to him. He met very kind men to whom he looked up with respect; they spoke a pleasant word and complimented him on his promptness, perhaps asked him to deliver a message on the way back to the office. I do not know a situation in which a boy is more apt to

---

[18] George Wells to Cornell, August 27, 1849, Cornell Papers.
[19] *American Telegraph Magazine* (November 15, 1852), 75-76; Jones, *Historical Sketch of the Electric Telegraph*, 98-99.
[20] *Ibid.*; Carnegie, *Autobiography*, 52-55.

attract attention, which is all a really clever boy requires in order to rise. Wise men are always looking out for clever boys."

With all their pleasures the messenger boys worked hard. Every other evening they were required to be on duty until the office closed, and on these nights Andy seldom reached home before eleven o'clock. On the alternating nights the boys were relieved at six, but this did not leave much time for self-improvement.

The incident in his messenger life which at once lifted Andy to the seventh heaven, occurred one Saturday evening when Colonel Glass, manager of the office, was paying the boys their month's wages. They lined up as usual and all received their pay of $11.25 except Andy. "My heart sank," relates Carnegie. "After the others had gone Colonel Glass took me behind the counter, said I was worth more than the others and gave me $13.50. My joy knew no bounds."

Having to sweep out the operating room in the morning, the boys had an opportunity of practicing on the telegraph instruments before the operators arrived. Young Andy soon learned to use the key well enough to talk with the boys at the other stations. Having a good mind and knowing how to use it, Andy soon learned the routine of the telegraph office and was promoted shortly from messenger boy to a position as telegraph operator at a salary of twenty-five dollars per month, which seemed like a fortune to the seventeen year old Scotch lad.

The operating room of the telegraph office was young Carnegie's school, and he proved himself an apt pupil. His slight knowledge of British and European affairs stood him in good stead. The foreign news was received by wire from Cape Race and the taking of successive "steamers news" was one of the most notable duties of the telegraphers. Young Andy liked this better than any other branch of the work, and it was soon tacitly assigned to him.

While working as a telegraph operator in Pittsburgh, Andy made the acquaintance of Thomas A. Scott, division superintendent of the Pennsylvania Railroad. Scott, having observed Carnegie's industry and good habits of work, offered him a position as clerk and telegraph operator for the Pennsylvania Railroad at a salary of thirty-five dollars a month. Carnegie promptly accepted the position, and on February 1, 1853, left the telegraph company to begin his new career.[21]

21 *Ibid.*, 35-67.

4 . . . . —

WHILE the telegraph, under the tutelage of private industry, had made rapid strides in many respects, its development on the technical side had been relatively slight. Copper wire had been supplanted by iron wire, which was cheaper and less subject to breakage under varying weather conditions. The discovery of gutta-percha as a coating for wires for submarine purposes had offered the first practical solution to the problem of river crossings. The use of heavier poles of such durable wood as cedar or cypress, and deeply set, had begun to give lines a greater degree of permanence. Improved methods of insulation had brought more efficient operation, but results were still far from satisfactory.[22] "In rainy and foggy weather all the telegraph lines in the country are unreliable, and worked (if at all) with extreme difficulty," declared the editor of the *American Telegraph Magazine* in an article on the subject of insulation, in the December 1852 issue of his publication.

Beginnings had been made in the transmission of long distance messages without intermediate rewriting between such points as New York and Mobile—a distance of nearly 1,800 miles. Such a feat, however, was possible only in good weather and under ideal conditions. A system had also been devised by which press and Congressional reports could be sent from a central station to a number of outlying points simultaneously. Congressional reports were being received at the same time in Baltimore, Philadelphia, and New York; and all that was necessary at the intermediate stations was for an operator to be present and receive the message as it was developed on paper by the instruments.[23]

But while such minor improvements were being made, the Morse instruments had undergone little change, and the old Grove battery continued to be the chief source of power for both main and local purposes.[24] Much as the electrical engineer was needed, he was unknown, and his work was carried on by well-meaning, but ignorant men, like the estimable James D. Reid, whose electrical knowledge had been gleaned through bitter experience. To serve as a goad to the ingenuity of its superintendent, the Washington & New

[22] *Report of Superintendent of Census* (1852), 108-109; *American Telegraph Magazine* (December 15, 1852), 123; Jones, *Historical Sketch of the Electric Telegraph*, 107-111.
[23] *Report of Superintendent of Census* (1852), 110; cf. Jones, *Historical Sketch of the Electric Telegraph*, 101, 108-109, 112, 114.
[24] *Report of Superintendent of Census* (1852), 109.

AMERICAN
TELEGRAPH MAGAZINE.

"CANST THOU SEND LIGHTNINGS, THAT THEY MAY GO AND SAY UNTO THEE, *HERE WE ARE!*"—Job.
"I'LL PUT A GIRDLE 'ROUND THE EARTH IN FORTY MINUTES!"—Shakspeare.

VOL. I.—No. 1.   **NEW YORK, OCTOBER, 1852.**   Donald Mann, Editor.

CONTENTS OF No. I.

With an Appendix of sixteen pages, containing
A Memorial from HENRY O'RIELLY, and accompanying Documents,
Proposing a System of Intercourse Across the American Continent,
By Mail and Telegraph, along a Military Route, through the public domain, between the Atlantic and Pacific States,
Including the Protection of Emigrants, the Formation of Settlements, and Promotiom of
Amicable Relations with the Indians,
Through Nebraska, Deserета, New Mexico, California and Oregon;
And thus facilitating Intercourse (across the American Continent) between
Europe and China, Hawaii, Australia, the British and Russian Possessions on the Northwest Coast, and other regions of
the Pacific World.
To which are added, Extracts from the Reports, Resolutions and Estimates published by the General Committee
of the "National Telegraph and Railroad Convention," at St. Louis, in 1849, expressing approbation
of the project, and commending it to the "favorable consideration of Congress."

NEW YORK:
PUBLISHED MONTHLY, BY DONALD MANN.

FROM THE STEAM-PRESS OF BAKER, GODWIN & CO., No. 1 SPRUCE STREET, NEW YORK.

Orleans line had ordered that he be paid but half his regular emolument when the line was working only one way, and nothing at all if the line was completely dead.[25]

The most marked improvement occurring during the era of methodless enthusiasm had been in the operators themselves. With constant practice and experience had come skill, so that by 1849 many were finding the "extraordinary feat" of taking their messages by sound to be quicker and more efficient than the former method of translating the dispatch slowly from a strip of paper upon which it had been recorded. Under the old system a copyist wrote out the message as it was translated by the operator, after which it was handed to a second clerk whose duty it was to copy it on official company telegraph blanks. Most officers and superintendents, apprehensive of error, had vigorously opposed sound reading at its inception, and in some cases, had made the practice grounds for dismissal. But despite their early strenuous protests, the ease, efficiency, and economy of sound reading gradually became apparent, and by 1850 a buzzer instrument known as a "sounder" was rapidly replacing the Morse register.[26] Of the change in attitude, Tal. P. Shaffner, writing in 1859, declared: "Some years ago, as president of a telegraph line, I adopted a rule forbidding the receiving of messages by sound. Since then the rule has been reversed, and the operator is required to receive by sound or he cannot get employment in first class stations."[27] Thus sound receiving, that had begun more or less by accident, became the accepted method. By decreasing operating costs and diminishing the likelihood of error and delay, it marked an important advance in practical telegraphy.

5 — — —

INCREASED efficiency on the part of the individual operators could not offset the distressing independence and lack of harmony among the dozens of petty telegraph companies, each operating in a limited area. The resulting anarchical conditions within the industry were vividly described by President Marshall Lefferts of the New York &

25 George C. Maynard, "The Telegraph in America," *Electrical Review*, February 20, 1892.

26 Shaffner, *The Telegraph Manual*, 462-463; Morse, *Letters and Journals*, II, 479-480; Reid, *Telegraph in America*, 190-191, 308-309, 383-384; A. B. Cornell to John Horn, Jr., May 14, 1869, in MS volume, *Horn's Old Time Telegraph History*, III, Cornell University.

27 Shaffner, *The Telegraph Manual*, 463.

New England, or Merchants' Telegraph line, in a report to the stockholders for 1851. The company's southern and western business had fallen off considerably during the preceding year, he explained, because of inability to perform this business "with either profit or credit." For example, declared Lefferts, "A presents himself to our Boston office to send a message . . . to New Orleans. We receive and send it to New York, and there hand it over to one of the Southern lines, paying them at the same time the price of transmission for the whole distance, we simply deducting for our service performed. And so the message is passed on, either to stop on the way, or by good luck to reach its destination. If it does not reach its destination—which is of such frequent occurrence—the sender of the dispatch presents himself at the counter of our office and demands the return of his money. After giving us on the spot the most undoubted evidence of the fact of the message never having reached its destination, we inform him we will make inquiries, and if we can learn which line is at fault we will return him his money. We make inquiry, and when I tell you we can get no satisfaction, it is almost the universal answer; for they all insist on having sent the message through."[28]

After giving several other examples of the sort of practices which were serving to bring discredit to the telegraph, Lefferts concluded his report with a ringing challenge to the leaders of the industry: "Clear the enterprise of the shackles which now weight it down, put it in the hands of men satisfied with a fair remuneration, and alive to its national importance, and who shall set bounds to its extension and usefulness [sic]!"[29]

6 . . . . . .

IN spite of the telegraph's numerous shortcomings, men from all walks of life had been obliged to draft the new means of communication into their service. The farmer found that as a result of telegraphic reports he was better able to get a satisfactory price for his wheat; bankers and brokers found the telegraph of inestimable value in transacting their business; the press had gone through a revolution in news gathering with the advent of the invention; and the railroads stood on the threshold of one. Lawyers, physicians, merchants, hotelkeepers, travelers, stage proprietors, and steamboat men—all found

---

28 Jones, *Historical Sketch of the Electric Telegraph*, 142-143.
29 *Ibid.*, 144.

their labors greatly expedited. In the springtime, steamboat men along the lower Mississippi were able to get telegraphic news from above concerning the going out of the ice and the stage of the river. Physicians could consult with fellow practitioners in distant towns. Merchants could check on the credit standing of a customer by corresponding with references hundreds of miles distant.[30]

Besides economic interests, social and political groups were likewise served. Men away from home made extensive use of the telegraph to correspond with their families. A gallant gentleman in Boston married a lady in New York by telegraph. A joke, an invitation to a party, an inquiry about health, the announcement of a birth or death—all were fitting subjects for telegraphic correspondence. The introduction of police and fire alarm telegraphs, moreover, brought to thousands of people residing in the principal towns a degree of security which they had not known before.[31]

Both the States and the Federal Government made extensive use of the telegraph in the performance of their duties. During the Mexican War it had been of some use in expediting the movement of troops. It had become invaluable as a measure of defense. Politicians used it to keep in close touch with their constituents; diplomats, to correct misapprehensions which might otherwise lead to serious complications endangering the peace of nations. It was of incalculable value to the United States Coast Survey and related government services in charting weather reports and spreading warnings of approaching storms, calculating longitude, establishing correct time at various points throughout the country, and in registering astronomical observations.[32]

Perhaps the greatest value of the telegraph to the country, however, was the part that it played in bringing the various isolated and diverse sections of the country into more intimate commercial and cultural contact with one another, and in fostering the feeling of nationality which developed in the wake of the telegraph and railroad. New England, the Middle Atlantic States, and the South were brought

[30] Prospectus for the Troy-Whitehall line issued by Ezra Cornell, January 21, 1848, Cornell Papers; National Telegraph Review, July 1853, 103; [Cornell], True and Firm, 109; Jones, Historical Sketch of the Electric Telegraph, 105-106; Highton, The Electric Telegraph, 174-175; B. H. Wilson, "Telegraph Pioneering," Palimpsest, VI, 388-389.

[31] Jones, Historical Sketch of the Electric Telegraph, 105-106, 110, 112, 158; Highton, The Electric Telegraph, 156, 172, 174-175; American Telegraph Magazine, December 15, 1852, 123-124.

[32] Jones, Historical Sketch of the Electric Telegraph, 154-157; American Telegraph Magazine, October 1852, 18-19; Report of Superintendent of Census (1852), 110.

into daily, even hourly contact. Goods, services, and ideas were exchanged more freely than ever before.[33] In the autumn of 1852 the *New York Herald*, discussing a recent allusion in Congress to the need for removing the Federal Capital from Washington to some location nearer the geographical center of the country, explained that it was now without point. "Some years ago, there were good grounds for supposing that the seat of government would be removed to a more central location, but telegraphs have entirely superseded the necessity for any such movement."[34] Dr. William F. Channing of Boston, viewing the development of the industry through the eyes of a medical man, very aptly compared the role of the telegraph in modern society with that of the nervous system in the human body. "The electric telegraph is the nervous system of this nation and of modern society by no figure of speech, by no distant analogy. Its wires spread like nerves over the surface of the land, interlinking distant parts, and making possible a perpetually higher cooperation among men, and higher social forms than have hitherto existed. By means of its life-like functions the social body becomes a living whole, and each of its new applications marks a step in the organization of human life."[35]

7 — — · ·

WHILE the extension of the telegraph to nearly all the settled portions of the United States was thus revolutionizing many phases of life in this country, a similar development was taking place in Canada, Europe, and other civilized regions of the world. By the close of 1852 more than half a dozen companies had built a total of 983 miles of telegraph in Canada, and hundreds of miles more were projected and under construction. Outstanding among the Canadian lines was the Montreal Telegraph Company under the efficient supervision of Orrin S. Wood, a brother-in-law of Ezra Cornell, who had gone to Canada to build lines in 1847. With the backing of such wealthy and able men as Andrew Shaw, James Dakers, H. P. Dwight, and Sir Hugh Allen, the company was a success from the start.[36] Dur-

---

[33] Jesse Macy, *The Anti-Slavery Crusade*, 98-99.

[34] *American Telegraph Magazine*, October 1852.

[35] William F. Channing, *The American Fire Alarm Telegraph* (pamphlet), 1855.

[36] *Report of Superintendent of Census* (1852), 115; Correspondence between Cornell and O. S. Wood, Cornell Papers; some material also in Morse and Vail Papers; Ernest Green, "Canada's First Electric Telegraph," *Ontario Historical Society Papers and Records*, XXIV, 366-372; Reid, *Telegraph in America*, 326-338.

ing the 1850's it was gathering all the important Canadian lines into a single great system, just as its American counterpart, the Western Union Telegraph Company, was shortly to do in the United States.

Among the European nations, England stood next to the United States in the extent of its telegraph lines with about 4,000 miles of wire in operation. Quality rather than quantity had been stressed by the English in the building of their lines, the cost of construction in some cases amounting to $600 per mile. As a result, the English lines were undoubtedly superior to those in the United States, and many of the operating difficulties which plagued the early American companies were avoided. Charges for transmission, however, were much higher than in the United States, one penny[37] per word being charged for the first 50 miles and one farthing per mile for any distance beyond 100 miles. While a message of twenty words could be sent a distance of 500 miles in the United States for one dollar, a similar message in England would have cost seven. As a result the telegraph was little used by the general public and the press. It is interesting to note, however, that the closest cooperation existed between the telegraph and the railroad companies; English railroads considered the telegraph an indispensable agent to the operation of their trains. In June 1852, a submarine cable had been completed between Dover and Ostend placing London in communication with such European centers as Paris, Trieste, Cracow, Odessa, and Leghorn; and wires were already being carried on to St. Petersburg and into India and Africa.[38] Not many years were to pass before much of the British Empire was joined to the mother country by telegraph.

Prussia, France, Austria, and the smaller European countries were also extending their lines rapidly. In Prussia there were some 1,700 miles of telegraph in operation; in France, where the telegraph was entirely government-controlled, only 750 miles; in Austria, 1,053 miles; in Saxony, 265 miles; and in Bavaria, 455 miles. Additional lines were either built or building in Holland, Belgium, Italy, Spain, Russia, and Sweden.

In fact, the telegraph was beginning to find its way into almost every civilized portion of the globe. Lines were being projected in Cuba, Mexico, Central and South America, Africa, India, and

---

[37] The English penny is the equivalent of two cents in American currency.

[38] *Report of Superintendent of Census* (1852), 114-116; Turnbull, "Telegraph Lines of the World," *Journal of the Franklin Institute*, LIV, 184-190; "British Newspapers," *Encyclopaedia Britannica*, XVI, 334-348.

Early Telegrams, 1848-1852

D. H. Craig

The Telegraph Station, Sandy Hook, New Jersey

Australia. And everywhere the simple Morse instrument—sturdy, inexpensive and easy to operate—was gradually replacing all rivals.[39]

By the close of 1852 over 40,000 miles of telegraph webbed the surface of the earth. The communication systems of the United States, Canada, England, France, Prussia, far-distant India, and many other regions had been completely revolutionized. Messages which had formerly taken days, weeks, or even months to reach their destination by coach, steamship, and railroad, now sped, as though by magic, hundreds of miles almost instantly. The whole civilized world was entering upon a new era of speed and interdependence.

[39] *Report of Superintendent of Census* (1852), 114-116; Turnbull, *op. cit.*; *American Telegraph Magazine* (October 1852), 20-21; *National Telegraph Review* (July 1853), 173.

BOOK FOUR

ERA OF

CONSOLIDATION

1853-1866

CHAPTER XVI

Emergence of the New York & Mississippi Valley Printing Telegraph Company

1 · — — ·

THE erratic movement toward cooperation and consolidation among the numerous telegraph companies which had already made itself strongly evident in the years 1847-1852,[1] progressed with amazing rapidity in the period from 1853 to 1860. Indeed, these years may well be termed the era of consolidation, for from them emerged a few clear-cut organizations having definite areas in which they were sovereign.

An important step in the direction of closer cooperation was taken when Kendall invited all the telegraph lines in America working the Morse system to send representatives to a meeting in Washington. The purpose of the meeting was to unify the telegraph system in matters pertaining to their common interest. A great majority of the Morse companies responded favorably and on March 5, 1853, the American Telegraph Convention was assembled in Washington with representatives from the Maine; the New York & New England Union; the Magnetic; the Washington & New Orleans; the New York, Albany & Buffalo; the Atlantic & Ohio; the Pittsburgh, Cincinnati & Louisville; the Ohio & Mississippi; the Illinois & Mississippi; the New Orleans & Ohio; the Western; and a number of minor telegraph companies. The leaders among the representatives of the sixteen companies attending were F. O. J. Smith, J. D. Reid, J. K. Moorhead, J. D. Caton, J. N. Alvord, Amos Kendall, B. B. French, James Eddy, William Tanner, Tal. P. Shaffner, and William M. Swain.[2]

Discussion revealed that one of the greatest evils of the system was the absence of due responsibility for messages sent over the lines of two or more companies. Such messages were often unreasonably delayed, or never delivered at all. While the delegates agreed that transmission could not always be perfect, they were unanimous in their demands that the company making a serious error or delaying a message unreasonably, be held accountable to the others and to the

---

[1] For a detailed account of this movement, see Chapter XII.

[2] Proceedings of the Meetings of the American Telegraph Convention, March 5 and 7, 1853, Caton Papers, Library of Congress; also Morse Papers, XXXII.

customer. It was further agreed that if a wire was inoperative, the companies were to be informed so that messages could be rerouted. More harm, declared one speaker, arose from the existing system of deceit than could possibly come from telling the truth. Additional topics such as the establishment of rules to regulate the dismissal and re-employment of operators, the treatment of signals and abbreviations, the establishment of a telegraph newspaper, and the impropriety of designating lines by the names of the builders, were also discussed.

Annual meetings were agreed upon; and to give the American Telegraph Confederation, as the organization came to be called, an administrative body and a certain degree of centralization and continuity, a committee of correspondence, or executive committee, consisting of French, Swain, Kendall, Caton, and Moorhead was elected. It was the duty of this committee to consider and act upon all disputed questions which might be referred to it by the member companies, to carry out such measures as might be agreed upon by the Confederation, and to promote the welfare of the telegraph industry in general, but not to interfere with the management or special interest of any given line.[3] As a further step toward closer cooperation Shaffner was elected paid secretary of the organization with an office in Washington. In addition to his regular secretarial work, he was empowered to act as central purchasing agent. By purchasing supplies in wholesale quantities, the companies would be assured of receiving high quality products at savings of from 25 to 200 percent.[4]

The American Telegraph Confederation was organized, not with any idea of bringing about a consolidation of the leading companies, but rather with a view to securing harmony of interests, uniformity in methods of transacting business, and cooperation in securing supplies at fair rates. While its formation was a step in the right direction, the organization possessed certain dangerous weaknesses. Resolutions passed at its meetings were not binding on the member companies unless ratified by their respective boards of directors, and a spirit of independence and local pride often prevented the necessary action. Some members paid lip service only to the Confederation and their connections continued to be for sale to the highest bidder. Many companies resolutely maintained the right to regulate their

---

[3] Proceedings of the Meetings of the American Telegraph Convention, March 5 and 7, 1853, Caton Papers.

[4] Ibid.; Shaffner's Telegraph Companion, I, no. 1 (January 1854), 30-45; Shaffner to Caton, March 20, 1853, Caton Papers; Ibid., October 29, 1853.

tariffs on whatever basis they chose, despite the confusion which resulted. Consequently, a New York telegraph company receiving a message for delivery in Columbus, Ohio, never knew with certainty what the actual charges would be. Finally, and most significant, certain important interests were not included within its membership. Cornell, obsessed with visions of controlling a great telegraph empire of his own in the West, had remained aloof, along with his lieutenants, Speed and Wade. Furthermore, the aggressive House lines, had not been invited to join the Confederation. They rightly looked upon it as an agency designed to crush them and prepared to do their utmost to break up this seemingly formidable new organization.[5]

Under the circumstances the strength of the associated Morse companies was more apparent than real; for while they controlled an impressive wire mileage, their loose confederation was to prove weak and ineffectual against the schemes of more closely knit organizations. The whole system was rank with dissension, distrust, and danger. Furthermore, the leading Morse companies were unfortunate in having for presidents men to whom the telegraph was only one of many interests. General J. K. Moorhead, able president of the Atlantic & Ohio and the Pittsburgh, Cincinnati & Louisville Companies, was too much interested in the Pittsburgh iron industry and various manufacturing projects to give the telegraph his undivided attention. William M. Swain of the Magnetic had his newspaper and other interests which demanded much of his time. Judge Caton of the Illinois & Mississippi continued to serve on the Supreme Court bench of the State of Illinois at the same time that he was rejuvenating the telegraph industry in Illinois and Iowa. On the other hand, Cornell, Speed, and Wade gave their entire attention to the management of their lines.

Moreover, the leading House lines, having undergone a considerable change in management by 1853, were controlled by alert, enterprising individuals to whom the telegraph business was no mere side line. Hugh Downing, it may be recalled, had held the House patent for the states bordering the Atlantic seaboard, but his accomplishment had fallen far short of his dreams.[6] Only two units of his proposed telegraph empire were ever completed—the Boston & New York Printing Telegraph Company, whose route was indicated

[5] Reid, *Telegraph in America*, 427; *National Telegraph Review*, I, no. 2 (July 1853); *Ibid.*, October 1853.
[6] For an earlier discussion, see Chapter x.

by the corporate title, and the New Jersey Telegraph Company extending from Philadelphia to New York. Both had been failures, and in 1851 the disillusioned Downing had sold his entire interest not only in the New Jersey line but also in the House patent to Freeman Edson, Robert W. Russell, Francis Morris, and Cambridge Livingston. The line of the New Jersey Telegraph was extended to Washington by the new owners, and after a complete rehabilitation, it was reorganized as the New York & Washington Printing Telegraph Company. The concern prospered under its new administration and was soon giving the pioneer Magnetic Telegraph formidable opposition on this important route.[7]

The following year (1852), Downing's Boston & New York Printing Telegraph went bankrupt, and in May it was liquidated and reorganized by a group of Boston merchants as the Commercial Printing Telegraph Company. The old wire cord, which had been the source of much of its trouble, was removed and an iron wire put in its place, but still the line did not pay expenses. In 1853 the discouraged owners had offered it to the New York Associated Press for $40,000, but the editors were opposed to the Association's entering the telegraph business. In order to encourage other parties to purchase and manage it, however, they agreed to send all their reports over the line, and under this pledge it was purchased on July 23, 1853, by John McKinney and several associates. Carefully rebuilt, ably managed, and enjoying the support of Daniel H. Craig and the Associated Press, the line became a force to be reckoned with on the New York-Boston route.[8]

On the New York-Buffalo route the House-operated New York State Printing Telegraph Company under the management of Samuel L. Selden, Freeman M. Edson, and their Rochester associates provided competition for the old New York, Albany & Buffalo Telegraph. The latter company had strengthened its position by purchasing one rival line, the Bain-operated Merchants' State Telegraph, on June 7, 1852, but competition with the House line continued to be a cause for concern.[9]

It was on the route from Buffalo west that the Morse companies faced the greatest danger. In this area the increasingly aggressive movements of another Rochester-controlled organization, the New

[7] Reid, *Telegraph in America*, 460-461.

[8] *Ibid.*, 410-411.

[9] For earlier discussion of this subject, see Chapters x, xii. For later discussion, see Chapter xvii.

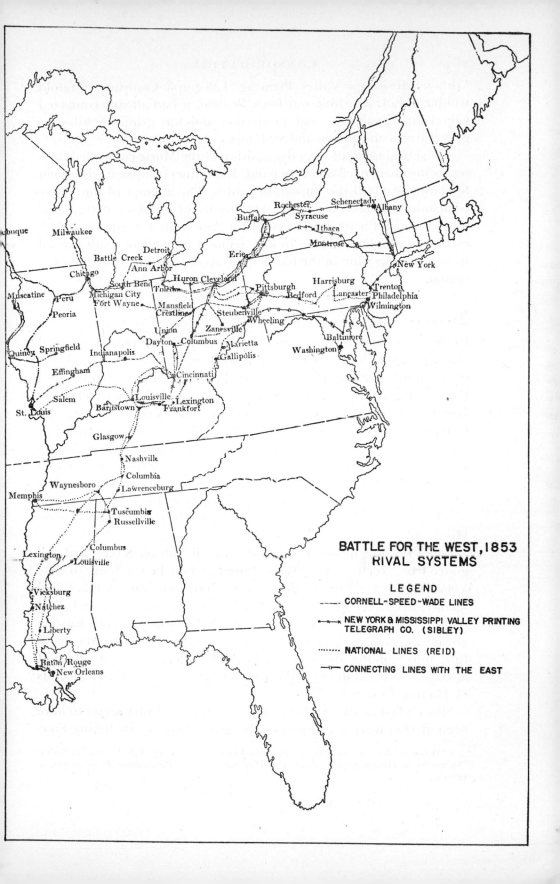

BATTLE FOR THE WEST, 1853
RIVAL SYSTEMS

LEGEND

------- CORNELL-SPEED-WADE LINES

-*-*- NEW YORK & MISSISSIPPI VALLEY PRINTING
TELEGRAPH CO. (SIBLEY)

········· NATIONAL LINES (REID)

-+-+- CONNECTING LINES WITH THE EAST

York & Mississippi Valley Printing Telegraph Company, foretold trouble ahead. Reaching out from Buffalo, it had already contacted Cleveland, Cincinnati, and Louisville, and was grimly fighting to gain entrance to Chicago and St. Louis.

At the beginning of 1853 the position of the Morse-controlled lines was being challenged on every hand. Rival lines competed with them for business on all the important routes. The attempt of the Morse companies to establish a closer community of interest among themselves through the establishment of the American Telegraph Confederation accomplished little. In fact, its most immediate result proved to be an acceleration of the bitter telegraphic warfare throughout the nation.

2 ·· — ··

IN the West the battle for supremacy developed into a three-cornered affair between the Cornell-Speed-Wade system; the National Lines system under the superintendency of James D. Reid, which enjoyed the backing of the American Telegraph Confederation; and the House-operated New York & Mississippi Valley Printing Telegraph Company. The first two organizations were "systems" composed of a number of separate companies, each of which had different officers and different ideas. The member concerns were only loosely bound together by voluntary agreements. In the case of the New York & Mississippi Valley, on the other hand, control was centralized in a small, able board of directors headed by a brilliant business leader, Hiram Sibley.

Following the pioneering instinct in his nature, Sibley had migrated from North Adams, Massachusetts, where he was born, to New York's Genesee Valley in the 1820's. Here the young Yankee had learned five different trades including those of machinist and wool carder before coming of age. In 1838 with the beginnings of a fortune already in hand, he had moved to Rochester where he entered successfully into banking and real estate. Politics came in for its share of attention also, and in 1843 Sibley was elected sheriff by the Democrats of Monroe County.[10]

Sibley's first contact with the new telegraph industry seems to have been in 1849 when a group of his business associates, including Free-

[10] "Hiram Sibley," *Dictionary of American Biography*, XVII, 145-146; Hiram W. Sibley, "Memories of Hiram Sibley," *Rochester Historical Society Publication Fund Series*, II, 127-134.

man M. Edson, Samuel L. Selden, and Royal Chamberlain organized the New York State Printing Telegraph Company. Under the primitive conditions of the time the new line with its complicated House printing telegraph instruments was no match for the well-built and excellently managed line of the New York, Albany & Buffalo with its simple Morse machinery, and during the next few years the newcomer was just about able to make expenses.[11] A careful study of the telegraph situation convinced Sibley that multiplicity of management, lack of coordination, mutual distrust, duplication of service, capricious tariffs, and the inability to fix responsibility—ills born through lack of centralization—were attacking the heart of the telegraph enterprise, making it unprofitable for its promoters and unsatisfactory for its patrons. Consequently when Selden had approached him in the spring of 1850 with a proposal for the organization of a company to carry a House line into the region west of Buffalo, his answer had been, "Why should we erect just one more line to add to the hopeless confusion of the West?"[12]

Sibley countered with a proposal that a company be organized whose aim would be to acquire *all* telegraphic interests west of Buffalo and bring them together into a single great system under a single and vigorous management.[13] Should such a company be established, and should he be able to obtain a sufficient interest in the House patent to assure himself of a voice in the management and a satisfactory share of the profits of the enterprise, then, and only then, would he become a party to it. Selden, believing he saw in Sibley just those qualities of aggressiveness, determination, and business acumen needed for the successful prosecution of the telegraph enterprise, agreed to his proposals. Thereupon Sibley, in conjunction with his friend, Isaac Butts, had proceeded on December 9, 1850, to buy a substantial interest in the House patent rights.[14]

11 Reid, *Telegraph in America*, 310, 315, 461-462.

12 "Telegraph History," *New York Evening Post*, February 27, 1885; Jane M. Parker, "How the men of Rochester Saved the Telegraph," *Rochester Historical Society Publication Fund Series*, v, 122-134; Reid, *Telegraph in America*, 463-464.

13 This idea was by no means original with Sibley. As has already been pointed out, leaders of the industry from its very inception had envisaged the establishment of monopolistic control over specific routes or regions. The attempts of men like Kendall, Reid, and Selden to achieve this goal had failed. Now Sibley proposed to try again in the region west of Buffalo.

14 This transaction is referred to in Article 9 of the Articles of Agreement, April 18, 1853, between Freeman M. Edson, Samuel L. Selden, Hiram Sibley, and Isaac Butts of the first part; and Francis Morris, Robert W. Russell, Cambridge Livingston and John B. Richards of the second part, O'Rielly Docs., Telegraph Pamphlets.

No exact details were available concerning division of the patent interest as of

3 · · · — ·

MEANWHILE, Selden and his colleague, Freeman M. Edson, had entered into a contract with Isaac Butts, Sanford J. Smith, and Charles L. Shepard, dated September 6, 1850, for the construction of a line of House telegraph from Buffalo to St. Louis via Cleveland, Cincinnati, and Louisville. The contractors agreed to complete and put into operation at least 100 miles of the proposed line on or before January 1, 1851, and to proceed with the construction of the remainder with all reasonable diligence.

From the very outset of the new project, it was clear that the primary aim of the Rochester promoters was the establishment of a monopoly over the telegraph business along their chosen route. In so far as possible this aim was to be achieved through the absorption of existing lines rather than by the construction of new ones. In their contract with Butts, Smith, and Shepard, for example, provision was made for canceling construction of the line between Buffalo and Cleveland should Edson and Selden succeed in absorbing the Lake Erie Telegraph Company's line between those cities. Another provision required all parties to the contract to work for the consolidation of their projected line between Buffalo and St. Louis with the lines already constructed between New York and Buffalo, so as to give one great telegraph system extending from New York on the seaboard to St. Louis on the Missouri.[15] In the years that lay ahead

~~~~~~

December 1850, but by December 1, 1851, several changes having occurred in the meantime, the patent interest, divided into eighty parts, was owned as follows:

Cambridge Livingston, five-eightieths or one-sixteenth of the whole
Francis Morris, ten-eightieths or two-sixteenths
William Ballard, five-eightieths or one-sixteenth
John B. Richards, five-eightieths or one-sixteenth
Freeman M. Edson, twenty-six and 2/3 eightieths } or together
Samuel L. Selden, thirteen and 1/3 eightieths   } one-half
Hiram Sibley, seven and 1/2 eightieths } or together
Isaac Butts, seven and 1/2 eightieths   } three-sixteenths

(Memorandum of an agreement made this first day of December 1851, between the New York & Mississippi Valley Printing Telegraph Company, of the first part; William Ballard, John B. Richards, Francis Morris, Cambridge Livingston, Hiram Sibley, Isaac Butts, Freeman M. Edson, and Samuel L. Selden, of the second part; and Smith and Butts, contractors for building of the line, of the third part. O'Rielly Docs., Telegraph Pamphlets.)

15 Agreement September 6, 1850, between Freeman M. Edson and Samuel Selden of the one part, and Isaac Butts, Sanford J. Smith and Charles L. Shepard of the other part, regarding construction of a line of telegraph, etc., O'Rielly Docs., Telegraph Pamphlets. This contract is given in full in Appendix 4.

Since the New York & Mississippi Valley Printing Telegraph Company was the nucleus the keynote of consolidation thus sounded was to remain the cardinal principle of the Rochester interests.

The next important step in the new enterprise was taken on April 1, 1851, when the New York & Mississippi Valley Printing Telegraph Company was organized under an Act of the New York State Legislature of April 12, 1848, providing for the incorporation and regulation of telegraph companies. The detailed articles of association and incorporation stated that the company was to continue in existence for one hundred years. Its authorized capital was set at $360,000, divided into shares of $100 each. One-half the capital stock was to be appropriated in payment for the exclusive right of constructing and using the House printing telegraph instruments on a line from Buffalo to St. Louis, while the other half was to be devoted to completing and putting the line into operation.[16]

The affairs of the company were to be managed by a board of nineteen directors who were to choose a president and vice-president from their number. The board was also to have the power to appoint a treasurer and a secretary, or, if they preferred, one person to act both as secretary and treasurer.[17] With the consent of two-thirds of the members of the board the line could be merged or united with any other line or lines using the House instruments on whatever terms appeared to be just and equitable. The directors with like consent were empowered to purchase or lease for the company any line or part of a line of telegraph already constructed, if in their judgment such action would be for the benefit of the company. These provisions clearly indicate the role which the promoters of the New York &

from which the Western Union Telegraph Company was to emerge in 1856, its corporate history has been followed in much greater detail than that of any other company. The account presented in the chapters on the emergence of the Western Union Telegraph Company may well serve as the general pattern for corporate development within the industry during this period.

16 Articles of Association and Incorporation of the New York & Mississippi Valley Printing Telegraph Company, April 1, 1851, O'Rielly Docs., Telegraph Pamphlets. These Articles of Association are given in full in Appendix 5.

17 Until the first annual meeting of the stockholders which was scheduled for the first Tuesday of April 1852, in the city of Buffalo, the board of directors was to be composed of the following persons provided they purchased stock in the company within sixty days:

Henry S. Potter	Gideon W. Burbank	Isaac Hills
Addison Gardiner	Joseph Hall	Samuel Medary
Freeman Clarke	George H. Mumford	Joseph Medbery
Isaac R. Elwood	E. Darwin Smith	James Chapman
Rufus Keeler	Freeman M. Edson	Hiram Sibley
Royal E. House	Samuel L. Selden	Isaac Butts
Sanford J. Smith		

Mississippi Valley proposed that it should play in the future development of the industry in the West.[18]

Now came the all-important task of raising the necessary funds to construct the proposed line. For various reasons men of means were reluctant to invest their money in the enterprise. Telegraph stocks in general had proved bad investments. Moreover, the favored position of the holders of the House patent right acted as a further deterrent. Under the circumstances, subscriptions were limited and their payment was slow and uncertain. To secure badly needed funds, holders of the patent right and the contractors for the line wisely decided to part with a liberal amount of their stock, hoping in this way to attract additional capital and induce subscribers to pay up in full. A contract was drawn up by which Royal E. House, William Ballard, John B. Richards, Freeman M. Edson, Samuel L. Selden, Hiram Sibley, and Isaac Butts as holders of the patent right, and Sanford J. Smith and Isaac Butts as contractors for the line,[19] were to turn over to acting secretary Isaac R. Elwood specified amounts of their stock for distribution to cash subscribers as a bonus. To those paying their subscriptions in full, a 50 percent stock bonus was to be issued. On the strength of this promise thirteen Rochester investors agreed to provide the company with $83,000. This sum constituted the financial backbone of the New York & Mississippi Valley in the spring of 1851.[20]

At the first annual meeting of the stockholders in April 1852, the provisional board of directors, appointed under the articles of association and incorporation the preceding spring, was duly elected to office. That body then proceeded to elect as the company's first president, Henry S. Potter, a public-spirited and wealthy merchant of

[18] Articles of Association of New York & Mississippi Valley Printing Telegraph Co., April 1, 1851, O'Rielly Docs., Telegraph Pamphlets.

[19] The name of C. L. Shepard, another of the original contractors, was omitted from this and subsequent contracts.

[20] The subscription list attached to this "bonus" contract follows:

A. Gardiner	$10,000	Hiram Sibley	5,000
F. Clarke	10,000	Freeborn G. Jewett	5,000
Henry S. Potter	10,000	J. B. Stillson	2,000
Isaac Butts	10,000	William Alling	2,000
J. Medbery	10,000	Ashley Sampson	2,000
G. H. Mumford	10,000	Edmund P. Willis	2,000
Bacon & Company	5,000		

(Article of Agreement between House, Edson, Selden, Sibley, and Butts holding an interest in the House patent right; Smith and Butts contractors for building the line; and Gardiner, Potter, Elwood and other stockholders [n.d., about April 1851], O'Rielly Docs., Telegraph Pamphlets. This "bonus" contract is given in full in Appendix 6.)

Rochester; Joseph Medbery, also of that city, became vice-president; and an able Rochester lawyer, Isaac R. Elwood, was selected as secretary-treasurer. The motivating force behind the company from the beginning, however, was Hiram Sibley. About this time the company secured as its superintendent, a young man named Anson Stager. As former manager of the Cincinnati office of the Pittsburgh, Cincinnati & Louisville Company he had shown outstanding ability, and as superintendent of the New York & Mississippi Valley he was to render that company invaluable services.[21]

4 . . . . —

THE course of events during the next few years was enough to discourage all but the most stout-hearted. New subscriptions were few, while old ones were only partly paid or repudiated entirely. As a result, the company's original plans could not be carried out. A series of proposals for consolidation were thwarted by the determined opposition of rival lines and by lack of funds. The close of the year 1853 found the New York & Mississippi Valley Printing Telegraph Company with but a single line of wire, connecting the cities of Buffalo, Cleveland, Columbus, Dayton, Cincinnati, Frankfort, and Louisville.[22]

In view of these facts, amended articles of association were filed on January 9, 1854, reducing the capital stock to $170,000, divided into shares of $100 each. Of this sum, $84,200 was to be distributed to the cash subscribers in proportion to their respective rights; $42,500 was to be given to the holders of the patent right for the exclusive privilege of using House instruments on the line; $10,000 had already been issued to Sanford J. Smith & Company, as contractors for building the line; another $7,500 had been issued to Freeman Clarke to be used as collateral for a loan of $3,000; and the remainder of the capital stock, amounting to $25,800, was to be issued to contractor Isaac Butts when he should secure for the company a clear title to the line. A further indication of the straitened financial condition of the company was the inclusion of a clause authorizing the executive committee to issue bonds "to an amount not exceeding fifteen thousand dollars for the purpose of paying off the existing debts of the said company."[23]

[21] Reid, *Telegraph in America*, 187-188, 469-470.
[22] A branch circuit to Lexington, which was under construction, was to be included.
[23] Agreement January 9, 1854, between New York & Mississippi Valley Printing

While the outlook for the New York & Mississippi Valley at the opening of the year 1854 appeared to be none too promising, Hiram Sibley had absolute faith in the efficacy of consolidation as a cure for the basic ills of the telegraph industry, and as the key to success for his company. So convinced was he of the soundness of his views that during the dark years 1851-1853, when others were growing discouraged and quitting, he had invested more and more heavily. By 1854, nearly everything that he owned was pledged to the success of the enterprise. On April 14, 1853, Sibley and Butts, in conjunction with several other wide-awake promoters, had secured a controlling interest in the unsold House patent rights for the entire United States, and had organized a patent association known as House's Printing Telegraph Company.[24]

On January 20, 1854, the board of directors of the New York & Mississippi Valley had convened in Secretary Elwood's office in Rochester and adopted a resolution calling for the reorganization of the company[25] under an amendatory act of the Legislature of the State of New York passed June 29, 1853. The more liberal provisions of the amendatory act exempted stockholders from personal liability, and provided for taxing the company only upon the value of its prop-

Telegraph Company of first part; Francis Morris and other assignees of House Patents, of the second part; Francis Morris, Freeman M. Edson, and Hiram Sibley, Trustees for the undisposed patent interests, of the third part; and Henry S. Potter and other cash subscribers for stock of the said company, of the fourth part, O'Rielly Docs., Telegraph Pamphlets. These amended Articles of Association are given in full in Appendix 7.

[24] All property, rights, and interests associated with the patent were divided into 320 parts, or shares, of unspecified value which were distributed among the individual owners as follows:

Freeman M. Edson	50 shares
Samuel L. Selden	14 shares
Hiram Sibley	48 shares
Isaac Butts	48 shares
Francis Morris	64 shares
Robert W. Russell	32 shares
Cambridge Livingston	32 shares
John B. Richards	32 shares
	320 shares

Under this arrangement Samuel L. Selden, the original promoter, was reduced to a minority interest, and control passed into more aggressive hands. (Article of Agreement, April 18, 1853, between Edson, Selden, Sibley, Butts, Morris, Russell, Livingston, and Richards respecting their shares in the House patent interest, O'Rielly Docs., Telegraph Pamphlets.) This Article of Agreement is given in full in Appendix 8.

[25] Certificate of a Resolution adopted by a majority of the Board of Directors of the New York & Mississippi Valley Printing Telegraph Company, on January 20, 1854, concerning reorganization of the company, O'Rielly Docs., Telegraph Pamphlets. This resolution for reorganization is given in Appendix 9.

Henry S. Potter, President

Joseph Medbery, Vice President

Isaac R. Elwood, Secretary-Treasurer

Anson Stager, Superintendent

OFFICERS OF THE NEW YORK & MISSISSIPPI VALLEY PRINTING
TELEGRAPH COMPANY, 1852

Hiram Sibley

Samuel L. Selden

Isaac Butts

SOME LEADING MEMBERS OF THE BOARD OF DIRECTORS OF THE NEW YORK &
MISSISSIPPI VALLEY PRINTING TELEGRAPH COMPANY, 1852 (Pictures of
Freeman M. Edson and Sanford J. Smith were not available)

erty within the state. The reorganized New York & Mississippi Valley Printing Telegraph Company was duly incorporated on February 21, 1854. While the capital stock remained fixed at $170,000 divided into shares of $100 each, the number of stockholders had now increased to twenty-nine.[26] The largest potential stockholder was Isaac Butts with 55 shares owned outright and 258 more earmarked for future delivery to him under certain specified conditions.[27] Next on the list was Isaac R. Elwood, who, as secretary of the company, probably held most of the 250 shares listed opposite his name in trust for others, or for the company. President Henry S. Potter followed with 125 shares. For him, this telegraph stock was merely one of many investments. Such was not the case with Hiram Sibley, who was the next largest stockholder, with 114 shares. The telegraph was not *an in-*

[26] Name of shareholder	Residence	No. of shares
J. L. Allen	New Haven, Conn.	11
A. Arnold	[address not given]	4
William Alling	Rochester, N.Y.	30
Bacon & Company	do.	47
Isaac Butts	do.	55
William Buffam	Stratford, Conn.	11
G. W. Burbank	Rochester, N.Y.	15
C. G. Brinsmaid	do.	1
James Chappell	do.	10
Freeman Clarke	do.	75
Dows & Carey	New York City	20
F. M. Edson	Flushing, N.Y.	30
I. R. Elwood	Rochester, N.Y.	250
A. Gardiner	do.	75
F. G. Jewett	Skaneateles, N.Y.	75
Cambridge Livingston	New York City	41
G. H. Mumford	Rochester, N.Y.	75
J. Medbery	do.	75
F. Morris	New York City	74
H. S. Potter	Rochester, N.Y.	125
W. H. Perkins	do.	4
J. B. Richards	New York City	40
R. W. Russell	New York City	36
E. F. Smith	Rochester, N.Y.	4
A. Sampson	do.	30
H. Sibley	do.	114
S. L. Selden	do.	55
J. B. Stillson	do.	30
E. P. Willis	do.	30
		————
		1,442

The above list accounts for 1,442 of the 1,700 shares authorized by the article of incorporation. There remained 258 shares which were to be issued to Isaac Butts whenever he should procure a release from the contractors, a clear title to the line, and upon the payment by him of $1,200 to the company. Certificate of Resolution, *Ibid.*

[27] For details on this point, see footnote 26 immediately preceding.

vestment to Sibley; it was *the* investment upon which he had staked most of his personal fortune, and the success of the enterprise was a matter of vital importance to him.

An examination of the remainder of the list reveals a group of men to whom the telegraph was only an investment. Success or failure would merely make them correspondingly richer or poorer. Another significant fact to be noted was the overwhelming preponderance of Rochester citizens among the stockholders. Of the twenty-nine, there were nineteen residing in Rochester who collectively controlled 1,110 of the 1,442 shares outstanding.

5 — — —

AN interesting, although somewhat inaccurate and romanticized account of developments during those dark years 1851-1853, was given by Hiram Sibley to a reporter of the *New York Evening Post* in 1885—three decades after the events.[28] According to Sibley, his plan for consolidating the numerous conflicting companies into a federation, or union, was considered so wild, that it came to be called "Sibley's crazy scheme," even by men who had reluctantly invested in it.

"It did seem like a crazy scheme," reminisced Sibley, ". . . the buying up of broken-down telegraph companies, accumulating their worthless stock, assuming their liabilities, etc." It was no secret that he had mortgaged his property and borrowed heavily to carry out the project. While he did not relish being called a "line gobbler," ridicule mattered little to him if the necessary capital for buying up companies and the controlling interests of patents could be secured.

Again and again he called the capitalists of Rochester together and presented to them his plan for consolidating all the lines in the West. "If I do invest in it, Sibley," said one as they walked home alone together after one of those meetings, "promise me it shall be a secret between us forever. I'll loan you $5,000—that means, give it to you, for you'll lose it, of course—but you are never to tell that I was such a fool. I believe in you, Sib, but I don't believe in this telegraphy."

As the months passed and pledges of financial assistance failed to materialize, Sibley grew increasingly impatient and disgusted, and decided to have a showdown. "I will give them one more chance," he said. "It shall be the last call." Accordingly, one evening some twenty-five Rochester men assembled in Sibley's office in the Arcade.

28 "Telegraph History" in *New York Evening Post*, February 27, 1885.

Chief among them were Isaac R. Elwood, Isaac Butts, Joseph Medbery, Henry S. Potter, George H. Mumford, Addison Gardiner, Samuel L. Selden, E. P. Willis, Don Alonzo Watson, G. W. Burbank, J. B. Stetson, Aristarchus Champion, and W. H. Cheyney.

After addressing them collectively, Sibley appealed to each in turn. Would they subscribe $5,000 each that evening, as the ultimate test of their faith in the project?

Finally Aristarchus Champion, a prudent millionaire, asked: "You admit, Mr. Sibley, that the telegraph is a failure?"

"I do," was the emphatic response.

"And you further admit that each company is a failure—that in particular and general the whole thing is a failure?"

"I do."

"Then how is the consolidation of failures to escape failure? If there is nothing in the result which is not in the cause, where is the element of success to come in? Would collecting all the paupers—the social failures of Monroe County—into one organization, composed entirely of paupers, insure their success and make them men of fortune?"

Conviction with Sibley was stronger than syllogism. Would Mr. Champion sign the paper? Champion refused.

"Admitting all that you have said, Mr. Sibley," said Judge Gardiner, "admitting that this organization by the investment proposed may reap a certain and increasing success, is it at all probable that you or I, or any here present, will live long enough to see your prophecy fulfilled, to reap the benefit of faith in your seership?"

Sibley would not discuss the question. There was the paper. Would Judge Gardiner sign it? The name of Addison Gardiner was the first on the list. After some hesitation, George H. Mumford signed his name.

"I agree with Mr. Champion," said Gideon Burbank. J. B. Stetson and W. H. Cheyney also refused to sign.

"Things looked serious," said Sibley, in describing the meeting, "and I began to think my cake was dough after all."

Don Alonzo Watson knit his brows. "I'll tell you in the morning. Perhaps I'll take all I can pay for." He did advance $5,000, but not because he believed he should not lose it in the end.

"The ninety thousand dollars subscribed at that meeting," says Sibley, "was all the money that was ever paid. The balance was money loaned on bonds of the company, and individual loans. Isaac Butts promised the other ten and paid it in stock of other lines. That one hundred thousand dollars, with what was gained by the consolidation with the House lines outside of the State of New York, constituted the property of the Western Union Telegraph Company [called the New York & Mississippi Valley Printing Telegraph Company during this period] and soon exceeded in value the whole assessed value of the property real and personal of the city of Rochester."[29]

[29] *Ibid.*

CHAPTER XVII

The New York & Mississippi Valley's
Career of Conquest

1 ·——·

WITH the reorganization of the New York & Mississippi Valley Printing Telegraph Company in February 1854, the turning point had been reached. That concern now embarked upon a career of conquest which has seldom been equalled in corporate history. The first great triumph came on February 7 when the company, as a result of the skillful negotiations of Sibley and his able lieutenant, Anson Stager, succeeded in arranging for the construction of lines to Detroit and Chicago through a contract with the Cleveland & Toledo, the Michigan Southern, and the Northern Indiana Railroad Companies. The contract provided that the railroads should build and equip the necessary lines for the telegraph company, receiving in return telegraph stock to the amount of $125 a mile and the free use of the lines for railroad business.

A detailed examination of the elaborate contract reveals an arrangement which seems highly favorable to the telegraph company.[1] First of all, the railroad companies agreed to construct lines of telegraph according to carefully stated specifications—wire of the best quality, weighing not less than six hundred pounds to the mile; poles, at least thirty to a mile, preferably white oak, yellow or red cedar, bark removed, set four to five feet deep in the ground; insulators of House design; and, for crossing streams, cables insulated with gutta-percha and sunk and secured in a proper and suitable manner. Furthermore, the telegraph company was to be permitted to furnish at least one, and, if necessary, two persons experienced in the building of House telegraph lines to superintend their construction at the expense of the railroad companies. Secondly, centrally located tele-

---

[1] Articles of Agreement, February 7, 1854, between New York & Mississippi Valley Printing Telegraph Company of the first part; Morris, Sibley, and Edson, trustees for House patents, of the second part; the Cleveland & Toledo Rail Road Company of the third part; and the Michigan Southern Rail Road Company, and the Northern Indiana Rail Road Company, of the fourth part; and the New York State Printing Company of the fifth part, concerning the construction of a line of telegraph, O'Rielly Docs., Telegraph Pamphlets. This contract is given in full in Appendix 10 as typical of those which were being made between the telegraph and the railroad companies during this period.

graph offices equipped with all necessary apparatus and with suitable fixtures and furniture were to be provided by the railroads. The cost of maintenance was to be borne by the telegraph company from the time it took possession of the lines. It was further agreed that upon completion of the lines according to specifications they were to become the property of the telegraph company, and pass under its complete control and management. The telegraph company, for its part, was then to issue an amount of stock equal to $125 a mile for the whole length of the lines. Additional stock equal to $30 a mile was to be issued for the House patent rights.[2] The increase in capitalization required to carry out this ambitious building program had already been approved by the New York & Mississippi Valley stockholders on February 1, when they had voted to increase the capital stock of the company by a sum not to exceed $92,500.[3]

Further important stipulations of the contract required the railroad companies to transport representatives of the telegraph company without charge when they were traveling on company business, and to carry the necessary materials for repairing the lines. Moreover, railroad repair men were expected to observe the condition of the telegraph lines and mend the breaks. The railroad companies, however, were not to be responsible for keeping the telegraph lines in order. They also agreed that during the continuance of the New York & Mississippi Valley Printing Telegraph Company, they would not allow any other telegraph line to be constructed along their roads.

In return for these favors, the telegraph company agreed to keep the lines in good working order, to maintain offices in specified towns and cities, and to transmit messages pertaining to railroad business without charge. Moreover, messages concerning the movement of trains or in any way connected with the operation of the roads, and requiring immediate attention, were to be given priority over all other business, in so far as the company lawfully could. As a further favor to the railroads, the New York & Mississippi Valley entered into an agreement with its ally, the New York State Printing Telegraph, by which the officers and agents of the railroad companies were to be permitted to transmit messages over the House line between Buffalo and New York without charge in return for a promise by the New

---

2 *Ibid.*

3 Agreement, February 1, 1854, by which the stockholders of the New York & Mississippi Valley Printing Telegraph Company authorized an increase in the company's capital stock issue, O'Rielly Docs., Telegraph Pamphlets.

York & Mississippi Valley that it would continue to connect with and transmit its messages over the New York State Printing Telegraph line.[4]

Thus Sibley and his associates, in spite of the strenuous efforts of their rivals to block them, and without the expenditure of any actual cash, had been able to conclude successfully a contract which would give the company between 500 and 600 miles of additional line, and bring it into telegraphic communication with the important cities of Chicago and Detroit, as well as numerous lesser towns and cities in the growing West.

Less than two months later came another conquest. O'Rielly's ill-fated Lake Erie Telegraph, with lines extending from Buffalo to Detroit and from Cleveland to Pittsburgh, was already on the friendliest of terms with the House interests. Its early promoters included in their number Samuel L. Selden who was a key man in promoting the House telegraph.[5] The leasing of the Lake Erie line by the New York & Mississippi Valley on March 30, 1854, was a natural outcome. According to the agreement entered into, Sibley's concern was to pay as rent, "a sum which shall be equal to the dividends, which the . . . [New York & Mississippi Valley] shall, from time to time, make upon fifty thousand dollars of its own stock. . . ." In addition, the New York & Mississippi Valley was to issue $50,000 of its stock in the name of the directors of the Lake Erie Telegraph Company. But for the time being, it was to be retained by Secretary Elwood and was to be delivered to the Lake Erie directors, only after they had turned over to him an absolute assignment and conveyance on the line and on all other company property, "together with the right to use Morse's patent thereon, executed by all the holders of stock in said Lake Erie Telegraph Company." In the meantime, the directors of the Lake Erie Company were to have the right of voting upon this stock at all meetings of the stockholders of the New York & Mississippi Valley. The agreement further stipulated that should the Lake Erie Telegraph, at any time, obtain an injunction restraining the use of Morse's telegraph upon the rival Erie & Michigan line, temporarily or otherwise, then the New York & Mississippi Valley would pay the Lake

---

[4] Articles of Agreement, February 7, 1854, *op. cit.*

[5] Samuel L. Selden had first become interested in the House patent at the time he was attempting to free O'Rielly from dependence on the Morse patent. For earlier discussion of this subject, see Chapters v, x, xvi.

Erie at the rate of $5,000 a year for such time as the restraint should continue.[6]

Once more Sibley and his aides, with no actual cash outlay, were able to bring under their control lines aggregating about 600 miles in length and reaching such important centers as Buffalo, Cleveland, Pittsburgh, and Detroit. Following the execution of this lease, Lake Erie stock soon found its way, at low prices, into the hands of the lessors, and within a few years the old Lake Erie ceased to exist.

This was the period in the New York & Mississippi Valley's history when Hiram Sibley, "grip-sack" in hand, journeyed up and down the land on line "forages"—that is, buying up telegraph stock at nominal prices. For example, the capital stock of one perishing company, valued at $240,000, was bought by Sibley at less than two cents on the dollar.[7]

2 ··—··

WITH his program of expansion now fairly launched, Sibley proceeded to lay the foundations for further progress. The New York & Mississippi Valley Printing Telegraph Company agreed to issue to the holders of the House patent interest $40,000 of its capital stock for the use and control of the patents in the States of Ohio, Indiana, Illinois, Michigan, Wisconsin, and Iowa, and the Territory of Minnesota, with the right of connecting its lines with St. Louis. Then to enable the company to purchase an interest in various lines, and to construct others in the six States and the Territory for which it controlled the House patent, either the Board of Directors, or the Executive Committee, was authorized to issue bonds to the amount of $100,000. The bonds bearing interest at a yearly rate of 7 percent were to be disposed of at discounts of not more than 25 percent. The board of directors was further authorized, with the written consent of those holding two-thirds of the capital stock, to issue additional stock for similar purposes. At the same time, the number of directors was reduced from nineteen to nine and a bare marjority of those was to constitute a quorum. In other words, the imperious Sibley

[6] Agreement, March 30, 1854, between the Lake Erie Telegraph Company, of the one part, and the New York & Mississippi Valley Printing Telegraph Company of the other part, concerning lease of the Lake Erie's property, O'Rielly Docs., Telegraph Pamphlets. This agreement given in full in Appendix 11.

[7] "Telegraph History," *New York Evening Post*, February 27, 1885.

with the support of any four of his associates on the board, could thereafter manage the company's affairs as he saw fit.[8]

Many a crisis had to be met and resolved, however, before Hiram Sibley was to achieve success. Times were hard and no market could be found for the company's bonds. The directors and their friends were compelled to take them, discounting their personal notes to pay for them.[9] Moreover, Sibley's further advance into the West seemed to be effectively blocked by the activities of the hostile Cornell-Speed-Wade lines, the National Lines under Superintendent J. D. Reid, and the closely allied, Illinois & Mississippi Telegraph Company under the direction of Judge J. D. Caton.[10]

But Hiram Sibley, resourceful and thoroughly conversant with every phase of the telegraph situation in the West, was not to be denied. Instead of a frontal attack upon the enemy, he proceeded to execute a brilliant flanking movement. Cornell's associates, John J. Speed and Jeptha H. Wade, were approached and asked confidentially to name a price at which they would sell out their entire interests. Their relations with their chief were such that there was no feeling of loyalty for Cornell to deter them. The price named—$50,000—was high, for they did not intend nor expect that their offer would be taken. Much to their surprise, however, their offer was promptly accepted, and a formal agreement was entered into on April 29, 1854.[11]

Thus at one blow the Cornell-Speed-Wade system was split asunder. Moreover, Sibley and his associates, in addition to securing control of a valuable range of lines throughout Ohio, Indiana, Illinois, and Michigan, and an important interest in the Erie & Michigan and a number of other telegraph companies, secured the future services of Jeptha H. Wade whose abilities as a promoter, negotiator, and organizer were second only to those of Sibley himself.[12] A further

8 An agreement made and entered into this twenty-ninth day of April, 1854, between the New York & Mississippi Valley Printing Telegraph Company of the first part; Francis Morris, Hiram Sibley and Freeman M. Edson, trustees to hold the undisposed interests in House's Telegraph Patents, of the second part; and Henry S. Potter, and others, stockholders of said telegraph company, of the third part, O'Rielly Docs., Telegraph Pamphlets.

9 A. R. Brewer, *Western Union Telegraph Company. A Retrospect*, 22.

10 Cornell to Caton, March 6 and March 24, 1854, Caton Papers; Cornell to E. Cobb, March 27, 1854 (copy sent to J. D. Caton by Cobb), Cobb to Caton, April 3, 1854, Caton Papers.

11 Speed to Caton, May 4, 1854, Caton Papers; agreement, April 29, 1854, between J. J. Speed and J. H. Wade of the first part, and the New York & Mississippi Valley Printing Telegraph Company, of the second part, O'Rielly Docs., Telegraph Pamphlets. This contract is given in full in Appendix 12.

12 Manuscript autobiography of J. H. Wade, in possession of the Wade family of

valuable consideration in this purchase was the unsold interest in the Morse patent for the States of Ohio, Illinois, Michigan, and Wisconsin, Iowa, and the Territory of Minnesota, in so far as Speed and Wade controlled it. For these properties and rights, the New York & Mississippi Valley Printing Telegraph was to pay the sum of $50,000 —$12,500 in cash upon the execution and delivery of the proper conveyances, and the remaining $37,500 "to be secured by the promissory notes of responsible parties, payable one-third in six, one-third in twelve, and one-third in eighteen months with interest at 7 percent, said notes to be guaranteed by the New York & Mississippi Valley Printing Telegraph Company."[13]

Cornell was almost beside himself at this betrayal. His plans for controlling telegraphy in the West were given a terrific setback; the very existence of his lines was endangered. To Judge Caton, whose friendship and cooperation he courted assiduously, he complained of the deception which had been practiced upon him. He related how he had left the West to take care of business in the East and upon arriving in New York City, had been surprised to find his associates, Wade and Speed, there. He had inquired of them if anything was going on, and was answered, "Nothing." Then a few days later he "was thunderstruck by information from Speed that he and Wade had sold out all their telegraph interest to the House folks." In the transaction, explained Cornell, "Speed sold all the Morse patent, my interest as well as his, thus giving the House folks our own tools with which to defeat us in our operations for extending our lines, and fortifying and protecting our business.

"I asked the Colonel mildly why he sold my interest in the patent. His answer was 'to make money, by God.'

"This is the foulest piece of treachery toward me that I have ever known and the reason assigned is appropriate; it is the reason for which Judas betrayed his Lord, and for which Arnold betrayed his country.

"How I stand, or what position I occupy, I am unable as yet to understand, as all parties to the foul bargain refuse even to let me see the contract. I am looking about me to see what can be done by way of protecting what I have left.

Cleveland, Ohio; J. H. Kennedy, "The Early Railroad Interests of Cleveland," *Magazine of Western History*, II, 608-609 (based on an interview which Kennedy had with J. H. Wade).

[13] Agreement, April 29, 1854, *op. cit.*

"I write this early to you that you may stand on your guard, if any of the conspirators approach you. . . . I hope you will stand firm, and hold on to your position and do the best you can for the stockholders."[14]

Ezra Cornell was not one to surrender weakly. Gathering together the scattered fragments of his former system, and making such new connections as he could, he prepared to carry on against the "House tribe" to the bitter end.[15]

In June the New York & Mississippi Valley gave warning of its rising position in the West through a widely circulated printed notice. Among other things the company claimed the exclusive control of all telegraph patents in Ohio, Indiana, Illinois, Michigan, Wisconsin, Iowa, and the Territory of Minnesota. It claimed also to control all the former Wade lines, several of the Speed lines, and O'Rielly's old Lake Erie line which, added to its own lines connecting Buffalo with Cleveland, Columbus, Dayton, Cincinnati, Lexington, Frankfort, and Louisville, afforded an efficient and complete service in the area covered. The notice pointed out the confusion that had existed in the telegraph industry up to this time due to the conflicting claims to the Morse patent, the competition between Morse and House systems, and the short, disconnected, and poorly built lines acting without coordination and without responsibility beyond their respective limits. Now, however, for the first time since the invention of the telegraph, the different patents, interests, and lines in the extensive midwestern territory could be controlled sufficiently to meet the public's needs. The confusion heretofore prevailing would now give way to harmony; the telegraph would be made to serve the purpose for which it was intended. The circular concluded with the advice that railroad and other companies or individuals wishing to arrange for lines of telegraph or the right to use the patents should communicate with the principal agent of the company, Jeptha H. Wade, Columbus, Ohio.[16]

Cornell promptly issued a circular hotly countering the claims put forth by his competitors. He denied that the New York & Mississippi Valley Printing Telegraph Company controlled either the Morse patent in the territory specified in its circular or any of the former

14 Cornell to Caton, May 5, 1854, Caton Papers.   15 Ibid., June 3, 1854.

16 Circular issued by the New York & Mississippi Valley Printing Telegraph Company [June 1854], reprinted by Cornell and sent with his refutation to Caton and others, June 22, 1854, Caton Papers; Brewer, Western Union Telegraph Company. A Retrospect, 20-21.

Speed lines. The claim of the House Company, Cornell wrote, was based upon a pretended purchase of the right to use the Morse patent from J. J. Speed, Jr., his former partner in the ownership of the patent. As the sole remaining partner, Cornell claimed that he had the exclusive control of the Morse patent in the territory in question. Railroad companies and others desiring to erect telegraph lines were warned not to contract with the New York & Mississippi Valley for the use of the Morse patents. All claims to the use of the patent would be contested by Cornell. Any correspondence or request relative to the use of the Morse patent must be addressed to the only persons having the right to grant license for its use—Ezra Cornell at Indianapolis or Judge J. D. Caton at Ottawa, Illinois.[17]

Meanwhile, Cornell's position had been considerably improved by the establishment of close working relations with Reid's National Lines. By the middle of June he had become so confident of the future that he was predicting to Caton, ". . . they [New York & Mississippi Valley] will be in the market in less than twelve months to sell out; there is [sic] no more traitors for them to buy and what they have got don't save them."[18]

At the annual meeting of the stockholders of the Erie & Michigan for the election of officers held in Detroit on July 5, a lively contest for control of the company occurred between the Cornell and House factions. Much to his satisfaction, Cornell was able to command enough votes to secure his election as president, and men whom he believed to be friendly to his interests as directors.[19]

Just at this critical juncture, however, a series of misfortunes descended upon Cornell. As the result of a serious accident he was confined to his house and unable to look after his affairs for months. Rumors spread abroad regarding his solvency.[20] A group of Utica capitalists who had advanced Cornell money for purchasing control of an important western link, the Southern Michigan Telegraph Company, demanded their money.[21] The House Company as lessees of the Lake Erie Telegraph obtained an injunction against the Erie &

17 Circular issued by Cornell refuting claims of the New York & Mississippi Valley Printing Telegraph Company, June 22, 1854, Caton Papers.

18 Cornell to Caton, June 14, 1854, Caton Papers; cf. Cornell to Caton, June 6, 1854, Caton Papers; *Ibid.*, June 30, 1854.

19 Cornell to Morse, July 7, 1854, Morse Papers, xxxIII.

20 R. Chadwick to S. A. Strong, October 12, 1854, Cornell Papers; [Cornell], *True and Firm*, 106-107.

21 Cornell to Caton, October 30, 1854, Caton Papers; George Curtiss, Silas D. Childs, and T. S. Faxton to Messrs. Cornell and Speed, November 8, 1854, Cornell Papers.

Michigan restraining it from the operation of its line between Buffalo and Cleveland.[22]

In numerous ways, Sibley and his associates tried to take advantage of the disabled and hard-pressed Cornell.[23] In a letter to Judge Caton he elaborated upon the ramifications of the conspiracy. Operators in his principal offices were being offered more money by the House Company and his officers, Cobb and Haviland, had obviously been bribed to betray him. Cornell related that he had recently met an agent of the Associated Press in Buffalo who had wished to know why the Erie & Michigan had refused to make arrangements with the press association to send reports west from that city. Further conversation revealed that Cobb and Haviland had informed the press agent that the Erie & Michigan would enter into no fixed agreement for the transmission of news reports. Cornell's perfidious associates had then suggested that such an arrangement might be made through the House Company, a suggestion upon which the press agent had acted.[24]

Every effort was being made, Cornell declared, to prevent him from securing the necessary money to meet his obligations, for should he fail, his Erie & Michigan stock, which was pledged for his debts, would be sold. "The House Company have pursued this policy ever since they bought Speed and Wade; they have been assured by them that if I was pressed hard, I could not get through and hold the controlling stock of the Erie & Michigan line."[25]

With grim determination Cornell carried on and managed somehow to weather the storm. By the summer of 1855, however, he had come to realize that the Rochester interests were too powerful to be driven from the field. Reporting to the stockholders of the Erie & Michigan Telegraph Company on July 1, President Cornell foreshadowed the future. The earnings of the past year, he told them, would have been larger except for the extension of rival House lines to Chicago. There was every reason to believe that their company could hold its own and make an 8 percent dividend, but a large amount of money could be saved if the rival companies were united on an equitable basis. Some earnest efforts had recently been made

22 Morse to Kendall, October 30, 1854, Morse Papers, Letter Book A.
23 Cornell to Caton, November 1, 1854, Caton Papers; E. Cobb to Cornell, [October] 31, 1854, Cornell Papers.
24 Cornell to Caton, November 16, 1854, Caton Papers; cf. *Ibid.*, November 23, 1854.
25 Cornell to Caton, November 26, 1854, Caton Papers; cf. Isaac R. Elwood to J. D. Caton, December 2, 1854, Caton Papers, for the rebuttal by the Rochester interests.

to consolidate the two companies, Cornell concluded, and it was to be hoped that a union might soon be effected.[26]

It was only after four months of intermittent and acrimonious negotiation that Sibley and his associates were able to secure Cornell's consent to terms of consolidation satisfactory to all the parties concerned.[27] The contract of union, which was to become effective November 1, 1855, was of far-reaching importance. Not only did the Rochester interests gain control of the Erie & Michigan Telegraph Company and all its many important tributaries and connections, but most valuable of all, they also acquired complete sovereignty over the use and sale of the Morse patent in the States of Ohio, Indiana, Illinois, Michigan, Wisconsin, Iowa, and the Territory of Minnesota. Already controlling the House patent rights for the West, Sibley and his associates were now in a position to determine the future development of the telegraph in that region. Any additional lines built would be obliged to apply to Rochester for permission to use either of the leading patents.

In order to carry out the consolidation, it was agreed that the New York & Mississippi Valley should increase its capital stock to $500,000 of which $150,000 was to be issued to the stockholders of the Erie & Michigan, while the remaining $350,000 was to be retained by Sibley and his associates. The Erie & Michigan was to be entitled to at least two members on the board of directors of the consolidated company at all times. It was further agreed, upon Cornell's request, that the consolidated company was to be reincorporated under the general law of the State of New York as "The Western Union Telegraph Company." In respect to earnings it was provided that after payment of current expenses, seven-tenths of the net earnings were to be set apart to be applied to the indebtedness of the New York & Mississippi Valley. Of the remaining three-tenths, the first $5,000 was to be applied to the payment of any outstanding indebtedness of the consolidated company, after which a dividend might be paid to the former Erie & Michigan stockholders not to exceed 6 percent

[26] Report of the President to the Stockholders of the Erie & Michigan Telegraph Company, July 1, 1855, Cornell University Library.

[27] Memoranda in Cornell's handwriting dealing with the negotiations for consolidation [n.d.], 1855, Cornell Papers; Contract of Union between the New York & Mississippi Valley Printing Telegraph Company and the Erie & Michigan Telegraph Company, September 20, 1855, to be effective October 1, 1855, Cornell Papers. (Cornell has written on the back "Consolidation Contract as signed by Howard and Walbridge [the other two members of the Erie & Michigan Telegraph Company's consolidation committee] which I declined to sign. E. C.")

per annum; any funds remaining were to be applied to the payment of the consolidated company's indebtedness until it was fully discharged.[28]

3 ···—·

MEANWHILE the Rochester interests had also begun the task of breaking up J. D. Reid's National Lines system, and the American Telegraph Confederation of which it was a part. Instead of building rival lines and embarking upon a policy of ruinous competition, Sibley and his confederates made use of more subtle weapons. Reid's National Lines, as has already been shown, had never been a very harmonious group.[29] While one important faction headed by Reid strongly favored outright consolidation of the various companies that made up the system, another faction dominated by the spirit of local autonomy was bitterly opposed.[30]

At the annual meeting of the Atlantic & Ohio stockholders in 1855, an attempt was made by a separatist faction, which was strongly suspected of being inspired from Rochester, to break up the National Lines system. In a bitterly contested vote on the question of continuing the working alliance with the other members of the system, Reid and his friends finally won, but by a very narrow margin. Having failed in this stratagem, Sibley and his lieutenants directed their attention in another direction.[31]

Only a few months had passed when ominous rumblings began to be heard from the Ohio & Mississippi Telegraph, the westward extremity of Reid's system. Certain directors declared their line was being used to enrich its eastern neighbors, the Pittsburgh, Cincinnati & Louisville, and Atlantic & Ohio Companies, while it received the crumbs. Balance sheets seemed to substantiate this contention.[32] Consequently when Joshua N. Alvord, superintendent of the company, offered to lease the line personally for a term of seven years at 5 percent yearly on its capital stock of $90,000, the offer was promptly accepted and a lease entered into on February 7, 1856.[33] Alvord's

---

[28] Agreement to consolidate between the New York & Mississippi Valley Printing Telegraph Company and the Erie & Michigan Telegraph Company, October 19-20, 1855, O'Rielly Docs., Telegraph Pamphlets. This contract given in full in Appendix 13.

[29] For earlier discussion of the disunity of the National Lines, see Chapter XII.

[30] Reid, *Telegraph in America*, 166-169, 227-230.   [31] *Ibid.*, 171-172.

[32] *Ibid.*, 229.

[33] Agreement between the Ohio & Mississippi Telegraph Company of the first part and Joshua N. Alvord of the second part, February 7, 1856, O'Rielly Docs., Telegraph Pamphlets.

willingness to assume this heavy responsibility was explained, when less than a week later on February 13, he sold his lease to the New York & Mississippi Valley Printing Telegraph Company for an added $2,700 per annum.[34] Ohio & Mississippi stock purchased at low prices soon found its way into the hands of Sibley and his associates, and another link of the original O'Rielly range was absorbed.

The loss of this valuable Louisville-St. Louis link was a serious blow both to the National Lines and to that larger association of Morse companies, the American Telegraph Confederation. Vigorous action was needed to forestall further aggressions, yet nothing was done. In striking contrast with the purposeful movements of the House concern were the confusion, indecision, distrust, and spirit of defeatism which characterized the activities of the leading Morse companies. The Magnetic proposed, for example, to test the legality of the House system by suing, for the benefit of all the companies concerned. Should the suit be successful and the House system proved an infringement, the various Morse companies would have to pay nothing and would profit by the suppression of their rival; on the other hand, the Magnetic refused to press the suit unless, in the event of failure, the companies would guarantee to pay their portion of the expense. The New York, Albany & Buffalo Telegraph Company declined to join in the proposed suit and the matter was dropped.[35]

Then early in April 1855—months before his consolidation with the House interests—Cornell had written George W. Curtiss, president of the New York, Albany & Buffalo, informing him of his intention to dispose of all his telegraph property, and promising that he would make his first offer to the New York, Albany & Buffalo. Failing in that, concluded Cornell, he would turn to the National Lines; and lastly, to the House interests. Here was a situation requiring speedy and intelligent action; but President Curtiss seemed to have no idea of how to deal with it. Writing to Morse on April 5, he announced: "The House Company are boasting that they will soon have the control of all the telegraph business west of Buffalo and consequently we shall be cut off from all western business; it may be

34 Agreement and assignment between Joshua N. Alvord of the first part, and the New York & Mississippi Valley Printing Telegraph Company of the second part, February 13, 1856, O'Rielly Docs., Telegraph Pamphlets.

35 S. F. B. Morse to the stockholders of the New York, Albany & Buffalo Telegraph Company, August 2, 1854, Morse Papers, XXXIII; Morse to Kendall, September 30, 1854, Morse Papers, Letter Book A; George Curtiss to William M. Swain, November 21, 1854, Morse Papers, XXXIV; Morse to Thos. R. Walker, April 9, 1855, Morse Papers, Letter Book A.

and very probably is the case that they are negotiating with Cornell for his interest West and thereby will get control of the business west of Buffalo. If they do, it will reduce our receipts very much and I see no way we can help it."[36]

It was against such feeble opposition that Sibley and his associates proceeded. Repeated attempts by the Rochester-controlled New York State Printing Telegraph Company to lease or buy the New York, Albany & Buffalo lines had failed.[37] Instead of engaging in a senseless war with the powerful, well-entrenched Morse company, Sibley resorted to diplomacy.

All the skill he could muster was needed, for a new patent—the Hughes patent, and a new company—the American Telegraph Company—had just entered the field to complicate the picture further. With the substantial backing of a group of New York City capitalists headed by Cyrus W. Field, the newcomer was trying to accomplish along the seaboard substantially the same thing that Sibley and his associates were attempting in the West. Desiring the New York, Albany & Buffalo line as a part of its system, the American Telegraph Company had offered to lease it for twenty years at an annual rental of 8 percent on its capital stock of $250,000. A number of the leading New York, Albany & Buffalo stockholders, including Morse and Kendall, favored the project.[38]

Sibley met this dangerous threat with a clever counter-proposal. He suggested that the New York, Albany & Buffalo lease the rival House line, establish a monopoly on the New York, Albany & Buffalo route, and then defy the Hughes interests, or any other, to invade that territory. Such an arrangement, hinted Sibley, should net the company 15 or 20 percent.[39]

While the New York, Albany & Buffalo directors were considering Sibley's proposals, Field withdrew the American Telegraph Company's offer. Whatever his strategy was, the result was unfortunate, for the New York, Albany & Buffalo directors hesitated no longer.[40] On February 15, 1856, they proceeded to lease the lines of the New York State Printing Telegraph for ten years at an annual rental of 7

[36] George Curtiss to Morse, April 5, 1855, Morse Papers, xxxiv.

[37] Ibid.; Morse to Thomas R. Walker, April 4, 1855, Ibid. For earlier discussion of this subject, see Chapters x, xvi.

[38] Morse to Thos. R. Walker, December 15, 1855, Morse Papers, Letter Book B.

[39] Ibid.; George Curtiss to Morse, January 14, 1856, Morse Papers, xxv; George Curtiss to E. Cornell, January 22, 1856, Cornell Papers.

[40] For discussion of this point, see Chapter xix.

percent, on its capital of $200,000. In return, Sibley and his associates received a promise from the New York, Albany & Buffalo that the New York & Mississippi Valley Printing Telegraph Company should be given an exclusive connection at Buffalo. For the benefit of the other House companies throughout the United States, the agreement contained a clause requiring the New York, Albany & Buffalo to give to the different House lines at least as large a proportion of business destined to points reached by them, as the New York, Albany & Buffalo received from them, provided the House lines could do the business with reasonable promptness and on terms as favorable as those of the Morse companies. It was further agreed that on March 1, 1866, the capital stock of the New York, Albany & Buffalo should be increased to $500,000 so that it might absorb the New York State Printing Telegraph Company. Of this amount, $300,000 was to be issued to the holders of the old New York, Albany & Buffalo stock, and $200,000 to the holders of the New York State Printing stock.[41]

By this single bit of masterly diplomacy, Sibley transformed a bitter enemy into a firm ally; and, at the same time, the Rochester interests were assured of a 7 percent return on their New York-Albany-Buffalo line, and an exclusive connection at Buffalo for their growing western system. Reid's National Lines, on the other hand, lost another valuable connection. The American Telegraph Confederation, which had never had any real strength, collapsed under the blow. Henceforth, the spirit of self-interest was to prove stronger than that of cooperation, among the leading Morse companies, and Sibley shrewdly capitalized upon this fact to conquer them one by one.

41 Thomas R. Walker to Morse, February 8, 1856, Morse Papers, xxxvi; Agreement between the New York State Printing Telegraph Company of the first part, and the New York, Albany & Buffalo Electro-Magnetic Telegraph Company of the second part, February 15, 1856, O'Rielly Docs., Telegraph Pamphlets.

CHAPTER XVIII

Colossus of the West:
the Western Union Telegraph Company

1 · — — ·

IN the spring of 1856 the New York & Mississippi Valley Printing Telegraph Company discarded its cumbersome name. Under the acts of the Wisconsin Legislature of March 4, 1856, and of the New York Legislature of April 4, 1856, the young concern was reincorporated as the Western Union Telegraph Company,[1] a name under which it was to rise in two short decades to become the largest and most powerful corporation in the United States.[2] Henry S. Potter, president of the old company, continued to hold that office in the new organization until July 30, when at the regular annual meeting Hiram Sibley was elected chief executive. Sibley was fortunate in having a group of remarkably able men to assist him in his labors. Isaac R. Elwood, secretary and treasurer of the company, performed his duties efficiently, while Jeptha H. Wade and Anson Stager made a splendid team for carrying out company policies. Wade—suave, persuasive, realistic—was chief negotiator, and he exhibited rare talent in arranging satisfactory terms of lease and consolidation by which lines were to be brought into the Western Union fold.[3] The heterogeneous lines secured by Wade's diplomacy were then taken by general superintendent Stager and skillfully fused into a unified system. Another valuable aid to President Sibley was the experienced board of directors made up largely of prominent Rochester business men: Henry S. Potter, Samuel L. Selden, Isaac Butts, Joseph Medbery, Alvah Strong, George H. Mumford, Freeman Clarke, Isaac R. Elwood, Ezra Cornell,[4] and J. M. Howard.[5]

[1] Western Union capitalization was set initially at $500,000, divided into shares of $100 each, with the right of increasing the capitalization to a sum not exceeding $1,000,000.

[2] An Act to change the name of the New York & Mississippi Valley Printing Telegraph Company, April 4, 1856, *New York Laws*, 1856, O'Rielly Docs., Telegraph Pamphlets; An Act to incorporate the Western Union Telegraph Company, March 4, 1856, *Wisconsin Laws*, 1856, *Ibid.*

[3] Reid, *Telegraph in America*, 468; Isaac R. Elwood to the Western Union stockholders [July] 1856, Cornell Papers.

[4] While Ezra Cornell and those writing about him in later years have maintained that he was a dominant figure in the early Western Union Telegraph Company, the existing

2 ··—··

THE tasks facing the Western Union management in the next few years were to require its utmost energy and ability. Hundreds of miles of line acquired by lease and consolidation had to be rebuilt according to improved standards of construction, numerous extensions had to be erected, the service had to be improved—in short, order and system had to replace confusion. By 1856 also the natural affinity of railroad and telegraph was becoming clear and the progressive leaders in both industries were eager to join wire and rail to their mutual advantage. Sibley, Wade, Stager, Caton, Green, and others labored ceaselessly to secure exclusive contracts for lines along the important railroad rights of way in their territories. To no small degree the future greatness of Western Union was built upon the dozens of exclusive railroad contracts drawn up by its founding fathers.[6]

Still another task of formidable proportions was the completion of the conquest of the West. James D. Reid's National Lines system, while it had lost the Louisville-St. Louis connection[7] to its rival in February 1856, was still an extensive and powerful combination consisting of the Atlantic & Ohio, the Pittsburgh, Cincinnati & Louisville, and the New Orleans & Ohio Telegraph Lessees, along with a number of minor tributaries. After several attempts to break up this combination proved abortive, Sibley and his chief lieutenants again resorted to their strategy of divide and conquer. With this in view, they turned their attention southward.

The southern lines—the People's and the New Orleans & Ohio—

records, including his own papers at the Cornell University library, fail to support this contention. After the consolidation of his telegraph interests with Western Union at the close of 1855, he became a minor figure in telegraph history. Except for his financial holdings in the company, his associations with it were limited.

[5] Reid, *Telegraph in America*, 468.

[6] Isaac R. Elwood to Caton, October 27, 1856, *et seq.*, Caton Papers; Caton to I. R. Elwood, March 11, 1857, Caton Papers; cf. Green to Morse, copy of minutes of executive board of New Orleans & Ohio Company, April 6, 1857, Morse Papers, xxxvii; a whole series of contracts between the New York & Mississippi Valley Printing Telegraph Company and the railroads; and later, between the Western Union Telegraph Company and the railroads are given in O'Rielly Docs., Telegraph Pamphlets. (Contract of the New York & Mississippi Valley Printing Telegraph Company with Cleveland & Toledo, the Michigan Southern and the Northern Indiana Railroad Companies, February 7, 1854; contract of New York & Mississippi Valley Printing Telegraph Company with the Buffalo & Erie Railroad, August 14, 1855; contract of Western Union with Cleveland & Erie Railroad, May 6, 1856; contract of Western Union with the Cleveland & Pittsburgh Railroad, January 21, 1857; *et seq.*)

[7] For detailed account, see Chapter XVII.

having become hopelessly entangled in financial difficulties following their consolidation in 1853,[8] had been leased the following year, as a last resort, to a group of Louisville business men. This group had proceeded to form an Association of Lessees, which was later formally incorporated as the New Orleans & Ohio Telegraph Lessees.[9] The dominant spirit behind the organization was Dr. Norvin Green, a young physician who had found politics more stimulating than his medical practice. At the time of his becoming one of the original Lessees he was the Government disbursing agent for a federal building project in Louisville. As his associate in the telegraph enterprise he was greatly aided by an able assistant, George L. Douglass. Under the progressive management of these two men the New Orleans & Ohio Lessees' line was thoroughly rebuilt along the rights of way of the railroads, and made one of the best in the country. The results were most gratifying; in July 1855, a dividend of 48.84 percent was declared on the then outstanding lessee stock of $32,500;[10] in January 1856, another dividend of 20 percent was paid;[11] and in April, still another dividend of 18 percent was paid.[12]

In the spring of 1856, Green and Douglass were alarmed by the appearance of Edward Creighton at strategic points along their route. Creighton, a native of Ohio, had been building telegraph lines for Sibley in the Middle West. His arrival in the South suggested at once that Western Union planned to build an opposition line to New Orleans. Telegraph messages regarding the prices of poles and the best routes for lines were wired to Sibley. Cipher messages added to the consternation of the southern directors. Upon Sibley's arrival in Louisville a short time later, therefore, Green and Douglass were

---

[8] For earlier discussion of this subject, see Chapter XII.

[9] The original Association of Lessees set up in June 1854, had a capital amounting to $31,500 which was held in the following proportions: S. F. B. Morse, $4,000; John M. Sharp, $3,000; G. L. Douglass, $7,750; William D. Reed, $6,000; Norvin Green, $5,000; and James D. Reid, $5,750. During the ensuing year there were admitted into the lease the following stockholders: A. E. Trabue, $1,000; John Kendall, $100; A. Kendall, $5,500; H. H. Forsyth, $200. These additions brought the total capital stock of the organization to $38,300. Finally on April 9, 1856, the Association of Lessees was formally incorporated as the New Orleans & Ohio Telegraph Lessees under acts passed by the legislatures of the various states through which the line was constructed. Norvin Green was elected president and G. L. Douglass, vice-president. (Kendall to Morse, June 17, 1854, Morse Papers, XXXIII; Kendall to Morse, November 1, 1854, cited in Kendall, *Autobiography*, 551; Norvin Green to Morse, July 20, 1855, Morse Papers, XXXV; W. D. Reed to Morse, January 16, 1856, Morse Papers, XXXV; *Ibid.*, March 18, April 13, 1856, Morse Papers, XXXVI.

[10] Norvin Green to Morse, July 20, 1855, Morse Papers, XXXV.

[11] W. D. Reed to Morse, January 16, 1856, Morse Papers, XXXV.

[12] *Ibid.*, April 13, 1856.

only too glad to listen to any reasonable proposal which the Western Union might have to make. Sibley complained of the exclusive connection which the New Orleans & Ohio maintained with the National Lines; he asked that his company be given a chance to compete for the transmission of the New Orleans & Ohio's business between Louisville and the East, if it could offer as good or better terms. Green and Douglass eagerly accepted this seemingly reasonable proposition and proceeded to notify the National Lines that they intended to terminate their existing exclusive contract. Henceforth, the forwarding of New Orleans & Ohio messages to points not reached by that company's own lines was to be open to competition, and messages would be sent over the line offering the largest rebate.[13]

The board of directors of the Pittsburgh, Cincinnati & Louisville Company, upon receiving this message, concluded that Sibley must have secured the southern business for his company. Having already lost their St. Louis connection to the aggressive Rochester interests several months previously, they were willing to believe the worst. So great was their sense of danger that upon Sibley's arrival in Pittsburgh, a lease was quickly arranged and executed by President Salmon P. Chase.[14]

The contract dated May 24, 1856, provided for the leasing of the entire property of the Pittsburgh, Cincinnati & Louisville, and the transfer of all contracts to Western Union for a term of ten years commencing June 1, 1856. The rental to be paid by Western Union was arranged upon a progressive basis; the first year it was to be $10,800; the second year it was to increase to $12,150; the third, fourth, and fifth years to $13,500; and during the remainder of the term it was to be $13,840 per annum. This lease was only a temporary measure. Western Union promptly took steps to secure the passage of legislation which would permit a complete consolidation of the two companies with a joint capitalization of $638,400, of which $500,000 would belong to Western Union.[15]

Instead of notifying their eastern ally, the Atlantic & Ohio Telegraph Company, of their action, the directors of the Pittsburgh, Cincinnati & Louisville remained silent. It was not until repeated rumors had reached the directors of the Atlantic & Ohio of the action

---

13 Reid, *Telegraph in America*, 209-210.

14 *Ibid.*, 196; cf. Kendall to Cornell, August 13, 1856, Cornell Papers.

15 Articles of Agreement between the Pittsburgh, Cincinnati & Louisville Telegraph Company, party of the first part, and the Western Union Telegraph Company, of the second part, May 24, 1856, O'Rielly Docs., Telegraph Pamphlets.

of their supposed ally that they finally made inquiry. On July 19, nearly two months after the lease had been arranged, a polite reply from President Chase informed them that the rumors were correct; but the Atlantic & Ohio directors were assured that the contract contained no provision which, in President Chase's judgment, would be prejudicial to their interests. "The contract," he declared, "was simply a measure of self-preservation on the part of the Pittsburgh, Cincinnati & Louisville Company against a competition ruinous to itself and its rival in business and beneficial to nobody."[16] Within a year the entire capital of the Pittsburgh, Cincinnati & Louisville Company had been converted into Western Union stock.

Following the lease of the Pittsburgh, Cincinnati & Louisville line, Sibley had nothing more to say to the New Orleans & Ohio Lessees about rebates; the southern company no longer had any choice but to send its messages East by way of the Western Union Lines. By its seemingly innocent act, the southern line had lost its independence and had become a vassal of the vigorous, young colossus of the West. It should be noted, however, that the new connection was not without its advantages to the New Orleans & Ohio Lessees. Western Union proceeded to turn over to its new associate all messages destined for delivery in the South which could be reached by the Louisville concern. The result was a marked increase in its business.[17]

Meanwhile, another company was being drawn irresistibly into the Western Union orbit. Judge Caton had managed the Illinois & Mississippi Telegraph lines admirably since taking control in 1852. As a member of the American Telegraph Confederation he had maintained a working alliance with the associated Morse lines for several years;[18] early in 1854 he had become the agent for the sale of the Morse patent right in the States of Illinois, Iowa, Wisconsin, and the Territory of Minnesota;[19] later he had cooperated closely with both Reid and Cornell in their battle with the Rochester forces. Then, as resistance to Sibley and his Rochester colleagues had become more

16 Salmon P. Chase to Messrs. Berryhill, Cummings and Swain, July 19, 1856, cited in Reid, *Telegraph in America*, 174.

17 Report of Norvin Green, president, to the stockholders of the New Orleans & Ohio Lessees for the year ending July [?], 1856, Morse Papers, xxxvi; Norvin Green to Morse, November 24, 1856, Morse Papers, xxxvii.

18 See the extensive correspondence of leaders in the industry with Caton, 1853-1854, Caton Papers.

19 Contract between John D. Caton of the first part, and J. J. Speed, Jr., of the second part respecting Morse patent rights in Illinois, Iowa, Wisconsin, and Territory of Minnesota, April 3, 1854, Caton Papers.

and more futile, Caton had adopted a policy of wary and limited cooperation with them, for only by such a policy could he hope to carry to fruition his plans for the development of the telegraph industry in his section of the country.[20]

On March 23, 1855, he had entered into an agreement with the New York & Mississippi Valley, which now controlled both the Morse and House patent rights in the West. Under its terms he was granted the exclusive right to make contracts with the railroad companies and others who might wish to construct telegraph lines within the States of Illinois, Wisconsin, Iowa, and the Territory of Minnesota under either patent. Two-thirds of the stock issue and approximately one-third of the construction profits on all lines built under the contract were to belong to the Rochester interests. Further, and most important, it was agreed that all such lines were to connect with and send messages only over the lines owned or controlled by the New York & Mississippi Valley.[21] About a year later, at the Rochester company's request, Caton had released a portion of the Territory of Minnesota and most of the State of Wisconsin.[22] Then, on April 24, 1856, a new agreement was entered into by which the Rochester company, now known as Western Union, sold to Caton for $10,000 its two-thirds interest in all lines either built or to be built under their earlier agreement; its share in the construction profits; and its rights in the House and Morse patents for Illinois and Iowa, as well as the rights for certain specified routes in Wisconsin and the Territory of Minnesota. The new agreement also contained a solemn reiteration of the covenant guaranteeing to Western Union an exclusive and perpetual business connection with all such lines.[23]

Under the terms of these agreements, Caton succeeded in closing a number of profitable contracts, especially with the leading railroads in Illinois and Iowa whose managers were gradually becoming aware of the invaluable aid which the telegraph could be in the

[20] See extensive correspondence of leaders in the industry with Caton, 1854-1856, Caton Papers: I. R. Elwood to Caton, December 26, 1854; T. Mason to Caton, January 24, 1855; Elwood to Caton, March 8, 1855; Cornell to Caton, March 19, 1855; et seq.
[21] Contract between John D. Caton of the first part, and the New York & Mississippi Valley Printing Telegraph Company of the second part, respecting Morse patent rights in Illinois, Iowa, Wisconsin, and Territory of Minnesota, March 23, 1855, O'Rielly Docs., Telegraph Pamphlets.
[22] Contract between J. D. Caton and New York & Mississippi Valley Printing Telegraph Company releasing a portion of the Territory of Minnesota, March 5, 1856, Ibid.
[23] Contract between J. D. Caton and the Western Union Telegraph Company respecting lines built under the 1855 agreement, April 24, 1856, Ibid.

operation of their roads.[24] As hundreds of miles of new line were constructed and the volume of business increased, Caton grew wealthy. But always in the background, watching every move, was Western Union. In a letter written to Caton by Secretary Elwood in October 1856, the nature of Western Union's relation with the Judge is well shown. Elwood had just learned that someone had made a contract with a railroad company in Iowa to build a line of telegraph from Davenport or Burlington to Ft. Des Moines and had applied to the "Hughes folks" for the right to use their instrument. The Hughes telegraph being still in the experimental stage, there was little immediate danger of an invasion of the West. But, concluded Elwood, "I felt it my duty to give you this intimation that you might take care of your interests which we consider intimately connected with ours."[25]

Caton, writing to Elwood some months later, expressed a similar sentiment when he declared, "We have undoubtedly a mutual dependence on each other and I trust we may ever zealously and in good faith endeavor to promote each other's welfare wherever we can properly."[26] While remaining nominally independent for another decade, and sometimes coming into conflict with certain of the Rochester company's policies,[27] Caton's Illinois & Mississippi and its satellites, the Illinois Central and the Chicago & Mississippi Telegraph Companies, had definitely swung into the Western Union orbit by 1856, and Sibley had no need to fear difficulty from this quarter.

In September 1856, still another of the former O'Rielly lines was engulfed by the onrushing Western Union flood. The Ohio, Indiana & Illinois, already under Rochester domination as a result of Western Union's purchase of the telegraph interests of Speed, Wade, and Cornell, was leased on September 22 for the remainder of its corporate existence at an annual rental of 1 percent on the outstanding stock issue so long as it did not exceed $240,050. Should it be found to exceed this sum, then there was to be a ratable reduction from the 1 percent.[28] The Ohio, Indiana & Illinois, following in the footsteps

[24] I. R. Elwood to Caton, September 7, 1855, Caton Papers; *Ibid.*, November 24, 1855; *Ibid.*, December 17, 1855; *Ibid.*, December 22, 1855; *Ibid.*, March 28, 1856; *et seq.*
[25] I. R. Elwood to Caton, October 27, 1856, Caton Papers; cf. Elwood to Caton, December 3, 1856, Caton Papers; *Ibid.*, December 15, 1856; *Ibid.*, December 26, 1856.
[26] Caton to Elwood, March 11, 1857, Caton Papers.
[27] E. D. L. Sweet to Caton, February 17, 1857, Caton Papers; E. Cobb to Caton, February 20, 1857, *Ibid.*; Elwood to Caton, February 21, 1857, Caton Papers; *Ibid.*, February 27, 1857; *et seq.*
[28] Articles of Agreement and Lease between the Ohio, Indiana & Illinois Telegraph Company of the first part, and the Western Union Telegraph Company of the second part, September 22, 1856, O'Rielly Docs., Telegraph Pamphlets; Reid, *Telegraph in America*, 475.

of its former companies, was soon completely assimilated by the omnivorous Rochester organization.

By the autumn of 1856 there remained but a single link of the old National Lines to dispute Western Union's hegemony over the telegraph industry in the West—the pioneer Atlantic & Ohio. Extending along the Pennsylvania Railroad's right of way from Pittsburgh to Philadelphia and holding vital connections with Baltimore and New York, it was a very valuable line; its stock was expensive and difficult to purchase, and its independent stockholders were imbued with local pride.

To Jeptha H. Wade was given the unenviable task of storming this final stronghold. Quietly he laid his plans. On May 27, 1856, it was announced that the Pennsylvania Railroad had granted a newly organized House concern, the Pennsylvania Telegraph Company, permission to place a wire upon a line of telegraph poles which the railroad had just erected between Pittsburgh and Philadelphia for its own use. The telegraph company in return promised to supply the chief offices of the railroad with new House printing telegraph instruments free of charge. These instruments, explained the House concern, were much superior to the Morse since information sent by the House instruments could not be taken off *en route*.[29] During the summer of 1856 the new Pennsylvania Telegraph Company rapidly opened offices along the Pittsburgh-Philadelphia route, and acting in close harmony with the now extensive Western Union system, it soon began to affect Atlantic & Ohio business seriously. Thoroughly outflanked, the Morse company listened eagerly to proposals for a union of interests.[30] The result was an agreement on January 9, 1857, by which the Atlantic & Ohio was to increase its capital stock to $650,000 of which $335,000—a majority—was to be issued in exchange for the stock of the Pennsylvania Telegraph Company. While the Atlantic & Ohio was continued in name, control of the company now passed into the hands of Wade and his Western Union colleagues.[31]

29 Memorandum of an Agreement between the Western Union Telegraph Company and the Pennsylvania Telegraph Company, an association formed for and now constructing a telegraph line from Pittsburgh to Philadelphia along the Pennsylvania Railroad, May 27, 1856, O'Rielly Docs., Telegraph Pamphlets; Contract between J. H. Wade and the Pennsylvania Railroad Company, February 12, 1856, *Ibid.*; Manuscript Autobiography of J. H. Wade.

30 Reid, *Telegraph in America*, 174-176.

31 Agreement between the Atlantic & Ohio Telegraph Company of the first part, and the Pennsylvania Telegraph Company of the second part, respecting the formation of "a perfect and perpetual consolidation," January 9, 1857, O'Rielly Docs., Telegraph Pamphlets; Agreement between the Atlantic & Ohio Telegraph Company of the first

By 1857 the Western Union Telegraph Company was dictator of the wires in the West. Through the construction of a few lines and the lease or purchase of many others, it had become a vast telegraph system with its lines reaching from Baltimore, Philadelphia, and New York on the Atlantic seaboard, to Buffalo, Pittsburgh, Cleveland, Cincinnati, Louisville, Detroit, Chicago, Milwaukee, and St. Louis in the west. Dozens of feeders extended out from the main trunk lines into nearly every profitable point in the States of Ohio, Indiana, Illinois, Michigan, and parts of Wisconsin and Missouri. The important Caton interests in Illinois and Iowa, while remaining independent, were closely circumscribed in their actions by the colossus of the West. Similarly, the New Orleans & Ohio Telegraph Lessees, dependent upon Western Union for connection with the rest of the nation, were in no position to oppose seriously the policies of their big neighbor to the north. The New York, Albany & Buffalo Company, bound by contract to give Western Union exclusive connection for all business west of Buffalo, was also a close ally.

Sibley and his associates with a relatively small amount of money, a large amount of determination, and a still larger amount of diplomacy, had accomplished in two years what others had failed to achieve in a decade. To be sure, conditions were right for consolidation at the time Sibley and his friends embarked upon their project, but that fact makes their achievement none the less brilliant.

3 · · · — ·

MANY a man might have been content to rest on his laurels after such an accomplishment. But Hiram Sibley, with true pioneer instinct and audacity, was already eagerly talking about and investigating the possibilities of a telegraph to the Pacific. Nearly two thousand miles of open plains and deserts, and savage Indian tribes, separated the telegraphic outposts of the nation in Missouri from the pioneer lines which had begun to spring up in the distant State of California. Friends warned of the impossibility of a transcontinental line, but in spite of all the hardships and risks involved, Sibley became convinced of its feasibility. Forcefully and eloquently he presented his project to the Western Union board at Rochester, but they had already ac-

part, and the Pennsylvania and Western Union Telegraph Companies of the second part, respecting future business relations, January 9, 1857, *Ibid.*

quired something of the conservatism of success and refused their assent to undertaking such a "crazy" scheme as a company venture.

Nor could the members of the board be entirely blamed for their conservatism. The company was already heavily involved in numerous undertakings, many of which were not yet thoroughly established. They maintained that if this latest brain-storm of Sibley's were undertaken at all, it should be under the auspices of an outside organization in which the Western Union and those directors of the company who favored the project could be properly represented. Under such an arrangement failure of the scheme—which many fully expected—would not imperil the Western Union Telegraph Company, or destroy its growing prestige.[32] The next few years were such busy ones in the industry that Sibley was obliged to let his transcontinental project rest, but it was not forgotten. The name of Western Union was to be carried to the far Pacific,[33] and made to embrace all the important telegraph interests in the United States, and even beyond, before Sibley and his chief lieutenants retired from the field.

[32] Reid, *Telegraph in America*, 488-489.
[33] For later discussion of the Pacific telegraph project, see Chapter xxv.

CHAPTER XIX

Emergence of the American Telegraph Company

1 · — — ·

WHILE the Western Union Telegraph Company was consolidating the telegraph interests in the West, a similar movement had been proceeding in the East. In 1854 Cyrus W. Field, a retired merchant of New York City, had become interested in telegraphic communication as the result of a series of conversations with an ambitious Canadian promoter, Frederick N. Gisborne. The Canadian had approached Field with a view to resuscitating an earlier project for a line of telegraph and cable to connect St. John's, Newfoundland, with the existing system of land telegraphs, which had been extended as far as Halifax, Nova Scotia, through the influence of the New York Associated Press. Such a circuit would shorten by at least forty-eight hours the time required for the news brought by the European steamers to reach the eager American public. Moreover, Gisborne felt confident that the patronage of the press and the important commercial interests of the great seaboard cities, would assure its financial success.[1]

Gisborne approached Field at a favorable time. Two years previously at the age of thirty-three, Field had retired from the wholesale paper business in New York City with a modest fortune. He had not found release from active participation in business enterprise to his liking. At the time Gisborne approached him, therefore, Field was looking for a new venture in which to engage an active mind. He listened with interest to Gisborne's proposal for extending the telegraph to Newfoundland, but in the course of their conversations Field's mind went one step further. Why not go ahead after reaching the easternmost point of Newfoundland and establish direct telegraphic communication by cable with England and Europe via Ireland?[2] The

[1] Philip B. McDonald, *A Saga of the Seas. The Story of Cyrus W. Field and the Laying of the First Atlantic Cable*, 30-34; Reid, *Telegraph in America*, 398-401.

[2] The idea of a submarine telegraph connecting Europe with the United States was not original with Cyrus W. Field. Projects for the construction of such a line had been under consideration for several years. The Superintendent of the Census in his report for 1852 mentions one such project—that of Tal. P. Shaffner—for a line of telegraph and cable to commence at the most northerly point of Scotland, run thence to the the Orkney Islands, and thence to the Shetland and Faeroe Islands. From the latter a cable of two hundred miles was to conduct the telegraph to Iceland, thence to Greenland, and across Davis Strait to Byron's Bay on the coast of Labrador. The entire length of

idea obsessed him, and after a careful examination of the project by experts, it was declared to be entirely feasible.[3]

Enthusiastically, Field now presented the grand enterprise to a group of wealthy acquaintances and fellow-entrepreneurs, Peter Cooper, Moses Taylor, Marshall O. Roberts, and Chandler White. The result was the organization on May 8, 1854, of the New York, Newfoundland & London Electric Telegraph Company, with a capital of $1,500,000. The new company proposed to construct a line of telegraph and cable linking St. John's, Newfoundland, with the existing line in Nova Scotia, and to lay a submarine cable from Newfoundland to Ireland. The charter which had been granted the company by the Newfoundland legislature was a liberal one. Under its terms Field and his associates were given an exclusive right to land ocean cables for a period of fifty years, a grant of $50,000 to aid in the work, fifty square miles of public land, and a bonus of fifty additional square miles when the cable was successfully laid.[4]

Peter Cooper was elected first president of the company, while Chandler White was chosen vice-president, Moses Taylor, treasurer, and S. F. B. Morse, honorary electrician. This last bit of subtle flattery bore abundant fruit. Morse, quite swept off his feet by the attentions of Field and his capitalist friends, was eager to aid in the great and noble plan of uniting the two continents by telegraph. He promised to allow the Newfoundland Company to use his patents on a line from the British Provinces to New York without charge, as far as he personally was concerned, and to do all in his power to persuade the existing telegraph companies in the United States to transmit messages for the Newfoundland Company at half price.[5] Moreover, by publicly supporting the enterprise, he lent it the weight of his name. So enamored had he become, that he even subscribed $10,000 to the capital stock of the company.[6]

the line was estimated at 2,500 miles—the submarine portions of it at 1,500 miles. The expense of this great international work, concluded the Superintendent, was estimated at £500,000. (Report of the Superintendent of the Census [1852], 114; *National Telegraph Review*, July 1853, 172; *Ibid.*, October 1853, 247-250.)

[3] Morse to Cyrus W. Field, February 24, 1854, Morse Papers, XXXII.

[4] "An Act to Incorporate a Company under the style and title of The New York, Newfoundland, and London Telegraph Company," passed by Newfoundland legislature, April 15, 1854, copy in Morse Papers, XXXIII; agreement between the corporators of the New York, Newfoundland & London Telegraph Company, May 8, 1854, copy in Morse Papers, XXXIII.

[5] Morse to Cyrus W. Field, July 16, 1855, Morse Papers, Letter Book A; Kendall to Morse, June 5, 1854, Morse Papers, XXXIII.

[6] Cyrus W. Field to Morse, July 13, 1854, Morse Papers, XXXIII.

This agreement entered into so innocently by Morse was to prove a source of embarrassment to him. Kendall warned that there were two features in the agreement which he very much regretted. The first was Morse's promise to use his influence to get the existing telegraph companies in the United States to transmit the messages of the New York, Newfoundland & London Telegraph Company at half price. Kendall pointed out to him that while there was not the slightest chance of any of the companies agreeing to such a proposition, Morse would be forced to vote his stock in all the companies to that end. Under the circumstances, the inventor would be liable to the imputation of using his power in the American companies to subserve a speculation in which they had no interest.

The second unfortunate provision, as Kendall saw it, was Morse's promise to allow the Newfoundland Company to use his patents, as far as he personally was concerned, without charge on a line from the British Provinces to New York. This had several untoward aspects. First, it was inconsistent with Morse's contract with Smith and Vail which bound the partners not to dispose of their individual interests without one another's consent. Secondly, it would be understood as a plan to coerce the New England companies, which had no direct interest in the speculation, to submit to any terms which might be dictated by the Newfoundland Company. The New England companies which had purchased Morse's patent right with a view to the business from the British Provinces, would have just cause for complaint if Morse compelled them to do it at an unfair price as a means of enhancing the value of his interest in the Newfoundland Company.

Kendall felt that there was no mistaking the object of that company in making the contract. It was to use Morse's rights and powers, as far as practicable, to make all the telegraph lines in the United States subservient to a grand speculation. In the months that followed, the inventor's dual role, as a leading stockholder in the Morse telegraph lines throughout the United States and as a stockholder in the Newfoundland Company, grew increasingly difficult.[7]

2 ·· — ··

NOT many months had passed before Field and his wealthy New York backers came to realize that a vigorous and successful transmission of European correspondence would require direct access to the great

[7] Kendall to Morse, June 5, 1854, *Ibid.*; cf. *Ibid.*, June 10, 1854; Morse to Kendall, June 13, 1854, Morse Papers, Letter Book A.

business centers of the United States. The numerous small lines already in operation along the eastern coast were slow, unreliable, and expensive, and such efforts as had been made at cooperation among them had not been very successful. Field determined, therefore, as part of a vast and ambitious program, to obtain control of the more important lines along the seaboard from Newfoundland to New Orleans and unite them into a single, effective telegraph system to be known as the American Telegraph Company.[8]

With this object in view, he approached the leading eastern telegraph interests—Morse, House, and Bain—in August 1855, and made offers to lease their lines. It was proposed, for example, that the Magnetic Telegraph Company be leased for twenty years with the privilege of renewal for a further term of thirty years at an annual rental of 8 percent on its capital of $369,300.[9] Leases on similar terms were offered the other eastern lines. The Washington & New Orleans was invited to lease its line for twenty years with a guarantee of 4 percent per annum on its capital of $561,700, and an equal division of net earnings over 8 percent. The New York, Albany & Buffalo was proffered a twenty-year lease at 8 percent on its capital of $250,000; the House concern over the same route, the New York State Printing, was offered 6 percent on its capital of $200,000.[10] Desiring to conclude arrangements as promptly as possible, Field requested early replies to his offers.[11]

Both Kendall and Morse, eager for the consolidation project to succeed, worked hard to secure the consent of the Morse companies to terms of lease. By the expenditure of much time and at considerable expense, they had finally secured the acceptance of terms by nearly all the important Morse companies. Plans had been made to convene special meetings for legally consummating the leases.[12] Then, just as success seemed about to crown their efforts, they were suddenly surprised by a formal withdrawal of the proposition and terms of lease without any satisfactory explanation of the reason for such an ex-

[8] Morse to Kendall, June 20, 1855, Morse Papers, XXXIV; Ibid., July 2, 1855, Morse Papers, Letter Book A.

[9] Wilson G. Hunt and Cyrus W. Field to the president and directors of the Magnetic Telegraph Company, August 1, 1855, copy in Vail Papers.

[10] For earlier reference, see Chapter XVII.

[11] Morse to Thos. R. Walker, July 21, 1855, Morse Papers, Letter Book A; Morse to Cyrus W. Field, July 21, 1855, Ibid.; Morse to Kendall, September 15, 1855, Ibid.

[12] Morse to Kendall, June 20, 1855, Morse Papers, XXXIV; Kendall to Morse, June 22, 1855, Ibid.; memorandum in Morse's handwriting in which he gives a brief history of the rise of the American Telegraph Company [n.d., probably 1856], Morse Papers, XL.

traordinary course. The letter sent to the president and directors of the Magnetic Telegraph Company, on September 14, simply announced: "The proposal made by Cyrus W. Field and Wilson G. Hunt on August 1st in reference to a company being formed for purpose of leasing certain telegraph lines, not having been answered on the part of the companies with the liberality anticipated is for the present withdrawn."[13]

In a conversation with Morse some days later, Field explained more fully his course of action. He and his associates had been disappointed at the course of negotiations, especially in so far as the line to Boston was concerned. Believing they recognized "the marplot hand of Fog Smith" in the deal, they had decided to teach him and a few fellow obstructionists a lesson. Withdrawal had, therefore, been made with a view to inducing "reflection in those who had been the cause of the difficulty" and in the belief that they would come to see how advantageous the offer had been. When they were in a properly repentant mood, the offer could be renewed.[14]

While such an explanation satisfied the trusting Morse, Amos Kendall was frankly skeptical. A series of attacks on the Morse system began to appear in the New York press a few weeks later, followed shortly by the announcement that a remarkable new printing telegraph instrument was soon to enter the field. Kendall's skepticism appeared to be well-founded. This new printer, the invention of David E. Hughes, a Kentucky professor of music, was declared to be so superior to existing telegraphs that it would supersede them all.[15]

In general appearance the Hughes instrument resembled that of House, but its operation was very different. In place of the clock-movement and the pendulum of the House apparatus, Hughes employed an ingenious contrivance called a spring-governor, which was nothing more than a vibrating spring. The spring-governor depended for its action upon the fact that a certain number of vibrations per second produced a specific musical tone. Therefore, if all the instruments on a telegraph line were set to the same tone, they would all run together. In short, it was a printing chronoscope in which minute divisions of time were translated by mechanical action into printed letters. The type-wheel while resembling that of the House instrument was different in application and movement. Instead of stopping

---

13 Wilson G. Hunt to William M. Swain, September 14, 1855, copy in Vail Papers.

14 Morse to Kendall, September 25, 1855, Morse Papers, Letter Book A.

15 Kendall to Morse, October 1, 1855, Morse Papers, xxxv; *New York Herald*, November 17, 1855; Morse to Cyrus W. Field, November 19, 1855, Morse Papers, Letter Book B.

for each letter to be printed, the Hughes machine printed the letters while moving at the rate of one hundred and thirty revolutions per minute. Moreover, it required but one-tenth the battery power needed to work the House system, and approximately one-third that of the Morse instrument.[16]

Hughes and his instrument had been unearthed by the wide-awake agent of the Associated Press, Daniel H. Craig, who now attempted by means of a flood of propaganda and vilification to discredit the Morse patent and the companies operating under it. While Field and his colleagues emphatically denied any association with the press campaign of Craig,[17] they exhibited a lively interest in the new printer; and on November 1, 1855, although the Hughes instrument was still very imperfect and not even patented, a contract was entered into for its purchase at a cost of $100,000.[18]

Morse, thoroughly alarmed at first, was reassured by his friends, Field and Cooper, that they had acquired the Hughes patent with the most friendly design toward the Morse interests. They had purchased it "to keep it out of the hands of men like Russell and Morris"— leaders of the House interests in the East.[19] Writing to Kendall, Morse explained that they had nothing to fear since the Hughes instrument was in the hands of friends.[20]

Kendall's reply must have shocked the good professor with its tone of stark realism. "As you say," counseled Kendall, "Field and Cooper are shrewd business men not unfriendly to you or me but more friendly to themselves. It was not friendship to us which induced them to buy the Hughes instrument; but it was, in fact, say what they will, to hold it in *terrorem* over our heads and the heads of our companies to induce us to let them have our lines at a reduced rent. This too is the source and object of their disparagement of our stocks with which they endeavor to alarm us. . . .

"Our policy is to keep on good terms with them without taking

---

[16] Prescott, *History, Theory and Practice of the Electric Telegraph*, 139-142.

[17] Morse to Kendall, November 23, 1855, Morse Papers, Letter Book B.

[18] The successful operation of the Hughes telegraph required perfect synchronization, and while readily obtained in laboratory tests, it proved difficult to maintain in practical tests upon the still imperfect telegraph lines of the day. As a result, the Hughes printer was of little practical value until after it had been greatly improved and altered by George M. Phelps during the years 1856-1857. It was on this improved Hughes instrument that a patent was finally granted on September 23, 1857. (Reid, *Telegraph in America*, 406.)

[19] For a more detailed reference to Robert W. Russell and Francis Morris, see Chapter XVI; cf. footnote 24 of Chapter XVI.

[20] Morse to Kendall, December 7, 1855, Morse Papers, Letter Book B.

alarm at their representations, satisfied (as I certainly am) that they have no thought of going into competition with us, and will in the end come up to their original offer."[21]

On the same day that the Hughes instrument was purchased—November 1, 1855—Cyrus W. Field, Wilson G. Hunt, Peter Cooper, H. Hyde, W. G. Crosby, Douglas B. Stevens, P. Jardine, Hiram O. Alden, James Eddy, and David E. Hughes, acting as corporators, proceeded to organize the American Telegraph Company under the laws of the State of New York, with a capital of $200,000 divided into shares of $100 each. The company was being established, stated the charter, "for the purpose of using under lease, purchase, construction or otherwise, a line or lines of telegraph both within and beyond the limits of this State, and of maintaining and operating the same, and of purchasing such letters Patent of telegraph instruments as they may see fit." Peter Cooper was elected president, Hiram O. Alden, vice-president, and James Eddy, treasurer and general superintendent.[22]

Prior to the formal organization of the American Telegraph Company preliminary arrangements had already been made for the establishment of an extensive telegraph system along the seaboard. A series of leases were now consummated with startling rapidity. The excellently managed line of the Maine Telegraph Company, which had been extended so as to connect Boston with the little town of Calais on the Maine border, was leased from January 1, 1856, for a term of fifty years, at an annual rental of 10 percent on its capital of $112,500.[23] The following month the New Brunswick Electric Telegraph Company was likewise leased for ten years with the privilege of renewal at an annual rental of $3,000.[24] On May 30, the House-operated Boston & New York Printing, or Commercial Telegraph Company,[25] along with a number of minor subsidiary lines in New England, were brought into the fold. The lines of the Commercial Telegraph had been controlled by D. H. Craig and several associates since 1853 in the interest of the New York Associated Press to rid

[21] Kendall to Morse, December 7, 1855, Morse Papers, xxxv.
[22] *Corporate History of the Western Union Telegraph Company* (typewritten unpublished document in the possession of the Western Union Telegraph Company), 30; Reid, *Telegraph in America*, 414.
[23] *Ibid.*, 396.
[24] *Ibid.*, 343.
[25] For earlier history of this company, see Chapter x.

that body of the obstructions thrown in the way of eastern press dispatches by F. O. J. Smith.[26] The leasing of the lines to the American
Telegraph served to strengthen Craig's hand in his battle with Smith,
and at the same time, provided another important link in the American Telegraph Company's rapidly growing system.

3 ··· — ·

PARALLELING these activities of the American Telegraph Company
were those of the closely allied New York, Newfoundland & London
Telegraph Company. During the summer of 1856, this aggressive
new organization had successfully established communication between St. John's and the Nova Scotian mainland by means of 400 miles
of land line and a short cable, at a cost of more than $800,000. While
engineer Matthew D. Field had been carrying this part of the project
to completion, promoter Cyrus W. Field was in England trying to
enlist British cooperation—both financial and technical—for the laying of an Atlantic cable to connect Newfoundland with Ireland.
Field's efforts resulted in the formation under English law of the
Atlantic Telegraph Company, with a capitalization of £350,000,
divided into shares of a thousand pounds each. Of the 350 shares, 262
were taken in England. Field returned to New York with the remaining 88 shares, but found American investors extremely reluctant to
invest in so hazardous an undertaking. As a result, he was left as the
largest American stockholder.[27]

The New York, Newfoundland & London Telegraph Company,
having transferred its monopoly for the landing of cables in Newfoundland to the Atlantic Telegraph Company, received in return
the promise of an exclusive connection with any cable which that
organization might lay across the Atlantic. The American Telegraph
Company, in turn, was granted an exclusive connection with the
Newfoundland Company. In this way the American Company was
placed in a position where it could control foreign news entering
the United States from the British Provinces, and, to a certain extent,
that leaving the United States destined for Europe.[28]

26 Reid, *Telegraph in America*, 407, 413. For the succeeding history of the Boston
& New York Printing, or Commercial Telegraph Company, see Chapter XVI.
27 McDonald, *A Saga of the Seas*, 34-40; Reid, *Telegraph in America*, 402.
28 *Ibid.*, 402.

4 . . . . —

LESS than a year after Field and his associates had formally launched their enterprise, the American Telegraph Company had become a force to be reckoned with in the industry. With its allies, it controlled a line of telegraph along the seaboard from St. John's, Newfoundland, to Boston and New York; and plans were well advanced for laying a transatlantic cable which would give the American Company's land lines an exclusive connection with Europe. Smith, Kendall, and the other leaders in the East found themselves confronted by a formidable new rival that daily threatened to extend its influence still more widely. The Hughes printing telegraph, should it come up to the claims made for it by Craig and a considerable portion of the press, would give the newcomer a weapon with which it could fight its way into every section of the country.

Accompanying the rise of the American Telegraph Company, but disavowed by Field and his associates, was the "war of nerves" which the press, under Craig's influence, conducted against both the House and Morse interests. In a typical news release Craig pointed out that there would not be a competing Hughes line if the House and Morse lines could be made to appreciate their true position. In that case, he claimed, they would see at once the folly of attempting to operate their rickety lines, and endeavor to sell or lease them to the American Telegraph Company which was willing to make arrangements with the old companies upon liberal terms which would pay the stockholders better dividends than they had ever received under existing managements.[29]

Kendall, Russell, Smith, and the other leaders in the East took the utterances of Craig for what they were—mere bombast—but they could not be sure that the American Company, although disclaiming connection with Craig, was not using him as a mouthpiece. Rumors began to circulate that Field and his associates planned to construct lines southward from New York to Philadelphia, Washington, and perhaps even to New Orleans. Field might be trying to frighten them into leasing their lines to him on favorable terms; then again, perhaps he really intended to build competing lines to be operated with Hughes instruments.[30] Confronted by a common danger, Morse and

[29] Open letter addressed to Amos Kendall by D. H. Craig, March 1, 1856, copy in Morse Papers, XXXVI.

[30] Kendall to Morse, March 5, 1856, Morse Papers, XXXVI; *Ibid.*, March 8, 1856; Morse to Field, March 8, 1856, Morse Papers, Letter Book B; Kendall to Morse, May 7, 1856, Morse Papers, XXXVI; Morse to Kendall, May 26, 1856, Morse Papers, Letter Book B.

House interests drew closer together. There was talk of a union between the Magnetic, the New York & Washington Printing, and the
Washington & New Orleans Telegraph Companies.[31] At the same
time, the American Telegraph Company renewed its offers to lease
these lines but at figures considerably reduced from those which had
been suggested originally in August 1855.[32] Proposals and counter-
proposals followed one another in weary succession.

Weeks passed without any action having been taken. Meanwhile,
Craig's "war of nerves" continued unabated. At last, Kendall and
the directors of the Magnetic decided to wait no longer. On June 19
they held a special meeting to consider the critical situation. The
opinion had become general that Craig was practically the instrument
of the American Company; and on the morning of the meeting he
issued one of his threatening news releases, obviously designed to
affect their deliberations.[33] Its effect was the reverse of that intended.

Instead of capitulating, the Magnetic board sent Field and his
associates a virtual ultimatum. A lease of the Magnetic line was once
more offered to them at 8 percent per annum for twenty-five years,
and it was moved that if the offer were not promptly accepted other
arrangements would be made. At the same time, the Magnetic board
resolved, in the event of refusal of this offer, to lease the Washington
& New Orleans themselves, and thus strengthen the Magnetic by
securing it against attack on its southern flank.

The American Telegraph Company having rejected their ultimatum, a lease of the Washington & New Orleans line was duly consummated by the Magnetic directors on July 7, 1856, for a term of
ten years at 4 percent per annum upon the southern company's
capital of $561,700; the next 4 percent earned was to be retained by
the Magnetic; and there was to be an equal division of all over
8 percent. It was further agreed that the Magnetic Company should
expend at least $25,000 in improving the line. This new arrangement
was in no sense intended to close the door upon future negotiations
with the American Telegraph Company. "I have no doubt," wrote
Kendall to Morse, who had the ear of Field and his associates, "the
Magnetic would now lease their line at 8 percent certain and transfer

31 R. W. Russell to William M. Swain, April 17, 1856, copy in Vail Papers.
32 Peter Cooper to William M. Swain, March 14, 1856, copy in Vail Papers; Kendall
to Morse, March 18, 1856, Morse Papers, XXXVI; Morse to Kendall, March 20, 1856,
Morse Papers, Letter Book B.
33 Kendall to Morse, September 16, 1856, Morse Papers, XXXVI; cf. Swain to Vail,
May 5, 1856, Vail Papers; *Ibid.*, May 9, 1856; Kendall to Morse, May 22, 1856, Morse
Papers, XXXIV.

the lease of the Washington & New Orleans if payments could be secured; so that the matter is still open to the American Company if they will give even less than the companies are now making."[34]

While keeping the door open for future negotiations with the American Telegraph Company, Kendall and the Magnetic directors proceeded with plans for a system of their own. In addition to leasing the southern line, a working alliance was established with the New York & New England Union Telegraph Company in the East, and negotiations were begun looking toward still closer ties with F. O. J. Smith's concern. There was also talk of arranging for additional connections so as to give the Magnetic Company a line into the West.[35] Kendall and his associates realized, as telegraph leaders all over the country were coming to realize, that the only hope for the security of their interests lay in powerful combinations.

[34] Kendall to Morse, September 19, 1856, Morse Papers, xxxvi; cf. *Ibid.*, July 7, 1856.
[35] Kendall to Morse, January 4, 1857, Morse Papers, xxxvii; cf. F. O. J. Smith to Kendall [January 1857], New York Public Library, MS Division.

CHAPTER XX

The "Treaty of the Six Nations," or Six Party Contract

1 ·——·

As the ambitious plans of the American Telegraph Company unfolded, leaders of other companies in the industry were disturbed. With the progress that company had made in absorbing and gaining control of telegraph interests northeast of New York, it threatened to become a formidable competitor, whether the Atlantic cable succeeded or not. And should the cable succeed, many felt that the whole telegraph interest would be almost at its mercy. In the general concern, leaders throughout the industry watched one another closely, and trips to New York for conversations were frequent in the spring of 1857.[1]

In March 1857, Kendall and Morse had an interview with Peter Cooper, Hiram O. Alden, and Wilson G. Hunt in which the leaders of the American Telegraph Company officially disavowed any responsibility for the injurious publications of Daniel H. Craig, and they authorized Morse to say that the publications in question were made without their knowledge, or authority, and contrary to their wishes. They stated that they had urged Craig to desist and, in consequence, he had promised to publish nothing further on the subject without first submitting the article to them. While thereby removing one of the causes for ill feeling, there remained others to prevent the establishment of entirely friendly relations. The following week Morse and Kendall met with committees of the Magnetic and the New York, Albany & Buffalo Telegraph Companies to discuss measures for self-protection should the American Company fail either to lease their lines or to give them satisfactory connections.[2]

Nor were the eastern leaders alone in their concern. Early in June 1857, Sibley, Wade, Clarke, Stager, and Elwood of the Western Union Company visited New York and had several interviews with

[1] Kendall to Morse, January 4, 1857, Morse Papers, xxxvii; Morse to Kendall, May 20, 1856, Morse Papers, Letter Book B; cf. Morse, *Letters and Journals*, ii, 372; Kendall to Morse, February 22, 1857, Morse Papers, xxxvii; Peter Cooper to Morse, March 10, 1857, *Ibid.*

[2] Morse to Thos. R. Walker, March 21, 1857, Morse Papers, Letter Book B; *Ibid.*, March 27, 1857.

the managers of the American Telegraph Company. The Rochester interests found the American Company disposed to form an alliance with them provided they would unite with the New York capitalists in the control of the Hughes patent and purchase from them the western rights to it. Although the Western Union leaders did not want this new patent for use upon their lines, they looked favorably upon its purchase inasmuch as it was in the hands of such "heavy capitalists" as Field, Cooper, Hunt and their associates.

Not long after this, Charles A. Mann, president of the New York, Albany & Buffalo, and Hiram Sibley, president of the Western Union, called upon Kendall at the Astor House in New York City, and after an apparently free interchange of views, they decided that it was time to require the American Telegraph Company to define its position and to agree to a business connection with them on reciprocal terms.[3] For the purpose of bringing the matter to an issue, committees appointed by the New York, Albany & Buffalo, the Western Union, the New York & New England Union, and the Magnetic were to meet in New York on June 30 and draw up a common proposal to present to the American Telegraph Company.

When Kendall reached New York on the evening of June 29, he was somewhat surprised to find there not only Sibley, but also Dr. Norvin Green, president of the New Orleans & Ohio Telegraph Lessees, Judge John D. Caton, president of the Illinois & Mississippi, and a number of other leaders connected with the western lines. Dr. Green told Kendall he was there merely by accident and talked freely of telegraph affairs. Delegations were also in the city from Smith's New York & New England Union, the Magnetic, and the New York, Albany & Buffalo Companies.

Kendall, therefore, determined to invite the representatives of all the companies in the city, including the American, to meet in a general convention "for the purpose of devising a plan for harmonizing all interests and protecting existing lines."[4] Three meetings were held. In the first two, the American Company, represented by Hunt and Eddy, evinced a disposition to join the other companies in some cooperative plan if those companies would share with the American Company the responsibilities of the Hughes patent which, it was intimated, might amount to $15,000 or $20,000. The prospects for the formation of an offensive-defensive alliance among the nation's leading telegraphic interests seemed highly promising and Kendall,

[3] Kendall to Morse, August 27, 1857, Morse Papers, XXXVIII.   [4] *Ibid.*

as chairman of the planning committee, applied himself eagerly to the task of devising a plan that would be acceptable to all the companies. The plan as finally drawn up was based upon the following general principles:

1. That the member companies should connect exclusively with other parties to the proposed agreement as to all points reached by their lines, and should by all proper means discourage new competing lines.

2. That where member companies had competing lines, the connecting lines should divide their business between them in proportion to the business received from them.

3. That the influence of the member companies should be exerted to produce a union of all competing lines.

4. That the Presidents of the companies, or delegates appointed in their stead, should constitute a Board of Control with authority to settle all disputes arising under the agreement and prescribe the necessary general rules.

The agreement was to take effect among the ratifying companies as soon as approved by any five companies, and it was to be perpetual. A company might withdraw after ten years, however, by giving the other companies one year's previous notice. Any telegraph company in North America was to be admitted as a party to the agreement by a vote of two-thirds of the Board of Control.[5]

At the meeting where this plan was presented, the American Company was represented by Peter Cooper and Cyrus W. Field. Field declared emphatically that his company would not go into the arrangement unless the others would join them in the purchase of the Hughes patent, a responsibility of about $60,000, he stated. Kendall remarked that he saw no reason why the other companies should share with the American the cost of the patent—that the Magnetic which he represented would certainly never use the Hughes instrument even if they had the right. For the sake of harmony, however, Kendall said that he would be disposed to pay something toward it. Since none of the delegates had come instructed upon that subject, it was finally decided to refer the matter back to their respective companies for consideration. Delegates with plenary powers upon all

[5] "Proceedings of a meeting of the representatives of a number of the principal telegraph companies in the United States," June 30 and July 1, 1857, Proposed Articles of Agreement, Smith Papers.

the points involved could then be appointed to convene at another meeting to be held on August 6.[6]

Kendall's report to Morse, who had gone to Europe to participate in the first transatlantic cable-laying expedition, was decidedly pessimistic. He had but faint hope, he wrote, of bringing the American Company into any alliance, and but little of organizing any effective union, so short-sighted had he found most of the managers of the several lines. Conferences with representatives of the different lines had merely confirmed his view that the American Company had not been frank in its dealings with them. The American Company's policy was "to dragoon the companies into their own terms, and . . . they would without hesitation destroy your property or mine if we stood in the way of their grasping ambition," declared Kendall. For this reason, he told Morse, he would be deprived of much of the satisfaction he would otherwise have felt should the Atlantic cable succeed. Indeed, he feared the utmost danger to all their telegraph property from the power which success would place in the hands of these men.[7]

2 ··—··

ALTHOUGH the convention had been formally adjourned on the evening of July 1, and Kendall was already on his way back to Washington, another meeting of carefully chosen delegates was in session the following day. It appeared to be a revolt of second generation telegraphers against the pioneers. To the forceful men in the industry, the aging Morse and Kendall were so exacting in their business relations as to be virtually ineffectual; while F. O. J. Smith had long since made it clear that there could be no harmony in the telegraph world so long as he was a power. A concerted effort was on foot to rid the industry of "Amos the pious" and the "fraudulent Fog." Upon the instigation of Hiram Sibley, therefore, representatives of the American, the New York, Albany & Buffalo, the Atlantic & Ohio, the Western Union, and the New Orleans & Ohio Lessees met in backstairs conclave to wrest control of the telegraph industry from Kendall, Smith, and their associates, through the formation of a

[6] Kendall to Morse, August 27, 1857, Morse Papers, XXXVIII; George Curtiss to E. Cornell, July 4, 1857, Cornell Papers; "Proceedings of a meeting of the representatives of a number of the principal telegraph companies in the United States," *op. cit.*; Norvin Green to Morse, January 27, 1858, Morse Papers, XXXVIII; Kendall to Morse, March 31, 1858, *Ibid.*

[7] Kendall to Morse, July 6, 1857, Morse Papers, XXXVII.

powerful offensive-defensive alliance.[8] Tentative articles of agreement were drawn up on July 7, 1857,[9] after which the conspirators returned home to recommend to their stockholders the ratification, not of Kendall's proposed contract, but of the articles as drawn up by Sibley and his conferees.

Between the drafting of the articles and their adoption in August, Caton's Illinois & Mississippi was also drawn into the alliance, thereby making six powerful companies party to the cabal. On August 10, meeting in plenary session, the "Treaty of the Six Nations" or the Six Party Contract, as it was more commonly called, was ratified; non-member organizations shortly began to feel its pressure.

By the terms of the agreement the member concerns were to join with the American Telegraph Company in paying for the patent rights to the Hughes invention. Of the total cost amounting to $56,000[10] the American Telegraph was to pay 45 percent; the New York, Albany & Buffalo, 13 percent; the Atlantic & Ohio, 10 percent; Western Union, 15 percent; New Orleans & Ohio, 12 percent; and Illinois & Mississippi, 5 percent.

Through a careful territorial division of the United States each "Nation" was to be absolutely sovereign in an area allocated to it. The American Telegraph Company was designated as the exclusive owner of the Hughes patent rights for all of Newfoundland, Nova Scotia, New Brunswick, the New England States, Long Island, Staten Island, the States of New Jersey, Delaware, North Carolina, South Carolina, Georgia, Florida, and for a line through Mississippi and Louisiana to New Orleans; also for that part of New York north of the latitude of Troy and east of the Champlain canal, as well as the rights for lines on certain additional routes. The New York, Albany & Buffalo received most of the remainder of New York State, while the Atlantic & Ohio was to have most of the State of Pennsylvania. The great power in the West, of course, was Western Union, which was to have hegemony over the States of Ohio, Indiana, and Michi-

---

[8] Kendall to Morse, August 27, 1857, Morse Papers, xxxviii.

[9] Proposed contract drawn up by representatives of the American Telegraph Company, the New York, Albany & Buffalo Telegraph Company, the Atlantic & Ohio Telegraph Company, the Western Union Telegraph Company and the New Orleans & Ohio Telegraph Lessees, July 7, 1857, pamphlet in Smith Docs.

[10] Hughes had been unable to meet the terms of his original contract with the American Telegraph Company. The price of $100,000 which Field and his associates had agreed to pay for the perfected patent was accordingly revised downward to $50,000. The other $6,000 of the above sum represented money expended by the American Telegraph Company in improving and perfecting the invention.

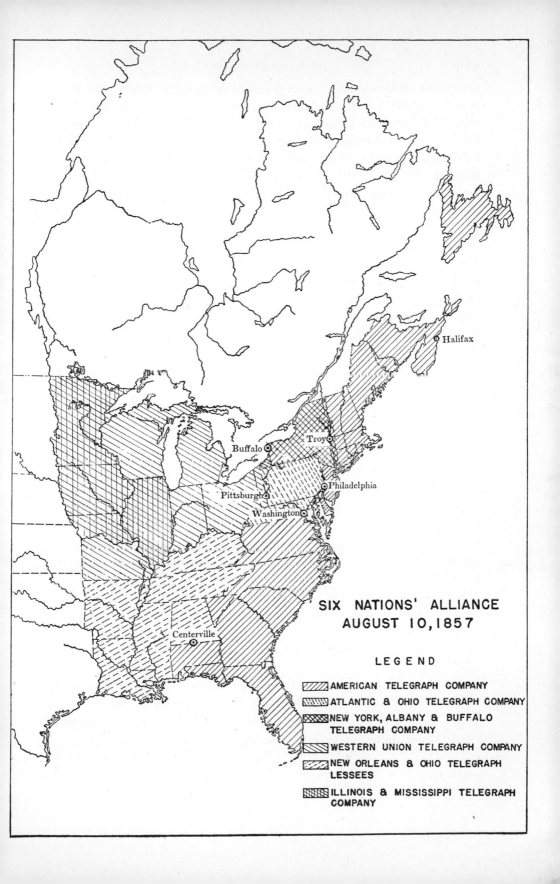

SIX NATIONS' ALLIANCE
AUGUST 10, 1857

LEGEND

AMERICAN TELEGRAPH COMPANY

ATLANTIC & OHIO TELEGRAPH COMPANY

NEW YORK, ALBANY & BUFFALO
TELEGRAPH COMPANY

WESTERN UNION TELEGRAPH COMPANY

NEW ORLEANS & OHIO TELEGRAPH
LESSEES

ILLINOIS & MISSISSIPPI TELEGRAPH
COMPANY

Halifax

Buffalo

Troy

Philadelphia

Pittsburgh

Washington

Centerville

gan; most of Wisconsin; small portions of western New York, Pennsylvania, and Virginia; and certain specified routes in Illinois, Minnesota, Missouri, and Kentucky. The New Orleans & Ohio Telegraph Lessees was to dominate the lower Mississippi Valley, having as its territory, Kentucky, Tennessee, Arkansas, Mississippi, Louisiana, and most of Alabama; while Caton's Illinois & Mississippi and allied lines were to dominate the upper Mississippi Valley, with exclusive privileges for most of Iowa, Illinois, and Minnesota, and for certain routes in Wisconsin and Missouri. Within its allotted territory, each party was entitled "to the exclusive enjoyment of all telegraph business."

To avoid competition between the contracting parties over certain routes where there was duplication of service, the business was to be carefully pro-rated among the parties concerned. As an additional step toward future harmony, no competing lines were to be built in the several territories as established, nor the patent rights sold therefor. Moreover, the "Six Nations" pledged themselves to exchange business exclusively with one another, except for existing contracts.

Any dispute arising between any two parties to the contract was to be referred to one or more disinterested persons to be mutually chosen by the disagreeing parties. If the parties in controversy were not able to agree upon referees, then the officers of each of the companies not involved were to nominate two disinterested persons. From this panel, the disputing parties were each to choose one person, and the two so selected were to choose a third. This tribunal was to hold a hearing, examine the evidence, and hand down a decision which was to be binding upon the parties concerned. Refusal to abide by the tribunal's award would result in expulsion from the association.

Representatives of the "Six Nations" were to convene annually—and as much oftener as necessary—"to *consult* and *advise* upon all matters of interest" to the member companies, but no changes were to be made in the Six Party Contract without the concurrence of all.[11]

In short, the new alliance aimed at nothing less than a monopoly of the nation's telegraph business by the signatories to the Six Party Contract. Within their assigned spheres of influence each member

[11] Articles of Agreement for the Union, Protection and Improvement of Certain Telegraph Lines in North America, August 10, 1857. O'Rielly Docs., Telegraph Pamphlets. The Six Party Contract, or "Treaty of the Six Nations," is given in full in Appendix 14.

company was to strive to consolidate with, or otherwise eliminate existing competition, and to prevent the erection of future rival lines.

3 · · · — ·

KENDALL was shocked to learn of this amazing bit of perfidy, and he grimly determined to fight to the death against the forces which sought to crush him. "I have a copy of the Treaty offensive and defensive," he informed Morse. "It is for *thirty years* and no one would know from the face of the paper itself that such a man as Samuel F. B. Morse ever existed."[12]

Kendall wrote to Peter Cooper for an explanation of his company's "hostile act." Cooper told him that information had reached the American interests through a reliable channel that two of the companies, the Magnetic and the New York & New England Union, were prepared to insist on terms of alliance to which his company could not assent. The American Company, therefore, had chosen allies more sympathetic to its interests. The reply did little to satisfy Kendall. He termed the explanation a "sheer fabrication" since no specific terms had been decided upon.[13]

A similar request addressed to President Norvin Green of the New Orleans & Ohio Lessees by Professor Morse threw further light on the intrigue. The previous June, Green explained to Morse, he had been urged "by parties identified with . . . [the Lessees] in interest" to come to New York immediately since a meeting of the Magnetic, the New York, Albany & Buffalo, the New England Union, and the American Telegraph Companies had been called to confer at the Astor House on the first of July. This meeting was represented as having been projected by the Magnetic with the object of forming a close and exclusive business connection among the companies named. Green pointed out that the New Orleans & Ohio Lessees could not remain idle spectators of a scheme so dangerous to their prospects. A working agreement which they had entered into with the American Company the year before had demonstrated too plainly the immense value of such an arrangement for the Lessees to see it pass from them without resistance.

On arriving in New York, Green found that much conversation had already passed between Sibley and the representatives of the American Company, looking to an exclusive interchange of business

12 Kendall to Morse, October 3, 1857, Morse Papers, XXXVIII.
13 *Ibid.*, August 27, 1857.

among the Western Union, the American, and the New Orleans & Ohio Lessees. All discussion, however, was predicated on the assumption that the Western Union and the New Orleans & Ohio Lessees would join with the American Company in the purchase of the Hughes patent. All plans were tentative pending the outcome of Kendall's meeting and the submission of his project to the companies.

Upon the conclusion of Kendall's meeting all hope of a general confederation embracing the American Company was abandoned. Several of the companies would not even entertain the idea of sharing in the purchase of the Hughes patent. Accordingly, the American, Western Union, and New Orleans & Ohio Lessees presented an alternative proposition to those companies that were willing to pay their share to get the Hughes patent out of the way. Thus the Six Party Contract came into being. Of course, admitted Green, it might have been more respectful to have awaited the outcome of Kendall's scheme, but the companies' annual meetings were near and failure would have left the field open for scheming during the ensuing twelve months. At his great distance from the theater of negotiation, it was a risk which Green believed he could ill-afford to take. In conclusion, Green summarized his position: "A union of the American and Magnetic Companies would at any time have ruined us; and a contract for exclusive connection between those companies and the New York, Albany & Buffalo, would have left us without sufficient business to pay our working expenses. We certainly believed that such was the original object of the meeting. . . ."[14]

After a careful study of the evidence, Kendall became convinced that the master mind directing the events leading to the Six Party Contract had been Hiram Sibley. It was he who had invited Green to New York; he who had sown the seeds of doubt and distrust in the minds of Cooper and his associates regarding Kendall's plans; and he who had directed the negotiations which terminated in the Six Party Contract.[15]

4 · · · · —

ON the very day that representatives of the American Telegraph Company in New York City were becoming signatories to the Six Party Contract, far out on the Atlantic Ocean a project dear to the

[14] Norvin Green to Morse, January 27, 1858, Morse Papers, XXXVIII.
[15] Kendall to F. O. J. Smith, December 26, 1857, New York Public Library, MS Division; Kendall to Morse, March 31, 1858, Morse Papers, XXXVIII.

Peter Cooper, President of the
American Telegraph Company

Norvin Green, President of the New
Orleans & Ohio Telegraph Lessees

John D. Caton, President of the Illinois & Mississippi Telegraph Company

LEADERS WITH SIBLEY IN THE SIX NATIONS ALLIANCE, 1857

Title Page of the Popular Sheet Music, "Atlantic Telegraph Polka" Dedicated to
Cyrus W. Field in Honor of the Laying of the Atlantic Cable, 1858

hearts of Field and his associates was ending in failure. On the morning of August 6, 1857, the cable-laying fleet had steamed out of Valentia Bay, Ireland, bound for the far off Newfoundland shore. The expedition had succeeded in laying about 380 miles of cable, when on August 10, the slender metal thread snapped, and half a million dollars vanished beneath the waves. While bitterly disappointed, Field lost no time in lamentations, but began at once to make plans for another expedition the following year.[16]

The task of raising the necessary funds, however, was to be fraught with grave difficulty. The panic of 1857 spreading from the West soon affected the entire nation, and by the autumn of that year stocks were down, banks had failed, and the richest people were hard pressed to salvage their rapidly diminishing resources. Field's own wholesale paper business in New York City went into bankruptcy, and so affluent a firm as Cooper & Hewitt warned of the "danger of starvation" although they promised to try to keep their men at work if money could be had on any terms.[17]

5 — — —

DEPRESSED conditions and the failure of the first Atlantic cable expedition, notwithstanding, the autumn of 1857 found the American Telegraph Company proceeding resolutely with a vigorous campaign to gain undisputed control of the telegraph industry along the seaboard. Much to the dismay of the Magnetic and the New York & Washington Printing Telegraph Companies, a line to be operated with Hughes instruments was constructed linking New York with Philadelphia, and a strenuous opposition was inaugurated against the older established companies. It was rumored, furthermore, that the American Telegraph Company intended to build on southward to Washington, and even beyond, unless the existing lines could be leased or purchased on reasonable terms.[18]

Kendall, Smith, and their associates, although well aware of the aggressive and wealthy combination against them, refused to be intimidated by the American Telegraph Company, or any other member of the Six Nations' alliance. A meeting of the Magnetic board

16 McDonald, *Saga of the Seas*, 52-53.
17 Cooper & Hewitt to J. D. Caton, October 2, 1857, Caton Papers.
18 Minutes of the meetings of the Stockholders and Board of Directors of the Magnetic Telegraph Company, July 8, 1858, Cornell University Library; Kendall to Morse, June 5, 1858, Morse Papers, xxxix.

was called to decide upon a future course of action. There was but one sentiment—"to carry the war into Africa"; and Swain, Barnum, and Kendall were appointed as a special committee with plenary powers.[19] F. O. J. Smith's New York & New England Union Telegraph Company took similar action. A series of offensive-defensive moves now followed one another in rapid succession. On September 18, 1857, the two companies, already bound in a close working agreement, signed a formal treaty of alliance. In so far as possible there was to be an exclusive exchange of business, and under no circumstances was one to come to terms with the enemy without the consent of the other.

At the same time offensive action was taken against their enemies on all fronts. Smith's New England Union Company proceeded to erect a line linking Boston with Portland, and plans were made to push it on north to the Canadian border.[20] The Nova Scotia Telegraph Company was notified that unless satisfactory arrangements could be made for the transmission of messages for the New England Union and Magnetic Telegraph Companies, that a new line would be constructed through Nova Scotia.[21]

Cyrus W. Field and his associates who were actively engaged in preparations for a second attempt to lay an Atlantic cable were also made to feel the weight of the new combination's displeasure. Acting jointly, Smith and Kendall asked Congress for the passage of a law to prevent combinations for the purpose of oppressing telegraph companies and monopolizing the business of telegraphy in the United States.[22] A combination entered into by parties and companies both in and out of the United States was endeavoring, the memorial declared, to force them to surrender their property under threat of destroying its value altogether. The combination of which they complained was composed of the New York, Newfoundland & London Telegraph Company, incorporated in the Province of Newfound-

---

[19] *Ibid.*, August 27, 1857, Morse Papers, XXXVIII.

[20] *Ibid.*, December 26, 1857.

[21] Minutes of the meetings of the Stockholders and Board of Directors of the Magnetic Telegraph Company, July 8, 1858, Cornell University Library; Minutes of the meetings of the Board of Directors of the New York & New England Union Telegraph Company, December 23, 1858, in *The Certificate of Formation, and The Articles of Association of the New York & New England Union Telegraph Company, together with the Records of the Meetings of the Directors*, Smith Docs.

[22] Memorial of the Magnetic Telegraph Company and the New England Union Telegraph Company by their Joint Committee to the Senate and the House of Representatives of the United States in Congress Assembled, March 10, 1858, O'Rielly Docs., Telegraph Pamphlets.

land; the American Telegraph Company, incorporated in New York State; and the Atlantic Telegraph Company, a British corporation.[23]

At the same time, Kendall, Smith, and their associates gave enthusiastic support to a rival cable project promulgated by the veteran promoter, Col. Tal. P. Shaffner. He proposed to connect Europe with America by means of a series of short cables via Greenland, Iceland, and the Faeroe Islands. Experience had already shown the utter impracticability of constructing and working a cable on a direct line across the Atlantic, declared a resolution passed by the Magnetic stockholders at their annual meeting on July 8, 1858. Believing the only feasible route to be that proposed by Col. Shaffner, they recommended that the directors of the company invite the cooperation of other companies in promoting the Shaffner cable project.[24]

6 · · · · · ·

CONCOMITANT with these developments in the East was the lively warfare on other fronts. The line of the Western Telegraph Company, extending from Baltimore to Wheeling, and already largely under Kendall's control, was rapidly pushed down the Ohio Valley to Cincinnati.[25] Then on August 13, 1858, the entire line was leased to the Magnetic Telegraph Company for thirty years at an annual rental of 6 percent per annum on its capital of $174,600.[26] Kendall and the Magnetic directors now let it be known that they intended extending the line on west to St. Louis unless Western Union and its allies arranged satisfactory terms of peace.

Nor was the southern front neglected. The line of the Washington & New Orleans, which had been leased by the Magnetic the preceding year, was carefully rebuilt, and a service between the North and South was inaugurated that could not be surpassed for speed and accuracy. At the same time, plans were made for an invasion of the

23 *Ibid.*; cf. Answer and Remonstrance of the American Telegraph Company to the Memorial of the Magnetic and New England Telegraph Companies, April 20, 1858, O'Rielly Docs., Telegraph Pamphlets; "British Telegraph Monopoly," a reply by the Magnetic and New England Union Telegraph Companies to the remonstrance of the American Telegraph Company, [April or May 1858], pamphlet in Library of Congress.

24 Minutes of the meetings of the Stockholders and Board of Directors of the Magnetic Telegraph Company, July 8, 1858, Cornell University Library; Kendall to Morse, March 15, 1858, Morse Papers, xxxviii.

25 Kendall to Morse, November 14, 1857, Morse Papers, xxxviii; *Ibid.*, April 19, 1858, Morse Papers, xxxix; *Ibid.*, April 27, 1858; minutes of the meetings of the Stockholders and Board of Directors of the Magnetic Telegraph Company, July 8, 1858, *op. cit.*

26 Reid, *Telegraph in America*, 151.

Mississippi Valley. Kendall, thoroughly aroused by what he considered the treachery of Dr. Green of the New Orleans & Ohio Lessees, had written Morse, "I feel a zeal to punish this perfidy even if my own interest suffer in the process."[27] Therefore, in spite of the fact that he and Morse held a large amount of stock in the New Orleans & Ohio Lessees, he now proceeded to grant the Magnetic the patent rights for a line of telegraph along the Mobile & Ohio Railroad from Mobile to Memphis, Tennessee. Having arranged for a connection at the northern terminus with a line already under construction from Memphis to Cairo, Illinois, the Magnetic Company became a real threat to the Lessees. The projected line upon its completion would be in a position to compete directly with the New Orleans & Ohio line for the business of the Mississippi Valley.[28]

Dr. Green, who had been talking rather confidently about the impossibility of any competing company entering his territory, ceased his boasting, and sent his chief lieutenant, George L. Douglass, North with proposals for a compromise. Since both sides were anxious to avoid a costly and unprofitable conflict, mutually satisfactory terms of peace were shortly arranged.[29]

The effect of the compromise, Kendall explained to Morse, "is to neutralize the Lessees and leave us to fight out the battle with the residue of the 'Six Nations.' We take the south end of the M & O [Mobile & Ohio] Railroad and they the north end, and we mutually agree not to reduce tariffs or do anything to create new or additional competition."[30]

By the summer of 1858 it had become quite clear to the American Telegraph Company and to the other members of the Six Party Contract that the alliance built up by Amos Kendall had fought them to a standstill. F. O. J. Smith's New England Union line, although hard pressed by the American, had managed to survive; while the Magnetic, in the course of a single year, had succeeded in developing an effective system which extended southward from New York via Philadelphia and Washington to New Orleans, westward from Baltimore to Wheeling and Cincinnati, and threatened momentarily to

27 Kendall to Morse, August 27, 1857, Morse Papers, xxxviii.

28 George L. Douglass to Morse, October 5, 1857, Morse Papers, xxxviii; George L. Douglass to J. D. Caton, October 5, 1857, Caton Papers; Kendall to Morse, November 23, 1857, Morse Papers, xxxviii; Kendall to Morse, March 15, 1858, Ibid.; Kendall to Vail, April 12, 1858, Vail Papers.

29 Kendall to Morse, April 19, 1858, Morse Papers, xxxix; Ibid., April 23, 1858.

30 Kendall to Morse, May 3, 1858, Morse Papers, xxxix.

extend its services to reach other important points of profit, especially in the West. The Six Nations were forced to face the unpleasant fact that Kendall and his allies were in no danger of being sold out at sheriff's sale, and that if they wished to add this property to their new order they would have to pay liberally for it.

7 — — · ·

SIMULTANEOUSLY came another heavy blow to the prestige of Field and his colleagues. After months of strenuous effort and at great expense, a second cable expedition had been organized. On June 25, 1858, four ships of the cable-laying fleet had met in the mid-Atlantic, spliced the cable ends, and sailed for their respective shores—Newfoundland and Ireland. All had gone well for the first eighty miles; then suddenly the cable parted. Returning to mid-ocean, they spliced the cable and set out hopefully. Once more their efforts were doomed to failure. When the two sections of the fleet were about two hundred miles apart, the cable again snapped and the ships were obliged to return to Ireland for further supplies and instructions.[31] Field was not to be discouraged. On July 17 the ships met at their mid-Atlantic rendezvous once more, spliced the cable, and headed for shore. This time all went well and on the evening of August 4, 1858, a cable linking the Old World with the New was a reality.[32]

The public was overjoyed at this most recent conquest of man over nature. Wild rejoicing occurred and plans were made for a great public celebration on September 1. But the rejoicing was premature; the insulation proved faulty, and the signals became more and more feeble. As the day for the great celebration drew near, the cable had become useless. Instead of receiving a public ovation, Field was denounced as a charlatan and his Atlantic cable was a subject of derision.[33] Nevertheless Field's faith in his grand design remained unshaken. He resolutely determined to try again as soon as the necessary money could be obtained.

8 — · · · ·

MEANWHILE, in the field of land telegraphy, events were moving to a climax.[34] On October 20, 1858, members of the Six Party Contract—the Six Nations—convened in New York and organized as the North

---

[31] McDonald, *Saga of the Seas*, 57.   [32] *Ibid.*, 59-60.   [33] *Ibid.*, 78-82.
[34] Kendall to Morse, May 11, 1858, Morse Papers, XXXIX; *Ibid.*, October 11, 1858.

American Telegraph Association with Peter Cooper as the first president. In addition to the six charter nations, membership was enlarged to include the Montreal Telegraph Company upon terms of full equality with the others. The chief object of the Association was declared to be the protection and advancement of the interests of the member companies by bringing about a closer union and concert of action among them.

Various subjects of mutual interest to the delegates were discussed during their four-day session, but two were of outstanding importance. One was the question of extending telegraphic facilities westward to the Pacific.[35] Hiram Sibley of Western Union, the chief exponent of this idea, presented it to the Association with clarity and force, but was able to arouse little enthusiasm. Such a project was too much of a gamble, and there were many other more pressing problems to be considered. Nevertheless, a committee was appointed to apply to Congress for government aid.

The second question, and of more immediate concern to the Association, was that of how to deal with Kendall and his alliance. Some of the delegates were for uncompromising war on the enemy, and a resolution was passed proposing that the Association meet competition in any given region, no matter how ruinous, and then divide the losses among the member companies until the enemy had been subdued. Some of the more far-sighted leaders, on the other hand, believed that a negotiated settlement would be infinitely better than a long and costly war of annihilation, and a special committee was appointed to confer with the New York & New England Union and the Magnetic Telegraph Companies.[36]

The Association launched an all-out peace offensive. Smith and Kendall were overwhelmed with peace proposals. Negotiations were almost continuous, and as the months passed, the proposals became more and more comprehensive in scope until they included the purchase by the Association of all unsold Morse patent rights for the entire United States, and the lease or purchase of all telegraph lines controlled by Kendall, Smith, and their allies.[37]

[35] For earlier discussion of this project, see Chapter XVIII.

[36] Proceedings of the First Annual Meeting of the North American Telegraph Association, October 20-23, 1858, in *Proceedings of the North American Telegraph Association, 1858-59 and 60*, Cornell University Library.

[37] Special meeting of the North American Telegraph Association, January 5-8, 1859, in *Proceedings of the North American Telegraph Association, 1858-59 and 60*.

9 — · · —

To fit itself for the larger role envisaged for it the American Telegraph Company inaugurated a series of important moves early in
1859. Application was made to the New Jersey Legislature for a
special act of incorporation with terms sufficiently broad to enable
the company to act with freedom and vigor. Proceeding on the assumption that the desired charter would be granted, a compact was
entered into on February 23 with Robert W. Russell and Francis
Morris, who acted not only for the New York & Washington Printing
Telegraph Company of which they were directors, but also as trustees
of the House patent. According to the terms of the agreement all
unsold House patent rights for the eastern and southern United
States, as well as the House line between New York and Washington,
were shortly to become the property of a reorganized and greatly
enlarged American Telegraph Company.[38] In addition to the material assets, two important telegraph leaders were brought into the
American Company by this consolidation—Francis Morris and Robert
W. Russell. Shortly thereafter, arrangements were also made by
which a number of important feeder lines throughout Virginia, the
Carolinas, Georgia, and Tennessee were to be brought into the
American Telegraph system for an issue of $100,000 of American
stock.[39]

10 · — — · —

MEANWHILE, negotiations of the North American Telegraph Association with Kendall, Smith, and their cohorts dragged on endlessly.
So numerous were the conflicting interests to be satisfied that the
task of effecting a settlement seemed hopeless at times. "When one
party was ready, the other was acting under cover in some way," complained Sibley.[40] A thorn in the flesh of all was F. O. J. Smith. Believing that the wealthy interests behind the Association would buy him
out at his own price rather than continue the war, he demanded an
outrageous figure for his holdings—about $250,000 at first, which
he later increased to over $300,000. "Perhaps it may be the cheapest
way to get rid of a man, to pay black mail," commented Theodore S.
Faxton savagely.[41] Writing to Morse on February 20, 1859, Kendall

38 Reid, *Telegraph in America*, 417.   39 *Ibid.*
40 Hiram Sibley to J. D. Caton, April 16, 1858, Caton Papers.
41 T. S. Faxton to J. D. Caton, January 11, 1859, Caton Papers.

declared that negotiations were "likely to fail in consequence of the exorbitant price put upon his interests by Smith, and the unwillingness of the western companies to pay a due proportion of the moneys necessary to buy out the patentees' rights and claims."[42] Nevertheless, the leaders of the North American Telegraph Association were determined that the consolidation project should not fail. It was imperative that peace and order be established within the telegraph industry before the expiration of the Morse patents[43] brought a host of wildcat companies into the field. Peter Cooper, Cyrus W. Field, Hiram Sibley, Norvin Green, and others gave without stint of their time and energy in an effort to work out the endless details and settle the petty jealousies that stood in the way of success. Writing to Judge Caton on April 10, Norvin Green pleaded with him to give the Association his support. If the Illinois & Mississippi and New York, Albany & Buffalo Companies were prepared to come up to their assessments, declared Green, he thought a satisfactory program of consolidation could be consummated. Every single company to the proposed deal, he explained, felt it was bearing too great a portion of the cost, but it was obviously impossible to make an apportionment which would please everyone. The all-important task was to settle the whole miserable telegraph quarrel before it was too late. Green then painted for the Judge a somber picture of what would happen if the consolidation project failed. The Magnetic would immediately extend its existing Cincinnati line to St. Louis and then spread over the West as fast as possible, while Smith would add new and insurmountable difficulties in the East. If the consolidation were not completed at this time, warned Green, he doubted if it ever would be.[44]

A few days later, Hiram Sibley added his plea to that of Green. "The New York, Albany & Buffalo Company have promised to pay their full assessment. . . . The time is short and may be now lost. If the matter shall still be open when this letter reaches you, you had better come on at once if you can. If not, telegraph the most you will do, personally . . . to effect this object."[45]

[42] Kendall to Morse, February 20, 1859, Morse Papers, xxxix; cf. Morse to Kendall, March 30, 1859, Morse Papers, Letter Book D.
[43] The first Morse patent issued June 20, 1840, and extended on June 20, 1854, for an additional term of seven years, was to expire on June 20, 1861. The second Morse patent issued on April 11, 1846 for certain improvements was to expire on April 11, 1860. While efforts were to be made to secure the extension of these patents the outcome was highly doubtful.
[44] Norvin Green to Caton, April 10, 1859, Caton Papers.
[45] Hiram Sibley to Caton, April 16, 1859, Ibid.

But two months later a settlement had still not been reached. Writing from the Astor House, New York City, on June 13, 1859, Kendall informed Morse that he proposed going home on the morrow without closing anything. "The parties are very near together and yet may never meet," he wrote.[46]

While numerous material considerations stood in the way of a settlement, the problem was further complicated by the unpredictable human factor. Smith might at any moment upset the whole arrangement with new and impossible demands. Robert W. Russell, "self-willed, conceited, and of unpleasant manners as a negotiator" had made himself obnoxious to nearly everybody.[47] Nor was Amos Kendall an easy man with whom to negotiate. Kendall and Russell were "both tenacious of their opinions, and neither [was] disposed to yield to the other, even on matters of form."[48] Sibley came in for his share of criticism also. "Sibley's policy is to bluff which won't do in all cases," Bassnett wrote his employer, Judge Caton.[49] The result was that nothing had been accomplished after weeks of fruitless negotiation, and it appeared doubtful whether any future discussions would terminate more favorably.

But at last, in August, notwithstanding all obstacles, the weary negotiators appeared to have reached a settlement. Then suddenly trouble appeared from another quarter. On August 13, D. H. Craig, agent of the New York Associated Press, informed William M. Swain, editor of the *Philadelphia Public Ledger* and a director of the Magnetic Telegraph Company, that after that day his paper would be cut off from all foreign news on account of some editorial remarks about the news reports. Obviously, such action would be impossible without the indirect cooperation of the American Telegraph Company which controlled the wires between Newfoundland and New York. Swain, Barnum, and Kendall, as negotiators for the Magnetic Company, determined, therefore, to submit a series of propositions as an ultimatum and inform the American Company that they must be accepted by August 19 or negotiations would be considered at an end.[50]

46 Kendall to Morse, June 13, 1859, Morse Papers, XL; cf. *Ibid.*, June 20, 1859; George L. Douglass to Caton, June 23, 1859, Caton Papers; Kendall to F. O. J. Smith, June 29, 1859, Kendall Papers, Library of Congress. (A small collection containing only a few telegraph items.)

47 E. D. L. Sweet to Caton, April 9, 1859, Caton Papers.

48 J. J. Speed, Jr., to Caton, June 29, 1859, Caton Papers.

49 Thomas Bassnett to Caton, October 6, [1859?], Caton Papers.

50 Kendall to Morse, August 24, 1859, Morse Papers, XL.

Kendall also wrote a private letter to Field explaining carefully the circumstances which had resulted in the ultimatum. He warned that the principle of "first come first served" was an indispensable one without which the Magnetic stockholders would "never agree to consolidate."[51]

Writing to Morse about the affair again on August 24, Kendall declared that it made his "blood boil" to witness the prostitution of the telegraph invention to purposes of fraud and oppression. Old as he was it roused within him a spirit of resolute resistance. He doubted whether he could end his life more worthily than in "a determined effort to break up this infamous combination to crush every independent Telegraph Line and reduce the Press to a condition worse than that of France." Their newspapers, explained Kendall, "may, in relation to private matters, keep silence; here they are made to speak lies."[52]

11 ·——··——·

ON August 31, 1859, representatives of the North American Telegraph Association assembled in New York for their second annual meeting. No attempt was made to minimize the seriousness of the situation. A long and costly battle with Kendall and his associates loomed on the horizon. Even the most skeptical was convinced by this time that Kendall was not bluffing. Here was a situation which called for prompt and decisive action.[53]

A committee acting in the name of the Association renewed negotiations for consolidation of the Magnetic and the American Telegraph Companies. A spirit of earnestness and compromise pervaded the series of conferences which followed. Reporting back to the Association on September 7, the committee declared that after a full and free conference, solutions had been found for all outstanding differences. On the question of news reports the American Company conceded fully that no news reporter or association should be entitled to either precedence or exclusive occupation of the lines, to the exclusion of equal facilities to other and rival reporters or associations.[54]

The obstacles in the way of a consolidation of the Magnetic and

51 *Ibid*.   52 *Ibid*.
53 Proceedings at Second Annual Meeting of the North American Telegraph Association, August 31 to October 12, 1859, in *Proceedings of the North American Telegraph Association, 1858-59 and 60*.
54 *Ibid*.

American Telegraph Companies having been removed, the log jam was broken, and activity followed all along the line.[55] The grand climax came on October 12 when a series of far-reaching agreements were entered into by the nation's leading telegraph interests. The members of the North American Telegraph Association agreed to important modifications in respect to the division of business upon certain routes, and of the territories assigned them by the original Six Party Contract of August 10, 1857.

At the same time, the American Telegraph Company, acting for the Association, purchased all the patent rights, stocks, and claims of F. O. J. Smith, with a few minor exceptions, for the grand sum of $301,108.50.[56] Of this amount, $51,108.50 was to be paid in cash on conveyance of the property, while the remainder was to be secured through the issuance of bonds bearing 7 percent interest per annum and payable over a period of four years.[57] "How the dog in the manger must relax his defiant display of teeth into a grin of delight at his eminent success. . . . Manger dogs are at a premium!" commented the usually mild-mannered Morse to Kendall upon the consummation of the deal.[58] The unsold patent rights belonging to Kendall, Morse, and their associates were also purchased through the issuance of American Telegraph Company stock to the amount of $107,000.

The cost of this ambitious program was borne by the members of the Association on a pre-arranged basis. By far the greatest burden was assumed by the American Telegraph Company, which was also the most benefited; its share of the total cost was fixed at one-half. The Western Union Telegraph Company, as the leader in the West, was allotted one-fourth of the cost, while the remaining one-fourth was divided as follows: New York, Albany & Buffalo, eight one-hundredths; Atlantic & Ohio and Pennsylvania Telegraph Companies together, five one-hundredths; New Orleans & Ohio Lessees, seven one-hundredths; and the Illinois & Mississippi and the Chicago & Mississippi Telegraph Companies together, five one-hundredths.[59]

The trend of the times was toward fewer but larger companies, and

[55] *Ibid.*

[56] A further sum of $2,500 was paid Smith later for a release of certain claims which had been exempted in the original contract with him.

[57] Proceedings of the North American Telegraph Association, August 31 to October 12, 1859, *op. cit.*

[58] Morse to Kendall, January 21, 1860, Morse, Letter Book D.

[59] [R. W. Russell] *Statistics, Etc. of the American Telegraph Company*, August 20, 1860. Pamphlet, New York Public Library.

those closely bound together by agreements. The goal toward which the North American Telegraph Association had directed its energies for sometime had been the establishment of a monopoly over the industry. That goal was virtually achieved by the agreements of October 12.

CHAPTER XXI

Titan of the East:
The American Telegraph Company

1 · — ·

THE American Telegraph Company was reorganized on October 12, 1859, to fit it for the prominent role it was henceforth to play in the industry. Under a special Act of the New Jersey Legislature the new company was capitalized at $740,000 with the right to increase its capitalization to $2,000,000. The capital stock was to be divided into shares of $100 each which were to be issued to the stockholders of the old American Telegraph Company of New York and those of the New York & Washington Printing Telegraph Company for the lines, patent rights, and other property owned by them, in the proportion of their interests.[1]

Then, taking immediate advantage of its right to increase its capitalization, the reorganized American Telegraph issued $100,000 of its stock to Dr. William S. Morris and several associates for a number of branch lines throughout Virginia, the Carolinas, Georgia, and Tennessee. A formal agreement was also entered into with the Magnetic Telegraph by which that corporation's capital stock of $369,300 was to be exchanged for $500,000 of American Telegraph stock. The American Company agreed, moreover, to assume the Magnetic Company's lease of the Washington & New Orleans Telegraph line.[2] And to relieve the Magnetic from the obligations of its contracts for exclusive connections with the New York & New England Union and the Western Telegraph Companies, the American agreed to lease

---

[1] *Charter and By Laws of the American Telegraph Company* (pamphlet), Wm. C. Bryant, New York, 1861. According to an informal report made to the stockholders by Secretary Russell on August 20, 1860, the capital was apportioned as follows:

To the old American Telegraph Company	$450,000
To the New York & Washington Printing Telegraph Company	200,000
To Messrs. Morris and Russell, trustees for the House Printing Telegraph patent rights for the East and South	40,000
	$690,000

Just what disposition was made of the remaining $50,000 of the original capital stock is not stated. (*Statistics, Etc., of the American Telegraph Company*, August 20, 1860.)

[2] Special meeting of the Washington & New Orleans Telegraph Company, May 10, 1860. Pamphlet, Library of Congress.

the lines of these concerns, together with those of the Marietta & Cincinnati Telegraph, or to make such other arrangements as would be acceptable to these companies. The purchase of F. O. J. Smith's interests had included 3,300 out of a total issue of 6,060 shares ($50 each) of New York & New England Union Telegraph stock. The American Telegraph now invited holders of the balance of the stock to exchange their shares at par for American Telegraph stock. Under this arrangement the New England Company was soon absorbed.[3] Several attempts were made by Field and his associate, Wilson G. Hunt, to obtain possession of the important lines of the New York, Albany & Buffalo at this time also, but without success.

To give the various interests included within the reorganized American Telegraph Company a voice in its management, a stock-holders meeting was convened on January 2, 1860, and a representa-tive board of directors was chosen. Zenas Barnum, Amos Kendall, William M. Swain and Samuel F. B. Morse represented the old Mag-netic interests; Robert W. Russell and Francis Morris, the former New York & Washington Printing Telegraph stockholders; John McKesson, the New York & New England Union Company; and Abram S. Hewitt, Cyrus W. Field, Wilson G. Hunt, Hiram O. Alden, and John H. Purdy, the old American Telegraph Company. Zenas Barnum, former president of the Magnetic, was made chief executive of the consolidated company, at a salary of $5,000 a year; Francis Morris became treasurer; Robert W. Russell, secretary and counsel; and John Kendall, general superintendent. An executive committee consisting of Zenas Barnum, Robert W. Russell, and Hiram O. Alden was also chosen.[4]

Under this conservative but enlightened management the Ameri-can Telegraph Company made very satisfactory progress during the following year. The elimination of competition with its attendant waste, and the introduction of improved methods, made possible by a unified management, quickly resulted in increased revenues. Net profits for the first quarter ending February 1, 1860, were $50,716.68; while second quarter profits rose to $57,961.68. Under the circum-stances the board of directors commenced the declaration of quarterly

[3] Notice to the stockholders of the American Telegraph Company, August 27, 1860; minutes of the meetings of the Board of Directors of the New York & New England Union Telegraph Company, September 6, October 1, 12, 28, 29, December 7, 1859, in *The Certificate of Formation . . . of the New York & New England Union Telegraph Company, together with the Records of the meetings of the Directors,* Smith Docs.
[4] [R. W. Russell] *Statistics, Etc., of the American Telegraph Company.*

dividends. One of 3 percent was paid on March 1, 1860; a second of like amount followed on June 1.[5] There was every indication that this rate could be maintained.

The position of the American Telegraph Company along the Atlantic seaboard was now believed to be almost impregnable. Within its territory it controlled the patent rights for all of the important telegraph systems in use. In addition it enjoyed numerous other advantages. It had the best, and in many instances, the only available routes for telegraph lines. It had inherited from its predecessors valuable franchises which had been granted by legislatures and municipalities. It held exclusive contracts for lines of telegraph along the leading railroads. It owned or controlled different sets of wires, over different routes, and connecting the principal cities. It held or controlled an extensive network of side lines. And as a member of the North American Telegraph Association, it enjoyed the benefit of exclusive business connections with all the great telegraph companies in the United States and Canada.[6] With 283 offices and 13,500 miles of wire, the American Telegraph Company dominated the telegraph industry along the Atlantic seaboard.[7] Stretching virtually unopposed from Newfoundland to New Orleans, the vigorous, young Titan of the East gave promise of a bright future.

[5] *Ibid.*   [6] *Ibid.*   [7] *Ibid.*

CHAPTER XXII

The Irrepressible Conflict

1 · — — ·

BY 1860 a complete transformation had taken place in the telegraph industry. Instead of dozens of little uncoordinated units operating under rival patents, there was one great telegraph fraternity—the North American Telegraph Association—whose members ruled the nation's communications. Within their respective territories the member companies had purchased the right to use the Morse, House, and Hughes patents.[1] Through consolidations and long-term leases they had absorbed or controlled hundreds of formerly independent companies, and they had begun to bring a semblance of order into a hitherto chaotic industry.

Had the companies which made up the North American Telegraph Association been willing to adhere strictly to the contracts which they entered into with one another, the years that lay ahead might have brought peace and harmony. But the aggressive managers who controlled the policies of the American and Western Union Telegraph Companies, were much too ambitious to abide by the *status quo*. No sooner had all important rivals been banished from the field, than these two powerful organizations began quietly to carry on an undeclared war with one another. While outwardly professing to be on friendly terms, the leaders of both companies seldom let pass a chance to take advantage of any situation which might improve their position at the expense of the rival concern.

Nor was it difficult for the telegraphic giants to find causes for disagreement. Leaders of the American Telegraph Company continued to sponsor actively Cyrus W. Field's project for an Atlantic cable, while those of Western Union, ably led by Hiram Sibley, earnestly advocated the construction of a telegraph line to connect the United States east of the Mississippi with California. Both projects were presented to the North American Telegraph Association for approval and support.[2] Since the success of the cable project would greatly

---

[1] The Bain patent was also purchased on March 24, 1863.

[2] Proceedings at special meeting of the North American Telegraph Association, March 12, 1860, in *Proceedings of the North American Telegraph Association, 1858-59 and 60*; *Ibid.*, July 27, 1860; *Ibid.*, August 29, 1860.

Constructing the Transcontinental Telegraph Line. A Scene from the Motion Picture, "Western Union"

"Building of the Transcontinental Telegraph"
A Painting by W. H. Jackson

Telegraph Office on Main Street, Salt Lake City, Where the Lines from East and West were Joined on October 24, 1861

The Long Bridge over the Potomac, 1861
Upper: from the Washington Shore. Lower: from the Virginia Shore

strengthen the position of the American Company in the industry, Western Union, while giving nominal support to it publicly, opposed it privately in every possible way.[3] The American Company, for its part, was not much interested in Sibley's transcontinental scheme, inasmuch as it would benefit chiefly the Western Union. Robert W. Russell and some of the other American Telegraph leaders shortly brought forward a scheme for a southern transcontinental line from New Orleans across Texas and New Mexico Territory to Los Angeles and San Francisco.[4]

Both companies continued to push aggressively the policy of absorption of such independent companies as remained; and in spite of the carefully worded agreements defining their respective spheres of influence, friction between the telegraph giants constantly increased. Each endeavored by persuasion and threats to secure for itself the collaboration of the various members of the North American Telegraph Association. The Atlantic & Ohio and the Illinois & Mississippi Telegraph Companies tended to collaborate with Western Union, while Dr. Norvin Green's progressive organization (formerly the New Orleans & Ohio Telegraph Lessees) which had been reorganized in January 1860 as the Southwestern Telegraph Company,[5] usually aligned itself with the American Telegraph Company. The remaining companies tried as best they could to maintain positions of neutrality.[6]

2 ·· — ··

ONE of the most bitter disputes between the Colossus of the West and the Titan of the East arose over the relations of the telegraph with the New York Associated Press. Beginning as a quarrel between D. H. Craig and the management of the American Telegraph Company, it soon involved the entire North American Telegraph Association and seriously threatened to bring about the dissolution of that organization.

[3] Thomas Bassnett to Caton, [n.p., n.d., received by Caton, August 8, 1860], Caton Papers.

[4] [R. W. Russell] *Statistics, Etc., of the American Telegraph Company*, August 20, 1860; cf. Hiram Sibley to Caton, December 6, 1860, Caton Papers.

[5] Reorganized under acts passed by the States of Kentucky, Tennessee, Mississippi, and Louisiana, with a capital stock of $600,000 (G. L. Douglass to Morse, October 18, 1861, Morse Papers, XLI).

[6] Thomas Bassnett to Caton, March 5, 1860, Caton Papers; *Ibid.*, [n.p., n.d., received by Caton, August 8, 1860]; Sibley to Caton, March 11, 1860, Caton Papers; *Ibid.*, April 9, 1860; Morse to Kendall, June 8, 1860, Morse Papers, XLI.

Since the successful conclusion of his battle with F. O. J. Smith in 1850,[7] the agent of the Associated Press, D. H. Craig, had worked unceasingly and very effectively to build up a news monopoly. He had aided the leading telegraph companies in establishing monopolies in their territories and they in turn had favored him. Discussing their relations some years later, Craig declared that for seventeen years previous to 1867 it was an unwritten law of the New York Associated Press, and of the various telegraph companies with which it did business, "that neither should do anything to the prejudice of the other's interests."[8]

At the time of the reorganization of the American Telegraph Company in October 1859, that company was refusing to forward the dispatches of a rival reporter until those of Craig had been transmitted, thereby driving his adversary from the field.[9] Craig, for his part, allowed no newspaper using the Associated Press reports to publish anything detrimental to the interests of the telegraph companies under contract with him. Furthermore, Associated Press vassals were forbidden to use opposition telegraph lines under penalty of being deprived of Associated Press reports and ruined, for without news reports no paper could hope to survive.[10]

The consolidation of the Magnetic with the American Telegraph Company had brought changes. Before consenting to consolidate with the American, it may be recalled the leading Magnetic stockholders had demanded and had been promised that the principle of "first come first served" would be a fundamental law of the new company.[11] Under guise of fulfilling that covenant, the executive committee of the American Telegraph Company which was comprised of Zenas Barnum, Hiram O. Alden, and Robert W. Russell, met on February 18, 1860, and decided to alter radically existing arrangements in respect to press messages. Notice was given of the termination after March 1 of the special contract under which the New York Associated Press and its satellites were enabled to monopolize foreign news distribution. Thereafter, reports for non-member papers were to be transmitted on exactly the same terms as reports

---

[7] For the account of Craig's battle with Smith for news supremacy, see Chapter XIV.

[8] [D. H. Craig], *Answer of Daniel H. Craig, Organizer and Manager of the New York Associated Press, 1850-1867 . . . to the Interrogatories of the United States Senate Committee on Education and Labor at the City of New York*, 1883, Pamphlet, New York Public Library.

[9] M. A. Zabriskie to F. O. J. Smith, May 28, 1859, Smith Papers.

[10] Craig, *op. cit.*

[11] For earlier discussion of this point, see Chapter XX.

for members of the Associated Press.[12] As a part of the new policy, rates to the evening papers were to be increased about 75 percent and those to the morning papers, about 150 percent.[13] Compared with the regular commercial tariffs and on the basis of actual work performed, the old rates had been too low. On the other hand, such an increase, accompanied by a clear-cut threat to the sovereignty of the New York Associated Press, was nothing less than an outright declaration of war.

Russell, the chief instigator of this radical move, badly miscalculated the strength of the opposition. Craig, with the support of the Associated Press, launched a vitriolic attack against him and his associates demanding their "ignominious discharge." At the same time, urgent appeals were addressed to the board of directors of the American Telegraph Company, asking that body to repudiate the action of the executive committee under threat of establishing an opposition line.[14] The board, while declining to interfere, recommended that the new rates should not become effective until a thorough investigation of the question of tariffs had been made by a special committee of five, consisting of the three members of the executive committee, Amos Kendall, and William M. Swain.

The report of the special committee submitted to the board of directors on April 18 upheld the action of the executive committee. Both groups agreed that it was the duty of the telegraph company to serve all the interests of the community alike, without making itself the slave or the partner of any one of them. This duty it would perform by holding is lines open to all on the same terms. In the opinion of the committee, the independence of the telegraph and the impartiality of its management were as important to the interest and safety of the country as the independence of the press.

In furtherance of the principles advanced in this report, the special committee recommended the adoption of the following resolutions:

1. Resolved that all arrangements giving one customer or one class of customers special advantages in time or price over

12 [American Telegraph Company], *The Telegraph and the Press. A report to the press of the actions of various committees and resolutions leading up to an increase in tariff on press messages,* 1860, Pamphlet, Cornell University.

13 [D. H. Craig], *"The Telegraph and the Press"; a reply to the American Telegraph Company's misrepresentations,* 1860, Pamphlet, Cornell University; [Amos Kendall], *Circular to the Stockholders of the American Telegraph Company,* August 27, 1860, Pamphlet, New York Public Library.

14 *Ibid.*

another customer or class of customers, under circumstances of a similar nature, are in violation of the duty of this Company to the community and should be discontinued.

2. Resolved, that the tariff rates on long messages should be so adjusted as to allow all customers the benefit of deductions allowed to any customer.

3. Resolved, that this Board fully approve of the resolution of the Executive Committee in reference to business of the press, . . . and that the same be confirmed and take effect next Monday, April 23rd.[15]

A majority of the board of directors accepted the recommendations, but a powerful minority headed by Cyrus W. Field, Wilson G. Hunt, and Abram S. Hewitt were strongly opposed. Field and his associates, while agreeing that the company's policy should be one of impartiality to all, one tariff for all, and "first come, first served," maintained that the right to combine to procure intelligence was as sacred as the right to build and operate telegraph lines. The American Telegraph Company, they insisted, had no more right to engage in the destruction of the Associated Press than it would have to break up a private firm in order that each partner might be made to pay separately for dispatches which would otherwise come to all in common. They were satisfied with the existing revenues of the company and felt that under a policy of *quieta non movere*, they would increase. All needed reforms could be effected without disturbing the friendly relations which had always existed between the company and the press. Failing to carry their point with the board of directors, they issued a call for a special meeting of the stockholders to convene the last week in June to consider the question.[16]

For the next two months the whole affair received publicity both in the daily press and by means of pamphlets and broadsides. Violent quarrels both private and public ensued. Charges and countercharges flew thick and fast. Craig presented his case in two pamphlets liberally sprinkled with such expressions as: "extortion of the rankest kind," "impudent monopolists," "autocrats of the telegraph," "numerous brood of yelping curs," "lottery swindlers, pettifoggers, illiterate cheats, rum sellers, drunken sots, and superannuated political

---

15 [American Telegraph Company], *The Telegraph and the Press, op. cit.*
16 [R. W. Russell], *Remarks of R. W. Russell . . . in reply to the statement of Messrs. Abram S. Hewitt, Cyrus W. Field, Henry J. Raymond and others, made at the meeting of stockholders on June 29, 1860.* New York, 1860, Pamphlet, Cornell University.

knaves."[17] Kendall in a pamphlet by way of reply began by asking the question, "Who is this D. H. Craig?" He then proceeded to answer it. "In the first place, he is a VULGAR BLACKGUARD, wholly unapproachable by any gentleman. The country abounds with evidence of this," and Kendall then presented some of it.[18]

Aside from such personal invective much space was given to a discussion of what constituted an equitable press rate, but that was not the real issue. The question of vital importance was, who should control the dissemination of news in the United States? Russell proposed to make the American Telegraph Company the purveyor of news, and to reduce the Associated Press to the position of a dependent not only for the transmission, but also for the matter of news. Craig, on the other hand, was resolutely determined to maintain the monopolistic position of the Associated Press at any cost.[19]

Field, Hunt, and Hewitt, occupying a middle ground between these two extremes, urged a policy of moderation and compromise upon both groups. The two great dangers of Russell's "wild policy," according to Field, were (1) that of driving the press to support the construction of a rival line; and (2) that of breaking up the North American Telegraph Association.[20] So long as the American Telegraph Company controlled all the important patents, the threat from the first source was somewhat remote. The second danger was very real. Hiram Sibley and many of the other leaders within the North American Telegraph Association were bitterly opposed to Russell's policy. They feared that the press would unite with Henry O'Rielly, who was trying to stage a comeback, in getting up opposition lines.

"O'Rielly has been to see the disaffected of the press," Sibley warned in a letter to Caton on March 11, 1860, "and nothing but the assurances given by the more sensible of the American Company and those comprising the Association, that Russell's policy should not be enforced against them has or will save us from competition. We must act together in this matter as in all others, and those who oppose the clearly expressed wish and unanimous purpose of the Confederation must be opposed by the united members of the Confederacy, or the

[17] *Circular to the Stockholders of the American Telegraph Company,* August 27, 1860.
[18] *Ibid.*
[19] [American Telegraph Company], *The Telegraph and the Press, op. cit.;* D. H. Craig, *op. cit.;* R. W. Russell, *op. cit.;* [Executive Committee of the American Telegraph Company, Z. Barnum, H. O. Alden, and R. W. Russell], *Letter: To the Stockholders regarding the American Telegraph Company and the New York Associated Press,* June 22, 1860, Pamphlet, Cornell University.
[20] R. W. Russell, *op. cit.*

six party contract becomes what Mr. Russell says it is, namely, 'a rope of sand.' "[21]

3 ···—·

SEVERAL months later the quarrel was assuming dangerous proportions. Russell proposed to break down the Associated Press by getting up a rival association. News was to be secured in Liverpool and then given preference upon its arrival at Halifax, St. John's, Newfoundland, or Cape Race. The Associated Press, meanwhile, was organizing formidable opposition to the American Company. Furthermore, there was reason for believing that in case of an all out conflict the six nation companies would break from the American and go with the press.[22]

Interesting light is thrown upon both the press quarrel and the dissension within the North American Telegraph Association by a letter which Thomas Bassnett, secretary of the Illinois & Mississippi Telegraph Company, wrote to Judge Caton following a special meeting of the Association held in New York on July 27. "Holding, as you know I do, certain settled convictions of the antagonistic positions of the two largest members of the Association, antagonistic in consequence of having laid down identical programs for the advancement of their own interests, I went [to the meeting in New York] with an intention of observing whatever might indicate final determination and results and their bearings on the future," wrote Bassnett.

Sibley's proposed Pacific line and the trouble with the Associated Press were the topics around which the controversy centered. Discussing the press controversy, Bassnett outlined the estranged positions of the protagonists. The Western Union professed an excessive deference to the press as an exponent of public opinion; the American Telegraph Company exhibited the Associated Press as a growing and dangerous monopoly which, if allowed, would soon destroy the independence of all the telegraph companies. It was Bassnett's opinion that both were primarily dominated by motives of self interest and that their professions of faith in their respective views were largely exaggerated.

[21] Hiram Sibley to J. D. Caton, March 11, 1860, Caton Papers; cf. *Ibid.*, April 9, 1860; Thomas Bassnett to Caton, March 5, 1860, Caton Papers.

[22] Morse to Kendall, June 8, 1860, Morse Papers, XLI; cf. *Ibid.*, June 25, 1860, Morse Papers, Letter Book D; Kendall to Morse, May 9, 1860, Morse Papers, XLI; *Ibid.*, June 18, 1860.

"The unfortunate aspect of our affairs just now," Bassnett concluded, "seems to me to be due more to personal traits and differences than to inherent difficulties. Sibley contends that Russell (who is head and limbs of the American Company) is so fond of ruling that he is continually acting contrary to his own interest. I think on the other hand his selfishness is paramount (not dishonorable selfishness) and that his views are always subordinate to that end, just as much as with Mr. Sibley with this difference; that the latter conceals his plans till it is safe to develop them, while the former offends by blurting out what he has concluded definitely and doggedly to stand by. I think also that if the six party contract is finally shown to be a rope of sand, it will be by the Western Union or under its auspices."[23] These were prophetic words.

4 · · · · —

MEANWHILE Russell had plunged recklessly on. As the battle lines had drawn closer, he had been forced into taking the extreme ground that all associations for dividing the expense of a single dispatch should be resisted by the company. Such an illiberal policy produced a further rift within the American Company's management. Morse, voicing the sentiments of the opposition, declared that the company could not rightfully take action against any group organized to share the expense of telegraphic communication, no matter how unfavorably such associations might affect the earnings of the company. In his opinion the company had no right to say how individuals or associations should use the dispatches sent over the wires. It was none of their business to look beyond the number of words sent them to carry. Who sent dispatches, what was their nature, whether they were intended for the use of one or a thousand, was not the province of the telegraph company any more than it was that of the Post Office to inquire as to who deposited a letter, what was its nature, or whether its contents were to be used by one or by thousands.[24]

At length, to secure increased weight in the administration of the company, Russell proceeded to buy out Cyrus W. Field and Abram S. Hewitt, who had become disgusted following the failure of the

23 Thomas Bassnett to J. D. Caton, [n.p., n.d., received by Caton on August 8, 1860], Caton Papers; cf. Proceedings at special meeting of the North American Telegraph Association, July 27, 1860, in *Proceedings of the North American Telegraph Association, 1858-59 and 60.*
24 Morse to Francis Morris, July 6, 1860, Morse Papers, Letter Book D.

stockholders at a meeting in June to modify Russell's policies.[25] He had then secured the election of Cambridge Livingston and Col. Edwards S. Sanford, manager of Adams' Express, as directors, thereby becoming the means of his own overthrow. "Russell is checkmated by his own moves," Kendall gleefully informed Morse in October. "Both Sanford and Livingston, though Directors of his own selection, in the place of Hewitt and Field, as soon as they understood his policy, took decided ground against it. The best of the joke is that he paid Field about $8,000 more than his stock was worth to get him out of the Board, and now finds the very man he selected for the place as much opposed to his views as Field ever was! He is now discouraged and proposes to sell out."[26]

Not long afterwards, following much excited discussion, the executive committee was completely reorganized leaving out Russell and Alden, and substituting in their places, Sanford and Livingston. At the same time, Col. Sanford was elected to the presidency. Cambridge Livingston became secretary, and Francis Morris took over the duties of treasurer.

Under this able and progressive administration, peace was readily made with the Associated Press. Early in November 1860, a new contract was entered into by which the rights of the public, of the telegraph, and of the press were fully recognized.[27] Talk of establishing a rival line now subsided, and the threatened dissolution of the North American Telegraph Association was averted; but rivalry between the Titan of the East and the Colossus of the West continued unabated.

5 — — —

By the close of 1860 it was becoming increasingly clear that the telegraph field was not big enough for six, or even two companies. There had developed within the industry an irrepressible conflict. The telegraph was a natural monopoly, and men like Hiram Sibley and Jeptha H. Wade would not rest content until the nation's telegraph interests had been brought under unified control. But the telegraph war which loomed on the horizon at the close of 1860 was soon engulfed by that larger conflict—the Civil War.

25 [R. W. Russell], *Remarks of R. W. Russell, op. cit.*; Morse to T. R. Walker, October 31, 1860, Morse Papers, Letter Book E.

26 *Ibid.* In his letter to Walker, Morse quotes a considerable section from a letter he has received from Kendall.

27 Frederic Hudson, *Journalism in the United States from 1690 to 1872*, 615. No specific information was available as to the terms of the new contract.

CHAPTER XXIII

The Telegraph in California

1 ·——·

DURING the 1850's while railroads, steamships, and telegraphs were binding the states east of the Mississippi closer together and laying the foundations for a new economic order, another nation looking out upon the mighty Pacific Ocean, yet also claiming to be a part of the United States, was growing up nearly two thousand miles away. The discovery of gold in California in January 1848 had brought thousands of people from all the ends of the earth pouring into this latest El Dorado; the single year 1849 saw an influx of over 80,000. Under the circumstances the need for laws and effective government was imperative. In September 1849 an antislavery constitution was adopted, and the next year California entered the Union in accordance with the provisions of the Compromise of 1850.

Separated as it was from the rest of the Union by two thousand miles of prairie, desert, and mountain country, the bonds which united the new state with the central government at Washington were more sentimental than real. Overland transportation by stage coach required about sixty days, while the trip by way of Panama or around the Horn took even longer. The average passage for sailing vessels between New York and San Francisco in 1850 was about one hundred and fifty days. During that year, to be sure, there came booming through the Golden Gate the clipper ship, *Sea Witch*, ninety-seven days out of New York. The following year another clipper, the *Flying Cloud*, made the voyage in eighty-nine days, a record never surpassed. Still the cry went up for speedier transportation between the two extremes of the nation, and Congress was bombarded with memorials and bills asking federal aid for the construction of a transcontinental railway.

Nearly as imperative as the prompt transportation of men and goods was the need for more rapid communication between East and West. As early as 1849 the irrepressible Henry O'Rielly had offered to solve this problem by building a line to link the westernmost outpost of the telegraph in Missouri with remote California, and Senator Stephen A. Douglas of Illinois had presented a memorial to that effect.[1] Like so many of O'Rielly's schemes, however, the project was premature.

Again three years later Senator Douglas presented a petition from O'Rielly in regard to a similar transcontinental project.[2] The Irishman asked for no appropriation of money or land, but only that he be protected in his enterprise. For that purpose he requested Congress to pass a law providing that instead of established forts, with hundreds of men at long intervals, the troops on the principal route through the public domain be stationed in small parties of twenty, in stockades about twenty miles apart. Two or three soldiers carrying the mails could ride daily each way between the stockades, thus providing a daily express mail across the continent. At the same time they could protect and comfort the emigrants and settlers, and incidentally, furnish O'Rielly with all the protection needed for a line of telegraph between Missouri and California. The establishment of such a system, declared O'Rielly, would revolutionize the nation's communications, promote the perpetuity of the Union, protect the traveler, encourage emigration, aid in colonizing the country along the route, and secure the friendship of the Indians by furnishing a market for their game and furs. The movement would also be useful as a preliminary to the stupendous railroad schemes just then exciting attention among the American people.[3] A bill embodying O'Rielly's ideas was submitted to the upper house of Congress by Senator Douglas on April 22, 1852, and its chances for passage looked favorable; but in the general scramble to secure money for other projects at the close of the session, it failed.[4]

From this time on, nevertheless, a transcontinental telegraph was a recurring subject of speculative thought, and at nearly every session of Congress petitions and bills were introduced with reference to the construction of a line to the Pacific.

[1] Henry O'Rielly to the Hon. Mr. Stephen A. Douglas, December 14, 1848, O'Rielly MS Coll. (December 1848); Henry O'Rielly to His Excellency James K. Polk, President of the United States, December 25, 1848, *Ibid.*; O'Rielly to Col. A. B. Chambers, Chairman of the Committee of Arrangements for the St. Louis Convention, October 2, 1849, O'Rielly Papers, Rochester Historical Society; J. Loughborough, *The Pacific Telegraph and Railway* . . . , 1849, Pamphlet, Rochester Historical Society.

[2] O'Rielly to J. D. Caton, October 14, 1851, Caton Papers; Senate Miscell. Doc. 67, 32 Cong., 1 sess.

[3] *Ibid.*

[4] Copy of a bill (S. 396) "for the protection of the emigrant route, and a telegraphic line . . ." reported by Stephen A. Douglas from Committee on Territories, April 22, 1852, 32 Cong., 1 sess., O'Rielly Docs., Miscell. Series, VII; H. H. Bancroft, *Chronicles of the Builders*, V, 332.

2 ··—··

MEANWHILE the lusty young state of California had awakened to the value of the telegraph as a means of rapid communication. Prior to 1852, its population shifted so rapidly from place to place that it would have been useless to set up telegraph poles. No sooner would the line have been completed than the community it had been intending to serve would have moved on to greener pastures. By 1852 the gold fever had begun to abate somewhat, business was settling down, and future commercial centers were fairly well indicated.[5]

In May of that year two enterprising promoters from New York, Oliver E. Allen and Clark Burnham, obtained from the legislature of California a franchise giving them the right to establish a line of telegraph between San Francisco and Marysville via San José, Stockton, and Sacramento. They were to enjoy exclusive rights over this route for fifteen years, and in return were obligated after three years to pay the state 3 percent of their net proceeds.[6] A further provision of their franchise required that the line be in operation by November 1, 1853. The California Telegraph Company, organized to carry out this project, met with many misfortunes, and as a result of severe losses from the great fire which swept San Francisco in 1852, the partners, Allen and Burnham, and their associates were financially unable to build the line.[7]

New capital was enlisted to save the valuable franchise, and on June 1, 1853, the concern was reorganized as the California State Telegraph Company, with a capitalization of $300,000. John Middleton was elected president; E. R. Carpentier, secretary; and Joseph C. Palmer, treasurer. After many delays, work was begun on September 13, 1853, with only six weeks remaining in which to complete the line before the expiration of the contract.[8] The company's superintendent, W. B. Ransom, had been fortunate in securing the services of a seasoned telegrapher, James Gamble, who had left the employ of Judge Caton's Illinois & Mississippi Telegraph Company the previous year to seek his fortune in the West. As supervisor of construction, Gamble with a little band of five men set out courageously to erect two hundred miles of telegraph through a rugged and unde-

[5] Alice L. Bates, "The History of the Telegraph in California," *Southern California Historical Society Publications*, IX, 181-187; Bancroft, *Chronicles of the Builders*, V, 327.
[6] The company was released from this provision in 1866.
[7] James Gamble, "Early Reminiscences of the Telegraph on the Pacific Coast," *The Californian Magazine* (1881), 321-326; Bates, *op. cit.*
[8] Bancroft, *Chronicles of the Builders*, V, 326-327; Gamble, *op. cit.*; Bates, *op. cit.*

veloped country. Working from sunrise to sunset, they were able to progress five or six miles on good days.[9]

Great was the amazement of the people along the route as work on the mysterious new "lightning line" progressed. Many of them, not understanding the use of the poles with their cross arms, believed that the Yankees were fencing in the country with crosses to keep the devil out. When a certain devout Mexican woman of San José beheld them she exclaimed, "Well, I believe those Americans are becoming good Catholics!"[10]

When the first regular telegraph office was opened at San José, interested spectators congregated in front of it hoping, in some manner, to fathom the mysteries of this strange new wonder called the telegraph. Observing the inquiring expressions on the faces of those who had managed to get near enough to thrust their heads through the open window, Gamble could not resist the impulse to act in a mysterious manner to see what effect it would have on his spectators. He had just received the first message from San Francisco which he had copied and placed in an envelope. On seeing him do this, his audience thought, as he supposed, that he was preparing a message for transmission. He then hid the dispatch under the table. As he did this he kept his eyes fixed intently on the wire out of doors, while, with his right hand, he began working the telegraph key. The moment the crowd heard the first click of the instrument they all rushed from under the veranda out into the street to see the message in the envelope pass along the wire. As they failed to see it their second supposition was that the wire was hollow and that the envelope with its message inclosed was forced through the hollow part to its destination.[11]

After many vicissitudes the line was completed to Marysville on October 25, six weeks from the day of its commencement, and the valuable franchise was saved.[12] Writing to his former employer, Judge Caton, about a month after the opening of the line, James Gamble, now manager of the company's office in Sacramento, reported enthusiastically, "The California State Telegraph connects five of the most important towns in the state, and is now doing a good business. I enclose the rates which you will perceive are pretty high, or at least they would be considered so in Illinois; they are paid without a murmur here. I am at present getting $200 per month and shall get $250 as soon as the other line [one under construction by

9 Gamble, *op. cit.*   10 Bancroft, *op. cit.*, 330.   11 Gamble, *op. cit.*   12 *Ibid.*

the Alta Telegraph Company between Sacramento and Nevada City] is finished, which will greatly increase our business here."

The rates referred to by Gamble were, indeed, "pretty high" as the following schedule shows:

RATES	1ST TEN WORDS	EACH ADD'L FIVE
Sacramento to Stockton and Marysville	$1.00	$.40
San José	1.50	.50
San Francisco	2.00	.75

But so great was the need for some means of rapid communication between San Francisco and the important interior towns that the new telegraph was hailed as a blessing in spite of these exorbitant tariffs.[13]

Within two years, monthly dividends of 1 percent were being declared regularly.[14] This rate was possible notwithstanding the fact that the line was capitalized at the rate of $1,500 per mile. "No line in the world, of the same length, has ever done so large and profitable a business as that of the old California State Telegraph Company," stated Gamble in discussing its affairs some years later.[15]

The prosperity of the California State Telegraph Company gave impetus to telegraph building in California. By January 1854, the Alta Telegraph Company had a line 121 miles in length completed and in operation extending inland from Sacramento via Mormon Island, Diamond Springs, Placerville, Coloma, Auburn, and Grass Valley to Nevada City. Within three years the company was earning 7½ percent a month on its capital stock of $70,000.[16]

Greedy promoters now organized companies and constructed lines with reckless abandon. The result was a period of fierce rivalry, litigation, and chaos—an era of methodless enthusiasm; but, as had been the case in the East, the end of the decade saw an irresistible movement toward consolidation.

[13] James Gamble to J. D. Caton, November 24, 1853, Caton Papers.
[14] Bates, *op. cit.*
[15] Gamble, *op. cit.*
[16] Bancroft, *op. cit.*, 328; Bates, *op. cit.*

The Pacific Telegraph Act

1 · — ·

AGITATION for a transcontinental telegraph was becoming more and more insistent by the mid-1850's. In May 1858, a group of Western promoters headed by two brothers, Frederic A. and Albert W. Bee, organized the Placerville, Humboldt & Salt Lake Telegraph Company for the purpose of constructing a telegraph line from Placerville to Genoa in Carson Valley and thence to Salt Lake City. Even prior to formal organization one of the directors had been sent to Washington to procure government aid in extending the line to Salt Lake City, or further east if possible, and to interest eastern telegraph companies in the enterprise.[1] The aid of those veteran promoters, Henry O'Rielly, John J. Speed, and Tal. P. Shaffner, was secured. Senator Broderick of California introduced a bill authorizing the Postmaster General to contract with O'Rielly, Speed, and Shaffner to carry government messages to and from Pacific stations for ten years at $70,000 per year. In addition, the above named trio were to receive preemption rights to 320 acres of land at ten-mile intervals along the route.[2]

For weeks while the bill was under consideration, the promoters and their friends lobbied energetically for the Pacific telegraph. "It is no small job to see Senators here," Speed wrote his former business associate, F. O. J. Smith. "Yesterday [March 26] we walked more than ten miles (we cannot pay for riding) and called at a dozen or more places, but saw only four Senators. . . . Shaffner and I have had to finance for Mr. O'Rielly as well as ourselves. . . . No money and a ragged coat is not calculated to exert much influence anywhere in this world, but is particularly objectionable at Washington. I have got to the end of my rope, and if we fail here, I will be worse off than you say Field will be when the cable breaks again."[3]

---

[1] Bancroft, *Chronicles of the Builders*, v, 331-332; *New York Herald*, November 8, 1858.

[2] Copy of a bill (S. 401) "to facilitate communications between the Atlantic and Pacific States by electric telegraph," reported by Senator Stephen A. Douglas, May 24, 1858, 35 Cong., 1 sess., O'Rielly Docs., Miscell. Series, VII.

[3] J. J. Speed, Jr., to F. O. J Smith, March 24, 1858, MS Division, New York Public Library; cf. E. D. L. Sweet to Caton, March 29, 1858, Caton Papers.

Unfortunately for the threadbare promoters, Broderick's fellow senator from California, William M. Gwin, was bitterly hostile to his colleague and opposed him at every opportunity. Moreover, a strong North-South cleavage colored every phase of political life in Washington at this time. Since the "black Republicans" backed the bill, the southern senators were against it, and the bill failed.[4]

But the Bee brothers and other parties interested in a transcontinental telegraph were more successful in their relations with the California Legislature, and in April 1859 an act was passed pledging a subsidy of $6,000 a year for ten years to the telegraph company first making connection with an eastern line, and $4,000 per annum to the one completing the second line.[5]

This legislation was designed to give impetus to the efforts of two California companies with transcontinental ambitions. One, of course, was the Placerville, Humboldt & Salt Lake City Telegraph Company of the Bee brothers. Encouraged by the subsidy, they pushed their line eastward to Carson City during the spring of 1859; early in 1860 it had reached Virginia City; and subsequently it was extended on to Fort Churchill. The line was a poorly constructed affair. The wire having been fastened to the trees in many places, was often broken by storms, and wagoners needing wire for repairing their outfits confiscated it. The luckless line came to be called derisively "Bee's grapevine."[6]

The other company with transcontinental ambitions was the Pacific & Atlantic Telegraph. Pushing its lines southward from San Francisco along the Butterfield overland stage route, it reached Los Angeles by the close of 1859. The promoters planned to construct a line on eastward through New Mexico Territory, Texas, and Louisiana to New Orleans, but lack of funds and the outbreak of the Civil War were to terminate this project.[7]

2 ··—··

THE real impetus for a transcontinental line came from the East where the indomitable Hiram Sibley was hard at work. His proposals

[4] James Gamble, "Wiring a Continent," *The Californian Magazine*, III (1881), 556-563.

[5] *Ibid.*; Bancroft, *op. cit.*, 333; Alice L. Bates, "The History of the Telegraph in California," *Southern California Historical Society Publications*, IX, 181-187.

[6] Gamble, *op. cit.*; Bancroft, *Chronicles of the Builders*, V, 331-333.

[7] Bates, *op. cit.*

for the extension of the telegraph to the Pacific coast, first announced in the autumn of 1857, had been somewhat delayed by lack of enthusiasm on the part of his associates, and the pressure of other important telegraph affairs.[8] But with the establishment of a reasonable degree of stability in the industry in the closing months of 1859, Sibley had once more begun a determined and aggressive campaign to carry his transcontinental project to completion.

In December a special meeting of the North American Telegraph Association was held at Cleveland, Ohio, to discuss the subject; the antagonistic positions of the Western Union and American Telegraph Companies became evident at once. Sibley outlined his plan for a line of telegraph extending westward from St. Louis to connect with the lines to the Pacific coast. Robert W. Russell and some of his American Telegraph associates were strongly opposed; they advocated a southern route through Texas which would bring the major portion of the transcontinental business over the American Company's wires. Norvin Green's Southwestern Telegraph also favored the southern route. Under the circumstances, a resolution was finally adopted appointing a committee consisting of Francis Morris, Charles A. Mann, Hiram Sibley, Norvin Green, John D. Caton, and J. Howells to devise a plan for compromising the two conflicting interests, so that a line or lines might be built over either or both of the proposed routes with the approval of the entire Association.[9]

January 1860 found Sibley in Washington. He urged Judge Caton to join him so that they might work out a plan of action. "If Congress ever gets organized," he wrote the Judge, "vigorous efforts will be made by various interests to obtain government aid for a telegraph line to California. It is to be feared that unless we of the West come into this measure actively and at once, the interests on the seaboard via New Orleans [American Telegraph] will secure a connection through the State of Texas and by that means leave us outside on a switch. You have often expressed a wish to be connected with the enterprise and it seems proper that you should, and the present is the time for some decided action."[10]

8 For earlier discussion of this subject, see Chapter XVIII.

9 Hiram Sibley to J. D. Caton, January 8, 1860, Caton Papers; Reid, Telegraph in America, 490.

10 Sibley to Caton, two pages dated January 8, 1860; two additional pages of same letter dated January 29, 1860, Caton Papers; cf. [R. W. Russell], Statistics, Etc., of the American Telegraph Company, August 30, 1860.

3 · · · — ·

EARLY in the first session of the Thirty-Sixth Congress several transcontinental telegraph bills were introduced both into the House and
Senate,[11] but the one which finally passed, after many modifications,
was that presented by Senator Gwin of California. This bill (S. No.
84), as introduced, empowered the Postmaster General to contract
with the Placerville, Humboldt & Salt Lake City Telegraph Company for the use of a line from San Francisco to Washington for ten
years at an annual rate not exceeding $50,000.[12]

Sibley and his friends now swung into action. The Committee on
the Post Office and Post Roads, to which the bill was referred, was
persuaded to strike out everything after the enacting clause and
substitute what amounted to a new bill which gave the contract to
a group of corporators—Zenas Barnum, Thomas R. Walker, John H.
Berryhill, Hiram Sibley, Norvin Green, John D. Caton, Frederic A.
Bee, Charles M. Stebbins, and James S. Graham—representing the
nation's leading telegraph interests. The amended bill also committed
the government to give the corporators a subsidy of fifty thousand
dollars annually, a right of way, and the use of land for stations.[13]

In the meantime, a special meeting of the North American Telegraph Association had been convened at Washington on March 12
to discuss the bill and conclude plans for harmonizing the conflicting
interests within the Association. Fortunately for Sibley and his
friends, the American Telegraph Company was represented by Amos
Kendall, Zenas Barnum, and Cyrus W. Field. These men, unlike
Robert W. Russell and his adherents, were willing to meet Sibley half
way. As a result an agreement was drawn up providing for a division
of the transcontinental business between a southern and a central
line, should two lines be found necessary to meet the needs of the
public and protect the interests of all. The business of the city of San
Francisco was to be equally divided between the first and the second
line; that of the State of California was to be apportioned so as to give
business originating north of a line running due east and west
through San Francisco, to the northernmost line, and that originating
south of it to the southernmost line. Such a division was to commence
whenever the second line was completed and in operation. It was also
stipulated that the proposed government subsidy of $50,000 a year,

11 *Cong. Globe*, 36 Cong., 1 sess., 647, 658, 668, 813.
12 *Ibid.*, 494, 1292.   13 *Ibid.*, 1292-1293.

or whatever subsidy might be appropriated, was to be divided equally between the lines so long as they were sustained and in working order. With that difficulty out of the way a resolution was passed declaring the Association unanimously in favor of the passage, with amendments, of Senator Gwin's bill.

And then lest his cable aspirations be placed in total eclipse by the transcontinental telegraph project, Cyrus W. Field introduced a resolution affirming the faith and interest of the Association in the final success of the Atlantic cable. The resolution was passed pledging the members to do all in their power to second the efforts of the Atlantic Telegraph Company.[14]

4 · · · · —

HAVING established a degree of harmony within the telegraph fraternity itself, leaders of the Association now bent every effort to secure passage of the telegraph bill by Congress.[15] In many respects the time was propitious for the passage of such a measure. The ominous political situation made speedy intercourse with California highly desirable; and the commercial interests both East and West were enthusiastic backers of a transcontinental telegraph. The semiweekly mail by the overland route took eighteen to twenty days. The inauguration of the Pony Express between St. Joseph, Missouri, and Sacramento, California, only reduced the time to nine days. There remained, therefore, a very real need for a line of telegraph to speed up communication and to bind the two extremities of the nation more closely together.

On March 26 the Senate proceeded to a careful consideration of the bill. A number of amendments were introduced and several of them adopted, including one limiting the charge for a single dispatch of ten words to four dollars. Then, a vote was taken and the bill was passed—28 yeas and 15 nays. Support for the bill had come largely from the North and West, while opposition centered in the South.[16]

Having passed the Senate, the bill (S. No. 84) was sent to the House where it underwent drastic changes. The Committee on the

14 Special Meeting of the North American Telegraph Association, March 12, 13 ff., 1860, in *Proceedings of the North American Telegraph Association, 1858-59 and 60.*

15 Norvin Green to Morse, March 19, 1860, Morse Papers, XL; cf. Sibley to Caton, April 9, 1860, Caton Papers; L. Trumbull to Caton, April 20, 1860, *Ibid.*; E. H. Beebe to Caton, April 8, 1860, *Ibid.*

16 *Cong. Globe*, 36 Cong., 1 sess., 1343-1345.

Post Office and Post Roads, to which it was referred, decided to reduce the government subsidy to $40,000, lower the charge for private messages of ten words to three dollars, and make numerous other changes to limit the powers which the telegraph companies might exercise. On April 12 the amended bill came up for consideration by the House. A young lawyer and politician, Schuyler Colfax of Indiana, presented the main features of the bill, and urged its acceptance. Perhaps it was his earlier experience as solicitor of funds for the pioneer telegraph line in Indiana that made him speak so warmly in its behalf. Arguments to prove the utility of establishing telegraphic communication between the Atlantic and Pacific States were hardly needed, declared Colfax, since every member knew it to be a necessity. Telegraphic communication with the Pacific would be of vital importance should the United States become embroiled in war with a foreign nation. Colfax pointed out how the United States had threatened to become involved in a war with England during the San Juan difficulty a short time before because of the delay in communicating with that distant region. "If that difficulty had ripened into actual hostilities," declared the Hoosier legislator, "the existence of such a means of communication as is contemplated by this bill would have been of priceless value to us—a thousand times more than the amount which it is proposed to expend by this bill." He went on to show how valuable telegraphic communication with Salt Lake Valley would have been during the recent troubles in Utah.[17]

In the extended debate which followed, all shades of opinion were to be found. Roscoe Conkling of New York, representing one extreme, demanded restoration of the bill as it had been received from the Senate; the House amendments he contended would discourage promoters of a transcontinental line. Henry C. Burnett of Kentucky, representing the other extreme, denied the constitutional power of Congress to engage this government in the building of telegraph lines. "If there is such a power," declared Burnett, "I do not know from what clause of the Constitution it is derived." Here was Congress, declared the Kentucky legislator, voting the public domain by millions of acres for every conceivable purpose. Now it was even asked to take money from the public treasury and put it into the pockets of private incorporators for the purpose of constructing a line of telegraph from the Atlantic to the Pacific states.[18]

17 *Ibid.*, 1563, 1692-1693.
18 *Ibid.*, 1693.

As the debate proceeded it became clear that a telegraph bill in some form was reasonably certain of passage. Burnett and several other opponents of the measure thereupon proceeded to offer amendments. If a line was to be built with the aid of a government subsidy, then at least the contract should be let in as democratic a manner as possible. Burnett accordingly offered an amendment striking out the names of the specific corporators and providing that the contract should be awarded on the basis of open bidding to the lowest responsible bidder. This amendment, along with several others, was accepted, and at last, on May 24, the bill was passed—101 yeas to 73 nays.[19]

The amended telegraph bill (S. No. 84), now so changed as to be scarcely recognizable, was returned to the Senate for its concurrence. An attempt was made to restore some of the provisions of the bill as originally passed by the Senate, but when the House disagreed to the amendments, the Senate receded and adopted the proposition as it came to them from the House.[20]

5 ———

THE much-amended measure which finally became law on June 16, 1860—commonly known as the Pacific Telegraph Act—authorized the Secretary of the Treasury to advertise for sealed proposals for a line of telegraph to be constructed within two years from July 31, 1860, from some point on the western boundary of the State of Missouri to San Francisco by any route which the contractors might select. The contract was to be awarded for a term of ten years to the lowest responsible bidder provided his proffer did not require more than $40,000 a year from the United States. During the ten-year term the party or parties to whom the contract was awarded should have the right to use such unoccupied public lands of the United States as might be necessary for the right of way, and for the purpose of establishing stations for repairs. Such stations were not to exceed in number, one for fifteen miles on an average of the whole distance and no station was to occupy more than one-quarter section of land. Authority was also granted for the construction and maintenance through the territories of the United States of a branch line to Oregon on similar terms. The privileges thus granted, however, were not to be

19 *Ibid.*, 2249-2252, 2279, 2328.
20 *Ibid.*, 2353, 2422-2423, 2856-2857. 3022, 3032, 3063, 3113.

construed as giving the contractors the right to preempt any public lands; nor did the act confer upon them any exclusive right to construct a telegraph to the Pacific, or debar the government from granting at some later time similar franchises and privileges to other parties.

In return for these privileges the government was to be entitled to priority in the use of the line, and with the approval of Congress might connect with it any of the military posts of the United States. The use of the line was to be given free of cost to the Coast Survey, the Smithsonian Institution, and the National Observatory for scientific purposes. The line was to be open to the use of all citizens on payment of the regular charges, which were not to exceed three dollars for a single dispatch of ten words with the usual proportionate reductions for longer dispatches; and all messages received were to be impartially transmitted in the order of their receipt. To safeguard the contractors against excessive use of the line by the government, the Act provided that if in any year during the continuance of the contract, the business done for the government should, at the ordinary rate of charges for private messages, exceed the $40,000 already contracted to be paid, then the Secretary of Treasury was to certify the amount of such excess to Congress and it would be paid.

Finally, no contract was to be made until the line was in actual operation, and payments under it were to cease whenever the contractors failed to comply with their contract. Congress, moreover, reserved the right to alter or amend the Act at any time.[21]

[21] An Act to Facilitate Communication Between the Atlantic and Pacific States by Electric Telegraph, June 16, 1860, *U.S. Stat. at Large*, 36 Cong., 1 sess., Chap. 137. This Act is given in full in Appendix 15.

CHAPTER XXV

On to the Pacific

1 ·——·

WHEN the North American Telegraph Association convened in New York for its third annual meeting on August 29, 1860, the chief topic of discussion was the recently enacted Pacific Telegraph Act. Leaders of the industry had been disappointed with the measure as finally passed by Congress, and showed little enthusiasm to promote a line under its terms. The subsidy, it will be recalled, had been reduced from $50,000 to $40,000 annually; the maximum charge for a single dispatch of ten words had been lowered from $4 to $3; and instead of a provision giving the building contract to a specific group of telegraph men, it was to be awarded on the basis of open bidding.[1] Moreover, quite a few believed the difficulties in the way of constructing and maintaining a Pacific telegraph line were almost insuperable. What was to prevent the Indians from tearing down the wires as fast as they were put up? Would not the poles be swept away by the irresistible movements of the immense herds of buffalo then roaming over the plains? In addition, there were other serious practical obstacles such as securing and transporting poles across the vast plains area, and repairing hundreds of miles of line stretching through uninhabited regions, as yet unpenetrated by the railroads. Finally, there was the important question of whether the amount of business to be depended upon after the line was constructed would be sufficient to pay the high cost of maintenance.[2] Under the circumstances quite a few of the Association members favored suspending all action pending the passage of a more satisfactory measure by Congress.

Such an attitude suited admirably the plans of Robert W. Russell who was determined to block any action which might favor the Western Union interests. He proceeded to introduce three resolutions. The first, which was promptly passed, asserted that the Act was so objectionable in principle and detail that the Convention declined to recommend its adoption by the associated companies forming the North American Telegraph Confederation. A second recommended

---

[1] Third Annual Meeting of the North American Telegraph Association, August 29, 1860, in *Proceedings of the North American Telegraph Association, 1858-59 and 60*.
[2] A. R. Brewer, *Western Union Telegraph Company. A Retrospect*, 25.

that another application be made to Congress requesting aid for a California line either by a central or southern route, but this was voted down. The third recommended that the associated companies appoint delegates to confer together on the subject to ascertain what legislation would be acceptable to all, and report at the next meeting of the Confederation.[3] This last resolution having been accepted, Russell congratulated himself on the ease with which he had shelved the whole troublesome matter for at least a year.

Up to this point the Western Union forces had remained strangely quiet, but Sibley had already made up his mind that if his allies in the North American Telegraph Association refused to aid him with the project, he would "go it alone." Such an intention was carefully concealed from Russell and his adherents, however. The resolution which Secretary Isaac R. Elwood of Western Union now presented appeared to be innocent enough:

Resolved, That nothing in the preceding resolutions shall be construed to prevent any company or companies of this Association, either alone or in connection with other parties, to bid under the said Act, upon the distinct understanding that the said line, when built, shall make exclusive business connections with the lines of this Association according to the provisions of the six party contract.

Sibley explained casually that the purpose of the resolution was merely to make it possible for a member of the North American Telegraph Association to put in a bid, if necessary, to stave off action by an outside company; and the resolution was passed without protest.[4]

Russell, without realizing it, had played into Sibley's hands. The meeting had scarcely adjourned before a bid was entered with the Secretary of the Treasury in the name of Hiram Sibley at $40,000— the maximum amount allowed by Congress. According to the terms of the Act, the contract should have been made with the lowest bidder; actually it went to the highest—Hiram Sibley. The other bidders, Benjamin F. Ficklin at $35,000, Theodore Adams at $29,000, and Harmon & Clark at $25,000, for reasons probably best known to Sibley, had withdrawn before the time came for giving bonds; and, thus, the highest was also the lowest bidder. Official acceptance of Sibley's bid for construction of the Pacific line was communicated

3 Thomas Bassnett to J. D. Caton [n.p., n.d., August 1860], Caton Papers.
4 Ibid.

by Howell Cobb, the Secretary of the Treasury, on September 20, 1860.[5]

2 ··—··

SIBLEY and his associates now set to work to carry the great project to a successful conclusion. Sibley's letters to Judge Caton during December 1860 furnish an interesting picture of Western Union's president at work and give some insight into the telegraphic developments of the day. On December 6 he wrote Caton asking him to join with the other members of the North American Telegraph Association in giving the transcontinental line support by granting it a 40 percent drawback on all transcontinental business. "Our company is making at our own risk and expense all the examinations of the several routes and securing to the enterprise all the benefits from contracts with other companies and parties. And we propose that after all is done that can be and all is learned that can be of the expense and business income, etc., to offer to each and all of the parties granting this drawback a full and fair proportion with us of the stock and equal participation with us in the management and profits if they choose to do so after a full consideration of the whole matter."

Sibley was also eager to have the Pony Express continue to run between the eastern and western extremities of the wires during the construction of the transcontinental line. The management of the Pony Express was unwilling to maintain this service unless offered some encouragement beyond the regular tariff. Sibley had agreed, therefore, to yield to the Pony Express its full share of all the drawback after January 1 and to continue to do so as long as the Express maintained its service between the wires.

The American Company, wrote Sibley, was for several reasons rather unfriendly. Kendall wanted the transcontinental projectors to buy the patent right for Texas. Russell wanted the line to go from New Orleans through Texas and Mexico. In short, the attitude of the American Telegraph Company was one of hostility and obstructionism.[6]

[5] Bancroft, *Chronicles of the Builders*, v, 335-336; Gamble, "Wiring a Continent," *The California Magazine*, III (1881), 556; Brewer, *Western Union Telegraph Company. A Retrospect*, 25; *Telegrapher*, October 31, 1864, I, 13-14.

[6] Sibley to Caton, December 6, 1860, Caton Papers; cf. Thomas Bassnett to Caton, December 18, 1860, Caton Papers; [Russell], *Statistics, Etc., of the American Telegraph Company*, August 30, 1860.

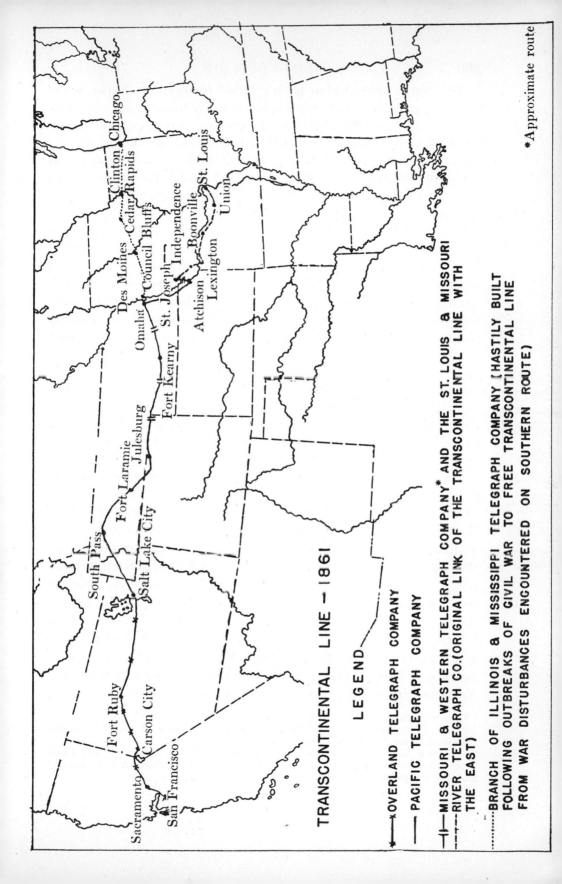

TRANSCONTINENTAL LINE — 1861

LEGEND

×—OVERLAND TELEGRAPH COMPANY

——PACIFIC TELEGRAPH COMPANY

╫—MISSOURI & WESTERN TELEGRAPH COMPANY* AND THE ST. LOUIS & MISSOURI
RIVER TELEGRAPH CO.(ORIGINAL LINK OF THE TRANSCONTINENTAL LINE WITH
THE EAST)

········BRANCH OF ILLINOIS & MISSISSIPPI TELEGRAPH COMPANY (HASTILY BUILT
FOLLOWING OUTBREAKS OF CIVIL WAR TO FREE TRANSCONTINENTAL LINE
FROM WAR DISTURBANCES ENCOUNTERED ON SOUTHERN ROUTE)

*Approximate route

Chicago
Clinton
Cedar Rapids
Des Moines
Council Bluffs
Omaha
St. Joseph
Independence
Boonville
St. Louis
Union
Atchison
Lexington
Fort Kearny
Julesburg
Fort Laramie
South Pass
Salt Lake City
Fort Ruby
Carson City
Sacramento
San Francisco

Two weeks later, Caton having failed to succumb, Sibley wrote another persuasive letter pointing out that five of the eight companies composing the North American Telegraph Association had signed contracts similar to the one which he had sent Caton, and urging the Judge to give the project his backing.[7] Sibley's salesmanship was evidently effective, for a short time later Judge Caton joined the others; only the American Telegraph Company remained outside the transcontinental agreement.

Meanwhile, Western Union had sent Jeptha H. Wade to California to organize the chaotic telegraph industry there. Upon his arrival in November he had found four rival companies all anxious to join the Western Union interests in building the transcontinental line. An agreement with one would have antagonized the others. Wade, therefore, told them that he would have nothing to do with any of them unless they would agree to consolidate; in which case they would be given the construction of the line from California to Salt Lake City, and an equitable share, according to distance, of the subsidies offered by the State of California and the Federal Government, as well as of the total receipts of the line. This incentive, along with the skillful negotiations conducted by Wade, shortly resulted in a consolidation of interests along the West coast under the California State Telegraph Company.[8]

For a number of reasons the promoters decided to place the execution of the transcontinental project, both east and west of Salt Lake, in the hands of outside organizations, in which the parent companies— Western Union and California State—were to be properly represented. On April 10, 1861, the telegraph leaders in California, with the approval of Wade and Sibley, proceeded to organize the Overland Telegraph Company with a capital of $1,250,000 to construct that section of the transcontinental line between Carson City, eastern terminus of the California State line, and Salt Lake.[9] Sibley and the Western Union interests had, in the meantime, established a similar organization, the Pacific Telegraph Company, with a capital of $1,000,000 to construct the section between Omaha and Salt Lake. An examination of the list of corporators is enlightening. Dominating

[7] Sibley to Caton, December 29, 1860, Caton Papers.

[8] J. H. Wade, Autobiography, manuscript in the possession of the Wade family, Cleveland, Ohio; *Telegrapher*, October 31, 1864, I, 13-14.

[9] [Western Union Telegraph Company], *Corporate History of the Western Union Telegraph Company*, 107; A. L. Bates, "The History of the Telegraph in California," *Southern California Historical Society Publications*, IX, 184.

the organization was the Western Union group—Hiram Sibley, Isaac Butts, Jeptha H. Wade, Isaac R. Elwood, Samuel L. Selden, and Joseph Medbery. The Missouri & Western Telegraph Company, whose line between St. Louis and Omaha was to form an important link in the transcontinental system, was represented by Charles M. Stebbins. In addition, there were Thomas R. Walker of the New York, Albany & Buffalo, John H. Berryhill of the Atlantic & Ohio, and Edward Creighton, contractor for the Pacific Telegraph line. Representing the California interests were Albert W. Bee and James S. Graham. Also included, significantly enough, were the names of Theodore Adams, John H. Harmon and Benjamin F. Ficklin, the bidders who had quietly withdrawn at the time Sibley had secured the contract for the transcontinental line from the Secretary of the Treasury.[10] Evidence, if any were needed, as to who controlled the Pacific Telegraph Company was furnished by the election of officers. Jeptha H. Wade was made president; Hiram Sibley, vice president; and Isaac R. Elwood, secretary.[11]

3 · · · — ·

ALL during the spring of 1861 the telegraph promoters were busy working out final plans for the construction of the transcontinental line. Much attention had been given the important question of the route. Upon the recommendation of Edward Creighton who had spent the entire summer of 1860 in the West surveying and gathering information, it was agreed that the Pacific Telegraph Company under his superintendence should construct a line from Omaha, Nebraska, up the Platte River via old Fort Kearney to Fort Laramie, then up the Sweetwater River, and through South Pass to Salt Lake. Simultaneously the Overland Telegraph Company under the superintendence of James Gamble was to push a line eastward from Carson City through Ruby Valley, Egan Cañon and Deep Creek to join with Creighton's line at Salt Lake. But transcontinental service was not to wait for the completion of the lines. Through an arrangement worked out with the Pony Express service was to cover the gap between the lines until their union was effected. As an incentive to speed up the work, it was agreed that the company completing its line to Salt Lake City first was to retain the full tariff received for

10 "An Act to Incorporate the Pacific Telegraph Company" passed by the legislature of the Territory of Nebraska, January 12, 1861, O'Rielly Docs., Telegraph Pamphlets.
11 *Telegrapher*, October 31, 1864, I, 13-14.

messages between Omaha and San Francisco, until the entire line
was complete. Should either party arrive at Salt Lake with their
completed line four months in advance of the other, they were to
receive $50 a day thereafter until the line was finished.[12]

The specifications for the construction of the line called for poles
of durable material and not less than twenty-five per mile; galvanized
iron wire of the best quality was to be used; and the line was to be
insulated in the best possible manner—on the eastern section the
"Wade" insulator was specified. Repeaters were to be provided so
that communication could be carried on by either party as far as the
junction of their respective lines at Salt Lake City without rewriting.
The whole structure was to be finished by July 31, 1861, unless Congress should extend the time on account of any necessity which might
arise.

The $40,000 annual subsidy offered by the Government was to
be divided in the ratio of 60 percent for the lines east of Salt Lake
City, and 40 percent for the lines west of that point, until the gross
annual receipts of the California interests on transcontinental business should exceed $70,000 per annum, when their proportion was
to be reduced to 30 percent.[13]

4 · · · · —

ALL the necessary business details having been arranged, gangs of
men were organized to commence the work at a number of different
points simultaneously. On the western section, Superintendent Gamble proposed to start one gang under the direction of James Street
westward from Salt Lake City, while another under I. M. Hubbard
was to push eastward from Carson City until the two should meet.
Superintendent Creighton planned to follow a similar course in the
construction of the eastern section. W. H. Stebbins was to direct the
work from Salt Lake City eastward some four hundred miles, while
Creighton himself would superintend the work on the remaining
seven hundred miles to Omaha.[14]

Wade, Sibley, and their fellow promoters hoped that the project
could be completed before the close of the year, but with nearly
2,000 miles of line to be constructed before winter should halt all

---

12 Wade, Autobiography; Gamble, *op. cit.*, 556-563; *Telegrapher*, October 31, 1864,
I, 13-14.
13 *Ibid.*; Reid, *Telegraph in America*, 495.
14 Gamble, *op. cit.*

activities, there was no time to lose. On May 27 a great telegraph expedition headed by Superintendent James Gamble and his assistant, I. M. Hubbard, left Sacramento with a train of 25 wagons loaded with telegraph materials and supplies, 228 oxen, 18 mules and horses, and 50 men. They had estimated 15 days to get through the Sierra Nevadas, but the long heavily-laden train passing along the narrow mountain roads was delayed by incoming trains for a day at a time. Finally the telegraph train was broken up into several sections and its progress was somewhat accelerated. As a result of delays the expedition did not reach Carson City until late in June. By the close of the month work was being pushed energetically from both Carson City and Salt Lake City.[15]

While Gamble and Hubbard were leading their expedition over the Sierra Nevadas, another large expedition was being organized at Omaha by Edward Creighton and his lieutenants. Nearly 400 men were fitted out with rifles, navy revolvers, and the necessary provisions for a hard season's campaign. For the transportation of the material and provisions for this army of workmen, 500 head of oxen and mules and over 100 wagons were purchased.[16]

On June 15, while in the midst of their preparations, came a startling announcement: "The Telegraph line through Jefferson City, Missouri, has been torn down by order of Governor Claiborne F. Jackson."[17] War had swept across the path of progress. Here was just one more problem for Creighton and his lieutenants to worry about; but for the moment the all-important task was that of pushing a line of telegraph on to Salt Lake.

When all was ready the great telegraph expedition rolled westward from Omaha; their first pole was set on the fourth of July.[18] On the same day in Washington, D.C., Congress was convening in special session to vote loans and taxes, and to authorize President Lincoln to recruit an army of half a million men for the bloody Civil War.

The problems which confronted the telegraph builders on this heroic venture were many and varied. Wire and insulators for the western section had to be shipped from New York via Cape Horn to San Francisco and then hauled over the Sierra Nevadas to Carson City and beyond; or sent up the Missouri River and then overland across hundreds of miles of plain and desert to Salt Lake and on to

15 *Ibid.*; cf. *Scientific American*, July 13, 1861.
16 Wade, *Autobiography*; *Telegrapher*, October 31, 1864, I, 13-14.
17 B. H. Wilson, "Across the Prairies of Iowa," *Palimpsest*, VII (August 1926), 243-255.
18 Wade, *Autobiography*.

their ultimate destination. Another perplexing problem was that of securing the necessary poles. Much of the territory that had to be traversed contained little native timber and in some cases poles had to be hauled several hundred miles.[19]

While building in the vicinity of Salt Lake City, Creighton was somewhat concerned as to the attitude Brigham Young might assume toward the intrusion of the telegraph into his domain. As chief elder of the Mormons, his word was law throughout the Mormon empire. To win Brigham Young's friendship, the telegraph company asked his son, who was engaged in the lumber business, to submit a bid for furnishing the telegraph poles in that section. His price, which appeared to be reasonable, was promptly accepted and a contract was drawn up accordingly. Some time later the son informed the contractors that his bid on the poles had been too low, and that he was losing money on the job. A new contract was at once made at a higher figure. Not long after the new contract had been drawn up, a messenger came saying that Brigham Young wished to see the telegraph contractor. With considerable apprehension Creighton went to the home of the Mormon leader. Upon being ushered into the library, he introduced himself as the representative of the telegraph company.

"Is it true that my son entered into a contract with you to furnish poles for the telegraph?" inquired Young.

"Yes, sir," replied Creighton.

"Is it also true that the price agreed upon in this contract was subsequently raised?"

Creighton nodded his assent.

"Let me see those contracts," said Young.

Creighton taking the documents from his pocket handed them over. After careful scrutiny Brigham Young crushed the new one in his hand and threw it into the fire.

"The poles will be furnished by my son in accordance with the terms of the original contract," he said.[20]

Gamble had a somewhat similar experience with the Mormon leader. Brigham Young, upon hearing of the failure on the part of the Mormon contractors to supply the specified number of poles, denounced the pole contractors from his pulpit and said the work of furnishing poles must be carried out. The contract was accordingly turned over to other parties and the poles supplied.

[19] Gamble, *op. cit.*   [20] Wilson, *op. cit.*

In crossing desert regions teams with barrels of water had to be kept abreast of the construction gang. In one instance sixteen miles of line were built in one day in order to reach a point where water might be obtained by nightfall.[21]

Still another problem of considerable importance and delicacy was that of gaining the good will of the Indian tribes through whose lands the line was to pass. On the western section of the line, Gamble's friend and associate in the enterprise, James Street, was sent to confer with the leading Indian chiefs west of Salt Lake to gain their support for the project. Shokup, chief of the Shoshones and an influential figure among the western tribes, after listening to Street's careful explanation of the telegraph, expressed great interest in the white man's "wire rope express," as he termed it. Street then invited him to journey to San Francisco and meet the Big Captain (President Horace W. Carpentier). Shokup, having gotten as far as Carson City, however, refused to go any farther, but before returning to his people he dictated the following dispatch: "Shokup, Big Chief of the Shoshones, says to Big Captain at San Francisco, that his Indians will not trouble the telegraph line. Shokup is a friend of the white man. His people obey him. He will order them to be friendly with the white man and not injure the telegraph. He would like to see Big Captain, but must return to his tribe, and cannot go to San Francisco."

The great chief's ready acceptance of the "wire rope express" quickly disposed the Indians in its favor. To further insure harmonious relations, gifts of food and clothing were made to the Indians, members of the various tribes were employed among the working parties to care for the stock, and a general order was issued by Superintendent Gamble warning that any man of the expedition getting into trouble with the Indians would be summarily dismissed. As a result, there was never any hostility between the construction gangs and the red men on the western division. Even in later years when Indian flare-ups occurred, relations with the telegraph men remained excellent. On the eastern division, unfortunately, there were some exceptions to this happy relationship.

An incident which tended to give the Indians respect for the telegraph is related by Gamble. One day as they were working on the line about two hundred miles east of the Sierra Nevadas a thunder storm arose. The telegraph men, provided with buckskin gloves to

21 Gamble, *op. cit.*

protect them from the shock occasioned by violent lightning, were working hard to finish the day's mileage quota. A member of an Indian tribe that was watching the workmen came forward eagerly and grasped the wire to help; being in his bare feet and on moist ground, he received a shock which sent him running down the road like wildfire. Thereafter, no Indian along that section of the line could be induced to go near the wire or touch the poles under any circumstances.[22]

In general, construction of the line proceeded very well. Creighton and Gamble communicated freely, advising each other at frequent intervals of progress made. Soon a friendly competition developed between them, and a wager was laid as to which would be the first to establish a complete circuit with Salt Lake. Early in September, the *Scientific American* reported that the western half would be in working order "before snow falls," while the eastern section was already up to Julesburg, 200 miles west of Ft. Kearney, and work on the remainder was going forward satisfactorily.[23]

In order that no time should be lost, Hubbard's expedition organized a system. First, the route to be followed by the line was measured and staked off; hole diggers followed; then pole setters; and next the wire party. Even with such efficient organization, the line could not be strung at a rate of more than three to eight miles a day, depending upon the terrain. An advance telegraph station was maintained at the head of the line and each day's progress reported. Thus every day found the operator "occupying a new station, like a wandering Arab."[24] At this advance station, news was received on the arrival of the Pony Express and telegraphed on to San Francisco and other points. Commercial dispatches also were sent and received daily, as the Pony Express arrived at or departed from the telegraph camp.[25]

The magnitude of the task had led to a general belief that completion of the line would require at least two years. The work had been so well organized and so energetically pursued, however, that contrary to all expectations, Creighton's eastern section was completed on October 19.[26] Nor was Gamble's party far behind; up to October 1, work on the western section had progressed well. Upon reaching the last stretch, however—the 50 or 60 miles between Ruby Valley and Schell Creek—it became apparent that the pole contractors were

22 *Ibid.*; cf. *Telegrapher*, III, 143, 167.   23 *Scientific American*, September 7, 1861.
24 *Ibid.*; Gamble, *op. cit.*   25 *Ibid.*   26 Bates, *op. cit.*

going to fail them in that section. Mountaineers and Indians were sent to scour the nearby mountains and procure poles, if possible. But the season was getting very late, and the men, fearing the danger of being sealed in the mountains by heavy snow, wished to return home. Gamble had apprehensions that the project could not be completed until spring. Then ascertaining that poles might be obtained on top of a high mountain about fifteen miles from Egan Cañon, he sent forth twenty wagons under the direction of the wagon-master and foreman of construction. Several days later he was informed by a note sent by the stage coach that the men had reached Egan Cañon, but refused to ascend the mountain, contending that it was too late in the season for so dangerous a venture.

Gamble held a conference with his assistant, I. M. Hubbard, and Jasper McDonald, the commissary of the expedition; they decided to take the next stage for Egan Cañon and enforce orders. Upon arriving Gamble told the men that they had entered into an agreement to stick by the work until it was completed and that he intended to hold them to their promises. If they refused they might forfeit their pay. The men expressed fear of being caught by a storm in the mountains, but upon being assured that Gamble and his assistants would accompany them, they reluctantly set forth. In two days the party had secured twenty wagon loads of poles with which they hurried off to finish the telegraph line.

The work was now rapidly pushed forward without further incident, and the last link in the great transcontinental chain was finally forged on October 24, just six days after Creighton had finished the eastern section.[27] In little more than four months a vast prairie and mountain barrier separating the two sections of the nation was spanned; and isolated California, whose only means of communication with the East had been the slow, hazardous journey over the plains, across the Isthmus, or around the Horn, was in close communication with the Atlantic coast—and that, nearly eight years before President Stanford of the Central Pacific drove the historic gold spike connecting the oceans by rail.

During the evening of October 24, Cyrus Field's brother, the eminent jurist, Stephen J. Field, transmitted the following dispatch to the heavily burdened man who sat in the White House:

27 Gamble, *op. cit.*

To Abraham Lincoln, President of the United States:

In the temporary absence of the Governor of the State, I am requested to send you the first message which will be transmitted over the wires of the telegraph line which connects the Pacific with the Atlantic States. The people of California desire to congratulate you upon the completion of the great work. They believe that it will be the means of strengthening the attachment which binds both the East and West to the Union, and they desire in this—the first message across the continent—to express their loyalty to the Union and their determination to stand by its Government on this its day of trial. They regard that Government with affection, and will adhere to it under all fortunes.

Stephen J. Field
Chief Justice of California

There followed a message from Horace W. Carpentier, President of the Overland Telegraph Company:

San Francisco, Cal.
October 24, 1861, 7:40 P.M.

To His Excellency, the President
Washington, D.C.

I announce to you that the telegraph to California has this day been completed. May it be a bond of perpetuity between the states of the Atlantic and those of the Pacific.

Horace W. Carpentier
President, Overland Telegraph Company[28]

5 — — —

SIBLEY's original intention had been to make St. Louis the eastern terminus or distributing point for Pacific news, but the tumult of the rebellion that had swept through the border states at the outbreak of the Civil War made it desirable to substitute some free-state center, and Chicago was selected.[29] On October 31, the *Chicago Tribune* carried the following notice: "It was announced yesterday at the Board of Trade that the Hon. J. D. Caton, President of the Illinois & Mississippi Telegraph Company, had secured for Chicago the honor of being the Eastern terminus of the Pacific Telegraph."

November found Caton's faithful lieutenant, E. D. L. Sweet, rushing construction on a line of telegraph across the State of Iowa so that transcontinental messages could be routed from Omaha via Council Bluffs, Des Moines, and Cedar Rapids to Chicago. Writing to his

28 *Ibid.*; Bates, *op. cit.*
29 Bancroft, *Chronicles of the Builders*, v, 337.

employer from Des Moines on November 9, Sweet complained of the difficulty of getting laborers and teams; all had been taken by the army recruiting officers. Further trouble was encountered in securing good poles, and in order not to delay construction he had been obliged to use cottonwood on part of the route.[30]

In spite of the difficulties, the line was finished early in January 1862. The first regular telegraphic news column appeared in the *Des Moines Register* on January 14. The jubilant editor gave free rein to his feelings:

Ever since Adam was an infant, the City of Des Moines, or the site where it is located, has been cut off from the exterior world. We have had no Railroads. We have had no telegraph. We have been excluded from the activities of commerce. Situated midway between the two great rivers of the continent, without anything but coaches and stage roads to connect us with the rest of mankind, our condition has not been the most pleasant in the world.

To-day our situation is immensely improved. We have the privilege of reading the latest dispatches in our own paper. The lightning and telegraph company have at length made us even with the Mississippi cities. . . .[31]

The fact that the new line gave Des Moines speedy communication with the outside world was incidental, of course, to the much more significant fact that transcontinental messages could now be sent eastward over a line free from the ravages of war.

6 ......

CONTRARY to the expectations of many, the transcontinental line proved immediately and highly profitable. A heavy business was done the first few days at one dollar a word, in spite of the clause in the Act of Congress fixing the charge at a maximum of three dollars for ten words. Within a week after the opening of the line through to the East the following rates were established:

San Francisco to St. Louis, first 10 words $5.00
    each additional word .... $ .45
To Chicago, first 10 words $5.60
    each additional word .... $ .50
To New York or Washington, first 10 words $6.00
    each additional word .... $ .75

[30] E. D. L. Sweet to Caton, November 9, 1861, Caton Papers; cf. *Ibid.*, November 4, 1861.
[31] Wilson, *op. cit.*

Moreover, the ten words had to include the name of the place from which the dispatch was sent, and the month and day when it was sent, leaving seven words for the message. A customer sending a message from San Francisco to New York, therefore, was actually charged 87 3/7 cents per word. At such rates only the rich could afford to use the telegraph. The State of California and the Federal Government found themselves subsidizing a luxury in the interests of a few. In an indirect way it could be contended that every American was benefited by the transcontinental project, but many of them were not convinced that the proprietors had the right to deprive them of its use through exorbitant rates. As rumors reached the public of the fabulous profits that had been made by its promoters, ominous rumblings of discontent began to be heard.[32]

For Sibley, Wade, Creighton, Gamble, and a small inner circle of telegraph men, the transcontinental telegraph had been a glorious triumph, both financially and strategically. The line of the Pacific Telegraph Company, extending some 1,100 miles from Brownsville, Nebraska, to Salt Lake City, Utah, had cost, according to the later testimony of one of its builders, even after considerable "financing" on the part of two of the Western Union directors, only $147,000. Upon this expenditure they had issued $1,000,000 of stock. This $1,000,000 stock issue was afterward taken into Western Union through the issuance of $2,000,000 of Western Union stock. A short time later, Western Union stock was tripled so that "an original expenditure of $147,000 (and part of that not honestly spent) came to represent $6,000,000 of Western Union Telegraph stock." A similar procedure was followed in respect to the line of the Overland Telegraph Company. The entire transcontinental line, conservatively estimated to have cost not more than $500,000, brought its promoters $460,000 in subsidies alone within a decade. In addition, profits amounting to many millions of dollars were reaped by the group through stock watering and the ultimate sale of the line to the thousands of stockholders of the Western Union Telegraph Company.[33]

If Western Union was made to pay dearly for the great transcontinental line, it also derived great benefits from it. It controlled lines extending from ocean to ocean. Its business was large, its outlook brilliant, its position excellent, and its influence immense. It stood confessedly one of the largest and most comprehensive private enter-

---

[32] Bancroft, *Chronicles of the Builders*, v, 338.
[33] Senate Report 577, 48 Cong., 1 sess.; Bancroft, *op. cit.*, 336.

prises in the world. Its directors were looked upon by many as business magicians. No project was too big, no venture too daring, so long as Hiram Sibley directed its course.

7 — — ··

As a matter of fact, Sibley had begun, even before the line to the Pacific was completed, to make plans for another big undertaking. For several years an energetic promoter, Perry McDonough Collins, had been at work upon a great international project for uniting the telegraph systems of the United States and Russia. Collins proposed to construct a vast overland line through British Columbia, Russian America, and northeastern Siberia to the mouth of the Amur River, on the Asiatic coast, where it was to be met by a Russian line which was already under construction from St. Petersburg. The plan possessed many obvious advantages. Everywhere the line would run overland except for a short distance at Bering Strait. There was the possibility also of extending it eventually down the Asiatic coast to Peking and the populous commercial centers of China.[34]

In February 1861, Collins had secured the introduction of a bill into the United States Congress looking to the appropriation of $50,000 for a "survey of the northern water, coasts, and islands of the Pacific Ocean and Berings' Strait having reference to telegraphic connection with Russia." The subject was discussed in both the House and the Senate, but no action was taken at this time.[35]

Meanwhile, Collins had turned quite naturally to Hiram Sibley for assistance in carrying out his project, and the Western Union president, after a careful study of the scheme, became Collins' enthusiastic backer. The construction of a line girdling half the globe and joining America and Europe telegraphically would make Western Union a world power, and Sibley a still richer and more renowned citizen. Writing to Collins in October 1861, Sibley declared, "Our men are pressing me hard to let them go on to Behrings' Strait next summer, and as you say to me 'if I had the money' I would go on and complete the line and talk about it afterwards.

"If the Russian government will meet us at Behrings' Strait, and give us the right of way, etc., through their territory on the Pacific, we will complete the line in two years, and probably in one. The

---

[34] Reid, *Telegraph in America*, 508-510.
[35] House Report 82, 36 Cong., 2 sess.; *Cong. Globe*, 36 Cong., 2 sess., 999.

work is not more difficult than we have already accomplished over the Rocky Mountains and plains to California; and, in my opinion, the whole thing is entirely practicable, and that, too, in much less time and with much less expense than is generally supposed by those most hopeful. No work costing so little money was ever accomplished by man that will be so important in its results. The benefit resulting to the world will pay the entire cost of the line every year after completion while the world continues to be inhabited by civilized man; and it is to me a matter of surprise," concluded Sibley, "that any intelligent person, at all familiar with building and working telegraph lines in the West, should doubt the practicability of the successful working, after built, of a line to Behrings' Strait."[36]

Professor Morse in reply to a query from Collins also pronounced the proposed project entirely feasible, asserting that there was no serious obstacle to be apprehended from climatic or geographic considerations.[37] The next few years, however, were consumed with the exigencies of the Civil War, and the Russian-American project, while not forgotten, was held in abeyance.

[36] Hiram Sibley to Perry McD. Collins, October 16, 1861, in Appendix of pamphlet, *Statement of the Origin, Organization and Progress of the Russian-American Telegraph* . . . , May 1866, published by Western Union Telegraph Company.
[37] Morse to Collins, November 29, 1861, *Ibid.*

CHAPTER XXVI

War Years: the American
and the Southwestern Telegraph Companies

1 ·——·

THE terrible War between the States which burst upon the nation in
the spring of 1861 had a profound effect upon nearly every phase of
American life. Its impact upon the telegraph industry was an important factor—perhaps the decisive factor—in the struggle between
the leading companies for control of the industry. The immediate
effect of the war was to swamp all of the lines with business. Armies
had to be raised, supplies provided, and countless details handled
quickly. President Lincoln's call on April 15 for 75,000 troops was
flashed to the governors of the loyal states; units of the regular army
were summoned and shifted by telegraph; banks and capitalists
telegraphed offers of money and credit; newspapers, eager for the
latest bulletins, made lavish use of the wires. Papers which prior to
the war had printed no more than two or three columns of telegraph
news a day were soon printing two or three pages.[1] Business men
throughout the nation tried frantically to settle their affairs before
all contact between the sections was broken. Revenues of the telegraph companies skyrocketed as North and South prepared for
combat.[2]

Some of the companies were more advantageously situated to
profit from the war than others. Those extending from north to south
across the Mason-Dixon line and the Ohio River were soon cut in
two; as the war continued, much of their property was destroyed,
and their development checked. Those extending from east to west,
on the other hand, were particularly favored. Being so situated as to
link the loyal states with one another, they found the war years a
period of golden harvest and growth.

2 ··—··

THE splendid communications system which the American Telegraph
Company had developed along the seaboard from Newfoundland to

---

[1] E. H. Davis, *History of the New York Times, 1851-1921*, 53.
[2] Harlow, *Old Wires and New Waves*, 260-261.

New Orleans was rudely torn asunder by the war. On April 19 a company of militia seized the Washington office and the next month was one of constant interference and confusion. Finally, on May 21, the northern and southern officials of the company held a conference on the Long Bridge across the Potomac which resulted in the severing of telegraphic communication between Washington and Richmond. Colonel Edwards S. Sanford continued to direct affairs in the North, while the southern part of the company's system, reorganized as the Southern or Confederate Telegraph Company, was operated as an independent unit with Dr. William S. Morris, an important southern stockholder, as president.[3]

Under the able management of Dr. Morris the Southern Telegraph Company soon dominated the industry in the Confederacy. Shortly after the outbreak of war, Confederate Postmaster General John H. Reagan on plea of military necessity assumed nominal control of all telegraphs in the South. Reagan, in turn, chose none other than Dr. Morris as chief of military telegraphs. The actual management of the individual companies was interfered with only as military purposes required; nevertheless, Dr. Morris had general supervisory powers over all the lines. The efficient manner in which he maintained an effective telegraph system throughout the South during the war years won for him the wholehearted praise of the Postmaster General. At the same time, the special interests of the Southern Telegraph Company were not forgotten.[4] That concern's chief rival in the South, the Southwestern Telegraph Company, for example, was subjected to various embarrassments which its leaders attributed to Dr. Morris's influence with the officials in Richmond.[5]

Notwithstanding the influence and success of the shrewd doctor in the handling of telegraph affairs in the Confederacy, leaders of the American Telegraph Company in the North viewed his activities with mixed feelings. Was it the intention of Dr. Morris merely to preserve and protect their southern property during the war years; or was he just waiting for an opportune time to declare it confiscated?

There were other causes for pessimism on the part of the American

[3] Amos Kendall to J. D. Caton, March 14, 1861, Caton Papers; William R. Plum, *The Military Telegraph During the Civil War in the United States* . . . , I, 135; Reid, *Telegraph in America*, 422-423; [Western Union Telegraph Company], *Corporate History of the Western Union Telegraph Company*, 52-53.

[4] Plum, *The Military Telegraph During the Civil War*, I, 134-137; Harlow, *Old Wires and New Waves*, 265; Confederate States of America, Post Office Department Statement, January 12, 1863; *Ibid.*, December 7, 1863; *Ibid.*, November 7, 1864.

[5] For a detailed discussion of this subject, see 376-377.

Telegraph Company's stockholders. As the fortunes of war ebbed and flowed, many miles of line in the battle zones were destroyed or damaged. At the same time, all plans for the laying of an Atlantic cable were brought to a standstill. With the outcome of the war in doubt, British financiers who had been the chief backers of the project had withdrawn their support.[6]

The temporary weakness of the American Telegraph Company at this critical stage in the development of the industry was unfortunate. With the company's property divided, much of it destroyed or damaged by the ravages of war, and the cable project completely halted, it was in no position to cope effectively with the bold tactics employed by that great rival, the Western Union Telegraph Company, in its campaign to dominate the industry. The major efforts of the American Telegraph Company's leaders during the war years had to be given to maintaining the properties already owned rather than attempting to secure new ones.

3 ··· — ·

THE lines of the Southwestern Telegraph Company, extending from Louisville south through the States of Kentucky, Tennessee, Alabama, Mississippi, and Louisiana to New Orleans, were also severed.[7] The company's affairs in Kentucky continued to be directed by its able president, Norvin Green, while a separate corporation with its headquarters at Nashville, Tennessee, was set up to look after affairs within the Confederacy. George L. Douglass, long treasurer of the Southwestern, became acting president of the Confederate corporation. With the cooperation of Secretary Thomas L. Carter and General Superintendent John Van Horne,[8] Douglass labored unceasingly to protect the property and to operate successfully the lines within the Confederacy. The task was not an easy one. On May 21, 1861, the Confederate Congress had passed an act declaring void the renewal

---

[6] H. H. Forsyth to Kendall, June 29, 1861, Morse Papers, XLI; Kendall to Morse, January 21, 1862, Morse Papers, XLI; George L. Douglass to Morse, February 24, 1863, Morse Papers, XLII.

[7] The wire mileage of the company in 1861 was distributed as follows:

Kentucky	605	Louisiana	253
Tennessee	567	Alabama	35
Mississippi	713		————
			2,173

(Answer of George L. Douglass, garnishee, Nashville, Tennessee, October 18, 1861, Morse Papers, XLI.)

[8] Van Horne shortly replaced Douglass as acting president in the South.

on Morse's patent, thereby depriving the Southwestern Telegraph Company of all patent protection within the Confederacy. That was only a beginning.[9]

Writing to Morse from Louisville, Kentucky, in the autumn of 1861, President Green described some of the other difficulties with which they had to contend: "At present our lines are operated some forty miles southward from here. There are then some seventy-five or eighty miles between the main bodies of the opposing armies, which we can get no permission to visit or otherwise ascertain its condition. The lines over this space are doubtless broken or cut in many places, and I fear being . . . permanently destroyed or carried off. South of Bowling Green in this State some 120 miles from here, our lines are under the present authority of the Confederate Government, and being managed, doubtless as best they can, by our Secretary, Mr. Carter, our Treasurer, Mr. George L. Douglass, and our General Supt., Mr. Van Horne, whose headquarters or Executive office is at Nashville. All communication with them by any means whatever, is entirely cut off; and since the fifteenth of Sept. I have had no intelligence of what they were doing."

With the through business almost entirely destroyed, and local business from Memphis to Nashville just about enough to pay expenses, the company had to observe the most rigid economy. All building activities had been suspended, and the teams usually employed to make repairs during the summer had been dispensed with. In the extreme South, New Orleans and the other principal offices were doing comparatively nothing. With the total suspension of commerce and the terrible animosity existing between the North and the South, Dr. Green told Morse he feared that the "through business would never—certainly not for years—be restored to what it was."[10]

As the war progressed the situation grew increasingly difficult. Official notice was given to the company that the stock of Professor Morse and other alien enemies of the Confederacy was to be sequestered. For several months acting President Douglass evaded the order on one pretext or another.[11] Then came a bombshell. On the ground that its officers were Unionists, an order was issued by the Confederate Government taking the Southwestern's lines out of its hands and

[9] Answer of George L. Douglass, garnishee, Nashville, Tennessee, October 18, 1861, Morse Papers, XLI; Kendall to Morse, September 16, 1861, Morse Papers, XLI.

[10] Norvin Green to Morse, October 21, 1861, Morse Papers, XLI.

[11] George L. Douglass to Morse, March 22, 1862, Morse Papers, XLI.

putting them under the direct charge of the Confederate superintendent of military telegraphs, Dr. Morris.

The Southwestern Telegraph Company's officers naturally believed this move to be the work of the shrewd doctor who was an influential figure in Richmond. What better way could he have devised for eliminating the chief rival of his own Confederate Telegraph Company? Dr. Morris had been at work ever since the beginning of the war, declared George L. Douglass, "striving to destroy the interests of our Company, in total disregard of the obligations of the six party contract—and I thought his intentions were equally hostile to the interests of the American Telegraph Company—whose lines he assumed the control of, when the war began."

Instead of weakly submitting to seizure of their lines by the Confederate Government, Van Horne and Carter went to Richmond, fought vigorously for their cause, and finally in November 1862, they were able to get the obnoxious order rescinded.[12]

While Van Horne and Carter were thus averting disaster, acting President Douglass at Nashville and President Green at Louisville had a host of other perplexing problems with which to deal. Many miles of line in the war zone were being destroyed. Receipts from the southern section, while as large as could be expected, were in Confederate currency. The lines under Confederate jurisdiction were controlled by an appointee of General Polk, while that part of the property within the Federal lines was under the military authority of the superintendent of the United States military telegraphs, Anson Stager, who was also the general manager of the Western Union lines.[13] As a result, the regular management of the company suffered from constraint whether operating under Union or Confederate jurisdiction.[14]

At the same time that Green and his associates were battling valiantly to protect and preserve the property of the Southwestern Telegraph Company, they were obliged to meet a serious threat to their independence from still another quarter. Early in 1864, Western Union had launched a determined campaign for the consolidation of the Southwestern Telegraph with the Rochester interests. One proposal after another was made, but the inflated condition of the

12 *Ibid.*, February 24, 1863, Morse Papers, XLII.
13 For a detailed discussion of Stager's influence over the telegraph industry through his role as superintendent of military telegraphs, see Chapter XXVII.
14 George L. Douglass to Morse, March 22, 1862, Morse Papers, XLI.

Western Union stock and the deflated condition of that of the South-western caused Green to refuse all offers as disadvantages to his company's stockholders.

In a letter to Morse, President Green gave an account of the nego-tiations with Hiram Sibley during the closing days of January. While in New York on business, Green had met Sibley who had proposed a consolidation of their respective companies. Green had replied that although he favored a consolidation of all the telegraph interests in the country, as between Western Union and the Southwestern, he thought it totally impracticable to agree on a basis which the South-western management would deem fair. Besides, Western Union was stocked so large as to swallow up and utterly obliterate all sign of the Southwestern. Sibley then proposed the establishment of mutual interests of the chief executive men by exchange of stocks. Green had replied that he and his friends did not want Western Union stock at existing market prices, but they would be glad to see Sibley and the Western Union management interested individually in the South-western Company. Green pointed out that while his company was under the cloud of war, it was a favorable time to buy, since the return of peace and the recovery of its property would probably result in a doubling of the company's stock. From this conversation Sibley apparently gained the impression that Green would unite with him in an effort to secure a majority of the Southwestern Tele-graph stock.[15]

President Green had promptly dispatched a letter to Sibley correct-ing this impression and making his position quite clear: "I have certainly never proposed or thought of uniting in a scheme of privately securing to you a majority interest of our stock, whilst expressing a desire that yourself and Wade might be interested in our Company. We are but few in number, with each (resident hereabout) having about half our fortunes in the enterprise; and the most open candor and consultation has always existed between us. In a matter of this sort I could not think of acting otherwise than openly and in good faith with my associates; nor can I weaken their confidence by private consultations, on a matter so vital to their interests. Our respective views on questions of mutual interest differ; but it is our habit to discuss such differences freely and frankly before acting,

---

[15] Norvin Green to Morse, January 30, 1864, Morse Papers, XLII; cf. Kendall to Morse, January 14, 1864, *Ibid.*; Copy of letter, Green to Hiram Sibley, January 18, 1864, *Ibid.*; Douglass to Morse, January 18, 1864, *Ibid.*

and then either act in concert or with a full knowledge of what each other do.

"Nothing could therefore be accomplished by an interview with me. Your object can only promise success by a liberal and open offer made to all, of more than the stock has been rated at, or has been considered its market value. It would, therefore, be decidedly better you should come here, and see and judge for yourself of the real value of our interests." The stockholders of the Southwestern might either, collectively or individually, entertain Sibley's proposition, concluded Green, but he did not think that any of them would accept terms which were not open equally to all other stockholders and for a sufficient time to enable all to consider.[16] In spite of continued pressure by Western Union during the ensuing months, the officers and stockholders of the Southwestern Telegraph Company stood firm and united.

[16] Copy of letter, Norvin Green to Hiram Sibley, January 30, 1864, Morse Papers, XLII.

CHAPTER XXVII

War Years: the Illinois & Mississippi
and the Western Union Telegraph Companies

1 · — ·

IN striking contrast with the difficulties and misfortunes of the American and Southwestern Telegraph Companies during the war years, were the experiences of the Western Union and the Illinois & Mississippi. Since these lines operated north of the Mason-Dixon line and the Ohio River, they were little subject to the ravages of war. At the same time both were recipients of a tremendous volume of governmental business. Some idea of the increased use of the telegraph as a result of the war is furnished by comparing the revenues of the Illinois & Mississippi line before and after the outbreak of hostilities. The average revenues in 1860 had been about $2,000 per month. After the bombardment of Fort Sumter in April 1861, revenues jumped to an average of $6,000 per month.[1]

Throughout the war the Illinois & Mississippi under the direction of Judge Caton, an ardent unionist, gave the Federal Government unwavering support. Disloyal operators were hunted out and removed. Military authority was cheerfully accepted where it was deemed necessary. Lines were promptly repaired and extended so that military and governmental business could be handled rapidly and efficiently.[2] At the same time, of course, every opportunity was taken to advance the interests of the company. A number of highly favorable contracts were closed with the leading railroads throughout Illinois and Iowa. Railroad leaders, having awakened to the necessity of the telegraph for the efficient operation of their roads, entered eagerly into agreements for the construction of telegraph lines along their rights of way.[3]

[1] Based on statements of the Illinois & Mississippi Telegraph Company for 1860 and 1861, Caton Papers.

[2] J. D. Caton to Col. B. M. Prentiss, May 7, 1861, Caton Papers; J. J. S. Wilson to Caton, September 13, 1861, *Ibid.*; A. C. Fuller, Adj. General, to Caton, August 9, 1862, and numerous others, 1861-1864, Caton Papers.

[3] Isaac R. Elwood to Caton, April 4, 1861, Caton Papers; Caton to Elwood, April 12, 1861, *Ibid.*; E. D. L. Sweet to Caton, March 1, 1861, *Ibid.*; J. J. S. Wilson to Caton, January 20, 1862, *Ibid.*; Col. Hammond to Caton, September 27, 1862, *Ibid.*; W. H. Osborn to Caton, October 18, 1862, *Ibid.*; E. D. L. Sweet to Caton, January 21, 1863, *Ibid.*; Sweet to Caton, July 20, 1865, *Ibid.*; and numerous others, 1861-1866, *Ibid.*

While the Civil War years were bringing prosperity to Caton and his colleagues, they nevertheless had to be on guard lest their allies under the Six Party Contract outwit them. The dominant Western Union gave them the greatest concern, and relations between the two companies were often strained.[4] A specific cause for ill-feeling was the unsatisfactory manner in which the Illinois & Mississippi Company handled transcontinental messages. As a result of the war these messages, it will be recalled, had been routed over Caton's lines through Iowa and Illinois to Chicago, instead of to St. Louis as originally planned. The cheap, hastily-constructed line through Iowa "suspended upon bean poles and corn stalks . . . was down with every breath of the wind." Just when it was needed most it was "utterly worthless."[5]

The spring of 1862 found E. D. L. Sweet, Caton's superintendent, constructing a new line across Iowa with all possible speed.[6] But Sibley and his Western Union associates refused to be pacified. The fundamental difficulty between the two companies was more deep-rooted than mere dissatisfaction on the part of Western Union with Illinois & Mississippi's service. Sibley was determined that every foot of the line to the Pacific coast should be controlled by Western Union.[7] No other company could supply a link of the transcontinental line and manage it to his satisfaction. What Western Union wanted was direct control of a line across the States of Illinois and Iowa for the transmission of transcontinental business. In return for such a privilege the Rochester interests were willing to make important concessions to the Illinois & Mississippi, in regard to local business in parts of Illinois, Iowa, and Missouri. Moreover, the Western Union management made it quite clear that until they had gained control over this important link in the transcontinental system, there could be no real harmony between Western Union and the Illinois & Mississippi. Caton, refusing to be intimidated, stood his ground. The versatile Sibley then changed his tactics and tried to achieve his objective by offering terms of consolidation. The

[4] E. H. Beebe to Caton, February 10, 1862, Caton Papers; cf. J. J. S. Wilson to Caton, September 1, 1863, *Ibid.*; E. D. L. Sweet to Caton, February 20, 1864, *Ibid.*; *Ibid.*, March 5, 1864; *Ibid.*, November 17, 1864; E. H. Beebe to Caton, March 23, 1864, *Ibid.*

[5] B. H. Wilson, "Across the Prairies of Iowa," *Palimpsest*, VII, 252-254.

[6] E. D. L. Sweet to Caton, April 17, 1862, Caton Papers.

[7] *Ibid.*, September 12, 1862.

terms were not to Caton's liking, however, and the friction between the two continued.[8]

There were numerous other problems growing out of the war with which the able Illinois & Mississippi president had to deal. For example, in July 1864, both of Caton's superintendents, E. D. L. Sweet and J. J. S. Wilson, wrote him asking for salary adjustments. "As greenbacks are at present worth but forty cents on the dollar, we receive sixty percent less salary than we formerly did with a still greater proportionate increase in many articles of expense," Sweet pointed out. To meet the increased cost to the company of salary increases, he added, "I would also urge that the local tariffs be increased fifty percent leaving the tariff as it is on messages going out on other lines as the Western Union Company have done."[9]

The requested wage increases were granted, and at the same time an increase of 50 percent on all local tariffs was ordered. The inauguration of this policy brought a strong letter of protest from the outspoken and democratic vice president, E. H. Beebe.

"Have you maturely considered the policy of the advance of 50 percent lately ordered on all local tariffs over our lines? I fear a material falling off in receipts, and think 25 percent would have been far preferable. Again the distinction between local and through tariffs is, in my opinion, the worst feature in the order because it favors those beyond our territory at the expense of those from whom we derive our main resources.

"Holding, as we do, almost a monopoly of telegraphing in this state and Iowa, . . . expecting strong competition, it, in my judgment, should be our policy to conciliate our people and make no radical changes in our charges, or any distinctions in favor of outsiders that could be used to our prejudice."

The fact that the railroads had inaugurated sharp rate increases was no justification for similar action by their company, argued Beebe, for he believed such a policy to be a shortsighted one. Being most odious to the public, it would bring punitive legislation that would seriously affect the profits and business of the companies. Of course, pointed out Beebe, Caton might be in possession of knowledge of which he was not aware. "But so far as I can see," he concluded,

[8] Thomas Bassnett to Caton, December 9, 1862, Caton Papers; J. J. S. Wilson to Caton, November 28, 1862, *Ibid.*

[9] Sweet to Caton, July 14, 1864, Caton Papers; Wilson to Caton, July 25, 1864, *Ibid.*

The Telegraph Construction Corps, Army of the Potomac, Brandy Station, Virginia, c. 1864

The Field Telegraph at the Battle of Fredericksburg, December, 1862

Light Field Service

Telegraph Operator Tapping Rebel Telegraph Line Near
Egypt, on the Mississippi Central Railroad

"I must say that I am fearful, that we are cutting open the 'goose that had been laying the golden egg.' "[10]

The difficulties encountered by Caton and his associates, however, were compensated for by the company's success as reflected in its balance sheets. Receipts in January 1865, were $6,000; in February, $12,000; April, $9,800; May, $11,000; June, $9,500; and July, $9,500.[11] By September 1865, the affairs of the now affluent Judge Caton were in such condition that he felt free to leave on a long-contemplated trip to Europe.[12]

2 ··—··

SUCH good fortune as had attended the Illinois & Mississippi during the war years was as nothing compared to the progress of the already powerful Western Union Telegraph Company. Sibley and his associates swept forward on a flood-tide of success. In addition to being comparatively free from the ravages of war and enjoying greatly increased revenues, the company profited from still other advantages. The American Telegraph Company, crippled by the war, was no longer able to serve as an aggressive leader of the opposition to Western Union policies. Consequently, as the war progressed, the smaller companies came to look more and more to Western Union rather than to the American Telegraph Company for direction. Employing a subtle mixture of persuasion, bribery, and coercion, Sibley and his associates labored strenuously to convince them that consolidation under Western Union management was the haven which they sought. Moreover, while the American Telegraph Company's Atlantic cable project was stalemated by the war, Western Union's vast Russian-American project was being pushed with vigor.[13] Still another development which Western Union skillfully turned to its advantage was the organization by the government of an extensive military telegraph system to supplement the services of the private companies. A little more than six months after the outbreak of war the general

[10] E. H. Beebe to Caton, August 1, 1864, Caton Papers.

[11] Statements of the Illinois & Mississippi Telegraph Company for year 1865, Caton Papers.

[12] J. D. Caton to Thomas D. Catlin, September 29, 1865, Caton Papers. (A thirty-four page letter of instructions to Catlin who was to be left in charge of Caton's extensive interests in the telegraph, copper and salt mines, a starch company, water works, bridge company, railroads and oil, while the Judge was in Europe.)

[13] For earlier discussion of the Russian-American project, see Chapter xxv. For later discussion, see Chapter xxix.

manager of Western Union had become chief for all the military telegraph lines of the United States as well.

3 ···—·

THE resistance to the passage of troops through the city of Baltimore, hastening to the relief of the Federal Capital, and the destruction of the bridges of the Wilmington & Baltimore and the Northern Central Railroads, together with the refusal of the Baltimore & Ohio to transport government forces and supplies, made it necessary for the War Department to take possession of such railroad and telegraph lines as were required to form a connection with the states from which troops and supplies were to come.[14] On May 23, Secretary of War Simon Cameron issued an order placing Thomas A. Scott, general manager of the Pennsylvania Railroad, in charge of all government railways and telegraphs. Colonel Scott set to work energetically to bring order out of chaos. To assist him in his labors, he called to Washington the young superintendent of the Pittsburgh Division of the Pennsylvania Railroad, Andrew Carnegie. While Scott was struggling with the difficult problems of railroad management, Carnegie was busily engaged in the task of organizing an effective military telegraph system to supplement the services of the privately operated commercial companies in the East.

A few of the Pennsylvania Railroad's best telegraph operators were ordered to report to Washington where they were organized into the first United States military telegraph unit. One of their number, David Strouse, was invested with the power to erect and maintain such telegraphs as should be required by the War Department. His first task was to connect the War and Navy Departments with a telegraph line. Later, stations were established at Alexandria, Burke's Station, Fairfax, and other points in Virginia and the territory surrounding Washington. Inasmuch as the War Department had no appropriation for such a purpose, Carnegie and Strouse were left entirely dependent upon the American Telegraph Company for nearly all the construction work and the operation and maintenance of the lines. The actual administration of the lines also remained largely in the hands of President Sanford of the American Telegraph Company, who, by his prompt and generous support of the Federal

14 Report of the Secretary of War, Simon Cameron to President Lincoln, July 1, 1861, in Appendix to *Cong. Globe*, 37 Cong., 1 sess.

Government during the critical early months of the war, rendered his country valuable assistance.[15]

Meanwhile, in the West, General George B. McClellan, Commandant of the Military Department of the Ohio at this time, had appointed Anson Stager, already general superintendent of Western Union, as superintendent for military purposes of all telegraph lines within the Department. His purpose, declared McClellan, was to centralize authority in the hands of one individual to whom he might commit "the execution of such plans as contemplate[d] employment of the telegraph wires."[16] Since the telegraph was not a military organization, express authority to supervise telegraphic communications, to facilitate business, and to intercept disloyal messages was conferred upon Stager and his aides by the governors of the states traversed by the lines, namely, those of Ohio, Indiana, and Illinois.[17] With the authority thus granted him, Stager proceeded to coordinate the operation of the military and commercial telegraph lines in the Department of the Ohio into a highly effective system. To supplement this regular system, a field telegraph system was also organized so that when McClellan's forces moved forward into western Virginia from Clarksburg through Buckhannon early in July 1861, "the first field telegraph that ever advanced with an army in America kept pace with this one."[18] It soon became fairly accepted practice on the part of the Union armies for the telegraph service to follow them to the very edge of the battlefield.[19]

4 · · · · —

WHILE Carnegie and his aides with the assistance of the American Telegraph Company were organizing a military telegraph system in

---

[15] S. R. Kamm, "Thomas A. Scott and the Pennsylvania Railroad, 1850-1880." (The author very generously permitted me to examine his material in manuscript). William B. Wilson, "Lincoln and the Military Telegraph Corps," *The Magazine of History*, XIII, 95-99.

[16] Copy of a letter, Major General George B. McClellan to Governor Yates of Illinois, May 13, 1861, Caton Papers; Plum, *The Military Telegraph During the Civil War*, I, 92-99.

[17] Copy of letter, Governor Geo. W. Dennison of Ohio to Major General McClellan, May 14, 1861, Caton Papers; Copy of letter, Governor Oliver P. Morton of Indiana to Major General McClellan, May 14, 1861, *Ibid.*

[18] Field telegraphs had been used to a very limited extent during the Crimean War, in which young George B. McClellan had served as a military observer for the United States. (Encyclopaedia Britannica, xx, 640-44; J. G. Randall, *The Civil War and Reconstruction*, 271.)

[19] Plum, *The Military Telegraph During the Civil War*, I, 125-126.

the East, and Stager and his aides with the assistance of Western Union and the other leading companies were performing a similar service in the West, cooperation and integration between the telegraph units in the different military Departments were lacking. The idea had pervaded the government that the war was to be a mere three months' conflict.[20]

Following the disastrous battle of Bull Run, however, a disillusioned North began to organize for war in earnest. General McClellan was called to Washington to replace General Winfield Scott as commander of the Union forces in the East. McClellan inaugurated at once a comprehensive program of military reorganization which included the establishment of a single telegraph bureau with centralized offices in Washington, designed to aid him in his plan for a unified command. Colonel Thomas A. Scott, now Assistant Secretary of War, and his able young associate, Andrew Carnegie, were unable to give proper attention to this phase of the work because of the press of railroad affairs. McClellan, therefore, requested his former superintendent of military telegraphs for the Department of the Ohio, Anson Stager, to join him in Washington and perform the task.[21]

Stager prepared a thorough plan of reorganization which, having been accepted by McClellan and the War Department, was promptly inaugurated by the Western Union general manager serving in his official military capacity of assistant quartermaster, with the rank of captain. Some weeks later on November 25, 1861, he was formally appointed superintendent of military telegraphs, a position which gave him extensive emergency powers over all the telegraph lines and offices under the jurisdiction of the government in Washington.[22]

Considering the extremely delicate nature of this new position, and the extensive powers which it placed within his grasp, Stager might have been expected to resign his position as general manager of the Western Union Telegraph Company. Instead, he returned to Cleveland and resumed the active direction of Western Union affairs, thereby making his management of military telegraphs rather remote. Much of the responsibility for their operation he placed upon the broad shoulders of an aggressive young man named Thomas T. Eckert.

20 *Ibid.*, 62, 351.

21 S. R. Kamm, "Thomas A. Scott and the Pennsylvania Railroad, 1850-1880." MS.

22 *Ibid.*; Plum, *The Military Telegraph During the Civil War*, I, 127-134; U.S. War Dept., Annual Report, December 1, 1861, 37 Cong., 2 sess.; John Hay to J. D. Caton, November 12, 1861, Caton Papers; Anson Stager to Caton, December 9, 1861, *Ibid.*

Superintendent Stager in his first report stated that from April 25 to November 15, 1861, there had been built for military purposes in the several departments 1,137 miles of line, on which were 106 offices worked by 163 operators; of this total, 857 miles of line, 56 offices, and 80 operators were outside the Department of the Potomac. Describing the efficiency and value of the telegraph as an aid to military operations, Stager declared that "in many instances the wires followed the march of the army at the rate of 8 to 12 miles per day, there being no other lines of communication upon the routes where these lines have been placed. The capacity of the telegraph for military service has been tested, and in affording rapid communication between the War Department, the Commander-in-Chief, and different divisions of the army; in directing the movement of troops and the transportation of supplies, it may safely be asserted, that it is an indispensable auxiliary in military operations. The organization of the Government Telegraph Department, under the direction of the Secretary of War, will add greatly to the efficiency of this branch of the service," concluded Stager.[23]

But in spite of the great improvement made during the closing months of 1861, General McClellan and his assistants continued to be seriously handicapped in their war efforts by the inefficiency and corruption which prevailed in the War Department under Secretary Cameron. At last on January 20, 1862, a much needed change was made; Cameron was replaced by the able and energetic Edwin M. Stanton. Under Stanton the War Department took on new life, and developments came rapidly in respect to the military telegraph system. Within two weeks the lines of the American Telegraph Company and those of Western Union had been connected with the headquarters of General McClellan thus placing him in direct connection with General Buell at Louisville, General Halleck at St. Louis, and Commodore Foote at Cairo. Stanton also clamped down rigorously on the circumstances that made possible the frequent "leaks" in military intelligence, which were usually due to the scheming of some over-ambitious newspaper correspondent. No military information was to be sent over the telegraph except by order of the War Department, the commanding general, or the commanding general in the field. Newspapers that printed matter obtained contrary to this order were to be excluded from receiving news and from sending their papers over the railroads. As a further check, a cipher system

23 Plum, *The Military Telegraph During the Civil War*, I, 125-126.

of dispatching military information was developed. President E. S. Sanford of the American Telegraph Company was named military supervisor—in reality, censor—of telegraph dispatches throughout the United States, while Western Union's Anson Stager was continued as military superintendent of all telegraph lines and offices in the country.[24]

In February 1862, there was some talk of the government's taking possession of a number of additional railroad and telegraph lines as a defense measure. Superintendent Stager staunchly defended the rights of the privately operated companies declaring, "In no place have I found the Government service upon a line large enough to justify the Government in assuming the entire running expense of the same, nor can I recommend such a course as long as the telegraph companies perform the service promptly and faithfully." The telegraph companies, he continued, had at all times evinced a most liberal and loyal spirit and tendered the government all the facilities possessed by them.[25] The result was that only in cases of absolute military necessity were the management and operation of the lines of private corporations taken out of their hands during the war.

5 — — —

In striking contrast with the fabulous profits being made by companies like the Western Union and the Illinois & Mississippi were the meager wages and unsatisfactory conditions of labor of the hundreds of faithful employees of these concerns. The salary of the average operator remained between $70 and $90 a month, although by 1864 the greenbacks with which he was paid were worth only about forty cents on the dollar. His working day averaged from ten to fifteen hours with no allowances for sickness. Sunday work was required of many of the men. The telegraph offices were small, dark, filthy, and poorly equipped.[26]

An interesting description of conditions in Western Union's Cincinnati office during the Civil War has been left by George Kennan who was an operator there in the autumn of 1863. At that time, Cin-

---

[24] Kamm, "Thomas A. Scott and the Pennsylvania Railroad, 1850-1880." MS; House Report No. 64, 37 Cong., 2 sess.

[25] Report of Anson Stager to Quartermaster General Meigs, February 1862, U.S. War Dept., Annual Report, 37 Cong., 2 sess.

[26] *Telegrapher*, II, 26; *Ibid.*, III, 30, 99; *Ibid.*, IV, 2-3, 40; Reid, *Telegraph in America*, 315; F. L. Dyer and T. C. Martin, *Edison: His Life and Inventions*, I, 81.

cinnati, although the most important distributing center in the Middle West, had few long distance circuits; and commercial telegrams going westward from the seaboard or eastward from Kentucky, Indiana, southern Illinois, and Missouri had to be written out at that point and forwarded to their destinations. The office had several Hick's repeaters by means of which Buffalo or Pittsburgh could be put in direct contact with Louisville and St. Louis; but in general, all business was received in Cincinnati by one set of operators and forwarded from there by another. The workers were divided into two shifts. The first shift was on duty from 8 A.M. to 6 P.M., and the second shift from 6 P.M. until all books were cleared. On alternate days the shifts were reversed. The irregular hours proved very trying on both the morale and the health of the men. Moreover, the volume of business was out of all proportion to the strength of the force; and after every battle in Virginia or the Southwest the "specials," Associated Press dispatches, and war telegrams in cipher were so numerous and so long that the telegraphers had to work all night. The order of business was, private messages until 9 P.M.; "specials" and news until the papers went to press about 2 A.M.; and then private messages again until morning. "Many a night," declared Kennan, "I went on duty at 6 P.M. and never left my chair until I was relieved by a man coming from breakfast at 8 A.M. Once I had 10 hours sleep out of 72."[27]

In the face of long hours, poor pay, and unsatisfactory working conditions, and in keeping with the spirit of the times, the telegraphers gradually turned to organization as a means of bettering their lot. In the autumn of 1863 the operators in Western Union's New York office met and appointed a committee to draft a constitution for a telegraphic union of national scope. A constitutional convention was called for the first Monday in November. Telegraph offices were to choose one delegate for every fifteen members. An excess of eight members was to entitle an office to an extra delegate. The smaller offices were to club together to elect their delegates.[28]

The preamble to the constitution adopted by the union set forth clearly its general purposes:

We, Telegraphers, uniting ourselves for the purpose of mutual protection in adversity, upholding and elevating the character and standing

---

[27] Geo. S. Bryan, *Edison the Man and His Work*, 31-41.
[28] Call "To All Telegraphers" to rally to the support of a Telegraphers Union, New York, October 7, 1863, Pamphlet, Cornell University Library.

of our profession, promoting and maintaining between ourselves and our employers just, equitable, and harmonious relations, and advancing the general interests of the fraternity; recognizing the principle that the interests of the employer and employe are identical, and firmly believing that a union among ourselves, established upon just principles, will result in manifold benefits, not only to us, but also to those who employ us, and to be the means of enlarging and establishing, upon a better foundation, the peculiar business to which we look for our support, with the hope that our endeavors will merit the commendation of our Creator, do hereby ordain and promulgate for our organization and future government, the following: [constitution.][29]

The association was to be known as the National Telegraphic Union. The constitution provided for a national organization which was to hold a convention once a year, and for subordinate district organizations which were to hold meetings monthly, or more often, if circumstances required. The annual convention of delegates representing telegraphers from all parts of the country was to be vested with extensive legislative powers and all by-laws passed by the convention and approved by the Union's president were to be binding "upon each and every member." Dues were to be $6.00 a year. The first convention was held in Philadelphia on September 5, 1864.[30]

The National Telegraphic Union was a mild sort of an organization whose principal functions were social and educational in character. Those incapacitated by sickness or accident that had not proceeded from immoral conduct were entitled to receive $6.00 a week after the first six days. A list of all unemployed members was kept and efforts were made to aid these men in securing positions. The use of profane or abusive language over the wires was discountenanced.

To disseminate information among its members and to provide them with general telegraphic news, the Union decided to publish a monthly review to be known as the *Telegrapher*.[31] The first number was issued on September 26, 1864; and for more than a decade thereafter, it advocated measures which were believed to be in the best interest of the telegraphic fraternity. The new telegraphic newspaper, declared its editor, L. H. Smith, was not confined to any one policy, and would seek "to correct abuses, give honor and praise

[29] Constitution of the National Telegraphic Union, Pamphlet, Cornell University Library; *Telegrapher*, III, 89-90.
[30] *Ibid.*
[31] Proceedings of the First Convention of the National Telegraphic Union held in Philadelphia, September 5, 1864, in *Telegrapher*, I, 1-2; *Ibid.*, III, 89-90.

"Is it not a feat sublime?
Intellect hath conquered. time."

where due, and endeavor to elevate the standard of operators both morally and scientifically."[32]

Some of the operators suggested that the National Telegraphic Union be more forceful in its demands on the telegraph companies, and if they were refused, to call a strike. "We do not think strikes are a very intelligent way of effecting the object sought," declared the *Telegrapher.* "It is a forcible way employed by those who are less intelligent, and is not becoming in a class of men such as the Union is composed of."

Many telegraphers were not attracted to such an idealistic organization. What they wanted was a union that would fight aggressively for better working conditions, shorter hours, and higher salaries. Moreover, the amazing expansion of both commercial and railway telegraphs had created a demand for telegraphers and employment was easy. Dozens of young operators roamed over the country working in one telegraph office a few months, and then passing on to another. Such a life was not favorable to the formation of steady habits, and gambling and drinking were common. Thomas A. Edison, who was wandering about the country as an itinerant operator during these years, has given some vivid descriptions of the demoralization and laxness of discipline which characterized the profession at that time. Under such conditions, growth during the war years was not rapid, and despite the earnest efforts of its leaders, the development of a strong, effective union was virtually impossible.[33]

6 · · · · · ·

WHILE hundreds of men and thousands of miles of wire under private ownership and operation were thus serving the nation's war needs,

[32] *Ibid.,* I, 134.   [33] Dyer and Martin, *Life of Edison,* I, 57-64.

THE TELEGRAPHER,

PUBLISHED BY THE

National Telegraphic Union.

The UNION is an association of telegraph-operators for their own mutual benefit and support, and THE TELEGRAPHER is published to disseminate information among its members, as well as general telegraphic news.

THE TELEGRAPHER is published in New York, on the last Monday of every month, and besides matters of associate interest is devoted to the interests of telegraphers all over the world, and will contain telegraphic information from all parts of the globe.

It is not confined to any one policy, but will seek to correct abuses, give honor and praise wherever and whenever due, and endeavor to elevate the standard of operators both morally and scientifically.

It will not support any one person or corporation, but will aim to treat all alike, censuring either or both, when merited, and praising alike when praise is won.

Its columns will not be open to any one for personal abuse, nor for personal profit at the expense of others, nor will it contain anything that the most fastidious would not read.

THE TELEGRAPHER will contain Original Articles upon any and all subjects of interest to the fraternity and profession; Extracts from Works on Telegraphy, Electricity and Magnetism; Statistics; Improvements in Telegraphy, Telegraph Instruments and Materials; Correspondence; Poetry upon Telegraphic subjects; Telegraphic Literature; Incidents and Items of Personal interest; Promotions; Removals; Resignations; Marriages and Deaths of Telegraphers; Newspaper extracts of Telegraphic Items from any and every City, Town, State or Country.

We invite the co-operation from every one who is directly or remotely connected or interested in Telegraphy, in this undertaking to establish and maintain a first-class telegraphic newspaper, and for any items of news or personal telegraphic interest, articles or newspaper extracts upon any of the above mentioned subjects. We will cheerfully pay a reasonable sum for any trouble or expense gone to in behalf of this paper, and for any Original Articles which we may use.

We request aid from all, whether high or low, and will make a fair return for the same.

THE TELEGRAPHER is a Medium Quarto of sixteen pages, (the last four of which will be devoted to Advertisements of Telegraphic Materials, or any other respectable business) with clear type and on good paper. It will aim to be a first-class telegraphic newspaper, and not to be surpassed in the vigor and spirit of its editorials, nor in the variety and freshness of its reading matter generally. On all subjects which it discusses will aim to be correct, independent, clear, conscientious and fearless.

Whatever the experience of its conductors—whatever industry, energy, and a liberal expenditure of money can accomplish towards making a good and powerful paper, are pledged to the subscribers of THE TELEGRAPHER.

TERMS:—Invariably in advance.

For a single number of the paper..... 17 cents.
For one copy for one year, by mail, 12 numbers..... $2 00
For Six copies for one year, by mail, to one address..... 10 00
For Ten copies for one year, by mail, to one address..... 18 00
For Twenty copies for one year, by mail, to one address..... 35 50

Club rates are not allowed to District Directors unless for persons not members of the Union.
The paper will always be discontinued when the paid subscription expires.

☞ Remittances for subscriptions may be made by mail, in National currency, at our risk—the attention of the Postmaster being called to the mailing of the letters; but Post-Office orders or drafts on New York being safer, are preferable.

ADVERTISEMENTS.—Terms Cash.

For each line, first insertion..... 15 cents
For each subsequent insertion each line..... 13 "
No advertisement inserted for less than..... 50 "

Leaded advertisements are charged for the actual space occupied.
Advertisements of Patent Medicines are charged double rates.
Advertisements of Quack Doctors excluded.

We have no travelling agents, nor has any one authority from us to collect money for subscriptions; but Postmasters or others who may interest themselves in procuring subscribers at our advertised rates, and remitting us the money, will receive our thanks—and an *Extra Copy for one year for every Club.*

All communications and letters relating to THE TELEGRAPHER must be addressed to the Editor, Box 3393, New York.

☞ Newspapers by inserting this Prospectus and sending a marked copy to the Editor, will be entitled to an exchange.

Circulation over 1,200 copies, from Italy to the Pacific Coast, from Canada to Panama.

NOTICE TO CORRESPONDENTS.

All communications to, or articles for insertion in, THE TELEGRAPHER, must be addressed to the Editor, P. O. Box 3,393, New York.

No notice will be taken of anonymous communications: the name and address of the writer must always accompany each article or communication.

Correspondents sending articles for insertion must write briefly, and on but one page of each half sheet of paper. We cannot return rejected articles.

an extensive government-owned-and-operated military telegraph system which included additional hundreds of men and thousands of miles of wire had also come into being. A splendid military telegraph corps which enrolled more than twelve hundred young men during the war labored unceasingly to maintain military communications under any and all conditions. "The operators have shown great zeal, intrepidity and fidelity," declared Quartermaster General Meigs in a report to Stanton. "Their duties are arduous and the trust reposed in them is great. I have seen a telegraph operator in charge of a station in a tent, pitched from necessity in a malarious locality, shivering with ague, lying upon his camp cot, with his ear near the instrument, listening for the messages which might direct or arrest the movements of mighty armies. Night and day they are at their posts. Their duties constantly place them in exposed positions, and they are favorite objects of rebel surprise."[34] Secretary of War Stanton, in his report to the President at the close of 1863, also warmly praised their work declaring, "The military telegraph, under the general direction of Colonel Stager and Major Eckert has been of inestimable value to the service, and no corps has surpassed, few have equalled, the telegraph operators in diligence and devotion to their duties."[35]

The role of the military telegraph in providing the Union forces with a thoroughly effective communications system had become increasingly important as the war progressed. On the first of July 1862, there were 3,571 miles in working order; during the following year an additional 1,755 miles were laid, so that at the close of the fiscal year ending June 30, 1863, there were 5,326 miles of line in operation. Military telegraph lines were to be found in the District of Columbia, parts of Pennsylvania, Ohio, Indiana, Illinois, Maryland, Delaware, Virginia, North Carolina, South Carolina, Louisiana, Mississippi, Alabama, Arkansas, Tennessee, Missouri, Kansas, and the Indian Territories. Approximately 1,200,000 telegrams varying in length from 10 to 100 words had been sent over these lines during the year, or about 3,300 per day.[36]

During the next two years the military telegraph came to be used even more extensively. Wherever a Union army went the military

[34] Report of Quartermaster General Meigs to Edwin M. Stanton, November 3, 1864, U.S. War Dept., Annual Report, 38 Cong., 2 sess.

[35] Report of E. M. Stanton to Pres. Lincoln, December 5, 1863, U.S. War Dept., Annual Report, 38 Cong., 1 sess.; cf. U. S. Grant, *Personal Memoirs*, II, 204-208.

[36] Report of Stanton to Pres. Lincoln, December 5, 1863, U.S. War Dept., Annual Report, 38 Cong., 1 sess.; Plum, *The Military Telegraph During the Civil War*, I, 131.

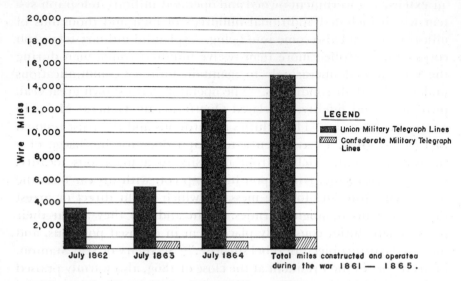

WIRE MILES OF MILITARY TELEGRAPH IN OPERATION BY THE
UNION AND CONFEDERATE FORCES DURING THE CIVIL WAR

Source: Figures on Union military telegraphs from Report of Secretary of War Stanton to President
Lincoln, December 5, 1863, U.S. War Department Annual Report, 38 Cong., 1 sess.; Plum, *The Military
Telegraph During the Civil War*, I, 131; figure for 1864 estimated on basis of expenditures for that year
(given in Report of Anson Stager to Quartermaster General Meigs, September 15, 1865, U.S. War De-
partment Annual Report, 39 Cong., 1 sess.) as compared with expenditures for earlier years.
  Figures on Confederate military telegraphs from Report of John H. Reagan, Postmaster General, to
C. G. Memminger, Secretary of Treasury, January 8, 1863, Confederate States of America, Post Office
Department Statement, January 12, 1863; *Ibid.*, December 7, 1863; *Ibid.*, November 7, 1864; Plum, *The
Military Telegraph During the Civil War*, I, 134-135.

telegraph went with it, "and it is a well established fact," declared
Stager in his annual report for 1865, "that the mobility of the army
has been greatly accelerated by its usefulness and assistance." The
military telegraph also proved an invaluable asset in the construction
and operation of military railroads. Trains were run and many of
the roads operated almost exclusively by telegraph.

Reviewing the situation at the close of 1865 Superintendent Stager
declared that from the commencement of the rebellion up to June 30,
1865, there had been constructed and operated about 15,000 miles
of United States Military Telegraph—land, submarine, and field lines.
Cost of the service averaged $22,000 per month from May 1, 1861, to
December 31, 1862; $38,000 per month during 1863; and $93,500
per month during 1864. Total expenditures for the construction,
maintenance, and operation of the United States Military Telegraph

during the period from May 1, 1861, to June 30, 1865, had amounted
to $2,655,500.[37]

While there is no evidence to show, nor reason to believe, that
Stager consciously misused the great sums of money or the extensive
powers which had been conferred upon him as chief of United States
military telegraphs, yet it would be artless not to recognize the fact
that during the war years he was first of all general manager of the
Western Union Telegraph Company, and only secondarily chief of
the United States Military Telegraph. Even the most objective of
men could not have completely dissociated the two functions. The
feeling of the leaders of the other telegraph companies toward Stager's
dual role in the industry was well expressed by Thomas Bassnett,
secretary of the Illinois & Mississippi, in a letter written to his chief,
Judge Caton. At the annual meeting of the North American Telegraph Association in August 1861, declared Bassnett, he had become
convinced that Western Union "had a grand and far reaching policy
calculated in time to swallow up or make tributary all other organizations." Taking this as the key, and knowing Western Union's political
influence as developed by the great events of the times to be immense,
declared Bassnett, "I see how easy it was for them, first to suggest to
the government (indirectly) the necessity of subordinating all the

---

[37] Report of Anson Stager to Quartermaster General Meigs, September 15, 1865, U.S.
War Dept., Annual Report, 39 Cong., 1 sess.; cf. Report of Major Thomas T. Eckert,
Asst. Quartermaster and Asst. Supt. of U.S. Milit. Teleg., to Quartermaster General
Meigs, October 9, 1865, Ibid.

It is interesting to compare the above expenditures of the United States Government
for military telegraphs with those of the Confederacy. The reports of Postmaster General
Reagan show that the expenditures of the Confederate Government from June 1, 1861
to September 1, 1862, had been $66,422.27, or approximately $4,428.15 per month. On
July 1, 1862, the Confederate Government had 16 military telegraph offices in operation
for which they employed 17 agents and operators; a year later "offices in operation"
had increased to 33, and operators to 33 also. Miles of line in operation on July 1,
1862, were 211; a year later mileage had increased to 422. The year ending June 30,
1864, showed a slight further expansion of the military telegraph system in the Confederacy; offices in operation, 45; operators employed, 51; number of miles of line, 461;
and total cost of building and operating for the year, $91,154.97, or approximately
$7,596.25 per month. These statistics show clearly how much less use was made of
military telegraphs by the Confederacy than by their northern opponents. The Confederates appear not to have regarded the telegraph as so essential as did the Federals.
Frequently telegraph lines were not extended from the main line offices to connect with
the Confederate armies in the field. The Southerners relied upon the private companies
to do most of their military telegraphing. The companies strove loyally to keep the
armies supplied with service and succeeded fairly well. Obviously though, the telegraph
system which served the Confederates was no match for its northern counterpart either
in efficiency or extent. (Report of John H. Reagan, Postmaster General, to C. G.
Memminger, Secretary of Treasury, January 8, 1863, Confederate States of America,
Post Office Department Statement, January 12, 1863; Ibid., December 7, 1863; Ibid.,
November 7, 1864; Plum, The Military Telegraph During the Civil War, I, 134-135.)

telegraph companies, to a certain extent, to one general supervision, and then to get Mr. Stager commissioned. Now I do not mean to insinuate that Mr. Stager entered into any improper engagements, but I believe he thinks, as it was supposed he would think by his friends, that the interests of the government, of the Western Union Company, and of Anson Stager are identical."[38]

Whether or not Bassnett's deductions regarding the role to be played by Stager during the war years was a just one, his belief that "Western Union had a grand and far reaching policy calculated in time to swallow up or make tributary all other organizations," was prophetic.

7 — — · ·

AT the same time that Stager was developing the nation's military telegraph system, Sibley and his associates, eager to take advantage of the temporary impotence of their rivals, launched a drive to bring about a consolidation of the nation's chief telegraph interests under Western Union. As a preliminary, Sibley had little difficulty in securing his election to the presidency of the North American Telegraph Association in the autumn of 1862.[39] Taking full advantage of the prestige of his new position, he began an intensive campaign for consolidation among the member companies of the Association.

The pioneer New York, Albany & Buffalo was the first marked for special attention. An opposition company had nearly completed a line through the State of New York in the autumn of 1863, and the conservative board of the New York, Albany & Buffalo had come to the reluctant conclusion that it was wiser to strengthen the position of their company by consolidation with Western Union, than to risk the hazards which a contrary policy would involve.[40] Morse, Kendall, and some of the other stockholders were slow to accept the proposed consolidation. They felt there was "more haste than good speed" about the Western Union proposal, and they refused to be rushed into a decision.[41]

[38] Thomas Bassnett to Caton, December 15, 1861, Caton Papers.

[39] Proceedings at Fifth Annual Meeting of the North American Telegraph Association, September 3-5, 1862, in *Proceedings of the North American Telegraph Association, 1858-1862.*

[40] Thomas R. Walker to George Vail, December 10, 1863, Vail Papers.

[41] Morse to Walker, November 28, 1863, Morse Papers, Letter Book O; cf. Kendall to J. D. Reid, November 26, 1863, *Ibid.*; Morse to J. D. Reid, November 26, 1863, *Ibid.*

The difficulties which stood in the way of consolidation were rapidly overcome, however, and on December 23, 1863, all the stock, property rights, and interests of the New York, Albany & Buffalo were formally leased to Western Union for ten years, to become effective January 1, 1864. Under the terms of the lease, Western Union agreed to pay 8 percent per annum on the $400,000 capital stock of the New York, Albany & Buffalo, and to permit it to appoint two Western Union directors. At the same time, the New York, Albany & Buffalo stockholders were offered two attractive options:

1. Western Union would pay $75 cash for each share (par value $50) to all who desired to sell their stock, if it were offered prior to January 18, 1864.

2. Or Western Union would issue three shares of its stock for every two shares of the New York, Albany & Buffalo, if it were offered before February 1, 1864.

Western Union stock was at this time highly regarded, and the future prospects of the company appeared to be excellent. As a result, New York, Albany & Buffalo stock was rapidly exchanged for that of Western Union and the splendid, old company was soon absorbed.[42] The conquest of the New York, Albany & Buffalo Telegraph Company pushed the powerful Western Union system to the seaboard at New York and added greatly to its strength and prestige.

A few months later a second great artery connecting the West with the seaboard was brought under direct Western Union control. On April 15, 1864, the lines of the important Atlantic & Ohio between Pittsburgh and Philadelphia were leased for ten years, under an agreement by which Western Union was to pay quarterly dividends of 2½ percent on all outstanding Atlantic & Ohio stock. Through a stock issue of $833,400, however, Western Union shortly absorbed the outstanding stock of the Atlantic & Ohio (about $654,000). One more of the pioneer lines had been lost in the rising tide of consolidation. According to James D. Reid's account of the merger, several of the Atlantic & Ohio leaders who had engineered the consolidation received $80,000 each for their labors.[43]

Fast on the heels of these consolidations came the announcement

42 [Western Union Telegraph Company], *Corporate History of the Western Union Telegraph Company*, Chart D; Reid, *Telegraph in America*, 319-320; T. R. Walker to George Vail, December 10, 1863, Vail Papers.

43 A. G. Davis to Morse, February 9, 1864, Morse Papers, xlii; [Western Union Telegraph Company], *Corporate History of the Western Union Telegraph Company*, 209-210; Reid, *Telegraph in America*, 176, 178.

that the Western Union, by an issue of $2,000,000 of its stock, had purchased the entire outstanding stock ($1,000,000) of the Pacific Telegraph Company. Thereafter, the line from Omaha to Salt Lake City was to be operated as an integral part of the growing Western Union system.[44]

8 — · · · ·

THE absorption of the Pacific Telegraph Company was closely associated with the arrangements then being made by Sibley and the Western Union management for the active prosecution of the great Russian-American project. As has already been pointed out, this ambitious enterprise for uniting the telegraph systems of the United States and Russia by the construction of an overland line through British Columbia, Russian America, and Siberia, had first been brought to the attention of Hiram Sibley early in 1861 by its originator, Perry McD. Collins.[45] The Western Union executive had become an enthusiastic convert to the daring project, but the exigencies of the war and the conservatism of the Western Union board of directors had delayed its active prosecution. In March 1864, however, the Western Union board formally accepted a proposition submitted by Collins under which control of the project passed into the hands of the Western Union Telegraph Company.[46]

When news of this formal acceptance reached the public there ensued a period of mad speculation in Western Union stock. Nor was it surprising, for by this time people had come to look upon Western Union as something of a phenomenon. A mere listing of the cash and stock dividends between 1857 and 1864 seems incredible. For seven years prior to 1857 the company's entire revenues had been devoted to the enlargement and improvement of its property; then came the abundant harvest. On December 1, 1857, a cash dividend of 8 ½ percent was declared on a capital of $369,700. The next year, cash dividends of 33 percent along with stock dividends amounting to 447.4 percent were dispersed. The years 1859, 1860, and 1861 brought modest cash dividends of 2 percent, 5 percent, and 5 percent,

<hr/>

44 E. D. L. Sweet to J. D. Caton, March 20, 1864, Caton Papers; Frank Parsons, *The Telegraph Monopoly*, 36; Senate Report 577, 48 Cong., 1 sess.

45 For earlier discussion, see Chapter xxv.

46 The Russian-American project, while occupying an important place in the history of Western Union during the war years, is merely touched upon here since its development is one of the principal themes of a later chapter. See Chapter xxix.

THE
TELEGRAPHER.

"Canst thou send lightnings, that they may go and | say unto thee, Here we are?"—*Job* 38, 35.

N. T. U.

"I'll put a girdle around about the earth in forty minutes."—*Shakespeare.*

Vol. 1.   New York, Monday, September 26, 1864.   **No. 1.**

GENERAL OFFICERS.

C. W. HAMMOND, Pres.,
   P. O. Box 1876, St. Louis, Mo.

W. H. YOUNG, Vice-Pres.,
   Am. Tel. Office, Washington, D. C.

JAMES PARTRICK, Treas.,
   Am. Tel. Office, Philadelphia, Pa.

J. C. UPHAM, Recording Sec.,
   U. S. Tel. Office, Boston, Mass.

KENNETH McKENZIE, Cor. Sec.,
   W. U. Tel., Office, St. Louis, Mo.

PROCEEDINGS OF THE
NATIONAL TELEGRAPHIC UNION CONVENTION
Held in Philadelphia, Pa., Monday, Sept. 5th, 1864.

First Session, 2 P. M.

Monday, September 5th.

The President being absent the Convention was called to order by the Vice-President, C. W. Hammond, at 2 o'clock, P. M.

The Recording Secretary being absent, Wm. H. Young was elected Recording Secretary, pro tem.

On motion of Mr. R. J. Black, a Committee consisting of three was appointed by the Chairman to examine the credentials of the delegates.

The Chair appointed R. J. Black, Kenneth McKenzie and A. H. Seymour on said Committee; after which the Convention took a recess of twenty minutes to enable the Committee to report.

On reassembling, the Committee reported the following persons entitled to seats as delegates to this Convention, viz: Robt. J. Black, Jno. W. McMullen and M. D. Buckwell, from the Philadelphia District; J. J. Flanagan and A. Ellison from the Louisville District; G. S. Silsbee from the Maine District; Wm. H. Young and H. H. Atwater from the Washington, D. C., District; M. H. Redding, W. Seymour, L. H. Smith and J. W. Burnham, Alternate R. M. Mattocks, from the New York District; S. C. Rice from the Albany District; Kenneth McKenzie and Chas. A. Paxson from the St. Louis District; E. B. Chandler, Wm. W. Ashley, A. H. Seymour and Sam'l Hott from the Chicago District; Wm. P. Potter, T. A. Davis and J. C. Upham from the Boston District; M. H. Korrner and Arch. Wilson, Jr., from the Baltimore District. Whole number 24.

Mr. T. A. Davis opposed the admission of the two delegates from Baltimore on the ground that not having complied with the requirements of the Constitution of the Union they were not entitled to seats. After considerable discussion Mr. L. H. Smith moved that the subject in relation to the Baltimore delegates be laid over until to-morrow, which was adopted.

On motion of Mr. T. A. Davis the above vote was re-considered, and Mr. M. H. Korrner was allowed to make an explanation; after which the Report of the Committee on Credentials was accepted.

Mr. T. A. Davis moved that Mr. Jas. Partrick, the Treasurer, be allowed to cast a vote by proxy for one of the delegates of the Boston District who was absent. The motion was amended by Mr. J. J. Flanagan that the delegates be allowed to vote by proxy for delegates who were absent; which was adopted.

The following letter accompanying the Annual Report of the President, Jas. G. Smith, was received and read.

New York, September 3d, 1864.

Gentlemen:

That I am unfortunate is well known and expected generally, but that I should be so unfortunate as to be deprived of the pleasure of being with you at the opening of the Convention, is far more than I anticipated, and could only have been occasioned by a combination of circumstances.

My arrangements were all perfected for going, with one or two exceptions, which I intended to jump, but late on Saturday night I received intelligence that my brother-in-law was at the point of death in Grant's Hospital on Long Island; also that my mother had left for New York to visit him, and requested me to meet her. She being elderly and a total stranger to this city would, under ordinary circumstances, be unable to get along, unaided; but, adding to this circumlocution necessary to be gone through with to enable her to obtain the proper passes and permission to go by the only conveyance (Government steamer), you will readily understand my position.

I trust the business of the Convention will not in any way be interfered with by my absence; and I hope to be able to meet you Monday night, should I be able to arrange my affairs before that time.

I trust everything will go forward harmoniously; and since I have been assured that the Vice-President will be present, my disappointment has been greatly lessened.

Yours respectfully,

JAS. G. SMITH, *Pres.*

PRESIDENT'S REPORT.

Gentlemen of the Convention:

Ten months ago the first Telegraphic Convention, elected from among the operators, that ever met in this country, came together in the city of New York.

At the time of the call for that Convention a feeling of the necessity of an organization similar to that designed was quite generally felt, but what the groundwork of action could be, what was really the amount of sympathy felt towards a Union, what under our peculiarly embarrassing situation could be done towards uniting ourselves, and what would be the tone and character of the Union, if established, were questions that few could settle to their own satisfaction. Sufficient, however, was ascertained to make it evident that an intelligent and respectable class among operators were anxious and willing to support a creditable Union; and the Convention came together representing, through indirect action, a large circle of operators.

The sessions of the Convention lasted three days, and it is a great pleasure to be able to say that, in my humble opinion, the first Convention was creditable, not alone to the Districts to which the members belonged, but to the profession generally, and considering the newness of the enterprise, the field to be covered by their action, the dangerous questions likely to arise to nullify the preliminary measures necessary to be taken, they brought to the meeting a unity of purpose, an intelligent appreciation of the position and the duties, which would, I think, challenge a favorable comparison with any similar Convention among any class of men.

Much of their success was undoubtedly due to the ability with which the presiding officer discharged his duties, and, although I regret that we are not similarly situated in that respect to-day, we still have his example before us, and I trust we may profit by it.

A Constitution and Code of By-Laws were adopted, which were well suited to the necessities of the occasion, and which were of such a character that any Telegrapher could feel gratified at and pleased to support, and the result of which has been that, notwithstanding the difficulties to be overcome, we have, as a body, advanced steadily, although slowly, and have during the short time become a permanent institution.

The Constitution was really the starting point—no organization previous to that having effected that much upon any basis that promised good results—and from the adoption of that instrument we must date the existence of our "Union."

We now number, of regular members whose names are enrolled upon the Treasurer's books, two hundred and fifty, comprising twelve Districts. Many others consider themselves members, and may eventually fulfil the duties required, but at present have not taken all the steps necessary to entitle them to privileges of membership.

Many of the obstacles in the way of rapid and thorough organization of Districts and the carrying out of all the necessary steps which would leave no question of the existence of full rights and titles, is owing to inattention or lack of interest on the part of the officers of the Districts.

The Treasurer informs me that he now has in his hands, to the credit of the Union, $393.27. But very few members have received aid on account of sickness or disability, although some individual demands have been large through this source. For details of the financial affairs of the Union I refer you to the report of the Treasurer.

The experience of ten months has shown to us that in many ways we can now improve upon the production of our first essay; and this present Convention is met, in accordance with the Constitution, to consider what further, or other action, can now be consistently be taken for our interest.

To complete and perfect the Constitution and By-Laws, and thus establish a permanent basis upon which our organization can go forward more rapidly, will, I think, be found sufficient to occupy the attention of the Convention at this session.

Our individual duties and our desire to be in no manner a hindrance to the general business of the profession (which we all know to be so conditioned at present that the continued absence of so large a body of practical men from its daily demands and requirements would be injurious), will be sufficient stimulus to prompt us to quick and decided action, so that we may return to our respective stations at the earliest possible moment.

One great impediment in the way of rapid and satisfactory progress has been found in the divided and scattered positions that we occupy. Many places contain but one member, one telegraph operator being sufficient for the locality; and in fact there are but a few places where a sufficient number of members are employed to make, when collected together, a respectable gathering for purposes of interchange of views and ideas. This has necessitated, on the part of the officers and those members who take the greatest interest, a large amount of correspondence and written communications, and, in consequence, a good deal of labor and devotion of all the time allowed from their daily duties, and still much has been left undone.

I would heartily recommend that some means be devised for more frequent, easier and more general communication among members and districts. Those situated in smaller places hear and know, in many instances, scarcely anything of what is going forward, and are very naturally, I think, inclined to believe that nothing is being done, and that no interest is felt in the affairs of the Union.

The First Issue of *The Telegrapher*, September 26, 1864. Official Publication of the National Telegraphic Union

General Grant and His Operator. Also included in the picture are
Generals Sheridan, Meade, and Rawlins.

A Field Expedient

respectively, on a capital varying slightly from year to year, but averaging about $2,300,000. A marked improvement once more in 1862 brought cash dividends amounting to 9 percent and stock dividends totaling 27.26 percent.[47]

By this time Western Union stockholders had come to expect miracles, and they were not disappointed. A cash dividend of 9 percent plus a 100 percent stock dividend was declared on March 16, 1863. The following December 23, a further stock dividend of 33 1/3 percent was paid. Up to this point, it was claimed, perhaps with justification, that stock dividends were based on actual mileage of restored property at a fair valuation. The capital of Western Union, now $7,950,700, was fairly representative of the property owned by the company.

Then in March 1864 had come news of Western Union's acceptance of the Russian-American project. The investing public visualized fabulous profits; New York, Chicago, and San Francisco were to be put into communication with St. Petersburg, Berlin, Paris, and London, with perhaps a branch line down the China coast to the great commercial centers of eastern Asia. There was even talk of extending another line from San Francisco and Los Angeles southward to Mexico, and Central and South America. The result was a period of dangerous excitement. "So much money had been made by the holders of the stock hitherto," declared James D. Reid, "and its value was held so great, that its possession even in minute quantities, was regarded as conferring on its holders all the golden possibilities of Aladdin's lamp." In Rochester, which was at that time the headquarters of the company, pianos, furniture of various kinds, mortgages, and homesteads were converted into cash to purchase Western Union stock. The stock at one time rose in value to $225 a share. While the public mind was thus excited, the board of the company, on May 11, 1864, declared a stock dividend of 100 percent, thereby increasing the capitalization to $21,063,400. "It was clear and unmixed water," asserted Reid. "This dividend, after a few years, seriously endangered the stability of the company, and, for a time rendered its administration obnoxious and perilous."[48]

[47] Reid, *Telegraph in America*, 484; Report of M. Guernsey, attorney-at-law, in *Talk on Telegraphic Topics*, anonymous pamphlet (1882), 33-34.

[48] Reid, *Telegraph in America*, 484-485; Morse to Thomas R. Walker, March 12, 1864, Morse Papers, Letter Book O; George Vail to Morse, March 14, 1864, Morse Papers, XLII; Morse to Walker, March 16, 1864, Morse Papers, Letter Book O; *Ibid.*, March 17, 1864; Walker to Morse, March 18, 1864, Morse Papers, XLII.

9 — · · —

ON August 17, 1864, the seventh annual meeting of the North American Telegraph Association assembled in New York, but of the seven companies which had once constituted the telegraph family only five remained to answer the roll call. During the preceding year the New York, Albany & Buffalo and the Atlantic & Ohio Companies had become merged with Western Union. The meeting was dominated throughout by Western Union. Hiram Sibley was re-elected president of the Association, Judge Caton was made vice president, and James D. Reid, secretary. The main topic for discussion was Western Union's Russian-American project. Sibley spoke at length on the brilliant prospects for the line and urged members of the Association to support the enterprise. The North American Telegraph Association was clearly losing its original character as an association of equals; it was fast becoming a mere Western Union tool.[49]

All during the autumn and winter of 1864 Western Union applied increased pressure to the remaining members of the Association in an attempt to force them into a consolidation. Anxious inquiries were exchanged among them regarding the frequent rumors that one or another of their number had succumbed to the telegraph octopus. The war-torn American Telegraph Company was approached again and again.[50] Offers were likewise made to the Southwestern,[51] the Illinois & Mississippi, and the Wisconsin State Telegraph Companies.[52] Executives were informed that they would find it to their personal advantage if they looked with favor upon Western Union's proposals.[53] Rumors were current that a merger had been agreed upon between Western Union and the California State Telegraph Company.[54] It was a period of apprehension and general uneasiness for the leaders of the remaining independent companies within the industry. They were forced to a realization that consolidation was, or soon would be, "an absolute necessity" for them. Each was working to place his company in the most advantageous position possible from which to bargain.[55]

49 Proceedings of the Seventh Annual Meeting of the North American Telegraph Association, August 17-20, 1864, 10 page pamphlet, Caton Papers.

50 Kendall to Morse, October [18?], 1864, Morse Papers, XLIII; Morse to Kendall, October 14, 1864, Morse Papers, Letter Book O.

51 Kendall to Morse, October [23?], 1864, Morse Papers, XLIII.

52 E. D. L. Sweet to Caton, October 26, 1864, Caton Papers; Ibid., November 28, 1864.

53 Ibid., April 15, 1864.   54 Ibid., October 26, 1864.

55 Ibid., April 15, 1864; Ibid., October 26, 1864.

While negotiations between the leading telegraph companies were dragging on month after month, numerous little lines were being quietly gobbled up by the rapacious Western Union. Then late in 1864, came word that Western Union had purchased a controlling interest ($1,265,000 out of a total stock issue of $2,500,000) in the important California State Telegraph Company.[56] That concern, shortly after completion of the transcontinental line had absorbed its puppet, the Overland Telegraph Company. During the next few years the California State had successfully carried out an ambitious program of consolidation which had brought all the important lines in the vast region from Salt Lake City westward under its management. At the moment that it came under Western Union control, the California State had just completed a line to Portland, Oregon, and was busily engaged in pushing it on northward via Olympia to Seattle. Moreover plans had already been made to lay a submarine cable to Victoria, British Columbia.[57] The addition of the California State lines gave Sibley and his associates control of a communications system that stretched from New York and Philadelphia on the Atlantic to San Francisco, Los Angeles, Portland, and Seattle on the Pacific. It also placed Western Union in a stronger position from which to prosecute its Russian-American project.

10 · — · —

ABOUT this time a slight cloud appeared upon the telegraph horizon. Numerous promoters and capitalists who had followed with interest and amazement the mercurial rise of Western Union, and had watched the fortunes of its leaders grow, became convinced that the telegraph industry offered a rich field for further exploitation. During 1863-1864, therefore, a number of companies were organized to build lines to compete with those of Western Union and the other old established firms. Several of these—the Inland, the Inland Extension, the Independent, the United States, and the United States Extension Telegraph Companies—proceeded to merge on August 3, 1864, the consolidated corporation retaining the felicitous name, United States Telegraph Company. The new concern, organized under the laws of the State of New York, was to have an authorized capital of

---

[56] Kendall to Morse, December 12, 1864, Morse Papers, XLIII; cf. Morse to T. R. Walker, December 15, 1864, Morse Papers, Letter Book O.
[57] Bancroft, *Chronicles of the Builders*, v, 340-341.

$6,000,000, divided into shares of $100 each. Nineteen thousand shares of stock amounting, at par value, to $1,900,000 were issued to the companies which were absorbed, in exchange for all of their stocks and other telegraph property. The merger brought under the control of the United States Telegraph Company nearly 10,000 miles of line leading to many important points; and its leaders announced their intention of extending the system until it should reach every important commercial center in the nation.

James McKaye was chosen president of this vigorous new corporation, and superficially, at least, its prospects seemed promising. The first board of directors was composed of prominent New York City business men: Lewis Roberts, Charles J. Martin, Silas C. Hay, Freeman Clarke, Charles Macalester, Thomas H. Wilson, John D. Taylor, John Hulme, G. W. Burbank, Theodore Adams, Josiah King, David Fleming, George F. Davis, Delos De Wolfe, George P. Plant, Samuel Munn, Henry Morgan, J. M. Schermerhorn, and Henry G. McKaye.[58]

The member companies of the North American Telegraph Association, in spite of their jealousy of one another, rallied against the common enemy and a bitter battle was soon being fought on a wide front. As early as the autumn of 1863, Hiram Sibley had written Judge Caton warning him to be on the lookout for trouble in his territory. "I have just been informed that the United States Telegraph Company have made proposals very favorable to the Keokuk & Des Moines Railroad and that one of the managers of that railroad has been induced to favor their scheme. . . . They are making efforts to get a contract with the Rock Island and its connecting line West, through their New York offices, and if they secure a contract over the K & D [Keokuk & Des Moines], it will aid them very much.

"You are aware, I suppose, that Mr. Tracy and Mr. Farnam [Rock Island Railroad officials] are very large stockholders in our Western Union Telegraph Company and their influence can be relied upon I think to defeat them [United States Telegraph Company]."[59]

A year later the battle was in full swing. Judge Caton's lieutenant, J. J. S. Wilson, writing to his employer from Springfield, Illinois, on September 23, 1864, told him that "the United States Telegraph folks" were setting poles along the Chicago & Alton Railroad just

[58] The Telegrapher, I (September 25, 1865), 156; Reid, Telegraph in America, 520-521.

[59] Hiram Sibley to Caton, September 10, 1863, Caton Papers; cf. Sweet to Caton, December 1, 1863, Ibid.

outside the railroad company's fence. "I propose to employ Virgil Hickox (who is well acquainted with farmers and citizens along the road and a man that will do what he undertakes to do) to make arrangements with landowners along the road to prevent them from constructing." Did Caton approve of such a course, and if so, how much money was he willing to spend in carrying it out? Wilson emphasized the fact that prompt action was required, since the opposition had a large force at work and were expecting to reach St. Louis by November 1.[60]

On the same day came a letter from another employee, L. A. Louis, with more bad news; agents of the United States Telegraph Company were claiming to have made arrangements to run a line along the Illinois Central Railroad on the opposite side from Caton's wire. They were also trying hard to employ the Illinois & Mississippi's operators, but without success, declared Louis.[61] Writing again on December 28, Louis informed Caton that the opposition forces were checkmated. They had failed to meet their contracts and would certainly not be able to keep their promise, "to be in full blast in Cairo" by January 1. "I do not see how they can get into Cairo at all," boasted Louis, "and Mr. Arthur and Mr. Hughitt [officials of the Illinois Central Railroad] will keep posted of their little plans and movements, and as you say—'Mr. Arthur will cut poles as fast as they set them on his right of way.' "[62]

By reckless promises and the liberal distribution of stock among prominent railroad and newspaper men, however, the United States lines progressed in spite of all attempts to stop them. J. J. S. Wilson, writing from Springfield on February 2, 1865, announced, "The United States folks have their office opened at this place and are trying to get hold of business but make a poor show thus far." The battle now entered a new phase. Illinois & Mississippi offices were instructed to refuse messages from the United States lines; rates were slashed at competitive points; and an unsuccessful attempt was made to halt the newcomer by injunction.[63]

Meanwhile, the other members of the North American Telegraph

[60] J. J. S. Wilson to Caton, September 23, 1864, Caton Papers.
[61] L. A. Louis to Caton, September 23, 1864, *Ibid.*
[62] *Ibid.*, December 28, 1864.
[63] Wilson to Caton, February 2, 1865; *Ibid.*, August 9, 1865; F. H. Kales to Caton, October 18, 1864, Caton Papers; much additional information in Caton Papers, 1863-1865.

Association were having similar difficulties.[64] The United States Tele-graph Company appeared to be irresistible; in spite of every obstacle the established companies could devise, its lines continued to reach out and embrace new territory daily. In July 1864, the company had secured the passage by Congress of an act authorizing the construc-tion of "a line or lines of magnetic telegraph between the Missouri River and the City of San Francisco, in the state of California, on such route as they [the corporators] might select, to connect with the lines of the said United States Telegraph Company, now constructed and being constructed through the States of the Union." The re-maining provisions were similar to those of the act under which the Western Union interests had constructed their transcontinental line three years earlier, except that the United States corporators were offered no subsidy.[65] The actual building of the proposed line was to be entrusted to a separate corporation to be known as the United States Pacific Telegraph Company. It was presented to the public as the knight in shining armor come to slay the dragon, "monopoly," and all were urged to support the noble cause by buying United States Pacific Telegraph stock. The response was so gratifying that by the close of the year, plans had been matured for commencing building operations in the spring.[66]

While the United States Telegraph Company was rapidly extend-ing its lines throughout the nation and apparently overcoming all opposition, the price it paid for its progress was out of all proportion to the value of the property secured.[67] The concern which ultimately was to profit from the activities of the United States Telegraph, strangely enough, was none other than Western Union. As the United States Telegraph lines had proceeded, the Western Union management had matured a plan for turning this development to its advantage. Sibley and his associates, who at first had joined whole-heartedly with the other members of the North American Telegraph Association in a war of extermination on the newcomer, seemed to lose interest in the contest; and by the close of 1864, Western Union had largely ceased fighting the opposition east of the Mississippi River.

[64] The Telegrapher, II, 127.
[65] "An Act for increased facilities of Telegraphic Communication between the Atlantic and Pacific States and the Territory of Idaho," July 2, 1864, Cong. Globe, 38 Cong., 1 sess., Appendix, 255.
[66] Reid, Telegraph in America, 521.
[67] The later history of the United States Telegraph Company develops this subject more fully. See Chapter XXVIII.

As Superintendent Sweet of the Illinois & Mississippi pointed out to Judge Caton: "The opposition will do no more than they have already done against the Western Union for some time, but [they will] build lines in the West to our injury, and I think Sibley believes it will cost but little more to buy us and them up, after a while, than it will take now to buy us."[68] The United States Telegraph lines were to be used as a club to drive members of the North American Telegraph Association into the Western Union fold.

11 ·——··——·

VIEWED in retrospect, the war years may be said to mark the turning point in the struggle for telegraphic supremacy. The American Telegraph Company with its lines extending from North to South had been torn asunder and its progress arrested by the conflict. The Western Union, on the other hand, with its lines stretching from East to West had been in a position to take advantage of the unusual opportunities afforded by the war. That aggressive newcomer, the United States Telegraph Company, appeared to threaten both of the older concerns. As the Civil War drew to a close in the spring of 1865, the strategic position of Western Union gave it a marked advantage over its rivals in the three-cornered contest for control of the industry which followed.

68 E. D. L. Sweet to Caton, October 26, 1864, Caton Papers.

CHAPTER XXVIII

The Great Consolidations

1 ·——·

ABOUT 9:30 on the morning of April 3, 1865, while William E. Kettles, a boy operator of fifteen, was in the Washington office attending to the service of the line which ran to Fortress Monroe, he was startled by a call from there to "Turn down for Richmond, quick!" With trembling fingers he obeyed, and in another moment the signal from Richmond flashed along the wire. "Do you get me well?" they said.

"I do; go ahead," was the reply.
"All right. Here is the first message for four years:
    Richmond, Virginia, April 3rd, 1865.
    Hon. E. M. Stanton, Secretary of War;
    We entered Richmond at eight o'clock this morning.
           G. Weitzel,
           Brigadier-General, commanding."

Kettles copied the message and rushed into the room of General Eckert, Assistant Secretary of War, where he found President Lincoln conversing in a low tone with Mr. Tinker, a cipher clerk. As Kettles handed the dispatch to Tinker, the President glanced through it and bounded from the room exclaiming, "Clear the track!" and made for the door of Secretary Stanton. The tidings flew like wildfire; soon the telegraph office was filled with officers of state, and the building was besieged by an enthusiastic crowd.[1]

At last that long-sought and elusive goal, Richmond, was within the grasp of the Union forces. Lee's army was in full retreat; the end was not far off. Six days later the great Confederate general's war-weary veterans laid down their arms and the conflict was virtually over.

2 ··—··

A CHANGED nation emerged from the crucible of war. Jefferson's dream of a great agrarian democracy had vanished and the Hamilto-

---

[1] "The Telegraph and the Civil War," *Chamber's Journal*, LXIX (1892), 23.

nian system emerged triumphant. The United States was on the way to becoming the leading industrial power of the world. Along the seaboard and westward through Pennsylvania, Ohio, Indiana, and Illinois, factories had sprung up by the hundreds, and the railroads and telegraph lines which served them had grown steadily more extensive.

At the same time there could be discerned in nearly every industry a clear and unmistakable trend toward fewer and larger units. That trend, as has already been shown, had progressed a long way in the case of the telegraph industry. In fact, the consolidation movement now entered its final phase, and the telegraph shortly emerged as the nation's first great industrial monopoly. In the decades that followed, the pattern described by the telegraph was to be repeated, with modifications, many times as the individual units in other industries followed the irresistible trend toward monopoly.

A survey of the telegraph situation at the close of the war will provide the basis for a clearer understanding of the developments of the post-war period. Western Union had outdistanced all its rivals, both old and new from the standpoint of capitalization, miles of wire in use, and number of offices. With a nominal capitalization of $22,000,000 (actual stock issued $21,355,100), possessing about 44,000 miles of wire, and 1,014 telegraph offices,[2] Western Union was far ahead of its nearest rival, the American Telegraph Company, with a capitalization of $2,000,000 and about 23,000 miles of wire.[3] The comparatively new United States Telegraph Company was a vigorous and rapidly growing third with an authorized capitalization of $6,000,000 (actual stock issued about $4,000,000) and nearly 16,000 miles of wire.[4]

A comparison of the gross receipts of the "Big Three" for the year 1865 provides additional significant detail. Once again Western Union was far ahead with $2,314,211.41; the American followed with $1,437,627.21; then came the United States with $668,422.26.[5] When gross receipts are compared with the capitalizations of the respective companies, however, the relative position of Western Union is seen to be much less favorable. The Rochester concern was capitalized at

[2] Statement of the Directors of the Western Union Telegraph Company to the stockholders, October 1, 1865; Senate Ex. Docs., No. 49, 39 Cong., 1 sess., 21-27.
[3] Report of President Sanford to the stockholders of the American Telegraph Company at their annual meeting, January 31, 1866, in The Telegrapher, II, 61-62.
[4] The Telegrapher, I, 173; Senate Ex. Docs., No. 49, 39 Cong., 1 sess., 21-27.
[5] The Telegrapher, I, 131; Ibid., II, 22; Ibid., III (September 1, 1866).

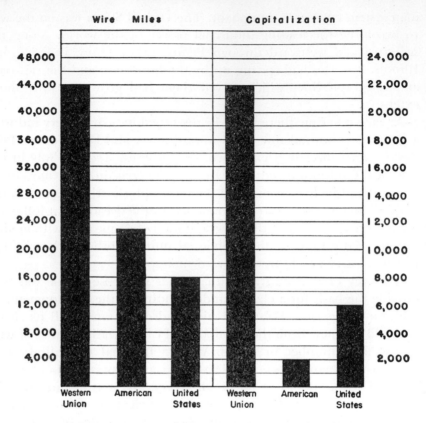

Wire   Miles   Capitalization

WIRE   MILES   OF   TELEGRAPH   IN   OPERATION   AND
CAPITALIZATION   OF   THE   BIG   THREE ,   CLOSE   OF   1865

Source: Statement of the Directors of the Western Union Telegraph Company to the stockholders, October 1, 1865; Senate Ex. Docs., No. 49, 39 Cong., 1 sess., 21-27; Report of President Sanford to the stockholders of the American Telegraph Company at their annual meeting, January 31, 1866, in *The Telegrapher*, II, 61-62; *The Telegrapher*, I, 173.

about 9.2 times its gross receipts, while the figure for the American was only 1.4 and that for the United States slightly less than 6.

In addition to the "Big Three" there were, of course, a number of smaller companies like the Illinois & Mississippi which controlled the lines in Illinois and Iowa; the Southwestern dominating the industry in Kentucky, Tennessee, and most of Mississippi, Louisiana, and Texas; and the newly organized Northwestern Telegraph Company, which had resulted from the consolidation of the principal lines in Wisconsin and Minnesota.[6] The interests of these companies being

[6] Senate Ex. Docs., No. 49, 39 Cong., 1 sess., 21-27.

confined to relatively limited regions, the concluding battles for national telegraphic supremacy, which now took place, were confined largely to the "Big Three."

3 · · · — ·

JUST as the outbreak of the war had served to give Western Union a decided advantage over its rivals, so the termination of hostilities tended to reverse the situation to a certain extent. In a period of falling markets and decreasing business, the 100 percent stock dividend which Sibley and the directors had declared so optimistically in May 1864 became a dead weight.[7] The actual property owned did not warrant a capitalization of $22,000,000. With its wire mileage of about 44,000, including many almost worthless duplications, the company was capitalized at slightly more than $485 per mile of wire— a very high figure, inasmuch as the average cost of constructing and equipping a first class line, according to Western Union's own estimates, was at most $220 to $250 per mile.[8]

Writing to his old friend and adviser, Thomas R. Walker, former president of the New York, Albany & Buffalo and now a director of Western Union, in July 1865, Professor Morse inquired uneasily, "I wish you would write me what you think of the management of the Company. There are some things which give me some anxiety. The watering of the stock, doubling it some time ago from eleven to twenty two million, I never approved, and I think it is injurious to the stock; but I suppose it cannot now be helped. . . . What is the price of the stock with you? When I last inquired in New York I think it was somewhere between 70 and 80; this seems strange for an 8 percent stock. Can you explain?"[9]

While Walker's reply is not known, the answer to Morse's question was clear enough. The name of Western Union had lost its charm for the investing public, which was justifiably skeptical of the company's ability to pay 8 percent on its twenty-two millions of capital.

Hiram Sibley, who had been in ill health for some time, now decided to retire from the presidency, and at the annual meeting held at the company's home office in Rochester on July 26, 1865, his resignation was accepted. Thereupon, his capable colleague, Jeptha H.

[7] Reid, *Telegraph in America*, 485.
[8] Senate Ex. Docs., No. 49, 39 Cong., 1 sess., 12-13.
[9] Morse to T. R. Walker, July 10, 1865, Morse Papers, Letter Book P.

Wade, was chosen to guide Western Union through the troubled months that lay ahead.[10] While lacking Sibley's boldness, and with less breadth of vision perhaps, Wade possessed to a far greater degree than his predecessor the quality that was especially needed at this time—the faculty of administration—the power of clear, accurate, discriminating systematization.[11]

To assist Wade in the management of the company there were chosen as directors: Hiram Sibley, George H. Mumford, Don Alonzo Watson, Isaac Butts, Henry R. Selden, Samuel Wilder, Fred Delano, and B. R. McAlpine, all of Rochester; Ezra Cornell of Ithaca; John Butterfield of Utica; Roswell S. Burrows of Albion; Anson Stager of Cleveland; Perry McD. Collins of New York City and H. H. Schillingford of Philadelphia.[12] An examination of this list shows that the Rochester group, which had controlled the company's policies since its organization, still shaped its course of action in 1865. The only new name of any significance was that of Collins, projector of the Russian-American overland line to Europe.

Wade set to work at once to put the Western Union house in order. The task was not a pleasant or easy one. Instead of disbursing dividends to the stockholders, he was obliged to call upon them to furnish the company with funds for a far-reaching program of reconstruction and extension. The continued prosperity of the company, declared Wade in a report to the stockholders on October 1, 1865, absolutely depended upon it. Many hastily and cheaply built lines were in an advanced state of decay and would have to be thoroughly reconstructed at once if the company's business was not to suffer.

Moreover, the construction of hundreds of miles of new line along railroad rights of way was imperative if Western Union was to retain its hegemony in the West. The war years had seen the consummation of the union between wire and rail. Railroad executives, convinced at last that the telegraph was essential to the efficient operation of their roads, hurried to make arrangements for the construction of lines. Telegraph leaders, likewise, had come to realize that lines built along the highways could not compete with those erected and maintained in cooperation with the railroads. A line along a railroad could use railroad stations for its offices. Breaks could be easily detected. Repair crews and materials could be transported rapidly. In

---

[10] *The Telegrapher*, I, 145.   [11] Reid, *Telegraph in America*, 518.
[12] Statement of the Directors of the Western Union Telegraph Company to the stockholders, October 1, 1865.

order not to let rival interests get a foothold, therefore, Western Union felt impelled to secure contracts with all the important railroads in its territory. The result was that in numerous instances the company was obliged to erect new lines along railroad rights of way even though they covered practically the same territory as those that had been erected earlier along highways.[13]

To add to the difficulties, the United States Telegraph Company showed its hand on the Pacific coast and directed James Street to build a line from San Francisco to the Missouri River, where it would connect with that company's already extensive system which stretched on eastward to the seaboard. It was imperative, therefore, that Western Union establish a reliable service between the east and west coasts to meet this new menace.[14]

During the spring and summer of 1865 that section of Western Union's transcontinental line between Omaha and Salt Lake City had been seriously interrupted by Indian raids and depredations; and an already hostile public criticized the management severely, not only because of the delays but also because of the suspected motives behind them. A San Francisco correspondent, writing to the *Telegrapher* declared: "Communication between here [San Francisco] and the East by telegraph is an illustration of the well known proverb that 'doubtful things are mighty onsartin!' The Overland line is 'out of order' about three-fourths of the time, being either 'interrupted by lightning between here and Salt Lake!' or else 'down somewhere east of Salt Lake,' if we may believe the official bulletins of the agent. Malicious and evil minded persons trace some remarkable coincidences between the ups and downs of this wire and similar fluctuations on the part of gold. Of course, being a member of the profession I ascribe it to the 'pesky Injuns.' "[15]

To meet the threatened transcontinental competition of the United States Telegraph Company, and to silence public criticism of Western Union's own erratic service, President Wade proposed to repair thoroughly the existing line upon the old northern route, and to construct a new one along a southern route via Denver. Western Union would then have two wires to the West, and one of them so far south of the region of Indian depredations as to be substantially free from disaster from that cause. "It is estimated," stated the new Western Union executive, "that the expenditures now absolutely essential in

13 *Ibid.*
14 *Ibid.*; Reid, *Telegraph in America*, 503.
15 *The Telegrapher*, I, 118.

respect to the Pacific line, and other important additions to our lines, will require about $1,000,000."[16]

Still another financial problem was that of raising the money needed to retire $2,000,000 worth of bonds which the company had issued in 1864 to construct new lines and to purchase a controlling interest in the California State Telegraph Company for the protection of Western Union interests on the Pacific Coast. At the time the bonds had been issued, the market value of Western Union stock was firm at par (100) and upwards, and there had been good reason to believe that before the maturity of the bonds, the holders would avail themselves of the convertible clause therein and exchange them for shares of the company's common stock. The amount would thus have become a part of the capital without provision of funds to meet the payment of the principal in cash. Western Union stock, however, dropped from par (100) in March, to 75 in September 1865, thereby removing the inducement to convert the bonds, and making it necessary to provide in some other way for their payment.

To meet the expense of retiring these bonds and making additions to the Pacific line, the board had authorized increasing the capital stock of the company by 30,000 shares of $100 each, guaranteeing annual dividends of 8 percent to the holders of the new stock and the privilege of converting this special stock, at their option, into common stock at any time within ten years.[17] The need for such heavy financing on the part of the already over-capitalized Rochester concern further undermined the confidence of the investment community, and by the close of the year Western Union stock was selling regularly at less than 50 cents on the dollar.[18]

The Western Union balance sheet was not quite so discouraging as here presented, for there were several important entries to be made on the credit side of the ledger. The United States Government, as compensation for the losses suffered by the company during the war, turned over to it a number of former military telegraph lines totaling many thousands of miles of wire.[19] Then, too, it was believed that the ultimate success of the vaunted Russian-American overland line to Europe, upon which construction was in full swing, would shortly bring to the parent company a tremendous increase in both business

[16] Statement of the Directors of the Western Union Telegraph Company to the stockholders, October 1, 1865.
[17] *Ibid.*   [18] Quotations on telegraph stocks in *The Telegrapher*, I (1865).
[19] Horace Coon, *American Tel. & Tel.*, 31; *Telephone and Telegraph Age* (Jan. 1, 1912), 16.

and profits in the same way that the transcontinental line had done five years earlier. Finally, Wade and his associates believed that their efforts to establish a telegraph monopoly were just about to be crowned with success. Negotiations for merging the lines of the remaining independent companies with those of Western Union were constant; and there began to appear signs that opposition to such a consolidation was beginning to weaken. If a monopoly could be established and maintained, generous dividends could be paid with ease on a far greater capitalization than $22,000,000.

4 . . . . —

THE American Telegraph Company was the one which profited most from the coming of peace. Just as soon as conditions permitted, regular communication with the states lately at war was restored; messages were being sent from Macon, Georgia, to Washington early in May; later in the month, dispatches were passing between New Orleans and New York.[20] By the autumn of 1865 the more important southern lines, although still under government control, had been repaired and were being operated by the private companies.[21] Then on December 1, full control of the southern telegraph lines was restored to the companies which owned them and the censorship of the press was removed except on cipher dispatches. Two months later all United States Military Telegraph lines and appurtenances within the states south of the Ohio River were turned over to the several commercial companies owning the patent rights for the different sections, in consideration of the relinquishment by the companies of all claims against the United States for use of the patents and as compensation for property losses incurred during the war.[22]

The American Telegraph Company's southern lines were naturally very much run down and needed rebuilding. It was also necessary to build many new lines to meet the increased business demand. On November 1, 1865, the directors announced, in a circular sent to the stockholders, that new stock was being issued for this purpose and that they were to have the privilege of buying at par (100) one share

[20] E. P. Oberholtzer, *A History of the United States Since the Civil War*, I, 107-108; *The Telegrapher*, I, 131, 175.

[21] Statement of the Directors of the American Telegraph Company to the stockholders, November 1, 1865.

[22] Plum, *The Military Telegraph during the Civil War*, II, 340-348; *The Telegrapher*, II, 17; *Ibid.*, III, 110.

of the new stock for every four shares then held. This was the equivalent of a stock dividend since at that time the market price of American Telegraph stock was about 140.

In describing the sound condition of the company to the stockholders, the directors announced proudly: "Our property could not now be replaced for the amount of our capital stock at par, and we are justified in stating that we have more than twice as much property, in proportion to our stock, as any other telegraph company in the United States. We have reason to expect, therefore, that the increase of business from our southern lines when they shall be put in good order, with additional facilities, will give us largely increased profits and add to the value of our stock."[23]

Well might the directors of the American Telegraph Company boast of its sound condition. When compared with Western Union, for example, the excellent position of the American was at once apparent. With a capitalization of $2,000,000 and well over 20,000 miles of wire, the capitalized value per mile of wire, including equipment, was less than $100, as compared with $485 per mile for the inflated Western Union lines.

Another source of strength to the American Company was its management. The able Col. E. S. Sanford, president since 1860, remained at the helm. To assist him in his labors, was an excellent and experienced board of directors. A mere enumeration of the names: Samuel F. B. Morse, Amos Kendall, Francis Morris, William M. Swain, John McKesson, Wilson G. Hunt, Hiram O. Alden, Cambridge Livingston, Caleb A. Burgess, Marshall Lefferts, Cyrus W. Field, and James Gordon Bennett, Jr., was enough to inspire the confidence of the public.

A further promising factor in respect to the future development of the company was its close association with the Atlantic cable project which had come to life once more with the termination of the war. If this undertaking was successfully concluded, it would mean a considerable increase in the revenues of the American, since the land lines which would be utilized to carry the messages from the western terminus of the cable in Newfoundland to New York were a part of the American Telegraph system.[24]

Of course, it was possible that serious antagonism might arise from

23 Statement of the Directors of the American Telegraph Company to the stockholders, November 1, 1865.
24 *The Telegrapher*, II, 61-62; Reid, *Telegraph in America*, 420-421.

Office of the American Telegraph Company. Corner of Broadway and Liberty Streets, New York, 1866

Edwards S. Sanford, American

Jeptha H. Wade, Western Union   William Orton, United States

PRESIDENTS OF THE BIG THREE, 1865

the aggressive operations of the United States Telegraph Company, but developments near the close of 1865 placed the American in a strong position to meet any competition its rival might offer. Both the American and Western Union Telegraph Companies had been wooing the strong and strategically situated Southwestern Telegraph for many months. Finally, in November, committees of the South-western and American had succeeded in arranging terms of consolida-tion satisfactory to both. The terms having been accepted by the stockholders of both companies, the merger was duly consummated in January 1866, by the issuance of $1,000,000 of American Telegraph stock in exchange for a like amount of Southwestern; this represented one-fourth of the American Telegraph's total capitalization.

The merger brought within the American Telegraph system an important network of lines in Kentucky, Tennessee, Mississippi, Louisiana, and Texas aggregating approximately 4,800 wire miles in length. Along with this property were acquired the valuable services of Norvin Green, George L. Douglass, and John Van Horne who were elected directors, and asked to continue their administrative duties over the lines between Louisville and New Orleans.[25] In their new role as representatives of the American Telegraph Company, Green and his associates had to confront a somewhat disgruntled and vindictive Western Union at the chief gateways to western traffic.

Concomitantly with this important consolidation came another; the American through an issue of $500,000 of its stock absorbed the lines of the Washington & New Orleans Telegraph Company.[26] These lines extending southward from Washington along the seaboard to New Orleans had been under lease to the American for a number of years; they now became an integral part of that corporation's system. Badly damaged during the war and in a dilapidated condition when handed over by the government, the lines needed extensive recon-struction and repairs, and half a million dollars was appropriated for the purpose. To meet the cost of this ambitious program of ex-

25 Report of President Sanford to the stockholders of the American Telegraph Com-pany at their annual meeting, January 31, 1866, in The Telegrapher, ii, 61-62; Morse to "My dear daughter," November 29, 1865, Morse Papers, Letter Book P; Morse to G. L. Douglass, December 9, 1865, Ibid.; Douglass to Morse, December 19, 1865, Morse Papers, xliii; Morse to Douglass, December 27, 1865, et seq., Morse Papers, Letter Book P.

26 Washington & New Orleans stockholders were given a choice between selling their stock at par ($50), slightly better than the market price; or exchanging it on the basis of two and one half Washington & New Orleans shares for one American (par $100), which was then selling for about $140 per share. (Morse to William M. Goodrich, January 8, 1866, Morse Papers, Letter Book P.)

pansion and reconstruction, the company proceeded to increase its capital stock from two to four millions of dollars. With the additional facilities thus furnished, the American management believed it would be able to meet successfully any competition the United States Telegraph Company or any other rival might offer.[27]

The real menace to the American Telegraph Company's future progress, as President Sanford and his associates realized only too well, was its pseudo-ally in the North American Telegraph Association, the Western Union Telegraph Company. Cooperation between the two concerns had long been more perfunctory than real. The frequent and acrimonious quarrels which had characterized their relations for years now grew more violent. At the same time the Western Union management exerted pressure by every means at its command to bring about a consolidation of the nation's two chief telegraph systems.

5 — — —

THE position of the United States Telegraph Company in 1865 was rather deceiving. During the year the company had constructed lines and opened offices with bewildering speed. Sixteen new offices had been opened in the States of Delaware, New Jersey, Pennsylvania, and Ohio during the month of April. Twelve more along a line extending through the State of New York to Montreal, Canada, were opened in June.[28] A short time later California was invaded by an organization designated as the United States Pacific Telegraph Company, and a line was begun from San Francisco eastward under the superintendence of James Gamble. By January 1866, it was already finished to Salt Lake City and plans had been completed for carrying it on to Missouri.[29]

During the early months of 1865, United States Telegraph stock was regarded with favor by the Wall Street community. Early in February, Judge John D. Caton's New York broker wrote him a long and enthusiastic letter about the United States Telegraph Company and its prospects for the future. The company had just declared a dividend of 4 percent from earnings, and its business was increasing

27 Report of President Sanford to the stockholders of the American Telegraph Company at their annual meeting, January 31, 1866, in *The Telegrapher*, II, 61-62.

28 *The Telegrapher*, I, 84, 115.

29 *Ibid.*, 165, 182; *New York Times*, January 6, 1866; S. Churchill to J. D. Caton, June 2, 1865, Caton Papers; Sweet to Caton, June 19, 1865, Caton Papers.

weekly. He predicted that United States Telegraph stock would be worth 150 by July. The company was rapidly extending its lines all over the country and expected soon to have as many miles of wire as the other two great systems. The United States Company did not plan as many little stations as its rivals, but proposed instead to concentrate its efforts upon linking the great eastern cities with the important commercial centers of the West. While difficulty had been experienced in getting the railroads to accommodate the wires of the United States Company, its management was not concerned. They preferred going over farms and on common roads, since they would not have to divide their earnings with the railroad companies. Everything considered, the broker believed that United States Telegraph stock at or near par (100) was a good speculation.[30]

Notwithstanding all the dash, wealth, and energy that had been exhibited by the United States Telegraph Company in its brief history, elements of fatal weakness had been allowed to creep in. Stock had been distributed freely in exchange for favors; contracts of prodigal liberality had been entered into in many instances; and lines had been extended into non-paying territory.[31] Then, too, there were suspicious signs that a small "inside" group were enriching themselves at the expense of the stockholders. In a letter to the editor of the *New York Tribune* which appeared on June 30, a writer who signed himself "A United States Stockholder" protested against the lack of information furnished to the ordinary stockholders about the conduct of their company. In a circular which President James Mc-Kaye had issued to the stockholders, it was proposed to construct a telegraph line to the Pacific to form part of the United States lines. Every stockholder was to have the right and privilege of subscribing for one share of Pacific extension stock for every two shares already held by him in the United States Telegraph Company, to be paid for at the rate of sixty-six and two-thirds dollars per share. What the protesting stockholders wanted to know was how much the proposed line to the Pacific was expected to cost, and how much extension stock was to be issued for the purpose.

"It may be, and I learn that such a suspicion exists," he asserted, "that while we, stockholders outside 'the ring,' are expected to furnish all the money to build the line, a still larger amount of stock

[30] S. Churchill to Caton, February 4, 1865, Caton Papers.
[31] J. J. S. Wilson to Caton, July 18, 1865, Caton Papers; Reid, *Telegraph in America*, 521.

is to be issued to members of 'the ring,' for which they are to pay nothing or next to nothing."

He went on to point out that certain significant facts of the greatest importance to the stockholders had been withheld from them. According to *Low's Telegraph and Railroad Directory* the United States Telegraph Company's wires covered substantially the same territories as those of the Western Union and American Telegraph Companies. Yet the gross earnings of these concerns for the last half of 1864, according to the returns of their respective officers, as stated in the *New York Herald*, were $1,791,415, as against $174,134 for the United States Telegraph. The United States Company, according to *Low's Directory*, had three hundred offices, and paid large rents and high salaries. Yet the gross receipts did not give $4.00 a day to the offices on an average. In addition, there were the salaries of sixteen superintendents and other high paid officials to be considered, as well as the expense of keeping the lines up. Still the managers were pretending to be paying liberal "dividends" from net profits.

Low's Directory gave the capital stock of the United States Telegraph Company at the opening of 1865 as $3,500,000 and stated that the last semi-annual dividend of 4 percent had been paid on February 1, 1865. A dividend of 4 percent on the above capitalization amounted to $140,000, while according to the official company reports gross receipts for the preceding six months' period had been only $174,134. Thus a balance of $34,134 remained to maintain 20,000 miles of wire, mostly along the highways, to pay the rent of three hundred offices, the salaries of hundreds of officers, operators, and other employees, and all other running expenses for six months. As a final indictment the protesting stockholder pointed out that one of the contractors for United States Telegraph lines had recently retired with a comfortable fortune, "the proceeds of his sharp bargains with us credulous stockholders."[32]

President McKaye replied to these charges in a letter to the editor of the *New York Tribune* dated July 5, 1865. While pointing out some errors in the statements of his critic, he failed to answer the really important questions raised. McKaye explained that out of $178,856 of gross receipts for the first six months of the company's existence, the semi-annual dividend of 4 percent was paid only on the $1,900,000 of capital which had been issued to the companies that were consolidated at the time of incorporation, August 3, 1864,

[32] *The Telegrapher*, I, 140.

and not on the entire capital stock of the company. This dividend had amounted to $76,000, leaving $102,856 to pay expenses on from 10,000 to 12,000 miles of wire instead of on 20,000 miles of wire as stated by the stockholder. McKaye's corrections did not alter the obvious conclusion that such "dividends" as were being paid were not from net profits. President McKaye also protested vehemently against the charges made concerning the Pacific Extension stock, but he failed to answer the stockholder's pertinent questions as to how much the line to the Pacific was to cost, or how much stock was to be issued in connection with this scheme.[33] As a matter of fact, the truth was even worse than the protesting stockholder had suspected; the company actually proposed to issue $7,000,000 of stock for the construction of a line worth only a small part of that amount.

President McKaye's letter brought a rebuttal from the protesting stockholder. He proceeded to ask McKaye another series of embarrassing questions:

Did or did not the Directors of the original United States Line let the job of building said line to a party composed mainly or altogether of Directors?

Did or did not this "ring" make a very "fat job" of their contract with themselves?

Did not one member of this contract "ring" retire with a very snug fortune?

And are not some or all the rest interested in the contract for building the Pacific Extension?[34]

President McKaye did not reply to these questions, but the investing public did. The stock of the United States Telegraph Company dropped from 98 in March to 52 in August 1865.[35] The monthly balances began to tilt heavily and persistently on the wrong side. Moreover, the opposition companies waged a relentless war upon their antagonist, not only in the courts over rights of way, but also by reducing rates below the cost of operation.[36] United States stock continued to slide; late in September it was selling at 30; and during the first week in October it dropped to 20.[37] Under such circumstances President McKaye began to find the work unpleasant and arduous, and he resigned.

[33] *Ibid.*, 156.   [34] *Ibid.*, 173; cf. 182-183.
[35] Quotations on telegraph stocks in *The Telegrapher*, I (1865).
[36] *The Telegrapher*, II, 16; Reid, *Telegraph in America*, 522; Oberholtzer, *History of the United States*, I, 194.
[37] Morse to G. L. Douglass, October 9, 1865, Morse Papers, Letter Book P.

Upon the resignation of McKaye the presidency of the company was offered to William Orton, Commissioner of Internal Revenue in Washington. Large of frame and dignified in bearing, Orton's qualities of leadership were readily apparent. His excellent habits of work and earnestness of purpose reflected the humble home in which he was raised. Born in a schoolteacher's family in New York State in 1826, the boy had soon learned to study and concentrate his energies. Following in his father's footsteps, Orton had qualified as a teacher by graduating from the State Normal School in Albany, and for a short time thereafter he taught. His frequent purchases of books brought him to the attention of George H. Derby, the head of a publishing company in Geneva, New York. This contact ultimately resulted in Orton's becoming a partner in the publishing firm of Derby, Orton & Mulligan, with offices in Buffalo. The company was transferred to New York in 1856, where Orton continued in the publishing business until the failure of his firm. In 1862 President Lincoln had appointed him Collector of Internal Revenue in New York City. His conduct of this office during the difficult war years was so successful that President Johnson had brought him to Washington as Commissioner of Internal Revenue.

Meanwhile the telegraph had been spreading throughout the length and breadth of the land. When the United States Telegraph Company, in desperate straits, had invited Orton to assume the presidency, he accepted. He resigned his office in the Revenue Department and entered upon his new task on November 1, 1865.[38] He was not long in discovering the true condition of the United States Telegraph. After a careful examination of the concern's records, he found that although it occupied valuable territory and was doing a comparatively large business, its income fell short of its expenses by over $10,000 per month. This condition was unknown to him when he accepted the presidency, and he began to suspect that he had become the captain of a foundering ship.[39]

6 ······

A REVIEW of the positions of the "Big Three" at the close of 1865 presents an interesting situation. The United States Telegraph was

    38 The Telegrapher, I, 184; T. D. Catlin to J. D. Caton, November 20, 1865, Caton Papers.
    39 Reid, Telegraph in America, 522-523. (J. D. Reid had become secretary of the United States Telegraph Company on November 8, 1865.)

in desperate straits, and there was little reason to expect any marked improvement in the near future. The conservatively managed American, recovering rapidly from its wartime difficulties, was well situated to take advantage of future developments. The over-capitalized Western Union was feeling the effects of its wartime excesses, and the outlook for it was clouded. J. H. Wade and his associates, however, believed they knew of a way to extricate Western Union from its difficulties. Their solution was monopoly. The price they would have to pay to eliminate all rivals might be high, but they were willing to gamble on the result. If a telegraph monopoly could be established they believed that handsome profits could be made on the resulting capitalization—"water" and all. As the new year dawned, the initiative lay with Western Union.

7 — — ··

THE year 1866 was to prove a memorable one in telegraph history. Talk of a consolidation of the American Telegraph Company with Western Union had been heard for many months, but all negotiations had failed.[40] Then suddenly, almost without warning, came the announcement that the United States Telegraph had accepted terms of consolidation with Western Union.

William Orton, following his acceptance of the presidency of the United States Telegraph Company in November 1865, had done his best to establish the concern on a paying basis, but without success. One day late in February he had received an invitation from President J. H. Wade of Western Union, who was visiting in New York, to stop in and see him. At the ensuing conference Wade offered Orton a proposition for the merger of the United States Telegraph with Western Union. He proposed as a basis of negotiations, the relation of 121½ for United States to 87½ for Western Union. Although this offer seemed unacceptable to Orton at the time, a careful comparison of the gross receipts showed him that the revenues of the United States Telegraph were to those of the Western Union as 13⅞ to 100. Wade's offer, therefore, was not unjust.

After a further study of the facts, Orton made a counter-proposal of union on the basis of the respective revenues of the two companies,

---

[40] Morse to Kendall, February 11, 1865, Morse Papers, Letter Book O; *The Telegrapher*, I, 83, 189.

and it was accepted by the Western Union.[41] A contract was entered into on February 27, 1866, by which the lines of the United States Telegraph were to be placed under the management of Western Union on March 1. The United States Telegraph secured four representatives on the Western Union board of fifteen directors, and Orton was made a vice president of the consolidated company. It was further agreed that the United States Telegraph was to receive for distribution upon its $6,000,000 of outstanding stock, 15 percent of the net earnings of the united lines. This amount was to be increased to 25 percent after completion of the United States Pacific line from Chicago to San Francisco, and after the United States Telegraph had purchased the line through the issuance of $5,000,000 of United States Telegraph stock. Holders of United States Telegraph stock were urged to exchange it for Western Union stock at the agreed ratio of three shares of United States stock for two shares of Western Union. This privilege was to be open for six months. As an added inducement the contract expressly stipulated that no part of the profits which might accrue to Western Union from the business of its Russian-American line, the prospects for which looked exceedingly bright at this time, was to be given to holders of United States Telegraph stock until it had been exchanged for that of Western Union. Stock to the amount of $7,218,500 was ultimately issued to absorb both the United States and the United States Pacific Telegraph Companies, thereby giving the former United States stockholders one-fourth of the total stock issue of the consolidated company.[42] On the basis of the actual property purchased and its generally poor condition, Western Union paid a high price to eliminate its rival.

News of the consolidation was not received with joy by the employees of the two companies, for it meant that fully one-third of them would be dismissed. A committee was appointed by the officers of the two concerns to select the best men from the forces of both to work the lines of the consolidated company.

The Telegrapher, lamenting the new arrangement, remarked:

We sincerely regret this consolidation. Although it is money in the stockholders' pockets, it will be death to telegraphers generally, and an

41 Reid, *Telegraph in America*, 523-525; Report of President William Orton to the stockholders of the United States Telegraph Company, March 16, 1866, in *The Telegrapher*, II, 93-94.
42 *Ibid.*; cf. *The Telegrapher*, II, 69, 76, 87; *Ibid.*, III, 230, 242; Annual Report of the President of the Western Union Telegraph Company to the Stockholders . . . (July 13, 1869), 19.

injury to the telegraphing public. With the power which this great monopoly puts into the hands of its officers, salaries will decrease as surely and naturally as water runs down hill, and the odds are so much against us that it will be useless to remonstrate. This monopoly is so vast in its proportions that no opposition can face it without an enormous capital, one larger than most organizations can boast, and the indulgent public must early conclude to put up with vexatious delays.[43]

Nor were the remaining members of the North American Telegraph Association entirely pleased with this latest development. As Thomas D. Catlin, who had been placed in charge of J. D. Caton's interests while the Judge was touring Europe, wrote to his principal early in March, the change might prove to be of benefit to the Illinois & Mississippi, or it might be just the opposite. Catlin hoped that Western Union would permit his company to buy all the United States lines in Illinois & Mississippi territory, and in that way rid the company of opposition for some time to come. He was planning an immediate trip to Chicago and Cleveland to see Wade and Stager and find out what had been done and what could be effected.[44]

The Western Union management, however, had no intention of strengthening the Illinois & Mississippi, or any of its other allies in the North American Telegraph Association by selling them the United States Telegraph lines in their respective territories. Instead, these newly acquired lines were to be used as a club to drive the remaining independent companies into the Western Union fold.

Caton's veteran superintendent, J. J. S. Wilson, writing to his employer on March 27, described Western Union's latest move. He was decidedly pessimistic. It looked as though Western Union proposed to use the lines of the United States Telegraph to invade the territories of all the other members of the North American Telegraph Association. Western Union was sending California business over United States lines in territory reserved to the American Telegraph Company by the Six Party Contract. The American Telegraph management had suggested to Wilson that if the worst came, and Western Union openly repudiated the provisions of the Six Party Contract, that the Illinois & Mississippi establish an outlet for its business by connecting with the American Telegraph system at Cairo. "The American folks say," concluded Wilson, "we shall not be forced to act against our judgment during your absence."[45]

43 *The Telegrapher*, II, 76.
44 Thos. D. Catlin to J. D. Caton, March 3, 1866, Caton Papers.
45 J. J. S. Wilson to Caton, March 27, 1866, Caton Papers.

Action might be delayed briefly, but the trend toward monopoly continued. There could be little doubt that the days of the independent companies were numbered.

8 — · · · ·

THE American Telegraph Company and the remaining independent units in the industry were now confronted by two alternatives. They could attempt to organize a nation-wide system to compete with that of Western Union; or they could try to negotiate satisfactory terms of consolidation. The former course would result in a bitter and protracted war, the outcome of which would be highly uncertain. The latter, while less glorious, was better business for all parties concerned. The advantages of consolidation were obvious—all would be benefited by the added strength, security, efficiency, and economy which the establishment of a monopoly would give them.

Intensive negotiations between the Western Union and American Telegraph Companies were carried on throughout the spring of 1866. Finally on June 12, an agreement was concluded by President Wade and President Sanford for the merger of the two corporations through an issue of Western Union capital stock to the amount of $11,833,100 in exchange for approximately $4,000,000 of American Telegraph stock outstanding. That is, for every share (par 100) held by an American Telegraph stockholder, he was to receive three shares (par 100) of Western Union stock; or, looking at it another way, the American Telegraph stock had to be watered sufficiently to place it upon an equitable footing with that of the inflated Western Union Telegraph Company. Holdings not exchanged were to receive a fixed income of 8 percent per annum, but American stockholders were urged to take advantage of the Western Union offer and exchange their shares for Western Union stock at once. Only in this way could they become active participants in the future development of the great telegraph monopoly. It was further agreed that for at least five years American stockholders were to have representation on the Western Union board of directors of not less than four out of fifteen.[46]

Following consummation of the merger, the headquarters of the consolidated company was removed from Rochester, New York, to

[46] Statement issued by the officers of the American Telegraph Company to the stockholders, June 20, 1866, Smith Docs.; *The Telegrapher*, II, 153; *New York Times*, June 14 and 15, 1866.

145 Broadway, New York City, which had previously been the home office of the American Telegraph Company. This change in the location of the Western Union headquarters was significant, for it presaged a shift in the control of the company. Gradually, during the next decade, control was to be transferred from Wade, Sibley, and the Rochester pioneers to a group of prominent New York City capitalists.[47]

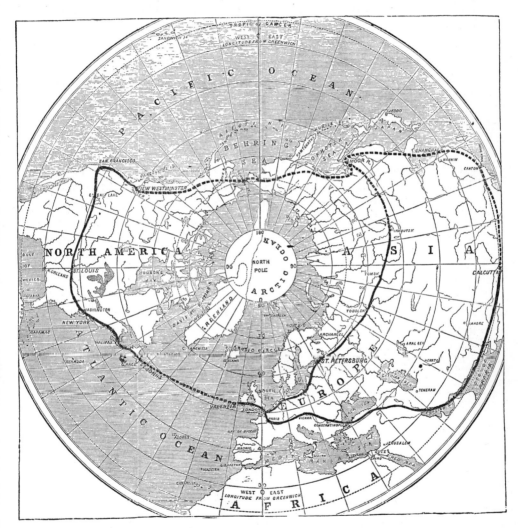

Linking the Continents, 1865. Proposed Routes of the Russian-American Telegraph Line and the Atlantic Cable

[47] Annual Report of the Western Union Telegraph Company, 1869, and ff.; A. R. Brewer, *The Western Union Telegraph Company. A Retrospect*, 28-30.

Professor Morse, commenting on these latest developments in a letter to his old friend, Amos Kendall, expressed his approval. "If I understand the position of our Telegraph interests, they are now very much as you and I wished them to be at the outset, not cut up in O'Rielly fashion into irresponsible parts, but making one great whole like the Post Office system. It is becoming, doubtless, a *monopoly*, but no more so than the P[ost] Office system, and its unity is in reality a public advantage if properly and uprightly managed, and this of course will depend on the character of the managers."[48]

The consolidations of 1866 created a mighty corporation with a combined capitalization of over $40,000,000 ($41,063,100). According to the figures given by the respective companies prior to the consolidations, the combined lines should have provided the great monopoly with nearly 100,000 miles of wire. However, many of the lines of all three concerns at the time of consolidation were either worn out and practically worthless, or they merely provided the consolidated company with a needless duplication of wires over the same routes. This was especially true in respect to the lines of the United States Telegraph which had been built to cover the same territory as those of the Western Union and American Telegraph Companies. According to an official report of Western Union published ten years later, the consolidations of 1866 gave the Western Union system control of 37,380 miles of line, 75,686 miles of wire, and 2,250 telegraph offices.[49] But far more significant than the great trust's increased size was the monopolistic position which it now commanded in the telegraph field.

48 Morse to Kendall, March 19, 1866, Morse Papers, Letter Book P.
49 Annual Report of the Western Union Telegraph Company (1877), 16.

Linking the Continents

1 · — ·

DURING the critical months that Western Union was engaged in bringing its great drive toward monopoly to a successful conclusion, another epic chapter was being written in the history of the telegraph industry. The struggle between the Western Union and American Telegraph Companies for the honor and profit of being the first to establish successful telegraphic communication with Europe was drawing to a close. The early months of 1866 found Western Union vigorously prosecuting its vast Russian-American project for linking the continents by a line through British Columbia, Russian America, and northeastern Siberia to meet a projected Russian line at the mouth of the Amur River on the Asiatic Coast; at the same time Cyrus Field and his British associates were equally busy preparing for one more attempt at the laying of a trans-Atlantic cable.

2 ·· — ··

As early as 1861, it will be recalled, Perry McD. Collins had approached Hiram Sibley with his Russian-American telegraph project and had won the Western Union president's hearty support for it. A formal proposal for the actual construction of a Russian-American telegraph line had been submitted to Western Union by Collins with Sibley's stamp of approval on September 28, 1863, and again at a meeting of the company's board on March 16, 1864.[1] Collins proposed to transfer to the company all the valuable rights and privileges held by him in exchange for one-tenth part of the stock in the new undertaking, free from call or assessment as paid up stock; the right to subscribe to one-tenth more upon the same footing as other subscribers; and the payment of $100,000 in cash as compensation for his services and expenses during the eight years he was engaged in securing the grants. It was foreseen, of course, that the Atlantic cable might succeed, and that such success would prove very damaging, if not fatal, to the prospects of the proposed "Overland Line." Such an event, however, did not seem probable, and after a careful

---

[1] For an earlier discussion of this subject, see Chapter XXV; cf. Chapter XXVII.

examination of all the circumstances, the Western Union board of directors had decided to assume the inevitable risk.[2]

The company thus came into possession of a series of valuable grants and privileges which included an engagement on the part of the Russian Government to complete the construction of a line of telegraph from St. Petersburg to the mouth of the Amur River (a distance of approximately 7,000 miles), of which three-fourths was already finished. Rebates of 40 percent on inter-continental messages were also promised to the projectors; and permission was granted for the construction of a line of telegraph from the mouth of the Amur up the coast of Asiatic Russia to Bering Strait and then down through Russian America[3] by any route desired. All the grants and concessions made by Russia were to be exclusive for thirty-three years, but were contingent upon the company's having the entire line in operation within five years.[4] Similar liberal grants by the British Government in respect to British Columbia were also included.[5]

With control of the project in its hands Western Union took active steps to complete all the details preliminary to the actual construction of the line. To finance the venture, special Russian Extension stock was authorized to the extent of 100,000 shares of $100 each, and a separate corporation known as the Western Union Extension Company was set up with Hiram Sibley as president and Oliver H. Palmer as secretary. Western Union stockholders were given the prior right to subscribe to the extent of 50 percent of the stock held by them. A 5 percent assessment was to be paid at the time of subscribing, with subsequent assessments to be paid as called for by the secretary. It was thought that not more than 20 percent in the way of assessments would be called for to finish the line. The whole stock was promptly taken, and such was the faith in the ultimate success of the enterprise that in less than two months the stock was selling for $60 per share with only one assessment of $5.00 paid in.[6]

Meanwhile, a bill having the enthusiastic support of Secretary of

[2] [Western Union Telegraph Company], *Statement of the Origin, Organization and Progress of the Russian-American Telegraph, Western Union Extension, Collin's Overland Line, via Behring Strait and Asiatic Russia to Europe* (May 1866), 5-6. (An excellent documentary account of the project to the close of 1865.) Will be cited subsequently as: *Statement of the Origin and Progress of the Russian-American Telegraph*; George Kennan, *Tent Life in Siberia*, 1-2.

[3] Purchased by the United States in 1867 and renamed Alaska.

[4] The date of the Russian grant was May 23, 1863.

[5] *Statement of the Origin and Progress of the Russian-American Telegraph*, 7-10, 54-60.

[6] *Ibid.*, 15, 63-65.

State William H. Seward was passed by Congress and signed by President Lincoln on July 1, 1864, granting the proposed line a permanent right of way through United States territory with timber and stone and as much land as would be required for stations. The Secretary of the Navy was authorized to furnish a steam or sailing vessel to assist in surveying, or laying cable, or to promote in any way the success of the undertaking. Upon completion, the line was to be safeguarded by government troops at the various military posts along the route. The act provided that the United States Government should have priority rights in transmission of dispatches. Satisfactory rate schedules were to be decided in conference by representatives of Russia, Great Britain, and the United States. To prevent combinations in restraint of trade or against the public interest, Congress stipulated that the new line should not contract with any newspaper or press association to transmit dispatches to them upon terms different from those obtaining in the case of all newspapers or press associations.[7]

"Whatever may be the ultimate fate of the Atlantic cable, there can be no doubt of the vast utility and importance of this Overland enterprise," declared the *Commercial and Financial Chronicle*, giving the project the general endorsement of the business community. "To promote the success of this great enterprise by every means in our power, and to facilitate the accomplishment of the grand changes which it is destined to produce in commercial and social affairs, should now be a paramount object of all Americans. We should never forget our mission as a nation—that of not only affording a sanctuary to the oppressed, but a free field of competition to the industrious—and every enterprise whose direct or collateral effects point to these noble ends should secure the unqualified approval and encouragement of our people."[8]

3 · · · — ·

THE execution of this mighty project was entrusted to Colonel Charles S. Bulkley, former superintendent of military telegraphs in the Department of the Gulf, who was appointed engineer-in-chief. In December 1864, he sailed from New York for San Francisco to organize and outfit exploring parties, and to begin active construc-

[7] *Ibid.*, 40-53, 60-62; *Cong. Globe*, 38 Cong., 1 sess., Appendix, Chap. CXIX, 245.
[8] *Commercial and Financial Chronicle*, I, 167-168.

tion of the line.[9] "Adventurous Micawbers, who had long been waiting for something of this kind to turn up; broken-down miners, who hoped to retrieve their fortunes in new gold-fields yet to be discovered in the North; and returned soldiers thirsting for fresh excitement—all hastened to offer their services as pioneers in the great work."[10] Soon a motley telegraph army of several hundred men had been recruited.

Colonel Bulkley organized it along military lines. "Working Divisions" and "Engineer Corps" were established. The working divisions were then sub-divided into "Parties of Construction," each under a chief foreman. The construction parties, in turn, were divided into four working squads, each under its foreman. Members of the expedition were furnished with a list of "General Rules of Organization and Government" so that there would be no misunderstanding as to what was expected of them.

Camp guard will be kept on duty at night and when necessary during the day, and will be responsible for property stolen from camp. Indians or others not engaged in work will not be permitted to loiter about the camps . . . strictest discipline must be enforced. . . .

Natives will be treated with the utmost kindness and consideration, and, as far as practicable, employed in the work. They are to be paid promptly and scrupulously. . . .

To avoid infringements upon the rights of regularly chartered trading companies, all trading with natives by employees of the expedition is expressly forbidden. . . .

Spiritous and intoxicating liquors will not be allowed in camp, nor under any circumstances, furnished to the natives. . . . Fire arms are intended for defense, and the greatest caution is requisite in their use. . . .

All work will be suspended upon Sunday. . . .[11]

To expedite the work, Bulkley decided to commence at several points simultaneously. One exploring party under the command of Major H. L. Pope was landed in British Columbia near the mouth of the Fraser River in the autumn of 1865. Another, under Major Robert Kennicott, established its base on an island near Norton Sound to conduct operations in Russian America. A third, under C. L. McRae, was landed on the Asiatic side of Bering Strait at the mouth of the Anadyr River. During the winter and spring of 1865-1866 each of these parties was engaged in extensive exploring trips.

[9] *Statement of the Origin and Progress of the Russian-American Telegraph*, 11-15; Kennan, *Tent Life in Siberia*, 3.

[10] *Ibid.*

[11] *Statement of the Origin and Progress of the Russian-American Telegraph*, 77-81.

Landing the Atlantic Cable in Heart's Content Bay, Newfoundland, July, 1866

The Progress of the Century. A Lithograph by Currier and Ives

All possible information with regard to climate, soil, timber, and inhabitants of the regions was obtained, and the location of a route for the proposed line was established.[12]

The line was to extend from New Westminster, British Columbia, the proposed terminus of the California State Telegraph Company's line which was already nearing completion, for 1,200 miles along the Fraser River and the famous Caribou wagon train—built shortly before to open the gold-mining country—to Russian America. It was to continue for 900 trackless miles through this practically unknown region to Bering Strait. Crossing to Asia at this point by means of a short submarine cable, it was to pierce the bleakest part of Siberia for another 1,800 miles to the mouth of the Amur River where the Russians were to meet the Americans with a 7,000-mile line of their own from St. Petersburg. The mere size of the Gargantuan undertaking, to say nothing of the physical difficulties to be overcome, was enough to make even the boldest pause.[13]

Reporting to the Western Union executive committee near the close of 1865, Colonel Bulkley announced excellent progress on all fronts. Explorations in British Columbia, Russian America, and Siberia were proceeding satisfactorily; both the lands through which the line would have to pass and their inhabitants were proving less formidable than originally supposed. The Indians along the American coast had been misrepresented, for the exploring parties found them to be friendly, honest, and hospitable. The wooded country through which the line was to pass made the problem of securing the necessary poles relatively simple and at the same time provided ample game. A whole fleet of steamers and vessels had been purchased and fitted for service; in addition, the United States Government had detailed the steamer *Saginaw*, and the Russian Government the steamer *Variag* to assist in the enterprise. Twenty-four steamers and vessels, in all, were at the disposal of the expedition. A series of "General Supply Depots" had been established at convenient points along the route and arrangements made for the delivery to them of teams, wagons, arms, supplies, and telegraph materials of all kinds— wire, insulators, instruments, batteries, and tools—in sufficient quantities to complete the entire line. Moreover, declared Bulkley, building parties in British Columbia had pushed construction work so vigorously that the line there had already been completed from New

---

[12] *Ibid.*, 11-12, 116-126; *The Telegrapher*, I, 114, 116, 131, *et seq.*; *Ibid.*, II, 24, *et seq.*
[13] W. H. Deppermann, "Two Cents an Acre," *North American Review*, CCXLV, 126-133.

Westminster, up the Fraser River to Fort Fraser, and on to Fort St. James, at the foot of Stuart Lake, a distance of about seven hundred miles. With the opening of navigation in the spring, he promised a spirited offensive all along the line.[14]

4 · · · · —

AT this stage of developments the Western Union management under the direction of its recently-elected president, Jeptha H. Wade, viewed the future with unbounded optimism. Through the construction of a network of subsidiary lines, the elated promoters visualized the commerce of all Europe, Asia, North and South America, as tributary to the Western Union system. Secretary O. H. Palmer in an extended report to the stockholders explained that while Western Union was at work connecting Europe and America through Asia, telegraph lines were also being projected in its interest to connect China and Japan. Russia, Western Union's partner in the great enterprise, already had lines to India and connections with the whole system of European telegraphs. In addition, a proposition, which the Western Union board judged entirely feasible, was under consideration to unite Mexico and Central and South America. The completion of this proposed network, Palmer declared, would "bring the commerce of the whole world upon the Russian Extension line and obviate the necessity of any trans-Atlantic cables."

As to the prospective earnings of the company the secretary estimated that a thousand messages a day could easily be transmitted and the charge for a dispatch could reasonably be put at $25. This would give $25,000 a day or $9,000,000 a year. Palmer did not believe that he was too optimistic in his calculations, for one thousand messages a day certainly was not an over-estimate for the telegraphic correspondence of the whole commercial world, to say nothing of that of governments, the public press, and the social dispatches of both hemispheres. But should revenues fail to meet his estimate by as much as 75 percent, the secretary estimated that the company would still have gross receipts of $2,225,000 of which operating costs would absorb no more than half.[15]

Secretary Palmer's enthusiasm was infectious. The stock was eagerly sought and a rosy glow illumined Western Union skies.

14 *Statement of the Origin and Progress of the Russian-American Telegraph*, 116-126; *The Telegrapher*, I, 129, 164;, *Ibid.*, II, 27.
15 *Statement of the Origin and Progress of the Russian-American Telegraph*, 15-16.

5 ———

IN the spring of 1866 Bulkley's telegraph army, which had now swelled in numbers to well over a thousand men, began its great offensive. Poles were set—some of them in solid rock—wires were strung, and supplies were distributed at convenient depots along the route. In spite of huge expenditures of both money and man-power, progress was somewhat disappointing. As a result of unavoidable delays the construction expedition for the Asiatic coast was not able to leave San Francisco until late in June. Then the British-Columbian party, instead of following the feasible route explored the year before, had struck out into unexplored regions nearer the coast, and after building three or four hundred miles of line had found themselves inextricably involved among impassable mountains. Major Kennicott, directing operations in Russian America, had been in failing health for some time, and on May 13, 1866, he was found dead by members of his party. Delay and confusion characterized the activity all along the way.[16]

6 · · · · · ·

WHILE the directors of the Russian-American project were busy trying to extricate it from these difficulties, the steamer *Great Eastern* at the docks of an English harbor was having coiled into her capacious hold over two thousand miles of gutta-percha-covered cable.[17] In spite of repeated failures the indomitable Cyrus W. Field was once more preparing to lay a trans-Atlantic cable.

"I would give $50,000," remarked the president of Western Union to the president of the Atlantic Cable when they met in London, "to *know* if you are ever going to succeed. I hope you will; but I would like to know for certain before we spend any more in Russia."[18]

In view of past failures, the successful landing of the cable was considered quite doubtful by many; and it was even more uncertain whether, if landed, its success would be permanent. In a letter to the editor of the *Washington Chronicle*, Tal. P. Shaffner, now a recognized telegraphic engineer, declared that with existing discoveries in

---

[16] *The Telegrapher*, III, 158; *New York Herald*, November 10, 1866; *Ibid.*, December 15, 1866; *American Annual Cyclopaedia and Register of Important Events of the Year 1866*, VI, 723-725.

[17] *New York Times*, June 7 and June 10, 1866.

[18] Jane M. Parker, "The Russian or Collin's Telegraph: A Defeated Success," *Overland Monthly* (new series), XII, 17.

the sciences he did not believe a line of that length could be made practicable for commercial telegraphy.[19]

Nevertheless, on Friday, July 13, the *Great Eastern* carrying the precious cable once more started across the ocean for far off New-foundland. Two weeks later, on July 27, the cable was landed at Heart's Content. Announcement of successful communication between the old world and the new was made the following day by Field, who more than any other man was responsible for this great and far-reaching achievement.[20] A short time later a cable which had been lost the year before was found, picked up, spliced, and continued to the American shore, thereby giving the world two intercontinental cables. Cable service between Europe and America was officially opened to the public on August 26, 1866. A large and remunerative business followed which soon handsomely repaid the projectors of the Atlantic cable.[21]

Fortunately for Western Union the land-line network, upon which the cable had to rely for the distribution of its inter-continental messages, had been brought completely under Western Union control with the absorption of the American Telegraph system in June. The success of the cable, therefore, brought greatly increased revenues to Western Union and at least partly compensated for the blow which the cable dealt to the company's pet project—the Russian-American line.

7 — — ··

THE success of the Atlantic cable sounded the death-knell of the Russian-American enterprise. All during the autumn of 1866, to be sure, the Western Union management by means of optimistic newspaper reports sought to lead the public into believing that work on the great Overland route was still going steadily forward.[22] Such was not the case. In British Columbia, the construction party of about two hundred and fifty men, on receiving news of the completion of the cable, had remained in camp two or three days awaiting developments; and at the end of that time, finding the cable continuing to work well, they had set out for civilization, "leaving their tools, stores

---

[19] Reprinted in *The Telegrapher*, I, 127.
[20] *New York Times*, July 29 and 30, 1866; *The Telegrapher*, II, 181; *American Annual Cyclopaedia* for 1866, VI, 719-722; S. F. B. Morse to R. C. Morse, December 8, 1866, Morse Papers, Paris Letter Book 1; P. B. MacDonald, *A Saga of the Seas*, 137-139.
[21] *Ibid.*, 149-152; Reid, *Telegraph in America*, 403.
[22] *The Telegrapher*, III, 63, 158-159.

and materials to the tender mercies of the Hudson Bay trapper and the native red man."[23] Major Pope, chief of that division, had submitted his resignation at once declaring, "I did not want to be banished to the ends of the earth if nothing was to come of it."[24] But perhaps another factor partly responsible for the promptness—almost eagerness—with which he resigned was the serious construction difficulties in which his division had become involved during the summer of 1866.

In the autumn of 1866 the action of the Western Union board of directors foreshadowed abandonment of the project. Up to September 15, assessments amounting to 25 percent of the capital stock of the Russian Extension line had been made. At this time a circular was issued by the executive committee to the Extension stockholders calling their attention to a resolution passed by the board of directors. The resolution, while making a further call of 5 percent on the stock, authorized holders of Extension stock to exchange it for bonds of the Western Union at any time prior to February 1, 1867. The exchange was to be made at the rate of one dollar of such bonds for each ninety cents of the amount paid in on the stock, together with 8 percent on the portion paid previous to September 18, 1866, in lieu of interest. These bonds, which were to come due on November 1, 1875, were to draw interest at the rate of 7 percent per annum. A similar proposition was made to holders of paid up or unassessable stock.[25] Accordingly, nearly all of the Extension stock was exchanged for Western Union bonds previous to February 1, 1867. Under this arrangement bonds to the value of $3,170,292 were issued.[26]

While this exchange of stock for bonds was going on, the public was assured, by means of occasional paragraphs in the newspapers, that the Russian-American telegraph scheme was an undoubted success.[27] Then on March 9, 1867, the *Commercial and Financial Chronicle* carried the following terse announcement: "It was decided at a meeting of Directors of the Western Union Telegraph Company last week that in view of the successful working of the Atlantic Cable, it is not advisable to expend any more money on the Russian extension at present."[28]

---

[23] British Columbia, Mines Department [Brief history of the British Columbia part of the overland telegraph line from America to Europe, largely from the notes of R. B. McMicking, 1865-1866], in *Annual Report of the Minister of Mines for the year ending December 31, 1905*, J90-92.

[24] Parker, *op. cit.*, 19.

[25] *The Telegrapher*, III, 158-159.

[26] Reid, *Telegraph in America*, 517.

[27] *The Telegrapher*, III, 159.

[28] *Commercial and Financial Chronicle*, IV, 300.

The questionable conduct of the Western Union board of directors now became quite clear. After the Extension stock—the greater portion of which was held by members of the board of directors—had been secured upon the property of the Western Union Company through the issuance of Western Union bonds in exchange for the Russian Extension stock, the Russian-American project was precipitately abandoned, and the hundreds of small Western Union stockholders were required to absorb a loss of over $3,000,000.[29]

"We would like to inquire," demanded the editor of *The Telegrapher*, "if there was any warrant for the issuance of these bonds, whereby the stockholders of the Western Union are compelled against their will to accept the gigantic expense of the huge failure? Mr. Collins made money, and the directors of the enterprise have saved themselves a great loss, but what do the stockholders of the Western Union Company gain?"[30]

The *Boston Traveler* in an editorial caustically remarked, "The impression is very general that the affairs of the company are managed solely with a view to the interests of a few, large stockholders who are represented in the Direction, and that although the net earnings, as shown by the balance-sheet are large, the smaller stockholders are not likely to realize much from them."[31]

Even if bad management had not interfered with the completion of the vast Overland line, it is doubtful whether it could have competed successfully with the Atlantic cable. It was a question of 2,000 miles of cable against 16,000 miles of land line, half of which was along an unpopulated coast.

The Government was officially notified of the discontinuance of work on the Russian-American line by Western Union's Vice-president William Orton, in a letter dated March 25, 1867, in which he explained the situation to Secretary of State, William H. Seward, who had done so much to encourage the enterprise:

The proof that the basis of revenue had been removed, was only needed to be complete, to make the duty of at once stopping the whole work a stern and peremptory necessity. That proof we have been from month to month receiving. So clear and cumulative has that evidence been, that we have been compelled, though with great reluctance, to acknowledge its completeness and power. All doubts concerning the capacity and efficiency

---

29 *The Telegrapher*, III, 159; cf. Morse to E. S. Sanford, January 4, 1867, in Morse, *Letters and Journals*, II, 444-446.

30 *Ibid.*, 146.   31 Reprinted in *The Telegrapher*, III, 166.

of ocean cables, are now dispelled, and the work of construction on the Russian line, after an expenditure of $3,000,000 has been discontinued.[32]

Meanwhile, the Asiatic division, blissfully ignorant of events in the United States, had continued to push work on its part of the line. George Kennan, chronicler of the division, has recorded that they had explored and located the whole route of the line from the Amur River to Bering Sea by the end of March 1867. Half a dozen working parties were in the field and arrangements had been made to supplement their number with 600 or 800 hardy native laborers from Yakutsk. Fifteen to twenty thousand poles had been cut and prepared, and awaited only the arrival of 600 Siberian ponies to distribute them. An abundant supply of tools and provisions as well as all the wire and insulators were on the ground. The men felt hopeful that they should be able to get their part of the Overland line to St. Petersburg in working order before the beginning of 1870. So confident were some of the men that they were singing in pole-cutting camps to the tune of a popular war song:

> In eighteen hundred and sixty eight
> Hurrah! Hurrah!
> In eighteen hundred and sixty eight
> Hurrah! Hurrah!
> In eighteen hundred and sixty eight,
> The cable will be in a miserable state,
> And we'll all feel gay
> When they use it to fish for whales.

> In eighteen hundred and sixty nine
> Hurrah! Hurrah!
> In eighteen hundred and sixty nine
> Hurrah! Hurrah!
> In eighteen hundred and sixty nine,
> We're going to finish this overland line;
> And we'll all feel gay
> When it brings us good news from home.

The next news which Kennan and his colleagues received from home, however, was not of a nature to make them feel gay. On May 31, 1867, the vessel *Sea Breeze* of New Bedford, Massachusetts, was

---

[32] William Orton to Secretary of State Seward, March 25, 1867, quoted by Reid, *Telegraph in America*, 516-517.

sighted. The next morning Kennan and some of his party boarded her and conferred with her master, Captain Hamilton. The Captain wanted to know if they had been shipwrecked. They explained to him that they were there trying to build a telegraph line.

"A telegraph line," he shouted. "Well, if that ain't the craziest thing I ever heard of! Who's going to telegraph from here?"

Having carefully explained their project to him, Kennan inquired about the Atlantic cable.

"Oh yes," he replied cheerfully, as if he were giving them the best news in the world, "the cable is laid all right."

"Does it work?" asked Kennan with sinking heart.

"Works like a snatch-tackle," he responded heartily. "The Frisco papers are publishing every morning the London news of the day before. I've got a lot of 'em on board I'll give you."

Returning to shore the dispirited telegraph builders stopped on the beach and read the papers. They were of various dates from September 1866 to March 1867. The men were not long in ascertaining not only that the new Atlantic cable had been successfully laid, but that the broken cable of 1865 had been picked up in mid-ocean, repaired and put in perfect working order. That information discouraged them more than anything else. If cables could be found in the middle of the Atlantic, picked up in 10 or 12,000 feet of water and repaired on the deck of a steamer, the ultimate success of submarine telegraphy was assured. The Asiatic division might as well pack up and go home.[33]

Kennan and his associates accordingly opened a sort of international bazaar and proceeded to dispose of their superfluous goods upon the best terms possible. They cut the price of telegraph wire until that luxury was within the reach of the poorest Korak family. They glutted the market with pickaxes and long-handled shovels which they assured the natives would be useful in burying their dead, and threw in a lot of frozen cucumber pickles and other anti-scorbutics which they warranted to fortify the health of the living. They sold glass insulators by the hundred as patent American tea cups, and brackets by the thousand as prepared American kindling wood. They offered soap and candles as premiums to anybody who would buy their salt pork and dried apples, and taught the natives how to make cooling drinks and hot biscuits, in order to create a demand for their redundant lime juice and baking powder. They directed all their

33 Kennan, *Tent Life in Siberia*, 411-418.

energies to the creation of artificial wants in that previously happy and contented community, and flooded the whole adjacent country with articles "that were of no more use to the poor natives than ice-boats and mouse-traps would be to the Quaregs of the Saharan desert."

In short, recorded Kennan, they dispensed the blessings of civilization with a free hand. But the result was not as satisfactory as the directors doubtless expected it to be. The market at last refused to absorb any more brackets and pickaxes; telegraph wire did not make as good fish-nets and dog-harnesses as some of the Americans confidently predicted that it would; and lime juice and water, as a beverage, even when drunk out of pressed-crystal insulators, beautifully tinted with green, did not seem to commend itself to the aboriginal mind. The saturation point having been reached, Kennan and his associates finally shut up shop.[34]

The final rites were performed over the body of the now defunct Russian-American enterprise on December 16, 1867, when the Russian minister, Baron Stoeckl, on behalf of his Government, and the officers of Western Union, on behalf of the company, executed the official papers releasing each other from the engagements which they had entered into so optimistically a few years before.[35]

The huge expenditure of man-power and money upon the Russian-American line had not been entirely in vain. The construction of the line through British Columbia had aided materially in opening up that country, and the large expenditure of money by the telegraph expedition proved a boon to the early colonists there.[36] Moreover, the enterprise had added greatly to the United States Government's knowledge of Russian America, and was thus indirectly a factor in its later acquisition. In October 1867, Russian America was purchased by the United States and renamed Alaska.[37]

[34] *Ibid.*, 428-429.   [35] *The Telegrapher*, IV, 148.
[36] *Annual Report of the British Columbia Minister of Mines for the year ending December 31, 1905*, J90-92.
[37] Parker, *op. cit.*, 18-20.

CHAPTER XXX

Retrospect

1 ·——·

IN the brief span of twenty years (1846-1866) the telegraph industry in the United States had undergone a revolutionary development. Beginning as a government experiment in speedier communication, the telegraph had soon passed into the hands of private enterprise. Congress could not, or would not, see that it was a natural adjunct of the country's postal system. As a result, the United States Government missed its opportunity to control the development of the new means of communication.

The growth of the telegraph industry under private enterprise was rapid. Starting with a few feeble lines along the eastern seaboard in 1846, a vast network of lines webbed the country by 1866. The establishment of telegraphic communication between the cities of the Atlantic and Pacific coasts had been achieved in 1861; the success of the Atlantic cable five years later brought the United States into communication with Europe and most of the civilized world. In two decades the American telegraph industry had grown from a business with a total capitalization of a few hundred thousand to one of more than $40,000,000; from a business with a few hundred miles of wire connecting several of the chief business centers of the country to one with more than 100,000 miles connecting nearly every village and town of any significance in the United States; and from a business employing a few hundred people to one employing thousands. In these two decades (1846-1866) the telegraph industry may be said to have come of age.

With growth had come an irresistible trend toward monopoly. The interaction of the forces working for and those working against consolidation during the early years of the industry's development produced a somewhat confused picture. Amos Kendall's original plan for organizing the telegraph industry had been a sound one. He had proposed to have a network of lines radiating out from New York City as a hub. While each trunk line was to have its own management, the activities of the lines were to be coordinated through the control exercised over them by the Morse patentees, who were to hold a substantial, and in most cases a controlling, interest in the lines operating under their patents. Quarrels within the Morse telegraphic family, however, soon split that group asunder. In addition, rival patents—such as the Bain, House, and Hughes—entered the field, destroying any semblance of unified control over the industry.

The resulting era of methodless enthusiasm saw a vigorous growth of telegraph lines, but competition on the more important routes often reduced profits to the vanishing point. Nearly all of the early companies were starved for working capital. Administration was loose and erratic. Rules and regulations were few, and frequently disregarded. Rate making was an enigma. Few of the companies could have explained how their tariffs had been determined. Repairs and reconstruction were generally undertaken only when service had become so erratic that action was imperative. Electrical engineering was an undeveloped science. Problems such as how to insulate effectively, how to get the lines across bodies of water, and how to improve the transmission of messages plagued the infant industry. Solutions were gradually worked out, but largely by trial and error.

Telegraph leaders came to realize quite early that many of the ills which beset them would be solved, or at least ameliorated, through consolidation. But to many of them the obstacles in the way appeared to be insurmountable. A few bold innovators attempted to bring about closer cooperation between some of the lines. There was O'Rielly's dream of a democratic council in which representatives of each of his lines would have a voice in determining matters of broad policy. Unfortunately the O'Rielly telegraph empire disintegrated before this plan could be given a trial. A number of former O'Rielly lines then tried to achieve a degree of unity by employing a common superintendent, James D. Reid. But petty jealousies, Reid's limitations as an administrator, and the pressure of outside interests, led to the early disintegration of the National Lines system. Still another attempt was that made by Amos Kendall to organize the principal lines operating under the Morse patents into a loose association. The American Telegraph Confederation, as Kendall's organization was called, proved a failure. Competing interests, distrust of one another, and the absence of any means for coercing members into working for the common good, made the confederation ineffectual. All of these early schemes exhibited the same fundamental weakness; they lacked implementation. The cooperation of the member companies was a voluntary matter. They merely pledged their allegiance to one another; there was no means for enforcing the decisions of the majority.

A very different type of organization was that resulting from the famous Six Party Contract of 1857. Engineered by shrewd, realistic business men like Hiram Sibley, Norvin Green, and Cyrus W. Field, it was a hard and fast legal contract. The members were given clearly defined territories and spheres of influence, in which they were sovereign. In all other matters the signatory companies managed their relations with one another in accordance with specific rules and regulations. Any member failing to abide by them was subject to joint action by all the other member companies. Similar rules and regulations governed the relations between the member companies of the North American Telegraph Association, which was an outgrowth of the Six Party Contract. From the time of its organization in 1858, until consolidations rendered it unnecessary, this association was the dominant force in the industry.

Men like Sibley, Wade, and Field realized only too well, however, that such a decentralized organization as the North American Telegraph Association had weaknesses which could best be overcome by actual consolidation. While heartily approving of the Association, Sibley and Wade never ceased their efforts to merge its members into a single corporation. They believed that real security and efficient management could be obtained only in this way. During the Civil War years they took advantage of every opportunity to strengthen the position of Western Union within the industry. One by one the independent companies were absorbed. Finally with the acquisition of the United States and the American Telegraph Companies in 1866, Western Union emerged as the nation's first great industrial monopoly and its largest corporation. Western Union's monopolistic position gave it many advantages not enjoyed previously, but it also brought with it a host of new problems.

2 ·· — ··

THE impact of the telegraph upon the political, social, and economic life of the nation was profound. There was hardly an individual or an institution which escaped its influence, for the whole tempo of life was quickened with the development of the telegraph industry. Long standing barriers of time and space were broken down, and the dissemination of ideas among the various sections of the country was both stimulated and accelerated. The telegraph, along with rail-roads, canals, and turnpikes, played its part in the rapid exploitation of the vast resources of a virgin continent.

The influence of the new means of communication upon the development of some of the leading industries of the day was marked. It revolutionized railway operation and management. The early distrust with which the railroad viewed the telegraph gradually gave way to mutual respect and understanding. Each industry had something of value to offer the other. The telegraph could provide the railroad with the intricate nervous system required for the effective operation of a great rail system. The management could be kept informed of the location of every train on its rail system, and endless delays and confusion could be avoided. The railroad, for its part, could provide the telegraph company with an exclusive right of way, free office space in every station, and cheap part-time help in the form of railway station masters. A rival telegraph company could not hope to enter the field against such odds. By the 1860's telegraph companies had come to regard their contracts for lines along the leading railroads as valuable assets. The railroads, in turn, were coming to regard the telegraph as indispensable to the operation of their roads.

Also closely associated with the development of the telegraph was the newspaper press. Fresh news has always been of primary concern to the press. Innumerable schemes and thousands of dollars have been employed by rival papers in their attempts to "scoop" the news. The advent of the telegraph revolutionized methods of news collection. Newspapers had no choice but to employ the new means of communication. Although editors might criticize the management of the early telegraph lines, the press continued to use their service. The high cost of telegraphic news, and the obvious impossibility of sending sufficient individual dispatches over the few unreliable lines suggested the need for some sort of a cooperative news-gathering agency. Competition had to give way to confederation before the press could enjoy the full benefits of the new means of communication. The New York papers were quick to recognize this fact and the result was the organization of the New York Associated Press.

In return for reduced rates on its business, the New York Associated Press entered into agreements with the leading telegraph companies promising to deal exclusively with them. It further agreed that member papers would print nothing that would be detrimental to the contracting telegraph companies. In short, the telegraph companies which entered into agreements with the Associated Press were to be favored in every possible way, while rival concerns were to be discouraged. Such agreements were valuable assets to a company like Western Union. Both Sibley and Wade declared upon several occasions that Western Union's railroad and press contracts were important factors in its rise to preeminence in the industry.

Both the States and the Federal Government were quick to recognize the value of the telegraph in carrying out their functions, and they made extensive use of it. The telegraph proved invaluable to the Federal Government in arranging for the movement of troops and supplies to distant battle fronts. As the Union armies advanced against the Confederate forces along the Mississippi, or into Northern Virginia, the telegraph proved its military worth over and over again. Politicians found it useful for keeping in touch with their constituents, while the people and interests back home made extensive use of it to let their representatives know their wishes and desires in respect to specific legislation and general policy. The American Government may be said to have become more responsive to the will of the people following the introduction of the Morse invention. Scientific and technical government agencies, such as the United States Coast Survey, used the telegraph to chart their weather reports; to spread warnings of approaching storms; to calculate longitude; to establish correct time at various points throughout the country simultaneously; and to register astronomical observations.

Men from all walks of life and for a variety of reasons, employed the new means of communication. Those away from home used it to correspond with their families. Families used it to inform relatives or friends of births or deaths. People residing in the rapidly growing urban communities of the country received a new degree of security from police and fire alarm telegraphs. The farmer and the business man used it to check the market prices for their produce or manufactures, in order to decide when and where to sell. As a result, local trade was increasingly affected by regional, national, and even international factors. The business man, the banker, the broker,[1] and the

---

[1] While bankers and brokers were among the earliest users of the telegraph, it was not until about 1868 that a special gold reporting telegraph system was established by means of which gold prices might be communicated to a number of brokers' offices and business centers instantly and simultaneously. Subscribers were provided with a direct wire connection to the Gold Exchange, while a gold indicator in each office furnished the subscriber with a visual picture of every fluctuation of the market. The gold indicators were shortly replaced by printing telegraph instruments which were capable of recording on ticker tape the sales of stocks, gold, and other commodities on the Stock,

capitalist were enabled to operate upon a constantly broadening basis, as it became feasible to reach out over hundreds or even thousands of miles and obtain intelligence within a matter of minutes. The increased scope of the operations which the telegraph made possible was a significant factor in the development of big business and the rise of finance capitalism.

Perhaps the greatest value of the telegraph to the country was the part it played in breaking down isolation throughout the length and breadth of the land, and in fostering the feeling of nationality. Upon the completion of the transcontinental telegraph in 1861, for example, California was no longer a distant province only nominally associated with the government in Washington; it became an integral part of the nation. Although it continued to be physically separated from the East by hundreds of miles of prairie and desert, the thin strand of wire stretching across the continent brought it within a few minutes of St. Louis, Chicago, or New York, so far as the transmission of intelligence was concerned. A stronger and more unified nation—a people possessed of a self-assurance based upon a new sense of security—emerged with the development of the telegraph and the railroad.

While lines of telegraph and cable reaching out from the world's great metropolitan centers—New York, London, Paris, Berlin, Vienna, and St. Petersburg—fostered the growth of nationalism within countries, they also encouraged closer international relations and a better understanding between nations. With the speedier interchange of ideas and goods came a growing realization of the interdependence of nations. Many of the doubts and suspicions which had existed when the leading nations had been separated by weeks or even months were dissipated with the establishment of telegraphic communication. If a misunderstanding regarding United States policy arose in London, a message could be dispatched to Washington and a reply received within a matter of hours. To be sure, speedier communication did not eliminate misunderstandings between nations, but it did reduce them. The telegraph proved a potent force

Gold, and related exchanges. A concern known as the Gold & Stock Telegraph Company soon came to dominate this field. Its services were so adapted to the needs of the banking and brokerage interests of New York that the company proved a striking success. By 1871 nearly 800 instruments were in use. (Reid, *Telegraph in America*, 602-608, 613-615.)

for good in the long and difficult struggle for international understanding.

But the telegraph was not in itself wholly a force for good. In the hands of men like Jay Gould the telegraph was used to stifle freedom of the press. It was made to spread false reports, so that unscrupulous men might manipulate the country's money and stock exchanges. It was employed to foster selfish monopolies detrimental to the interests of the American people. Moreover, it was used to sow the seeds of international strife as well as those of international understanding.

By 1866 the telegraph had become a powerful force for good or evil. Congress, which twenty years before had washed its hands of the new means of communication, was now confronted with the problem of how to regulate this great force in the best interests of the people.

· · · — · —

APPENDIX 1

ARTICLES OF AGREEMENT AND ASSOCIATION, CONSTITUTING THE MAGNETIC TELEGRAPH COMPANY AND PROVIDING FOR THE GOVERNMENT THEREOF, MAY 15, 1845.

Whereas Samuel F. B. Morse, Leonard D. Gale, and Alfred Vail, by their Attorney, Amos Kendall, and Francis O. J. Smith in his own right, sole Proprietors, under the Letters Patent of the United States, of the right to construct and use Morse's Electro-Magnetic Telegraph on the main line of communication from the city of New-York, through Philadelphia and Baltimore, to the city of Washington, have, by Deed of Trust bearing even date herewith, conveyed the said exclusive right to W. W. Corcoran and B. B. French, in trust for the use of the said proprietors and the subscribers to the stock of the Magnetic Telegraph Company, with the limitations, under the conditions, and in the manner set forth in said Deed and in these Articles of Association, we, whose names are hereunto affixed, do hereby constitute ourselves into a Joint Stock Company, to be called The Magnetic Telegraph Company, for the purpose of constructing and carrying on a line of said Telegraph from New York to Washington, as aforesaid, according to the following principles and regulations, viz:—

FUNDAMENTAL CONDITIONS

1. No member of this Company shall be held to any individual liability beyond the amount of capital stock subscribed by him. No Trustee, or Agent of the Company shall be authorized to contract any debt or obligation creating a charge upon the members individually, or upon any other fund than the capital stock, property, and income of the Company. This limitation of their power shall be advertised in every State, District, or Territory, where they may transact business, and shall in the most effective form, be incorporated in every contract.

2. The line or lines of Magnetic Telegraph which may be constructed by this Company, shall be opened alike to all men and all public authorities who shall tender and pay the regular charges which may be fixed upon for its use, and the first to come shall be first served, without regard to sex, wealth, or station; subject to reasonable limitations as to time, as may be hereafter prescribed: except that a preference may be given to the Government in great public emergencies, and to promote the arrest of fugitives from justice, and prevent the commission, or consummation of crimes.

3. The Grantors of the Patent Right shall not establish, nor shall they grant to others the power to establish, any other line of Telegraph for the purpose of communicating between any two points on the line conveyed

by them in trust for the use of this Company, nor shall they send, or authorize the sending of communications, which should appropriately pass over this line, by any more circuitous or indirect line; but this Company shall be also bound to transmit such communications over their line without other charge than a due proportion of the revenue arising therefrom, based on the relative distance they may pass over this and other lines. This Company shall also be bound to connect with local side lines, on conditions of receiving all the charges arising on matter sent over any part of their lines and outward upon such local lines, or on such other terms as may be agreed upon by the parties interested.

4. The Grantors of the Patent Right reserve to themselves, and their assigns, the right to decide when any extension or improvements, other than mere repairs, not provided for by the funds already subscribed, shall be made to this line of Telegraph; but the subscribers who shall have advanced the first fifteen thousand dollars, or the assignees of their stock, shall be offered the privilege of furnishing the necessary funds to make such extensions or improvements, on the same terms with their original subscriptions. If, after due public notice, they fail or refuse to do so, for the period of thirty days, the Grantors shall be at liberty to procure such funds from others, who, in subscribing to the Articles of Association and the Regulations of this Company, shall become members thereof, with all the rights and privileges of original subscribers.

5. Should the Grantors of the Patent Right, or their assigns, desire to construct lines of Telegraph east, west, north, or south, on any of the great lines of communication connected with the line owned by this Company, they shall give a preference to the members of this Company in raising the necessary funds.

6. The Grantors of the Patent Right reserve to themselves and their assigns, the power to dispose of the entire exclusive privilege secured by Morse's Patent for the whole United States, to the Government of said States in one general bargain or arrangement, under any law or resolution that shall be passed by the twenty-ninth Congress for that purpose; but in that event, they shall pay over to the holders of the stock which may have been issued to those subscribers, who shall have paid in the first forty-five thousand dollars, or any part thereof, of the capital stock of this Company, twice the amount paid in; and if the stock representing such payments shall be, at the time, bona fide above par in the stock market, the amount paid to them shall be the market value of such stock. On the completion of such payments, this Company shall be ipso facto dissolved.

7. For fifty dollars paid in by subscribers to construct, extend, or improve this line of Telegraph, a certificate for one share of one hundred dollars shall be issued by the Trustees, another share to be added, or another certificate to be issued, for every additional fifty dollars. Cotemporaneously certificates of stock in the same form, and to the same amount, shall be issued to the Grantors of the Patent Right, to each in proportion to his interest, so that the amount of stock issued to them and to the subscribers respectively, shall always be the same. These certificates of stock

shall state on their face, that the shares they represent are not subject to future assessment, and also the mode of their transfer.

8. If any subscriber to the capital stock shall fail to pay any instalment for a period exceeding fifteen days after notice given by the Trustees, he shall forfeit all the rights and privileges herein secured to him, and new subscribers may be admitted to supply the deficiency, on the same terms.

The foregoing provisions shall be unalterable by any vote or act of the Company, so as to effect any right or privilege herein reserved or secured to any subscriber, or any of the Grantors of the Patent Right, without the direct consent of every individual to be thus affected.

POWERS AND DUTIES OF TRUSTEES

9. The Trustees shall have the power, and it shall be their duty, forthwith to appoint the necessary agents, and take steps to secure the right of way, to construct a line of Telegraph, consisting of one or two wires, from New York to Philadelphia, and from time to time, call in such instalments of the capital stock as may be requisite for that purpose. After the Company shall provide a Treasurer, all monies collected for or belonging to the Company shall be paid to the Treasurer for the time being, who shall pay out the same only upon the written order of a majority of the Trustees.—But until a Treasurer shall be appointed, the Trustees shall perform the duties of Treasurer.

10. They shall prepare forms of certificates, and regulate transfers of stock, and audit all accounts for expenditures made in the construction or management of the Telegraph, and generally to superintend the financial interests of the Company.

11. They shall prepare a tariff of charges, and a system of regulations for the management of the Telegraph, which they shall submit to a meeting of the stockholders, to be called in due time, before the line from New-York to Philadelphia shall be ready to go into operation.

12. They shall call special meetings of the stockholders whenever emergencies may require it; and it shall be the duty of the Trustees, to call a special meeting of the Stockholders whenever they are requested in writing so to do by Stockholders owning or representing one third or more of the stock, and if either of said Trustees shall neglect or refuse to call such meeting when so requested, it shall be competent for the other Trustee, or in case their number be increased beyond two, for a majority of the Trustees to call such meeting; and in case they shall neglect or refuse to act in the premises aforesaid, then the Stockholders owning or representing one third or more of the Stock, shall have power to call such meeting by advertisement in some newspaper in the city of Washington.

13. They shall keep a record of their proceedings, and a record of emission and transfer of stock, all of which at every meeting shall be laid before the Stockholders.

14. They shall execute all papers necessary to vest a joint interest in the trust property in any additional Trustee or Trustees, who may be ap-

pointed by the Stockholders, in pursuance of these articles of agreement.

15. A Trustee shall not be responsible for acts of which he knows nothing, or knowing them, records his dissent.

GENERAL PROVISIONS

16. In all meetings of the Company, after the issue of Certificates of Stock, the Stockholders shall be entitled to one vote for each share held by them respectively; but no one Stockholder shall give more than one sixth part of the aggregate vote of the Company. The holders of a majority of the Stock shall constitute a quorum to do business; and every question shall be decided by a majority of votes, provided such majority shall embrace one third of the Stock. Stockholders may vote in person, or by agents constituted for that purpose in writing.

17. Regular meetings shall be held annually or semi-annually, as the Company may hereafter decide. At any regularly called meeting of this Company, it shall be competent for the Company in the manner of deciding any other proposition to divest the Trustees of all the powers herein vested, excepting the trust of the title of said Letters Patent, and the issuing of Certificates of Stock, and to transfer the same to and invest them in a Board of Directors to consist of not less than five persons, to be thereafter elected at each annual meeting of the Company, and to continue in office until new Directors shall be elected; and thereafter such Directors shall do and perform all the duties otherwise devolved upon the Trustees as herein provided, and generally to superintend the administrative concerns of the Company, and all officers and agents not herein specially provided and instructed, shall be subject to the direction of the Directors. And in like manner, the Company shall elect from time to time a President, and Secretary, and Treasurer; the former of whom shall preside at all meetings of the Stockholders, and the Secretary shall keep and preserve the records of the doings of the Stockholders at all meetings by them holden; to be opened at all times to the inspection of Stockholders. The President for the time being, shall countersign all Certificates of Stock that shall be issued by the Trustees.—The Treasurer shall, when required, give bond to the Trustees for the benefit of the Company; satisfactorily secured, for the faithful discharge of his duties; he shall keep an account of all his receipts and disbursements, and return a true transcript thereof quarterly to the Trustees, who shall lay the same before the Stockholders, at their next succeeding meeting.

18. One or more Trustees may be added to the number now appointed, at regular meetings of the Company, or at special meetings called for the purpose.

19. The compensation of the Trustees shall be fixed by the Stockholders, and that of all other agents by the Trustees, subject to revision by the Stockholders at their next regular meeting, or at a special meeting called for the purpose.

20. The powers of the Trustees may be enlarged or diminished by the Stockholders at any regular meeting, or any meeting specially called for

that purpose; but no such enlargement or diminution shall affect the title to the trust property, or the rights of subscribers, of Stockholders, or of the Grantors of the Patent Right and their assigns, as secured and set forth in the fundamental articles of this Association, without their unanimous consent.

The undersigned having read the foregoing articles of agreement, do each for himself, and not jointly with others, hereby approve and ratify the same, and agree to be governed thereby, and we do, severally and not jointly, hereby ratify and confirm all acts of the Magnetic Telegraph Company, or of the members thereof, done by them jointly or individually, under the limitations and restrictions in accordance with the provision in the foregoing articles contained, in as full a manner as if we were at all times present and consenting thereto, and do adopt them as if done by ourselves.

Done at the City of Washington, on the Fifteenth day of May, A.D., 1845, as witness our hands respectively:

Samuel F. B. Morse,
 Leonard D. Gale,
 Alfred Vail
   By their Attorney in fact
     Amos Kendall
	Chas. G. Page,
	 T. L. & A. Tho. Smith,
	 A. Tho. Smith,
	 Jno. M. Brodhead,
	 J. C. Brodhead,
	   By J. M. Brodhead

Francis O. J. Smith,
 B. B. French,
 Keller & Greenough
   By J. J. Greenough
 Charles Monroe,
 Daniel Gold,
 E. Cornell,
 A. Warren Paine,
 Jas. A. McLaughlin,
	Amos Kendall,
	 P. G. Washington,
	 John E. Kendall,
	 Corcoran & Riggs,
	 Jno. J. Haley,
	 Eliphalet Case,
	   By F. O. J. Smith

Witness to and including all to the name of C. G. Page.

J. A. KENNEDY.

(Source: O'Rielly Collection, Miscell. II.)

APPENDIX 2

"AN ACT TO FACILITATE THE CONSTRUCTION OF MORSE'S ELECTRO-MAGNETIC TELEGRAPH,"[1] PASSED BY THE STATE OF NEW YORK, MAY 13, 1845.

The proprietors of the patent right of Morse's electro-magnetic telegraph may be and hereby are authorized to construct lines of said tele-

[1] The first general easement and protective telegraph act passed in this country, it served as a model for similar legislation in other States.

(Source: Laws of the State of New York, 68th Session, 1845, Chapter 243, p. 264.)

graph from point to point and across any of the waters within the limits of this State, by the erection of posts, piers or butments for sustaining the wires of the same: Provided, that the same shall not in any instance be so constructed as to endanger or injuriously interrupt the navigation of such waters; and provided also, that the private rights of individuals shall be in no wise impaired by the provisions of this act; nor shall this act authorize the construction of any bridge or other similar erection across any of the streams or waters in this State. Any person or persons who shall knowingly or wilfully injure, molest or destroy any of said lines, or the materials or property pertaining thereto, shall, on conviction thereof, be deemed guilty of a misdemeanor, and be punished by fine or imprisonment, or both, at the discretion of the court which shall have and take cognizance thereof.

The legislature may, at any time, alter, modify or repeal this act, and the same shall take effect immediately.

APPENDIX 3

"THE O'RIELLY CONTRACT"

CONTRACT BETWEEN THE MORSE PATENTEES AND HENRY O'RIELLY FOR EXTENDING THE ELECTRO-MAGNETIC TELEGRAPH FROM THE SEABOARD TO THE MISSISSIPPI AND THE LAKES, JUNE 13, 1845.

ARTICLES OF AGREEMENT

This memorandum of an agreement between Henry O'Rielly of the one part, and Samuel F. B. Morse, Leonard D. Gale, Alfred Vail and Francis O. J. Smith, of the second part, witnesseth as follows:

That the said O'Rielly undertakes on his part, at his own expense, to use his best endeavors to raise capital for the construction of a line of Morse's Electro-Magnetic Telegraph, to connect the great Seaboard Line at Philadelphia, or at such other convenient point on said line as may approach nearer to Harrisburg in Pennsylvania, and from thence through Harrisburg and other immediate towns to Pittsburg; and thence through Wheeling and Cincinnati, and such other towns and cities as the said O'Rielly and his associates may elect, to St. Louis, and also the principal towns on the Lakes.

In consideration whereof, the said parties of the second part agree and bind themselves, their representatives and assigns, that when the said O'Rielly shall have procured a fund sufficient to build a line of one wire from the connecting point aforesaid to Harrisburg, or any points farther west, to convey the patent-right to said line so covered by capital, in trust, for themselves and the said O'Rielly and his associates, on the terms and conditions set forth in the Articles of Agreement and Association constituting the Magnetic Telegraph Company, and providing for the government thereof, with the following alterations, viz:—The amount of stock or other interest in the lines to be constructed, reserved to the grantors and their assigns, shall be one-fourth part only, and not one-half of the whole, on so much capital as shall be required to construct a line of two wires; but in all cases of a third wire, or any greater number, the stock issued on the capital employed on such additional wire or wires shall be divided equally between the subscribers of such capital and the grantors of the Patent Right, or their assigns. No preference is to be given to the party of the first part and his associates in the construction of connecting lines, nor shall any thing herein be construed to prevent an extension, by the parties of the second part, of a line from Buffalo to connect with the Lake Towns at Erie; nor to prevent the construction of a line from New Orleans, to connect the western towns directly with that city; but such lines shall not be used to connect any western cities or towns with each other, which may have been already connected by said O'Rielly.

In case of a sale of the entire Patent Right to the Government, the grantors shall be bound to pay the actual reasonable cost of the lines constructed under this agreement, with twenty per cent thereon, and no more, to vest the Government with the entire ownership of such lines—provided, as specified in the Articles of Agreement of the Magnetic Telegraph Company, the purchase be made or provided for by Congress before the 4th March, 1847, (eighteen hundred and forty-seven.)

The tariff of charges on the lines so constructed, shall conform substantially to the tariff of charges on the great Seaboard Line before named, and in no case to be so arranged as to render the lines unequal in this respect, to the prejudice of either.

Unless the line, from the point of connection with the seaboard route, shall be constructed within six months from date, to Harrisburg, and capital provided for its extension to Pittsburg, within said time, then this agreement, and any conveyance in trust that may have been made in pursuance thereof, shall be null and void thereafter; unless it shall satisfactorily appear that unforeseen difficulties are experienced by said O'-Rielly and his associates in obtaining from the State Officers of Pennsylvania the right of way along the public works; and in that event, the conditional annulment shall take effect at the end of six months after such permission shall be given or refused. And any section beyond said last point, embraced within the purview of this agreement, which shall not be constructed by said O'Rielly and his associates, within six months after said parties of the second part shall request said O'Rielly to cause such lines to be constructed, so as to extend the connection at least one hundred and fifty miles beyond said last point, and in like ratio during each succeeding six months thereafter,—*then*, in relation to all such sections of the Line, this agreement shall be null and void, provided that such request shall not be made prior to the first day of April next, 1846.

And the party of the second part shall convey said patent right, on any line beyond Pittsburg, to any point of commercial magnitude, when the necessary capital for the construction of the same shall have been subscribed within the period contemplated by this agreement, by responsible persons, and not otherwise.

Done at the city of New York, this 13th day of June, in the year of our Lord eighteen hundred and forty-five.

(Signed,)　　Henry O'Rielly,
　　　　　　Francis O. J. Smith,
　　　　　　Samuel F. B. Morse,
　　　　　　L. D. Gale, by his Attorney,
　　　　　　S. F. B. Morse.

(Source: O'Rielly Collection, Telegraph Pamphlets.)

APPENDIX 4

CONTRACT OF SANFORD J. SMITH AND ISAAC BUTTS FOR BUILDING A LINE OF HOUSE PRINTING TELEGRAPH (NEW YORK & MISSISSIPPI VALLEY PRINTING TELEGRAPH COMPANY) FROM BUFFALO, NEW YORK, TO ST. LOUIS, MISSOURI, SEPTEMBER 6, 1850; ALSO SUPPLEMENTAL AGREEMENT OF SEPTEMBER 13, 1850.

This Agreement made this sixth day of September 1850, between Freeman M. Edson, and Samuel L. Selden, of the one part, and Isaac Butts, Sanford J. Smith and Charles L. Shepard, of the other part, witnesseth as follows:

1. That the said Edson and Selden, being the proprietors of the exclusive right of constructing and using the Printing Telegraph invented by and patented to Royal E. House, of the city of New York, within and throughout the United States and its Territories, with the exception of the State of New York and the New England States; and the said Selden having jointly with Hugh Downing and others a like right within the States so excepted, they, the said Edson and Selden, do hereby agree that the said Butts, Smith and Shepard be and they hereby are authorized and empowered to construct and put in operation a line of said printing telegraph from the city of Buffalo, in the State of New York, to the city of St. Louis, in the State of Missouri, to pass in its course through the cities of Cleveland and Cincinnati, in the State of Ohio, and Louisville, in the State of Kentucky.

2. That the said line of telegraph shall be constructed by the formation for that purpose of an Association or Company, which shall be incorporated under the general telegraph laws of this State and the State of Ohio, and also in any other State, through which such line shall pass where laws for the purpose exist; which Company shall furnish the means necessary for building said line. The capital stock of said Company shall be equal at least to four hundred dollars per mile for the distance the line shall traverse; one-half of which shall be appropriated and issued to the proprietors of the patent for such printing telegraph as a compensation for the right to use the same, and the other half to the subscribers of the capital stock of said Company, in proportion to the amounts subscribed

by them respectively; and the Articles of Association of the Company shall contain an unalterable provision that any increase of wires upon such line, or additions to or extensions of the same shall be made by an addition to the capital stock of the Company, and not otherwise; one-half of which increased stock shall in like manner be issued to the proprietors of the patent as aforesaid; the share of stock so appropriated to the patentees or proprietors of the patent, to be issued as soon as any stock shall be issued to subscribers, and to be delivered in the first instance to the said Edson and Selden, to be by them distributed according to the respective interests of those entitled thereto.

3. The said line shall have two conductors of iron wire, one designed for the through business, and the other to connect the various way stations, and shall be constructed in the following manner, to wit:

There shall be at least thirty poles to the mile where the line is straight, and whenever curves or angles occur, the number and size shall be increased as far as may be necessary to render the line as substantial and permanent as with thirty poles upon a straight line; such poles to be in ground, thirty feet in length, and to vary from that height only where the location may render it expedient; and shall be so placed that the wire or conductor shall not come in contact with trees or any other obstructions; and shall be at least twenty-seven inches in circumference, four feet and a half from the butt and not less than four inches in diameter at the top. The line or route to be surveyed by a competent person before the poles are set, whose duty it shall be to drive a stake wherever a pole is to be set, and to prescribe the size and height of the pole for each locality; the poles to be delivered and set in accordance with such survey, and all reasonable and practicable efforts shall be made so to adapt and set the said poles that the wire shall never come in contact with other telegraph lines or any obstructions whatever. And in all cases where the line built under this contract shall cross other lines, poles of sufficient height shall be set to carry this line at least six feet above the line so crossed.

The through conductor shall be a single iron wire, weighing not less than six hundred pounds to the mile; and the way-conductor of like wire, weighing not less than four hundred and fifty pounds to the mile. The joints in the wire shall be made in the manner which shall or may be, at any time, directed by the said Royal E. House, and the insulator of the upper wire to be that recently invented by said House, and which is used upon the line now erecting between New York and Buffalo.

The poles, wherever it is practicable, shall be set five feet in the ground; and the wires shall be placed at least four feet apart upon the poles, unless more than two wires are used upon one set of poles; but in no case shall they be put less than three feet apart.

The poles to be of the most durable kind of timber that can be obtained upon the route of the line.

The offices at the various stations upon the line, shall be equal in convenience and appearance to offices on other lines upon the same route, and all proper stations upon the said line shall be furnished with telegraphic instruments, equal in construction to those now in use between New York, Philadelphia and Boston.

Whenever it shall become necessary in constructing such line to cross any river or stream, the said Royal E. House shall be consulted as to the manner of crossing the same; and the best mode, all things considered, shall be adopted.

All messages delivered from any office upon the line, shall be enclosed in envelopes having the words: *"By House's Printing Telegraph."* printed upon the outside, and any other appropriate words which said House may direct.

4. The said Butts, Smith and Shepard may make such contract between themselves and the persons who shall subscribe to the capital stock of said Company, not inconsistent with the provisions of this contract, as they may see fit; and they shall be entitled to receive for their own use and benefit, all profits and emoluments which may accrue upon any contract which they may thus make for the construction of such line; and they shall also be entitled to receive and appropriate to their own use, one-half of the share of the said Freeman M. Edson, in the portion of stock to be issued and assigned, or a compensation for the use of the patent.

5. The said Butts, Smith and Shepard agree to construct, complete and put in operation at least one hundred miles of the said line from Buffalo to St. Louis, on or before the first day of January, 1851, and to proceed in the construction of the residue of said line with all reasonable diligence; and all such portions of said line, as shall not be completed by the first day of September, 1852, shall be forfeited by the said Butts, Smith and Shepard, and the said Edson and Selden shall be at liberty to complete the same; and in case any suit or suits shall be prosecuted against the said Company, or against any person or persons interested in said line, for the infringement of any patented rights by the use of said printing telegraph, the said Butts, Smith and Shepard agree to bear one-half of all the expenses attending the defence of such suits, the other half to be borne by the proprietors of the patent, in proportion to their respective interests in said patent.

6. The said Edson and Selden, on their part, agree that no other line of said printing telegraph shall be constructed, commencing at the city of Buffalo, and terminating at the city of St. Louis, during the continuance of the patent, for said printing telegraph or of any renewal thereof; nor any line directly connecting any two points connected by the said line from Buffalo to St. Louis.

7. It is understood that in case the said Edson and Selden shall, on or before the 20th day of October next, make an agreement with the Lake Erie Telegraph Company, by which the section of the telegraph line now belonging to that Company, between the cities of Buffalo and Cleveland,

shall be made, and shall become a part of the line provided for by these articles, between Buffalo and St. Louis; then so much of said line, to wit: That portion between Buffalo and Cleveland, shall be considered as excepted from and taken out of the contract, which shall nevertheless continue in full force, for the residue of said line from Cleveland to St. Louis, except as in hereafter provided.

8. It is further understood and agreed to be an express condition of this contract, that the line to be built under it, shall never connect with, or send messages over any other telegraph line than those built under the said House Patent, provided, there is a line of said printing telegraph with which it can connect, or over which such messages can be sent.

9. It is further agreed that all the parties to these articles shall endeavor to produce a consolidation of the two companies from New York to Buffalo, and from Buffalo to St. Louis into one, extending from New York to St. Louis, and that each of said parties shall use their power as stockholders and their personal influence to bring about such consolidation.

10. In case an arrangement shall be made with the Lake Erie Line, to take the section of that line from Buffalo to Cleveland, as a part of the line from Buffalo to St. Louis, then the said Butts, Smith and Shepard agree to make the necessary advances to fit the said line with two wires; that is, with one additional wire to that which it now has, which shall weigh six hundred pounds to the mile, insulated with House's new insulator for the top of the poles, receiving for such advances the stock of the Company at par, and being entitled to the portion of Pattentee's [sic] stock, provided for by this contract in the same manner as if they had built the entire line.

In witness whereof, we have hereunto set our hands and seals respectively, the day and year first above written.

Freeman M. Edson,	(L.S.)
Samuel L. Selden,	(L.S.)
Isaac Butts,	(L.S.)
Sanford J. Smith,	(L.S.)
C. L. Shepard,	(L.S.)

It is hereby stipulated and agreed that the subscribers, Edson and Selden, shall receive stock to the amount of twenty-four thousand dollars each in the telegraph line to be built from Buffalo to St. Louis, under the contract this day made for the construction of said line, as their proportion of the stock reserved to the Patentees in said line; it being understood that the capital stock of the Company which constructs said line shall not exceed three hundred and sixty thousand dollars, unless the whole distance traversed by said line shall exceed nine hundred miles, in which case an amount may be added not exceeding four hundred dollars per mile for such excess.

Rochester, Sept. 6th, 1850.

Freeman M. Edson,	(L.S.)
Samuel L. Selden,	(L.S.)

It is understood that we are to arrange with Messrs. Downing and Backus in regard to their shares of Patentee's stock between Buffalo and the State Line.

Freeman M. Edson, (L.S.)

Samuel L. Selden, (L.S.)

SUPPLEMENTAL AGREEMENT

An Agreement made this thirteenth day of September, eighteen hundred and fifty, between Freeman M. Edson and Samuel L. Selden, of the one part, and Isaac Butts, Sanford J. Smith and Charles L. Shepard, of the other part, supplemental to the agreement and stipulation between the same parties, made on the 6th day of September, 1850:

The said Selden and Edson agree to convey and transfer to the Association or Company incorporated to construct the telegraph line mentioned in the original agreement, the right of the patentee [sic] to such line, including the use of House's insulators, upon the distribution of the capital stock, according to the provisions of the said agreement; and they further agree in like manner to convey and transfer to said Association or Company all the rights of any renewals of said patent and of all improvements to be made by said House, Ballard and Richards, or either of them.

And it is further stipulated and agreed that in case the stock of said Company shall be increased for an additional wire or wires, the said increased stock shall be distributed in the same proportion or proportions that the original stock is to be distributed, according to the aforesaid original agreement and stipulation.

It is further agreed that the said Butts, Smith and Shepard may change the route of said line of telegraph between the cities of Cincinnati and St. Louis, so as not to pass through or connect the city of Louisville, if they think proper.

Signed and sealed, the day and year first above written. } F. M. Edson, (L.S.)
Saml. L. Selden, (L.S.)

(Source: O'Rielly Collection, Telegraph Pamphlets.)

APPENDIX 5

ARTICLES OF ASSOCIATION AND INCORPORATION OF THE NEW YORK & MISSISSIPPI VALLEY PRINTING TELEGRAPH COMPANY, APRIL 1, 1851.

Whereas, Sanford J. Smith and Isaac Butts, under and by virtue of a contract between them of the one part, and Freeman M. Edson and Samuel L. Selden of the other part, are entitled to the exclusive right of establishing and constructing a line of telegraph, to be operated by the instrument known and patented under the name of "HOUSE'S PRINTING TELEGRAPH," between Buffalo, in the State of New York, and St. Louis, in the State of Missouri; and whereas, the said Sanford J. Smith and Isaac Butts are now engaged in constructing a line of telegraph between the places and for the purposes above mentioned:

Now, therefore, for the purpose of completing, owning, and operating said Telegraph Line, the subscribers hereto have agreed, and do hereby agree, to form an Incorporated Association or Company, pursuant to the Act of the Legislature of the State of New York, entitled "An Act to provide for the incorporation and regulation of Telegraph Companies," passed April 12, 1848, upon the terms and conditions following, to wit:

ARTICLE I. The name of the said Company shall be "THE NEW YORK & MISSISSIPPI VALLEY PRINTING TELEGRAPH COMPANY."

ART. II. The route of the said Telegraph Line shall pass through this State, from the City of Buffalo, to the State of Pennsylvania, along the south side of Lake Erie.

ART. III. This Company shall own and operate the residue of the said Telegraph Line, from the boundary of the State of New York, through the several States, to the City of St. Louis, touching at Cleveland, Columbus and Cincinnati; and thence to St. Louis, by such route as shall be designated by the Directors; to be constructed by the said Sanford J. Smith and Isaac Butts, under and by virtue of authority from the said States respectively, or from the persons whose lands the said line may cross.

ART. IV. The capital stock of said company shall be three hundred and sixty thousand dollars, to be divided into 3600 shares of one hundred dollars each; but the amount of said stock may be increased in the manner hereinafter prescribed.

ART. V. The persons whose names are hereto subscribed, are the shareholders of said capital stock, and their places of residence, and the number of shares held by each, are set opposite to their names respectively.

ART. VI. This Company shall commence on the first day of April, one thousand eight hundred and fifty-one, and terminate on the first day of April, one thousand nine hundred and fifty-one.

ART. VII. This Company is to have the exclusive right, subject to the rights of the aforesaid Smith and Butts, of constructing and using said Printing Telegraph, upon the line aforesaid, under letters patent issued to Royal E. House, as the inventor thereof, during the life of said patent, and of any renewals thereof; and the right of constructing and using House's insulators, and of all improvements made or to be made by said Royal E. House in the Printing Telegraph, or in the apparatus or machinery connected therewith.

The assent of the patentees to these articles, is to be obtained, and properly attested prior to the payment of any part of the subscriptions to the stock. As soon as practicable after twenty-five per cent of the cost of building said line shall have been paid by the subscribers to the said stock, the rights above specified shall be transferred to the Company by deed or other good and sufficient conveyance.

ART. VIII. The one-half of said capital stock, to wit: one hundred and eighty thousand dollars, shall be appropriated in payment for the exclusive right of constructing and using the said Printing Telegraph, upon the line aforesaid, under the letters patent issued to Royal E. House, as the inventor thereof, during the life of said patent, and of any renewals thereof; the other half shall be devoted to the object of constructing, completing and putting in operation the said line.

ART. IX. The line is to be constructed by Sanford J. Smith and Isaac Butts, above named, who are to receive therefor the sum of one hundred and eighty thousand dollars, to be paid to them out of the moneys subscribed to the capital stock of said Company: and provided the full amount shall not be realized from subscription, they shall be entitled to receive, and shall accept, the balance of the stock.

ART. X. The affairs of this Company shall be managed by a Board of nineteen Directors, who shall choose a President and Vice President from their number. The Board shall also have power to appoint a Treasurer and Secretary, who shall hold their offices respectively during the pleasure of the Board; or they may appoint one person to act both as Secretary and Treasurer.

They shall have power to fix the salaries of the President and of all the other officers and agents of the Company, and to adopt such resolutions and by-laws, not conflicting with any provisions of these articles, as they may think proper, for the regulation of the business of the Company. A majority of the Directors, including the President or Vice President, shall constitute a quorum to do business. Special meetings of the Board may be called by the President as often as occasion may require.

They shall hold regular quarterly meetings on the third Tuesdays of January, April, July and October respectively, of each year, and may declare dividends at such meetings, or as often as they may deem expedient.

They may also designate three of their number, who, with the President and Treasurer, shall constitute an Executive Committee, who shall, for the time being, have charge of the affairs and business of the Company, subject to the control of the Board.

ART. XI. The Directors shall be chosen by the Stockholders, at their annual meeting, and shall hold their offices for one year, and until others are chosen.

No person shall be Director, unless he is a Stockholder in the Company. Any vacancy in the Board of Directors, may be filled for the residue of the year by the remaining Directors.

The Stockholders shall at the same time choose three persons to act as Inspectors, to preside at the next succeeding annual election.

Until the first annual election of Directors, or until other persons are appointed in their places, as hereinafter provided, the following persons shall compose the Board of Directors, to wit:

Henry S. Potter, Addison Gardiner, Freeman Clarke, Isaac R. Elwood, Gideon W. Burbank, Joseph Hall, George H. Mumford, E. Darwin Smith, Isaac Hills, Samuel Medary, Joseph Medbery, James Chapman, Rufus Keeler, Royal E. House, Freeman M. Edson, Samuel L. Selden, Isaac Butts, Sanford J. Smith and Hiram Sibley.

In case any of the aforesaid persons shall not become Stockholders of this Company, within sixty days from the organization thereof, they shall cease to be Directors, and the remaining Directors may supply the vacancy until the said election.

ART. XII. The President shall preside at all meetings of the Directors, and also of the Stockholders, except during the election of Directors. He shall draw all drafts upon the treasury for the disbursements of the Company, according to the rules prescribed by the Board. He shall sign all certificates of stock; and shall be ex-officio, President of the Executive Committee. In the absence or inability of the President, the Vice President shall act in his stead, and possess all the duties of the President.

ART. XIII. The Secretary shall keep the minutes of the proceedings of all the meetings of Stockholders, and of the Directors, and of the Executive Committee, which, at all reasonable hours, shall be open to the inspection of any Stockholder; he shall countersign all certificates of stock; he shall keep the general accounts of the Company, as well as a record of all issues and transfers of stock; and shall perform all such other duties as may be imposed upon him by resolutions or by-laws adopted by the Board of Directors.

ART. XIV. The Treasurer shall receive all moneys collected, pay all drafts and dividends made pursuant to the rules and regulations of the Board of Directors, and shall keep a faithful account of his receipts and disbursements; and at each quarterly meeting of the Directors, and oftener if required, he shall exhibit to them a true transcript thereof. He shall also, when required, give security to the Company, in such form and to such amount as the Board of Directors may prescribe, for the faithful discharge of his duties.

While the line is in progress of construction, the Treasurer shall also receive and have the custody of the moneys subscribed for building said line; which subscriptions shall be payable to his order; and he shall pay to the said Sanford J. Smith and Isaac Butts the moneys so received by him, under the direction of the Executive Committee, as fast as the same shall be required for the construction of the said line; but the amount so to be paid, shall not, at any time, exceed the value of the work actually done and materials delivered or procured, which materials so delivered or procured, shall thereupon become and be the property of the Company.

The Board of Directors or Executive Committee may exact from the said Smith and Butts adequate security for the faithful appropriation of all moneys paid to them for the purposes herein specified.

ART. XV. The said Sanford J. Smith and Isaac Butts, are to construct said line from the city of Buffalo to the city of St. Louis, according to the contract hereinbefore mentioned, in the manner following, viz:

There shall be at least thirty posts to the mile, which shall be not less than thirty feet long; they shall also be twenty-seven inches or more in circumference, four and a half feet from the butt, and twelve inches in circumference at the top; and they shall be set into the ground five feet. The posts shall be of the best timber—reference being had to durability—

which is readily accessible on the route through which the line is to pass.

Upon these posts shall be stretched two conductors of single iron wire of the best quality, one of which shall weigh not less than six hundred pounds, and the other not less than four hundred and fifty pounds to the mile.

The insulation used for the upper wire shall be that recently invented by the said Royal E. House, consisting of a heavy glass insulator, cast or moulded, with a screw to secure it at the top of the pole, and enclosed in a cast-iron cap, to which it is also secured with a screw; the side insulator shall be such as shall be approved by the said House.

One of HOUSE's PRINTING TELEGRAPH instruments is to be furnished by said Smith and Butts, for each of the following places, to wit: Erie, Cleveland, Columbus, Dayton, Indianapolis, Terre Haute, Louisville; and two each at Buffalo, Cincinnati and St. Louis—provided the line shall intersect each of these places. But in no case shall the number of telegraph instruments be less than that herein specified; provided, that so many be required at those and other places, upon the completion of the line.

Suitable offices shall be procured at the several stations on the line in which the machines shall be set up in a proper manner for use; but the rent and all expenses of fitting up said offices, except furnishing and setting up the instruments, and connecting them properly with the line, shall be borne by the Company.

The whole line is to be put in complete working order by the said Smith and Butts, according to the aforesaid contract.

ART. XVI. Whenever the first payment on stock is made, the Treasurer shall give a scrip certificate of stock, stating the amount of each share, the number of shares which the holder thereof is entitled to, the amount paid thereon, and that the same is only transferable on the books of the Company, and on the surrender of such certificate.

ART. XVII. The Board of Directors shall not be authorized to issue the portion of the stock which is appropriated to be paid or given for the rights specified in Article Seventh, until such rights are fully transferred, conveyed, or assigned to this Company in such manner as to vest the same in this Company, according to the true intent and meaning of said article.

ART. XVIII. Every part and portion of the aforesaid telegraph line, as fast as the same shall be constructed, together with all posts, wires, insulators, or other materials procured for said line, shall become and be the full and complete property of this Company; and every member of this Company shall be bound to execute to the corporation such conveyance and assignment as shall be necessary to vest the said corporation with all the rights of property aforesaid, and all the rights of constructing and using on the said line, the aforesaid Printing Telegraph and Insulators, and all improvements thereof, and all renewals of the same, as specified in the aforesaid Seventh Article.

ART. XIX. The first annual meeting of the Stockholders shall be held at the Mansion House, in the city of Buffalo, on the first Tuesday of April, in the year 1852; or at some earlier day, to be appointed by the Executive

Committee, in case the line shall be in working order through its entire length prior to January 1, 1852; of which earlier meeting the same notice is to be given as for a special meeting of the Stockholders. The subsequent annual meetings shall be held on the same day in each year.

ART. XX. Special meetings of the Stockholders shall be called by the President at any time, on the written request of the persons holding, or entitled to, one-third of the capital stock of this Company. Such request shall specifically state the object or objects of the desired meeting. The President shall appoint such meeting, and the Secretary shall give a written notice thereof, stating the object of the proposed meeting, which notice shall be sent by mail, at least thirty days prior to the time of such meeting, addressed to the several Stockholders, at their respective places of residence, as they appear on the books of the Company; but no such meeting shall be held to be irregular or invalid for want of due notice to all the Stockholders, unless the omission to give such notice was wilful and fraudulent.

ART. XXI. The Board of Directors, with the consent of two-thirds of all the members thereof, whose names are to be entered in the minutes of their proceedings, may merge or unite this line with any other telegraph line or lines which may be authorized to use HOUSE's PRINTING TELEGRAPH, on such terms as shall appear just and equitable; and the Stockholders in this Company shall be entitled to at least the same amount of stock in the said incorporated Company to which this Company shall be united, as they were respectively entitled to in this Company.

The said Directors with the like consent may also purchase for the Company, any line or part of a line of telegraph already constructed, to form a part of this line, if in their judgment such purchase will be for the benefit of this Company. And in case of any such purchase or purchases, so much of the cost thereof as would be equal to the cost of the same extent of new structure, shall be borne by the said Sanford J. Smith and Isaac Butts; and the balance, if any, shall be chargeable to the Association.

The said Directors may also lease for the Company any line or part of a line of telegraph, if in their judgment such leasing will be for the benefit of this Company.

ART. XXII. Whenever the President shall receive notice from the said Sanford J. Smith and Isaac Butts that the line from the city of Buffalo to the city of St. Louis is completed and ready for operation, he shall call a meeting of the Directors, for the purpose of taking such measures in relation to the inspection of the said line and the acceptance thereof by this Company, as they may deem advisable; in the proceedings of which meeting, neither the said Sanford J. Smith nor Isaac Butts shall have any voice. Or, the directors, at their option, may at any time accept any portion or section of such line as may be in working order. And from the date of such acceptance, such portion or section of line shall be operated by and for the benefit of the Corporation; and all liability of said Smith and Butts, as regards any particular section or portion of line, shall be terminated by the acceptance thereof, as herein provided for. But with the restrictions here specified, the said Sanford J. Smith and Isaac Butts shall be liable for all defects and deficiencies of said line, until it is duly accepted by the Directors.

ART. XXIII. The subscriptions to this stock shall be payable in four instalments of twenty-five per cent. each. The first instalment shall be payable on demand, or within thirty days thereafter. The others shall be payable at the call of the Executive Committee; and the Treasurer shall give a written notice of such call, which shall be deposited in the Post Office at least thirty days prior to the time of payment, and addressed to the several Stockholders, at their respective places of residence, as they appear on the books of the Company.

In case any subscriber shall fail to pay the amount thus called for at the time specified in such notice, he shall forfeit his stock and all previous payments thereon, or remain liable on his subscription, at the option of the Board of Directors; all payments to be made to the Treasurer of the Company, or to his order, for the benefit of this Company.

ART. XXIV. Whenever the person holding one-fourth of the stock shall present a written request to the President for an increase or decrease of the number of Directors, at least two months before the annual meeting of the Stockholders, he shall direct the Secretary to give thirty days notice through the Post Office to each Stockholder, that the question of an increase or decrease of the number of Directors will be presented at such annual meeting; at which time the number of Directors may be increased or decreased by a majority of the votes given thereon, but the number shall not at any time be less than that fixed by these articles.

ART. XXV. Whenever the Board of Directors by a vote of a majority of all the members thereof, shall determine that it is for the interest of the Company to extend its business, by adding to the number of wires or conductors upon the line aforesaid, or by constructing any other line or lines to operate in connection therewith, (in case the patent rights can be obtained from the proprietors thereof,) they shall enter their determination upon their minutes at large; and all such additions shall be made by an increase of the capital stock, and in no other manner. The Board shall fix the amount of increase necessary for the purpose aforesaid. They shall cause thirty days' notice to be sent by mail addressed to each of the Stockholders, at his place of residence, of a meeting of the Stockholders, at which the question of increasing the stock, specifying the object thereof, is to be submitted. If at such meeting the persons owning two-thirds of the stock shall vote in favor of such increase, or if within two months thereafter, the persons holding two-thirds of said stock shall give a written assent thereto, the Directors shall be authorized to increase the stock accordingly. No meeting shall be held irregular or invalid for want of due notice to all the Stockholders, unless the omission to give such notice was wilful and fraudulent.

ART. XXVI. These articles shall be and form a part of the by-laws and regulations of this Corporation, until the same shall be altered as herein provided. And the said Directors shall provide for the distribution of the capital stock of the said corporate body among the persons entitled thereto, in proportion to their respective rights and shares therein.

ART. XXVII. Every person subscribing to these articles, shall designate his place of residence; and every person becoming the assignee of any stock or share, shall in like manner designate the place of his residence, to which places all notices required by these articles may be sent.

ART. XXVIII. At all meetings of the Stockholders, each Stockholder shall be entitled to one vote on each share of stock, appearing by the books of this Company to have belonged to him for at least thirty days prior to such meeting; but no one Stockholder shall give more than one-fourth part of the aggregate vote of the Company. Any Stockholder may vote either in person or by proxy.

ART. XXIX. Every person who shall take stock in this Company by subscription, transfer, or otherwise, shall be deemed to assent to the foregoing Articles; but the same may be altered at any annual meeting of the Stockholders, by the vote of the persons holding a majority of the stock, except the Article in relation to the increase of stock, which shall not be altered without the vote of the persons holding two-thirds of the said capital stock; and excepting also all those Articles which embrace some matter of contract between the Company and the patentees or contractors for building the line, which last Articles shall be and remain unalterable, without the consent of each and every party thereto.

ART. XXX. The Board of Directors shall cause certificates of the stock of this Company to be issued to the several parties entitled thereto in proportion to their respective rights; and for the purpose of enabling them to do so, duplicate copies of all contracts, by virtue of which any person shall be entitled to any of the said stock, shall be filed with this Company. But the portion of stock representing the patentee interest, shall be issued to Samuel L. Selden and Freeman M. Edson in trust, to be by them distributed to the respective parties entitled thereto.

(Source: O'Rielly Collection, Telegraph Pamphlets.)

APPENDIX 6

"The Bonus Contract"

ARTICLE OF AGREEMENT BETWEEN THE HOLDERS OF THE PATENT RIGHTS FOR HOUSE'S PRINTING TELEGRAPH, THE CONTRACTORS FOR THE BUILDING OF THE NEW YORK & MISSISSIPPI VALLEY PRINTING TELEGRAPH COMPANY'S LINE, AND THE STOCKHOLDERS OF THAT LINE, PROVIDING STOCK BONUSES OF 50 PERCENT TO THOSE FURNISHING FUNDS FOR THE LINE [ABOUT APRIL 1851].

ARTICLE OF AGREEMENT,

Between Royal E. House, of the City of New York: Freeman M. Edson, Samuel L. Selden, Hiram Sibley and Isaac Butts, of the city of Rochester, each of whom has an interest in the Patent Right for House's Printing

Telegraph, and Sanford J. Smith, of St. Louis, and said Isaac Butts, Contractors to build the Telegraph Line hereinafter mentioned, parties of the first part, and Addison Gardiner, Henry S. Potter, Isaac R. Elwood, and such others as shall subscribe hereto, witnesseth:

Whereas, it is proposed to form an Association or Company to construct a line of telegraph to be operated by House's Printing Telegraph, from the city of Buffalo to the city of St. Louis, with a capital of three hundred and sixty thousand dollars. Now, therefore,

1. The parties of the first part severally agree to and with the parties of the second part, that in case such an Association or Company is formed, they, the parties of the first part, upon the completion of said telegraph line and upon the transfer to said Association or Company of the right to use said printing telegraph, as specified in the Articles of said Association, will be entitled to amounts of capital stock, exceeding the amount which they respectively herein agree to set apart, appropriate and transfer for the benefit of the parties of the second part upon the terms and conditions herein provided.

2. The parties of the second part severally agree to become parties to, or stockholders in the said Association or Company, and to subscribe and pay for the construction of the said telegraph line, according to the Articles of Association, the several sums by the parties of the second part hereto respectfully subscribed; and they also severally agree to use their influence to induce others to subscribe for, or take stock in, said Association or Company, and to promote the interest and success of the printing telegraph.

3. The parties of the first part severally agree, and each for himself agrees to set apart, appropriate and transfer an amount of the capital stock in said Association or Company, that is to say:

Said Edson agrees to set apart and transfer one hundred dollars.

Said Sibley agrees to set apart and transfer three thousand one hundred and twenty-five dollars.

Said Selden agrees to set apart and transfer seven thousand five hundred dollars.

Said Butts agrees to set apart and transfer eighteen thousand one hundred and twenty-five dollars—fifteen thousand dollars as contractor to build line, and thirty-one hundred and twenty-five dollars as holder of patentee interest.

Said Smith agrees to set apart and transfer fifteen thousand dollars as contractor to build line.

Said House agrees to set apart and transfer

Said Ballard agrees to set apart and transfer

Said Richards agrees to set apart and transfer

Which said several amounts of the capital stock be issued to Isaac R. Elwood, by him to be held in trust for the benefit of the parties of the second part, and to be transferred to them respectively on the conditions following, that is to say: To each of the parties of the second part, who shall pay the amount subscribed by him as required by said Articles of

Association, shall be transferred an amount of said trust stock, as shall be equal to fifty per cent on the sum so subscribed and paid by him, and which shall be in addition to the stock for which he subscribed and paid; and no default on the part of either of the parties of the second part shall effect the right of the parties performing.

Freeman M. Edson,
Hiram Sibley,
Samuel L. Selden,
Isaac Butts,
Sanford J. Smith.

A. Gardiner, ten thousand dollars.
F. Clarke, ten thousand dollars.
Henry S. Potter, ten thousand dollars.
Isaac Butts, ten thousand dollars.
J. Medbery, ten thousand dollars.
G. H. Mumford, ten thousand dollars.
Bacon & Co., five thousand dollars.
Hiram Sibley, five thousand dollars.
(Reserved per order by letter to J. Thompson for
(Freeborn G. Jewett, five thousand dollars.
J. B. Stillson, two thousand dollars.
William Alling, two thousand dollars.
Ashley Sampson, two thousand dollars.
Edmund P. Willis, two thousand dollars.

(Source: O'Rielly Collection, Telegraph Pamphlets.)

APPENDIX 7

ARTICLE OF AGREEMENT BETWEEN THE NEW YORK & MISSISSIPPI VALLEY PRINTING TELEGRAPH COMPANY AND THE HOLDERS OF THE HOUSE PATENT RIGHTS, ETC., JANUARY 9, 1854.

AN AGREEMENT,

Made the ninth day of January, 1854, between the New York & Mississippi Valley Printing Telegraph Company, in its corporate or associate capacity, of the first part; Francis Morris, and other Assignees of, or interested in, House's Telegraph Patents, of the second part; Francis Morris, Freeman M. Edson and Hiram Sibley, Trustees appointed in and by a certain deed bearing date the 18th day of April, 1853, to hold the undisposed of interests in the said patents upon certain trusts therein mentioned, of the third part; and Henry S. Potter, and other Cash Subscribers for Stock of the said Company and their Assignees, of the fourth part, witnesseth as follows:

Whereas, the said New York & Mississippi Valley Printing Telegraph line has not been completed, according to the original Articles of Association and Incorporation, or as provided for in the subsequent agreement; therefore, for and in consideration of the premises, and for other good and valuable considerations, it is hereby mutually agreed by and between the parties and persons executing this agreement, that the original Articles of Association and Incorporation and all subsequent agreements and resolutions, be and the same are hereby modified, according to the articles hereinafter contained and set forth.

ART. I. The said Company or Association is to own and operate the existing line of electric telegraph with one wire or conductor, known as House's Line, from Buffalo to Louisville, including a branch line to be constructed from Frankfort or Georgetown to Lexington, Kentucky, with one wire or conductor, by a route reasonably direct between the last mentioned cities. And the said company is to be at liberty to renew or alter the said line or any part thereof, or change the route thereof, or any part thereof, from time to time, not deviating at any point more than twenty-five miles from the route first selected. And the said Company is to be entitled, in manner hereinafter mentioned, to the use of House's Printing Telegraph upon such line, original or altered, as aforesaid.

The parties hereto of the second and third part, do hereby severally and respectively grant, bargain, sell, assign and convey unto the said party hereto of the first part, all their and each of their right, title and interest in and to the exclusive use of House's patented invention of the Magnetic Letter Printing Telegraph on the said line of telegraph with one wire or conductor. The grant and assignment, hereby made, are to include the rights of the said parties hereto of the second and third parts respectively, (so far as relates to the said line with one wire or conductor,) in and to any extension, re-issue, renewal or renewals of the patents granted to Royal E. House, and in and to any and all improvements that have been or may hereafter be made upon, or added to, the said printing telegraph in any of its parts or connections, by the said Royal E. House, and in and to the said House's mode of insulating wires, and in and to any patent or patents that may be issued to the said House or his assigns by the Government of the United States for any such improvements, and all renewals and re-issues thereof.

And it is hereby declared, that it is the meaning and intention of the said parties hereto of the second and third parts respectively that the grant and assignment, hereby made, shall operate and extend so as to exclude and prevent any grant hereafter by the said parties hereto of the second part, or their assigns, any or either of them, or by the said Trustees or their successors to any person or persons, bodies politic or corporate of any right, title or authority to use the said invention, or any, or either of them, for the purpose of transmitting intelligence between the towns of Buffalo, Cleveland, Columbus, Lexington, Frankfort and Louisville, any or either of them, by any route whatever, directly or indirectly, during the continuance of the patents aforesaid or of any renewal thereof. But in case the said telegraph line shall not be operated in good faith for the transmission of Messages between the said towns, any or either of them, then messages may be transmitted indirectly by other House lines between any or either of the said towns between which the said line shall not be operated in good faith as aforesaid.

Provided, and the said grant and assignment are made upon the following express condition, and it is hereby declared by and between the parties hereto, that if the use of House's Printing Telegraph machines for the transmission of messages between Buffalo and Cincinnati, and Louisville and Cincinnati, shall at any time hereafter be superseded by other instruments on said line, or shall not be used in good faith for the transmission of messages, then and in either of the said cases the said parties of the third part, or their successors, for the time being, or a majority of them, shall have full power to grant, bargain, sell, assign and convey to any person or persons, company or companies, the right to use the said inventions upon any line of telegraph on the route aforesaid, or upon any part thereof; and such new grant or assignment may include all improvements, extensions and renewals as aforesaid. And the grant and assignment made as aforesaid to the said party hereto of the first part, shall be modified accordingly.

ART. II. All messages, delivered from any office upon the line, shall be enclosed in envelopes, having the words: "*By House's Printing Telegraph.*" legibly printed upon the outside.

ART. III. The line of this Company shall never connect with, or send messages over, any other telegraph line than those upon which House's Printing Telegraph may be used, provided, there is a line of said printing telegraph, with which it can connect, or over which such messages can be sent. But the parties hereto of the third part, or their successors trustees, for the time being, or a majority of them, shall have power on application of the said Telegraph Company, to modify, change or entirely dispense with the last two provisions in this article contained, respecting envelopes and connections.

ART. IV. The capital stock of the said Company, for the purpose aforesaid, it is to be one hundred and seventy thousand dollars—of the said capital stock, eighty-four thousand and two hundred dollars is the property of, and shall belong to, and be assignable to, the cash subscribers or their assignees, in the shares or proportions of their respective rights. Forty-two thousand and five hundred dollars shall belong to, and be issued in the names of, and be delivered to, the parties of the second part, upon their severally subscribing these presents in the shares or proportions of their respective rights, as set forth in the schedule hereto annexed, marked "A."

Ten thousand dollars of said stock heretofore issued to Sanford J. Smith & Co., as contractors for building the line, and seven thousand five hundred dollars heretofore issued to Freeman Clarke, as cash subscriber at the request and for the benefit of said Sanford J. Smith & Co., is now held by Isaac R. Elwood, as security for a loan of three thousand dollars and interest made by said Elwood to said S. J. Smith & Co., to aid them in building said line, or defraying the expense thereof.

And in consideration that the said Isaac Butts shall pay to the said

Telegraph Company the sum of twelve hundred dollars from time to time, as the same shall be wanted for the purpose of constructing the branch line or circuit to Lexington, then the residue of the said capital stock being twenty-five thousand and eight hundred dollars, shall be issued to said Isaac Butts, and shall be delivered to him on his procuring a release from the contractors and from persons claiming under them by assignment or by guaranteeing with satisfactory security the said Telegraph Company against all claims from said contractors, and those claiming under them as aforesaid, or by any other proceeding, by which such claim should be effectually barred; and upon said Butts procuring such release, or guaranteeing said Company against such claims, or by any proceedings by which the same shall be effectually barred, the said Telegraph Company is to release said Butts from all claims against him as cash subscriber or as contractor.

But nothing herein shall be construed as an acceptance of the said line as having been built according to the contract or contracts, or as an admission that the said contractors have any claim whatever, or as exempting them from liability for not fulfilling the said contract or contracts.

Schedules "A" and "B," hereto attached, exhibit the shares of the cash subscribers and of the persons interested in the patents.

ART. v. Whenever the Board of Directors shall deem it expedient to put up a second wire or conductor, or to extend the telegraph line, or to lease the same, or any part thereof, or to construct branch lines, or to take a lease or leases of any other line or lines, or to merge, unite or consolidate any other line or lines with this line, and to operate the same by House's instruments, or by other instruments, they shall have power to do so with the written consent of two-thirds of all the directors upon the procuring of the right to use such instruments; and for these purposes the said Board of Directors shall have power to increase the capital stock from time to time to such sum or sums as shall be necessary, to be specified in the written consent of the Directors. But the power and authority by this article given to, or conferred upon, the Board of Directors, shall not be exercised in any respect within three years from the date hereof, without the written consent from time to time, of a majority of the said parties hereto of the third part, or their successors, trustees, for the time being under the said deed of trust, or a majority of them. And no further wire or conductor shall be used on the said line, or any part thereof at any time hereafter, without the authority of the said trustees, or their successors, or a majority of them.

ART. vi. There shall be an election of Directors of the Company or Association, on the last Wednesday of July next, at the office of the Secretary, in the city of Rochester, and thereafter the annual election of Directors shall be held at the same place, on the last Wednesday in July in each year.

ART. vii. The Executive Committee shall have power to do, transact and manage all the business and affairs of the Company, except where the Articles of Association as amended by this agreement, expressly give the power to, or require the Board of Directors to act, and the Board of Directors may prescribe rules and regulations from the government of the Executive Committee, and may limit their power.

ART. VIII. The Executive Committee of said Telegraph Company shall have the authority to take an assignment of the claim of Isaac R. Elwood against S. J. Smith & Co., and an assignment of the said seventeen thousand and five hundred dollars of stock pledged for said debt, and pay said Elwood the amount of the aforesaid claim and interest thereon; and in case the said Board shall take the said stock, it shall take the necessary steps to foreclose the right of redemption of said stock, and shall be authorized to buy in the same, or any part thereof; and in case the said Company became the absolute owners of the said stock the same shall be held for the payment of the debts of the said Company.

ART. IX. The Executive Committee shall have the authority to issue the bonds of the said Company to an amount not exceeding fifteen thousand dollars for the purpose of paying off the existing debts of the said Company, including the claim of Isaac R. Elwood against S. J. Smith & Co., in case the said Board of Directors shall take an assignment thereof, such bonds shall be payable on or before the first day of January, 1860, bearing interest at seven per cent per annum, payable semi-annually on the first day of January and on the first day of July in each year; such bonds shall contain a clause that no dividend shall be made until all of said bonds shall be paid; such bonds may be sold at a discount of not more than ten per cent.

ART. X. It is hereby further mutually understood and agreed, that this agreement is in no way to affect any assignment or transfer of stock, or to affect any agreement for the assignment or transfer of any stock heretofore made by any of the parties hereto, but all and every such assignment, or transfer, or agreement, to assign or transfer, shall remain of the same force and validity as if this agreement had not been made, and shall apply to the stock to be issued under this agreement in the same manner as it would apply to the stock to be issued in case this agreement had not been made.

ART. XI. The original Articles of Association and of Incorporation shall remain unchanged, except where the same have been modified by this agreement.

In witness whereof, the parties hereto of the second, third and fourth parts, have hereunto set their hands and seals, and the President and Secretary of the said Telegraph Company have hereunto subscribed their names and affixed the corporate seal of the said Company, the day and year first above written.

{ L.S. }   Executed by the President and Secretary of said Telegraph Company pursuant to a resolution of the Board of Directors, passed March 8, 1854.   HENRY S. POTTER, President

Isaac R. Elwood, Secretary.

PERSONS INTERESTED IN PATENT RIGHT:

F. Morris,	(L.S.)
R. W. Russell,	(L.S.)
F. M. Edson,	(L.S.)
Saml. L. Selden,	(L.S.)
Hiram Sibley,	(L.S.)
Isaac Butts,	(L.S.)
John B. Richards,	(L.S.)
Cambridge Livingston,	(L.S.)

TRUSTEES

F. Morris,	(L.S.)
F. M. Edson,	(L.S.)
Hiram Sibley,	(L.S.)

CASH SUBSCRIBERS AND ASSIGNEES OF STOCK:

Hiram Sibley,	(L.S.)
Isaac R. Elwood,	(L.S.)
Henry S. Potter,	(L.S.)
F. Clarke,	(L.S.)
A. Gardiner,	(L.S.)
F. G. Jewett,	(L.S.)
G. H. Mumford,	(L.S.)
Bacon & Co.,	(L.S.)
G. W. Burbank,	(L.S.)
Wm. Alling,	(L.S.)
J. Medbery,	(L.S.)
J. B. Stillson,	(L.S.)
J. Chappell,	(L.S.)
W. H. Perkins,	(L.S.)
E. P. Willis,	(L.S.)
E. F. Smith,	(L.S.)
By W. H. Perkins.	
C. G. Brinsmaid,	(L.S.)
By H. Brinsmaid.	
Dows & Carey,	(L.S.)
By David Dows,	
Surviving Partner.	

"Schedule A,"

Exhibits the names of persons interested in the Patent Right and their respective portions of stock belonging to them or their assignees.

Francis Morris, ...	$7,400
R. W. Russell, ...	3,600
F. M. Edson, ...	7,500
S. L. Selden, ...	4,000

Hiram Sibley,	7,900
Isaac Butts,	4,000
J. B. Richards,	4,000
Cambridge Livingston,	4,100

$42,500

ISAAC BUTTS.

"Schedule B,"

Exhibits the names of the Cash Subscribers, and the respective portions of Stock belonging to them or their assignees.

William Alling,	$3,000
Bacon & Co.,	4,700
Freeman Clarke,	7,500
Addison Gardiner, and Assigns,	15,000
Freeborn G. Jewett,	7,500
George H. Mumford,	7,500
Joseph Medbery,	7,500
Ashley Sampson	3,000
Hiram Sibley, and Assigns,	7,500
Jerome B. Stillson,	3,000
E. P. Willis,	3,000
Henry S. Potter, and Assigns,	15,000

(Source: O'Rielly Collection, Telegraph Pamphlets.)

APPENDIX 8

ARTICLE OF AGREEMENT PROVIDING FOR A REDISTRIBUTION OF THE HOUSE PATENT INTEREST, APRIL 18, 1853.

ARTICLE OF AGREEMENT, made and entered into this 18th day of April, 1853, between Freeman M. Edson, of the City of Brooklyn, in the State of New York; Samuel L. Selden, of the City of New York, in the said State; Hiram Sibley and Isaac Butts, of the said City of Rochester; and Francis Morris, Robert W. Russell, Cambridge Livingston, and John B. Richards, all of the City of New York.

Whereas, on the 18th day of April, 1846, Letters Patent were granted by the Government of the United States, to Royal E. House, for his invention known as the Magnetic Letter Printing Telegraph.

And whereas, on the 28th day of December, 1852, Letters Patent were also granted by the said Government, to the said Royal E. House, for certain Improvements in said Magnetic Letter Printing Telegraph.

And whereas, by a certain agreement in writing, bearing date the 28th day of February, one thousand eight hundred and fifty, and made between the said Royal E. House, William Ballard and John B. Richards, assignees of certain shares and interests in the said invention of the first part, and the said Freeman M. Edson and Samuel L. Selden, of the second part, the said parties thereto of the first part, did assign to the said parties thereto of the second part, all their interests in and to the exclusive right of constructing lines of said Letter Printing Telegraph, and of using the same within and throughout the United States and its Territories. And the said parties thereto of the second part did thereby agree to proceed to construct lines of said Letter Printing Telegraph, the one-fourth part of which, when completed was to be the property of the said parties thereto of the first part, which said assignment was made, subject to certain assignments which had been already made to certain parties to enable them to use the said invention upon lines of telegraph, upon certain terms in such assignments respectively set forth.

And whereas, by virtue of divers assignments, the said Patents and all renewals and re-issues thereof, and all improvements thereon made or to be made by the said Royal E. House, have been assigned to and are now subject as hereinafter mentioned, the property of the said Hiram Sibley, Isaac Butts, Francis Morris, Robert W. Russell, Cambridge Livingston and John B. Richards, in the several shares or proportions following, that is to say:

Hiram Sibley and Isaac Butts, ...	15	fortieths
Francis Morris, ...	10	"
Robert W. Russell, ...	5	"
Cambridge Livingston, ...	5	"
John B. Richards, ...	5	"

subject to the said assignment to the said Freeman M. Edson and Samuel L. Selden, and to certain assignments to and contracts with various Telegraph Companies and individuals affecting the right to the said patents on certain routes and in certain territories.

And whereas, it has been agreed by and between the parties hereto, that the said assignment to the said Samuel L. Selden and Freeman M. Edson, shall be cancelled; and that they shall in lieu thereof be entitled to a certain interest in the said patents as hereinafter mentioned; and that for the purpose of facilitating the extension of the said Letter Printing Telegraph, all the rights of the parties hereto shall be vested in three Trustees with the powers and subject to the duties hereinafter set forth.

Now these presents witness, that in consideration of the premises and for other good and valuable considerations, the receipt and satisfaction of which are hereby acknowledged, it is hereby mutually agreed and declared by and between all the parties hereto as follows, that is to say:

ARTICLE 1. The said patents and all the rights, titles and interests of all the parties hereto in and to the same in and to all re-issues and renewals thereof, whether under any present or future law, and in and to all improvements made or to be made by the said Royal E. House thereon (save and except the stocks or shares of the Telegraph Companies or Telegraph Lines mentioned and referred to in Article 7, and the other rights therein mentioned), shall be and are hereby divided or considered as divided into three hundred and twenty parts or shares which shall be the property of the parties hereto in the following proportions, that is to say:

Freeman M. Edson, ...	50 shares
Samuel L. Selden, ...	14 ”
Hiram Sibley, ...	48 ”
Isaac Butts, ...	48 ”
Francis Morris, ...	64 ”
Robert W. Russell, ...	32 ”
Cambridge Livingston, ...	32 ”
John B. Richards, ...	32 ”

$$\overline{320}$$

ART. 2. The said Francis Morris, Freeman M. Edson, and Hiram Sibley, and their successors appointed as hereinafter mentioned, are hereby constituted and appointed Trustees of the said several rights, titles and interests in the said patents and in any re-issues or renewals thereof, and in such improvements thereof as aforesaid, save and except as aforesaid, and all the said rights, titles and interests (except as above excepted), are hereby assigned and transferred to the said Trustees and their successors as aforesaid—to hold the said patent rights, titles, and interests in trust; that the said Trustees or a majority of them may and they are hereby irrevocably authorized and empowered to bargain, sell, assign and transfer, or otherwise dispose of the same from time to time, or any part or parts thereof, absolutely or conditionally, or any partial interest therein to any person or persons, company or companies, upon the best terms that can be obtained by the said Trustees, and either for cash or on credit, for an absolute or contingent consideration, or for any property or advantage to accrue to the said parties hereto, according to the discretion of the said Trustees or a majority of them, and as to them may seem best for the advantage of the said parties hereto.

ART. 3. The Trustees are to account at the end of every quarter of a year, from the first day of May next, to each of the parties hereto, and to their and each of their executors, administrators and assigns, according to their and each of their said shares, rights and interests in the said patents for, and pay or pass over all stocks, monies, and other properties which the said Trustees shall have received upon any such grants, sales, assignments, or transfers as aforesaid, after deducting all costs, charges, and expenses laid out or incurred by the said Trustees in the performance of the said Trust and the exercises of the powers vested in them as aforesaid. But no charge is to be made for the time and trouble of the Trustees, nor for the travelling expenses of the said Freeman M. Edson, except in cases where the other Trustees may deem it advisable and proper to allow such expenses.

ART. 4. The said Trustees or a majority of them shall, for the purpose of avoiding competition with any company or companies, person or persons, owning or claiming any right or interest under any patent or patents for electric telegraphs, or in any improvements therein, have full power, from time to time, to contract with such person or persons, company or companies to share with him or them, any or either of them, the proceeds of any such grant, sale, assignment, or transfer as aforesaid, in such manner and proportions as to the said Trustees or a majority of them may seem advisable. And the said Trustees or a majority of them shall have full power to compound and compromise all claims which may be brought against them, or which they may have, at any time or times hereafter against any company or companies, person or persons, arising under or by virtue of the trusts and powers herein contained.

ART. 5. It shall be lawful, at any time and from time to time hereafter, for the owners of a majority of the said three hundred and twenty shares to appoint, by writing under their hands, new Trustees, or a new Trustee in lieu of the said Trustees, any or either of them, (but not so as to reduce the number of trustees,) to perform the said trusts, and execute the said powers; and if any or either of the said Trustees shall die or resign, or become incapable of executing the said trust, the remaining or other Trustees or Trustee shall, from time to time, have all the powers vested in the said Trustees until the appointment of another or others in manner aforesaid.

ART. 6. The receipts or receipt of the said Trustees or a majority of them, shall in all cases be a full discharge to all purchasers, grantees, assigns, and others, claiming under or dealing with them in respect of the said trust and powers vested in them as aforesaid. And each of the Trustees, acting under these presents, shall be liable or accountable only for his own receipts, acts and deeds, and not for the receipts, acts and deeds of his associates or of either of them.

ART. 7. Nothing herein contained is to affect the rights of the parties hereto, any or either of them, to the stocks or shares of the House Printing Telegraph lines running from New York to Washington, New York to Buffalo, and Buffalo to Louisville via Cleveland and Cincinnati; nor is the right of any of the parties hereto to the use of the said invention and patents on any route or routes between the cities of New York and Boston, or to any line of telegraph between said cities, or the stock of any company owning or to own any such last mentioned line to be affected in any manner whatsoever. But the said trustees are invested with the patent right for any and all additional wires on the said three first mentioned lines, with all the powers, rights and duties aforesaid concerning the same.

ART. 8. The said Freeman M. Edson, in consideration of the premises, agrees to devote his time and attention to the extension of the said printing telegraph, and for that purpose to take all necessary journeys at his own expense during the continuance of the said trust, not exceeding the period of five years from this date. But this covenant is not to effect [sic] the discretionary power of the Trustees under the said Article 3, respecting the travelling expenses of the said Freeman M. Edson. And in case the said Freeman M. Edson shall at any time hereafter cease to be one of the

Trustees, then the Trustees for the time being, or a majority of them, shall have the like power in respect to the same.

ART. 9. The said recited assignment to the said Freeman M. Edson and Samuel L. Selden, bearing date the 28th day of February, 1850, is hereby surrendered, cancelled and determined without prejudice to any grants, assignments, or contracts, which may have been heretofore legally made by the said Freeman M. Edson and Samuel L. Selden, or either of them, under or by virtue of the same. And all the rights of any of the parties hereto, under or by virtue of the Second and Fourth Articles of a certain agreement, bearing date the ninth day of December, eighteen hundred and fifty, and made between the said William Ballard, of the first part, the said Hiram Sibley, and Isaac Butts, of the second part, and the said Royal E. House, of the third part, are hereby released and extinguished. And it is hereby agreed and declared, that all claims upon the said Freeman M. Edson and Samuel L. Selden for damages under or by virtue of the covenants contained in the said assignment to them, shall be and the same are hereby relinquished, released and discharged.

ART. 10. The said parties hereto do hereby form themselves into a Joint Stock Company or Association, under the name and style of "House's Printing Telegraph Company." And the said property, rights and interests of the parties hereto, subject to the said trust, are hereby declared to be a joint stock interest, divided into three hundred and twenty shares, to be owned by the parties hereto in the several proportions or shares aforesaid, and by their respective executors, administrators and assigns. And the said parties hereto do hereby declare that the Trustees or Trustee, acting for the time being under the above Articles, shall be the Directors or Director of the said Company. Said Trustees and Directors shall have power to elect a President and Treasurer from time to time, and also to appoint a Secretary and suitable Agents, and to pay such Secretary and Agents a reasonable compensation for their services. And it is agreed that certificates of the ownership of the said three hundred and twenty shares, shall be issued in due form to the several owners thereof, signed by the President and Secretary. The said shares shall be transferable. Such transfer to be made only on the books of the Company, and new certificates thereof, signed by the President and Secretary, shall be issued upon surrender of the previous certificates. And the Directors may provide for the issuing of new certificates in place of any that may be lost.

ART. 11. The Trustees and Directors shall, at all times during the continuance of the trust and association aforesaid, keep an office in the city of New York, wherein the papers and books of the Trustees and Directors shall be kept, and among others there shall be kept proper books showing who are the shareholders for the time being and the amounts of their interests. The books, contracts, assignments, conveyances, and minutes of the proceedings of Trustees, shall at all reasonable times be open for inspection and examination by any and all shareholders and their agents.

It is hereby expressly declared and agreed, that the Trustees and Directors shall not, nor shall any or either of them have any authority whatever to incur or create any debt or obligation, by or on behalf of the owners of the said three hundred and twenty shares for the time being, any/or either of them; it being the intention of the parties hereto to constitute a power to sell, assign, or otherwise dispose of the said patent rights, titles, and interests in manner aforesaid, to the best advantage of the parties who may, for the time being, be entitled to the said three hundred and twenty shares.

In witness whereof, the said parties hereto have hereunto set their hands and seals, the day and year first above written.

In presence of,		F. M. Edson,	(L.S.)
(as to F. M. Edson,		Samuel L. Selden,	(L.S.)
Isaac Butts, Francis		Hiram Sibley,	(L.S.)
Morris, Robert W.		Isaac Butts,	(L.S.)
Russell, Cambridge		F. Morris,	(L.S.)
Livingston, and John		R. W. Russell,	(L.S.)
B. Richards.)		C. Livingston,	(L.S.)
Marcus Hughes.		John B. Richards,	(L.S.)

As to Samuel L. Selden,
  L. A. Ward.
As to Hiram Sibley,
  Isaac R. Elwood.

(Source: O'Rielly Collection, Telegraph Pamphlets.)

APPENDIX 9

CERTIFICATE OF A RESOLUTION REORGANIZING THE NEW YORK & MISSISSIPPI VALLEY PRINTING TELEGRAPH COMPANY, JANUARY 20, 1854, UNDER AN ACT OF THE NEW YORK STATE LEGISLATURE.

CERTIFICATE

Of a Resolution, adopted under and by virtue of an Act of the Legislature of the State of New York, entitled "An Act to amend an Act entitled An Act to provide for the incorporation and regulation of Telegraph Companies," being chapter 471, of the Laws of 1853, by a majority of the Board of Directors of The New York and Mississippi Valley Printing Telegraph Company or Association, owning and using a telegraph line, partly within this State.

At a meeting of the Board of Directors of the New York & Mississippi Valley Printing Telegraph Company, duly convened, held at the Office of the Secretary of said Company, in the City of Rochester, in the State of New York, on the twentieth day of January, 1854:

Resolved, by this Board, That the New York & Mississippi Valley Printing Telegraph Company, now owning and using, and having owned and used, on the 29th day of June, 1853, and long prior thereto and ever since a line of wires of telegraph, or a telegraph line, partly within the States of Pennsylvania, Ohio, and Kentucky, that is to say: from a point in the City of Buffalo, in the State of New York, to the City of Louisville, in the State of Kentucky, passing through Dunkirk, in the State of New York; through Erie, in the State of Pennsylvania; through Cleveland, Columbus, Dayton and Cincinnati, in the State of Ohio; through Covington, Georgetown and Frankfort, in the State of Kentucky, to the City of Louisville aforesaid, (and to include a branch circuit to Lexington, in said State of Kentucky, to be completed), shall organize under the Act of the Legislature of the State of New York, passed June 29, 1853, entitled "An Act to amend an Act entitled an Act to provide for the incorporation and regulation of Telegraph Companies," passed April 12, 1848, in order that the said Company may become a body corporate, and be entitled to the benefit of the provisions in the said Amendatory Act contained, on filing in the office of the Secretary of State, a certificate of a resolution adopted by a majority of this Board of Directors to organize under the said last mentioned act.

And thereupon be it farther [*sic*] resolved as follows:

First: That the name assumed to distinguish the said Company, and to be used in its dealings and by which it may sue and be sued, is to be and is "The New York & Mississippi Valley Printing Telegraph Company."

Second: That the general route of the said line of telegraph is from a point in the City of Buffalo, in the State of New York, to the City of Louisville, in the State of Kentucky, passing through Dunkirk, in the State of New York; through Erie, in the State of Pennsylvania; through Cleveland, Columbus, Dayton and Cincinnati, in the State of Ohio; and through Covington, Georgetown and Frankfort, in the State of Kentucky, to the City of Louisville aforesaid, (including a branch circuit to Lexington, in the last mentioned State); which several places above mentioned are indicated as the points to be connected thereby.

Third: That the capital stock of said Company is to be and is one hundred and seventy thousand dollars, divided into seventeen hundred shares of one hundred dollars each share.

Fourth: That the following list exhibits the names and residence of the shareholders of the capital stock aforesaid, and the number of shares held by each of them respectively:

Names of Shareholders.	Residence.	No. shares.
J. L. Allen,	New Haven, Conn.,	11
A. Arnold,		4
William Alling,	Rochester, N. Y.,	30
Bacon & Co.,	do.	47
Isaac Butts,	do.	55
William Buffam,	Stratford, Conn.,	11
G. W. Burbank,	Rochester, N. Y.,	15
C. G. Brinsmaid,	do.	1

James Chappell,	Rochester, N. Y.	10
Freeman Clarke,	do.	75
Dows & Carey,	New York City,	20
F. M. Edson,	Flushing, N. Y.,	30
I. R. Elwood,	Rochester, N. Y.,	250
A. Gardiner,	do.	75
F. G. Jewett,	Skaneateles, N. Y.,	75
Cambridge Livingston,	New York City,	41
G. H. Mumford,	Rochester, N. Y.,	75
J. Medbery,	do.	75
F. Morris,	New York City,	74
H. S. Potter,	Rochester, N. Y.,	125
W. H. Perkins,	do.	4
J. B. Richards,	New York City,	40
R. W. Russell,	do.	36
E. F. Smith,	Rochester, N. Y.,	4
A. Sampson,	do.	30
H. Sibley,	do.	114
S. L. Selden,	do.	55
J. B. Stillson,	do.	30
E. P. Willis,	do.	30

                                                1442

The remaining two hundred and fifty-eight shares is to be issued to Isaac Butts on the payment of twelve hundred dollars to this Company, and is to be delivered to him on his procuring a release from the contractors for constructing the line, and from persons claiming under them by assignment or by guaranteeing with satisfactory security the said Telegraph Company against all claims from said contractors, and those claiming under them as aforesaid, or by any other proceeding by which such claim should be effectually barred.

Fifth: That the present Directors of the said Company and all the officers thereof shall remain and continue to act as such Directors and officers of the new Company organized under this resolution until others are duly elected or appointed in their places respectively.

Sixth: That said Company shall and doth commence as a body corporate, this twentieth day of January, 1854, and shall terminate on the first day of April, 1951.

And be it further resolved, that the above resolution having been adopted by a majority of the said Board of Directors, a certificate thereof in due form shall be proved or acknowledged and filed and recorded, according to the requirements of the said act, passed June 29, 1853, entitled "An Act to amend an Act entitled an Act to provide for the Incorporation and Regulation of Telegraph Companies," passed April 12, 1848.

This certifies, that the foregoing are true and correct copies of Resolutions passed or adopted by a majority of the Board of Directors of the New York and Mississippi Valley Printing Telegraph Company, at a meeting held at the office of the Secretary of the said Company, the twentieth day of January, 1854.

In witness whereof, the President and Secretary of said Company, have {L.S.} hereunto subscribed their names, and caused the seal of the said Company to be hereunto affixed the day and year last above written. Isaac R. Elwood, Secretary.

HENRY S. POTTER, President.

We, the undersigned, being a majority of all the Directors of the aforesaid New York & Mississippi Valley Printing Telegraph Company, do certify that at a meeting of the said Board, duly convened, held at the office of the Secretary of the said Company, in the City of Rochester, on the twentieth day of January, 1854, the foregoing resolutions were adopted by a majority of the aforesaid Board of Directors; and that the above specifications in said resolutions contained; that is:

1. Of the name assumed to distinguish the Company, and to be used in its dealings, and by which it may sue and be sued;

2. Of the general route of the telegraph line owned and used by said Company, designating the points to be connected;

3. Of the capital stock of said Company, and of the number of shares, into which such stock is and shall be divided;

4. Of the names and places of residence of the shareholders, and the number of shares held by each of them respectively; and

5. Of the period at which said Company shall commence and terminate, are, in all respects, full, true and correct.

In witness whereof, we have, pursuant to the Statute in such case made and provided, made this certificate under our hands and seals at the City of Rochester, in the County of Monroe and State of New York, this twentieth day of January, in the year of our Lord, one thousand eight hundred and fifty-four.

Henry S. Potter,	(L.S.)
Isaac R. Elwood,	(L.S.)
F. Clarke,	(L.S.)
Hiram Sibley,	(L.S.)
Isaac Butts,	(L.S.)
W. H. Cheney,	(L.S.)
J. Medbery,	(L.S.)
J. B. Stillson,	(L.S.)
E. P. Willis,	(L.S.)
William Alling,	(L.S.)

CITY OF ROCHESTER, }
  In Monroe County. }

On the twentieth day of January, 1854, personally before me, the subscriber, appeared Henry S. Potter, Isaac R. Elwood, Freeman Clarke, Hiram Sibley, Isaac Butts, William H. Cheney, Joseph Medbery, Jerome B. Stillson, Edmund P. Willis, and William Alling, known to me to be the persons described in, and who executed the foregoing certificate, and severally and each for himself acknowledged that he had executed the said certificate for the purposes therein mentioned; and the said Henry S. Potter also acknowledged that he executed the foregoing official certificate as and being President of the New York & Mississippi Valley Printing Telegraph Company; and the said Isaac R. Elwood acknowledged that he executed the said last mentioned certificate as and being the Secretary of the said Company.

DANIEL B. BEACH,
Commis. of Deeds for said City.

Monroe Co. Clerk's Office, Rochester:

I certify, that Danl. B. Beach, Esq., was, at the date of the certificate of proof or acknowledgment of the annexed instrument in writing, a Commissioner of Deeds for the City of Rochester, in said county, duly authorized to take the same; that I am well acquainted with his handwriting, and verily believe that the signature to said certificate is genuine. And that the annexed instrument is executed and acknowledged according to the laws of this State.

{L.S.} In testimony whereof, I have hereunto set my hand, and affixed the seal of said county, this 7th day of February, A.D. 1854.

W. B. WILLIAMS, Clerk.

STATE OF NEW YORK, } ss.
Secretary's Office. }

I have compared the foregoing with a certificate of incorporation of the New York & Mississippi Valley Printing Telegraph Company, filed in this office, February 21, 1854, pursuant to chapter 471, of the Laws of 1853, and do certify that the same is a correct transcript therefrom and of the whole of said certificate.

{L.S.} Given under my hand and seal of office at the City of Albany, this twenty-second day of February, 1854.

A. G. JOHNSON,
Dep. Sec'y of State.

Fees, $3.25, paid.

(Source: O'Rielly Collection, Telegraph Pamphlets.)

APPENDIX 10

CONTRACT OF THE NEW YORK & MISSISSIPPI VALLEY PRINTING TELEGRAPH AND THE NEW YORK STATE PRINTING TELEGRAPH COMPANIES WITH THE CLEVELAND & TOLEDO, THE MICHIGAN SOUTHERN, AND THE NORTHERN INDIANA RAILROAD COMPANIES, FEBRUARY 7, 1854; WITH CERTAIN LATER ADDITIONS AND AMENDMENTS.

ARTICLES OF AGREEMENT, made and entered into this 7th day of February, one thousand eight hundred and fifty-four, between The New York and Mississippi Valley Printing Telegraph Company, of the first part; Francis Morris, Hiram Sibley and Freeman M. Edson, Trustees, appointed in and by a certain deed, bearing date the 18th day of April, 1853, to hold the undisposed of interests in House's Telegraphic Patents upon certain trusts therein mentioned, of the second part; the Cleveland and Toledo Rail Road Company, of the third part; and the Michigan Southern Rail Road Company, and the Northern Indiana Rail Road Company, of the fourth part; and the New York State Printing Telegraph Company, of the fifth part, witnesseth:

ARTICLE I. The Cleveland and Toledo Rail Company, parties of the third part, for and in consideration of the covenants and agreements hereinafter contained, do hereby covenant and agree that they will within twelve months from the date hereof, construct a Telegraph Line from Cleveland to Toledo, on or along the track of their Rail Road which passes nearest the shores of Lake Erie, and through the City of Sandusky, in the manner hereinafter particularly described; and that they will furnish the said line with at least, three printing instruments, and as many signal or rail road instruments as the Telegraph Company shall be willing to keep stations or offices for.

ART. II. The Michigan Southern and Northern Indiana Rail Road Companies, parties of the fourth part, for and in consideration of the covenants and agreements herein contained, do hereby covenant and agree that they will within twelve months from the date hereof, construct a Telegraph Line from Toledo to Chicago, on or along the track of their present Rail Road, running through Adrian, in the manner hereinafter particularly described, and they will furnish the said line with five or six printing instruments as shall be deemed necessary, and as many signal or rail road instruments, as the Telegraph Company shall be willing to keep stations or offices for.

ART. III. The said parties of the third and fourth parts are to have the right to put up and use on the said Telegraph Line at their own expense, signal or rail road instruments at any station or stations, along their roads respectively, where the said Telegraph Company are unwilling to keep stations, but the operation and management of the instruments at all such stations, are to be under the direction and control of the said Telegraph Company in the same manner as the instruments at other stations on said Telegraph Line.

ART. IV. The said Telegraph Line shall be constructed in a workmanlike manner and substantially, according to the following specifications, viz:

1. The wire shall be of the best quality, weighing not less than six hundred pounds to the mile.

2. There shall be at least thirty poles to the mile, which shall be firmly and securely set from four to five feet deep in the ground, according to the character thereof. They shall be either white oak, yellow cedar, or red cedar, or such other kind of timber as shall be satisfactory and approved by the person appointed as hereinafter provided to superintend the construction of the said Telegraph Line. They are all to be four

inches in diameter at the top, and at the surface of the ground, when set, they are to be at least seven inches in diameter, if of red cedar, and at least nine inches in diameter if of white oak or other timber. They shall be at least twenty-five feet in length, and at all crossings of rail roads, streets or highways, they shall be of suitable length to avoid all danger of contact with the wire. Wherever the Telegraph Line is not in a straight line, the poles shall be longer and stronger, and more firmly and securely set, than the others.

The bark shall be taken off the poles before setting, and those in cities or incorporated villages shall be such as the municipal authorities shall require.

3. The insulators shall be those commonly known as the "House-top-insulator," and shall be put on at the top in the most approved manner.

4. Wherever the said Telegraph Line is to cross streams where there are draw bridges, the same shall be crossed with wire insulated with Gutta Percha, and to be sunk and secured in a proper and suitable manner, something like the crossing of the line of the said Telegraph Company at Cincinnati, or in such other manner as the person superintending the construction of the line shall direct.

5. The said Telegraph Line shall be extended to some central and suitable point for an office, in the several cities and villages where offices are to be opened; and offices shall be rented by the said parties of the third and fourth parts, along their respective roads, but the rent of which is to be paid by the Telegraph Company from the time they take possession of the Line.

6. Such offices are to be provided with all necessary battery apparatus and with suitable fixtures and furniture, (but the aggregate expense thereof is not to exceed one thousand dollars,) to be paid by the Michigan Southern and Northern Indiana Rail Road Company, and by the Cleveland and Toledo Rail Road Company, not to exceed four hundred dollars.

7. The said Telegraph Company, parties of the first part, are to furnish at least one person, and, if necessary, two persons experienced in the building of House Telegraph Lines, to superintend the construction of said Telegraph Line, and whose compensation is to be paid by said Rail Road Companies.

ART. V. The said parties of the third and fourth parts do severally agree, each for themselves, that they will transport on their respective roads all officers, operators and agents of the Telegraph Company when traveling on the business of the Telegraph Company, without charge, and also to convey and carry all implements and materials, necessary for repairs, or for rebuilding the line, without charge; but such materials are to be carried at such reasonable times, and in such reasonable manner, as shall be most convenient to the said Rail Road Companies. The said parties of the third and fourth parts, do further agree as aforesaid, that the persons employed by them in repairing their respective Rail Roads, may observe the condition of the Telegraph Line along the sections where they are engaged and may mend breaks wherever discovered, without charge; but said Rail Road Companies shall not be responsible for keeping the Telegraph Line in order.

ART. VI. The said Telegraph Company, parties of the first part, for and in consideration of the several covenants and agreements herein contained do hereby covenant and agree, that within one month after the Telegraph Line shall be completed and furnished with instruments and apparatus as hereinbefore provided, and shall be in good working order, the same shall be taken and constitute a part and portion of their line, and that they will issue to the said Cleveland and Toledo Rail Road Company, or their order, such number of the shares of their capital stock, as shall be equal to one hundred and twenty-five dollars a mile, for the whole length of said Telegraph Line, from Cleveland to Toledo; and to the Michigan Southern and Northern Indiana Rail Road Companies, or to their order, such number of the shares of the capital stock as shall be equal to one hundred and twenty-five dollars a mile, for the whole length of said Telegraph Line, from Toledo to Chicago.

And the said Tele[graph]¹ Company, party of the first part, do further agree that they will [perform] the telegraph business of the said Rail Road Companies or, tran[smit over] their line all messages for the agents and officers of said [railroad com]panies, on rail road business, in the same manner [as] other business is [done] or messages transmitted, at all times, without charge; and they further agree to give the business of the said Rail [Road] Companies, touching the running of cars, or of anything con[cerned] with the operation and management of the said roads, req[uiring] immediate attention, the preference over all other business, so far as said Telegraph Company lawfully may.

ART. VII. It is further mutually agreed by and between the parties hereto of the first, second and third parts, that the said Cleveland and Toledo Rail Road Company, party of the third part, after they shall have constructed and completed the Telegraph Line from Cleveland to Toledo, along the Lake Shore Road as hereinbefore specified, shall have the right at any time, within five years from the date hereof, to construct a Telegraph Line from Toledo to Cleveland, along the track of their South or Norwalk Road, which line shall be constructed in the same manner as the line upon the Lake Shore Road, except as follows: that the wire may be smaller, but weighing not less than four hundred pounds to the mile, and poles may be one inch less in diameter at the surface of the ground, and the said wire may be strung on the same poles as the other wires, from Toledo to the point where the two tracks of said Rail Road divide; and from Grafton to Cleveland, the same may be strung on to the poles of the present line, unless it shall be deemed inexpedient by the Telegraph Company to string the second wire on said poles, and in that case new poles shall be set from Grafton to Cleveland, by and at the expense of the Telegraph Company. Where the said wire is strung on poles with another wire, as above provided, the insulator to be used shall be what is called the "Lewis' Side Insulator," or such other side insulator as the

¹ Material in brackets was obliterated in text.

Telegraph Company shall direct, which shall not be more expensive than the Lewis' Side Insulator.

The said Cleveland and Toledo Rail Road Company, in case they build the line in this article mentioned, shall furnish at least two printing instruments therefor, and as many rail road or signal instruments as the Telegraph Company shall be willing to open offices or keep stations for—and the said Rail Road Company shall have the right, to put up and use on the said Telegraph Line, at their own expense, signal or rail road instruments at points thereon where the Telegraph Company shall be unwilling to keep stations.

In case the said Rail Road Company shall construct the Telegraph Line in this article mentioned in manner aforesaid, and the same shall be in good working order, the said Telegraph Company, parties of the first part, agree that the same shall constitute a part and portion of their Line, and they shall issue to the said Rail Road Company, parties of the third part, or upon their order, eighty-five shares of the capital stock of the said Telegraph Company.

ART. VIII. It is further mutually agreed by and between the parties hereto, of the first, second and fourth parts, that the said Michigan Southern and Northern Indiana Rail Road Companies, parties of the fourth part, after they shall have constructed and completed the Telegraph Line from Toledo to Chicago, on or along their road through Adrian as herein specified, shall have the right at any time, within five years from date, to construct a Telegraph Line from Toledo to Chicago, by their new road, now being built from Toledo to intersect their present road at Elkhart, which line shall be constructed in the same manner as the other line, except that the wire may be smaller, but weighing not less than four hundred pounds to the mile, and the poles may be one inch less in diameter at the surface of the ground, and the said wire may be strung on the same poles from Elkhart to Chicago, using the insulator, known as Lewis' Side Insulator, or such other insulator as the Telegraph Company shall direct, and which shall not be more expensive than the Lewis' Side Insulator.

ART. IX. And it is further mutually agreed that the Telegraph Company is to do the telegraph business on the said Lines, in the two preceding articles mentioned, for the said Rail Road Companies, upon the same terms and in the same manner as upon the residue of their said Telegraph Line, and the said Rail Road Companies are to carry persons and materials for the Telegraph Company; and their repairers are to mend breaks in the same manner and upon the same terms, as upon their other tracks of Rail Road as hereinbefore provided.

ART. X. The Michigan Southern and Northern Indiana Rail Road Companies, parties of the fourth part, upon the completion of the said Telegraph Line from Cleveland to Chicago as first hereinbefore provided, are to have the right to build a Telegraph Line on their branch road, from Adrian to Monroe, which is to be operated by and to be under the control and management of the Telegraph Company, and instruments are to be furnished for as many stations as the Telegraph Company will keep; and the Rail Road Companies shall have the right to put up and use as many signal instruments on said line as they see fit, at their own expense.

ART. XI. In case the said Michigan Southern and Northern Indiana Rail Road Companies shall construct a Rail Road either from Toledo, or Monroe, to Detroit, and shall within five years from date, construct a Telegraph Line along said Road, to Detroit, aforesaid, and shall furnish at least two printing instruments, and as many signal instruments as the Telegraph Company shall be willing to keep stations for; and the said line to be constructed in the manner herein first described, then the said Telegraph Company, parties of the first part agree to issue to said Railroad Companies, or to their order, so many shares of their capital stock as shall be at least equal to one hundred and twenty-five dollars a mile for the length of said Telegraph Line from Toledo or Monroe to Detroit, according as the same shall be built, and shall also issue to the order of the said Trustees, parties of the second part, so many shares of stock for the patent right, as shall be equal to thirty dollars a mile for the length of the said Telegraph Line. All the covenants and agreements herein contained, in relation to doing the telegraph business of the Rail Road Companies, and in relation to the Rail Road Companies' carrying persons and materials of the Telegraph Company, and of the Rail Road repairers mending breaks, shall be applicable to the Rail Road and Telegraph Line in this article mentioned.

ART. XII. Francis Morris, and others, Trustees, parties of the second part, for and in consideration of the several covenants herein contained, covenant and agree, that upon the said Telegraph Line being completed from Cleveland to Chicago, as provided for in the first, second, third and fourth articles of this agreement, and upon receiving certificates for twelve thousand and seven hundred dollars of the Telegraph stock of the Telegraph Company, parties of the first part, for the benefit of the persons interested in the patent, they, the said Telegraph Company, shall be entitled to a grant of the right to operate, and may operate the said line from Cleveland to Chicago, by House's Printing Telegraph as hereinafter set forth, and they shall also be entitled to a like grant of the right to operate and may operate the Telegraph Lines mentioned in the seventh, eighth, tenth and eleventh articles of this agreement; provided the same are constructed within the period in said articles mentioned, and upon the completion of the line to Detroit, mentioned in article eleven of this agreement, as therein specified, and upon issuing upon the order of the said Trustees, the stock for the patent right as therein mentioned, the said Telegraph Company shall be entitled to a grant of the right to operate and may operate the same as aforesaid, and the said Telegraph Company is to be at liberty to renew or alter the said line or lines, or any part thereof, or change the route thereof, from time to time, deviating not more than twenty-five miles from the route as hereinbefore indicated or described, the said Rail Road Companies assenting thereto, and the said Telegraph Company is to be entitled in manner hereinafter mentioned to the use of House's Printing Telegraph upon such line or lines, original or altered as aforesaid, and the said Trustees, parties of the second part, do hereby further covenant and agree to grant, bargain, sell, assign and convey unto the said Telegraph Company, parties of the first part, upon the terms and conditions herein specified all their right, title and interest in, and to the exclusive use of House's Patent Invention, of the Magnetic Letter Printing Telegraph, on the lines of Telegraph as hereinbefore described, and set forth, and such grant and assignment hereby agreed to be made, are to include the rights of the said Trustees, parties of the second part, in and to said lines as herein described, in and to any extension, reissue, renewal, or renewals of the patent granted to Royal E. House, of, in and to any and all improvements that have been, or may hereafter be made upon, or added to the said Printing Telegraph in any of its parts or connections by the said Royal E. House and in, and to the said House's mode of insulating wires, and in and to any patent or patents that may be issued to the said House, or his assignees by the Government of the United States for any such improvements, and all renewals and reissues thereof.

And it is hereby declared that it is the meaning and intention of the said Trustees, parties of the second part, that the grant and assignment hereby agreed to be made, shall operate and extend so as to exclude and prevent any and all grants by the said Trustees, parties of the second part, or their successors to any person or persons, bodies politic or corporate, of any right, title, or authority, to use the said invention or improvements, or any or either of them, for the purpose of transmitting intelligence between any two telegraph offices or stations on the telegraph line of the said Telegraph Company, parties of the first part, as the same shall be owned by said Telegraph Company, if constructed according to the terms of this agreement, by any route whatever, directly or indirectly, between any such telegraph offices or stations on said line. But in case the said Telegraph Line shall not be operated in good faith, for the transmission of messages between the said Telegraph offices or stations on said lines so to be extended as aforesaid, or any or either of them, then messages may be transmitted by other House Lines indirectly between any or either of the said offices or stations, where the said lines shall not be operated in good faith as aforesaid.

And it is further declared, that it is the intention of the said Trustees, to exclude and prevent any grant by them or their successors, and they hereby covenant not to grant to any person or persons, bodies politic or corporate, any right, title or authority to use the said inventions or improvements, any or either of them, for the purpose of transmitting messages or intelligence on or along the Michigan Central Rail Road, or between places situated on said Central Rail Road, without the consent of the said Michigan Southern and Northern Indiana Rail Road Companies, parties of the fourth part.

Provided always, and the said grant and assignment herein agreed to be made are upon the following express conditions, and it is hereby declared by and between the parties hereto, that if the use of House's Printing Telegraph Machines for the transmission of messages between Chicago and Toledo, Sandusky and Cleveland, shall at any time hereafter be discontinued, or superseded by other instruments on said line, or shall not be used in good faith for the transmission of messages, then and in either of the said cases, the said Trustees, parties of the second part, or their successors for the time being, or a majority of them shall have full power to grant, bargain, sell, assign and convey to any person or persons, company or companies, the right to use the said inventions upon any line of Telegraph on the route or routes in this agreement set forth, or any part thereof, and such new grant or assignment may include all improvements, extensions and renewals as aforesaid, and the grant and assignment hereby agreed to be made, shall be modified accordingly.

ART. XIII. It is hereby expressly declared and agreed that the present stock of the New York and Mississippi Valley Printing Telegraph Company, is only one hundred and seventy thousand dollars, divided into seventeen hundred shares, of one hundred dollars each share.

ART. XIV. The said New York State Printing Telegraph Company, parties of the fifth part, for and in consideration that the said Telegraph Line of the parties of the first part, shall be constructed and extended to Chicago by the said Rail Road Companies, as herein provided in articles one and two, and in consideration that the said parties of the first part, shall continue to connect with and transmit their messages over the line of said parties of the fifth part, then they the said parties of the fifth part agree to transmit over their Line, the messages of the officers and agents of the said Rail Road Companies, on the business of their respective Rail Roads, without charge, in the same manner that other messages are transmitted.

ART. XV. The said Rail Road Companies, parties of the third and fourth parts, do hereby severally agree, each for themselves, that they will not during the continuance of the New York and Mississippi Valley Printing Telegraph Company, permit or allow any other Telegraph Line to be constructed upon and along their respective Rail Roads hereinbefore mentioned, or either of them, or any part thereof; but nothing herein shall be construed to affect or impair the existing right of the Telegraph Company now having a line on or along a part of the Michigan Southern and Northern Indiana Rail Road.

ART. XVI. All the existing debts and liabilities of the said Telegraph Company, parties of the first part, shall be a charge upon, and be paid out of the income or profits accruing on the present capital stock thereof, or from a portion of said capital stock, held as security by said Company, and no part of the said debts or liabilities shall be paid out of the income or profits accruing on the capital stock to be issued under and by virtue of this agreement, but such rateable proportion of said income, or profit (after paying current expenses,) as the stock so to be issued bears to the then capital stock of said Telegraph Company shall be set apart for the benefit of, and from time to time shall be divided among the owners of said stock, so to be issued under this agreement, till the aforesaid debts and liabilities shall be fully paid and discharged.

In witness whereof, the President and Secretary of the New York and Mississippi Valley Printing Telegraph Company, parties of the first part, have hereunto set their hands and caused the corporate seal of the said Company to be hereunto affixed; and Francis Morris, Hiram Sibley, and Freeman M. Edson, Trustees, parties of the second part, have hereto set their hands and seals: and [blank]
   of the Cleveland and Toledo Rail Road Company, parties of the third part, have hereunto set their hands, and caused the corporate seal of said Company to be hereunto affixed; and [blank]
 of the Michigan Southern Rail Road Company, and of the Northern Indiana Rail Road Company, parties of the fourth part, have hereunto set their hands, and cause the corporate seals of the said Companies respectively, to be hereunto affixed; and the President and Secretary of the New York State Printing Telegraph Company have hereunto set their hands and caused the corporated [sic] seals of the Company to be hereunto affixed.
   (Signed.)

       HENRY S. POTTER,
     President N. Y. & M. V. P. Tel. Co.
Isaac R. Elwood,
 Secretary N. Y. & M. V. P. Tel. Co.
       LEVI A. WARD,
     Pres't N. Y. & S. P. Tel. Co.
Isaac R. Elwood,
 Secretary N. Y. & S. P. Tel. Co.
F. Morris,   ⎫
Hiram Sibley, ⎬ Trustees of House Patent.
F. M. Edson. ⎭
 THE CLEVELAND & TOLEDO R. R. Co.
    BY SAMUEL F. VINTON, its Pres't.
THE MICHIGAN SOUTHERN AND NORTHERN RAIL ROAD COMPANY, [sic]
  BY THEIR PRESIDENT AND TREASURER.
      JOHN B. JERVIS, President.
Edwin C. Litchfield, Treasurer.

MEMORANDUM.

The following additions and explanations are made to, and become a part of, the contract between the New York and Mississippi Telegraph Company—Messrs. Morris, Sibley and Edson, Trustees; the Cleveland and Toledo Rail Road Company, and the Michigan Southern Rail Road Company, and the New York State Printing Telegraph Company, under date of the [blank]

I. The 6th specification of the fourth article of the said contract is intended to provide that the necessary battery apparatus, with suitable fixtures and furniture for the offices embraced in the 6th specification of the said 4th article, shall cost in the aggregate, a sum not exceeding fourteen hundred dollars, which shall be paid by the Michigan Southern Rail Road

Company, and by the Cleveland and Toledo Rail Road Company, in the proportion of one thousand dollars by the former, and four hundred by the latter.

II. The contract aforesaid is hereby declared to be so limited and interpreted, that the said first party doth hereby bind itself to the third party and the fourth party, severally, that it will maintain its line of Telegraph upon and over the several and respective Rail Roads of the said third and fourth parties, in good working order, and that it will at all times transact the business of, and maintain its communication with, the fifth part for the reception and transmission of messages and business; or will open and maintain an equally good telegraph communication with New York and the intermediate places, on terms equally advantageous, for the accommodation of the third and fourth parties.

III. The fifth article shall not be interpreted to require the third or fourth parties to transport persons and materials other than on ordinary trains.

IV. The compensation of the Superintendent, under the seventh specification of the fourth article, shall not exceed the rate of fifty dollars per month and found.

(Signed and sealed.)

The Cleveland and Toledo Rail Road Company,

By S. F. VINTON, its President.

The Michigan Southern Rail Road Company, and the Northern Indiana Rail Road Company, by their President, and by their Treasurer.

JOHN B. JERVIS.

Edwin C. Litchfield.

(Source: O'Rielly Collection, Telegraph Pamphlets.)

APPENDIX 11

AGREEMENT OF THE NEW YORK & MISSISSIPPI VALLEY PRINTING TELEGRAPH COMPANY LEASING THE LAKE ERIE TELEGRAPH COMPANY, MARCH 30, 1854.

AN AGREEMENT,

Made and entered into this thirtieth day of March, in the year one thousand eight hundred and fifty-four, between The Lake Erie Telegraph Company, of the one part, and The New York & Mississippi Valley Printing Telegraph Company, of the other part, as follows:

1. The Lake Erie Telegraph Company is to lease in perpetuity to the New York & Mississippi Valley Printing Telegraph Company, its line extending from Buffalo to Detroit, and from Cleveland to Pittsburgh, and all its property of every kind, including its right to the use of Morse's telegraph patent upon such line.

2. The New York & Mississippi Valley Printing Telegraph Company is to pay to the Lake Erie Telegraph Company, as rent, a sum which shall

be equal to the dividends, which the former Company shall, from time to time, make upon fifty thousand dollars of its own stock, that is to say: the sum to be paid, as rent to the Lake Erie Company, shall be the same as the said Company would receive, if fifty thousand dollars were added to the capital stock of the New York & Mississippi Valley Printing Telegraph Company, and held by the Lake Erie Company, and shall be payable at the same time with dividends to Stockholders.

3. In case the Lake Erie Telegraph Company, shall, at any time, obtain an order, decree or injunction restraining the use of Morse's Telegraph Patent upon the line, known as the Erie & Michigan (or Speed's) Telegraph Line, temporarily or otherwise, the New York & Mississippi Valley Printing Telegraph Company is to pay to the Lake Erie Telegraph Company at the rate of five thousand dollars per annum, for such time as the said restraint shall continue, and said Erie & Michigan Line shall be actually stopped, by reason of such restraint; whether it be for one year, or for a longer or shorter period, such payment to be made semi-annually, except that for all periods less than a half-year, payment shall be made at the termination of such period.

4. The New York & Mississippi Valley Printing Telegraph Company is not to make any arrangement for a consolidation with the Erie & Michigan (or Speed's) Line, or to purchase, lease or hire the same, or in any way to obtain the control of such line or a controlling interest therein without the previous consent by resolution of the Board of Directors of the Lake Erie Telegraph Company. This article, however, is not to be construed to prevent the former Company from purchasing the stock of said Erie & Michigan Line, to an amount not exceeding thirty thousand dollars.

5. The New York & Mississippi Valley Printing Telegraph Company is to add to its capital stock, the sum of fifty thousand dollars, which is to be issued in the name of the Directors of the Lake Erie Telegraph Company, but to be retained in the hands of the Secretary of the New York & Mississippi Valley Printing Telegraph Company, to be delivered to such Directors or to such persons, as they shall direct; whenever they shall procure and deliver to such Secretary an absolute assignment and conveyance to the New York & Mississippi Valley Printing Telegraph Company of its line, and all property connected therewith, together with the right to use Morse's Patent thereon executed by all the holders of stock in said Lake Erie Telegraph Company, the said Directors to have a right in the meantime, to vote upon such stock, in person or by proxy, at all meetings of the Stockholders of said New York & Mississippi Valley Printing Telegraph Company.

6. It is understood that the Lake Erie Telegraph Company is to retain all its legal rights and claims against the line, known as Speed's, or the Erie & Michigan Line, or any persons connected therewith for violations, either past, present or future, of the rights of the said Lake Erie Telegraph Company, by the use of Morse's Patent upon said Erie & Michigan Line.

It is also understood that the New York & Mississippi Valley Printing

Telegraph Company, from the time this agreement takes effect, is to bear every expense, connected with the line of the Lake Erie Telegraph Company, including taxes upon said line, or upon the stock of the Company, assessed to such Company; and that each Company is to pay and discharge all its present debts and obligations; that is to say: the New York & Mississippi Valley Printing Telegraph Company is not to assume or pay any debts or liabilities of the Lake Erie Telegraph Company, nor is the fifty thousand dollars of stock herein provided for, or the interest of the Lake Erie Telegraph Company, which it represents, to be charged with any portion of the present indebtedness of the New York & Mississippi Valley Printing Telegraph Company.

In witness whereof, the President and Secretary of the New York & Mississippi Valley Printing Telegraph Company, have hereunto subscribed their names, and affixed the corporate seal of said last named Company.

{L.S.}

H. S. POTTER, President,
Of the N.Y. & M.V.P.T. Co.

Isaac R. Elwood, Secretary,
Of the N.Y. & M.V.P.T. Co.

And in witness whereof, the Directors of the Lake Erie Telegraph Company, or a major part of them, have hereunto subscribed their names, the said last named Company having no common seal.

Samuel L. Selden,
S. P. Ely,
Alvah Strong,
Jonathan Child.

(Source: O'Rielly Collection, Telegraph Pamphlets.)

APPENDIX 12

AGREEMENT OF THE NEW YORK & MISSISSIPPI VALLEY PRINTING TELEGRAPH COMPANY WITH J. J. SPEED AND J. H. WADE, APRIL 29, 1854; AND CERTAIN SUPPLEMENTAL AGREEMENTS.

This Agreement made this twenty-ninth day of April, 1854, between J. J. Speed and J. H. Wade, of the first part; and The New York & Mississippi Valley Printing Telegraph Company, of the second part, witnesseth:

That the said Speed and Wade, in consideration of the sum of fifty thousand dollars to be paid and secured to them as hereinafter provided, and of the provisions and conditions of this agreement, have agreed and do hereby covenant and agree that they will sell, assign and transfer to the said Telegraph Company, or to such person or persons as the Directors of said Company shall designate, all and singular the stocks, rights, property and interests hereinafter specified, viz:

1. All the rights and interests which they or either of them have in and to any patent or patents, issued to S. F. B. Morse or his assigns, for any invention or improvement in or upon the electric telegraph, including their rights and interests in any re-issue, renewal or extension of such patent or patents; and especially all their rights acquired under or by virtue of two certain conveyances to said Speed, one from said Morse and Alfred Vale [sic], executed by Amos Kendall as the attorney of said Morse & Vail, and bearing date June 20, 1853; the other from F. O. J. Smith, and the other proprietors of said telegraph patents, executed by Henry O'Rielly as attorney for the said proprietors, and bearing date Dec. 25, 1852.

2. The avails of all sales which may have been made by Ezra Cornell or by J. D. Caton of the said telegraph patent or patents, or of any right or interest therein, as attornies for the said Speed or Wade, or either of them, together with the benefits of all contracts which may have been made by the said Cornell and Caton, or either of them, for the construction of any line or lines of telegraph, or for the sale or transfer of any rights in relation to any such line or lines as well as all profits which have accrued, or shall accrue from the construction of any such line, or from the sale or transfer of any such rights, so far only as such avails, benefits or profits appertain or belong to the said Speed and Wade, or either of them, either at law or in equity, excepting, however the line known as "The Illinois & Mississippi, or Caton's Line," extending from Chicago to St. Louis, with branches, and the Ohio, Indiana and Illinois Line, which are not included in this transfer.

3. The following stock and rights to stock, viz: All the stock which the said Speed & Wade, or either of them, have or to which they are entitled in the line known as the Erie and Michigan (or Speed's Line,) being about $30,000: whole capital, $114,000.

Also all the stock to which they or either of them are entitled in the New York & Erie Line, being about 6-20 of the whole stock.

Also all the stock to which they or either of them are entitled in the Cleveland & Cincinnati Line, being about $22,500: whole capital $89,100.

Also all the stock to which they or either of them are entitled in the Cincinnati & St. Louis Line, being about $15,000: whole capital $61,500.

Also all the stock or rights to stock or interest of them or either of them, in the following lines owned by the Association, called "The Ohio Telegraph Company," such rights amounting to about 3/4 of the entire lines, viz:

> The line from Pittsburgh to Crestline.
> The line from Crestline to Fort Wayne.
> The line from Mansfield to Huron.
> The line from Galleon to Union.

4. One-half of the bonds of the Cincinnati & St. Louis Telegraph Company held by said Wade, the whole of said bonds amounting to $4,735.81.

5. All the rights and interests of the said Speed & Wade, or either of them, in the Cleveland & Pittsburgh and Cleveland & Zanesville Lines.

6. All other rights and interests which the said Speed & Wade have either jointly or severally in connection with Ezra Cornell or otherwise in any telegraph contracts or lines of whatsoever nature the same may be, except as provided in Article II of this agreement.

The New York & Mississippi Valley Printing Telegraph Company, party of the second part, agrees to pay to the said parties of the first part for the rights and property above specified, the sum of fifty thousand dollars, in manner following, viz: twelve thousand five hundred dollars in cash upon the execution and delivery of proper conveyances of said rights and property, and of the leases hereinafter specified.

The remaining thirty-seven thousand five hundred dollars to be secured by the promissory notes of responsible parties, payable one-third in six, one-third in twelve, and one-third in eighteen months with interest at seven per cent, said notes to be guaranteed by the New York & Mississippi Valley Printing Telegraph Company.

The said party of the second part also agrees to take leases of the following lines for the term of five years each, and upon the following terms, viz:

The Cleveland & Cincinnati Line, at an annual rent of four thousand five hundred dollars.

The Cincinnati & St. Louis Line, at an annual rent of eighteen hundred dollars after the expiration of the first year.

The four lines of the Ohio Telegraph Company, at an annual rent of three thousand dollars.

The said party of the second part is to covenant in said leases to keep up and maintain and work the said lines, and to return them to the respective Companies, at the expiration of such leases, in as good working condition as now, natural wear of instruments and wire excepted.

Said Wade is to be entitled to ten per cent of the avails of all sales of such patent or patents, which the party of the second part may make to Rail Road Companies for the period of three years from the date of conveyance of such patents. He also undertakes to devote his time and attention to the interests of the said party of the second part for the like period or so much thereof as he may choose, and the said party of the second part may require at the rate of $3,000 salary per annum, in addition to the said percentage.

It is understood that the time for the payment of the Cincinnati & St. Louis Line bonds is to be extended one year.

It is agreed that the New York & Mississippi Valley Printing Telegraph Company shall issue to me, said Wade, ten thousand dollars of the capital stock of said Company in lieu of the ten per cent of the avails of sales of patents provided for above, and the provision entitling the said Wade to the said ten per cent, is hereby modified accordingly.

And it is further agreed that in case the party of the second part shall, within ten days from the date hereof, give written notice by mail to said Speed & Wade that this contract will not be carried out on the part of the said party of the second part, such notice to be addressed to said Speed at Ithaca, Tompkins county, New York, and to said Wade at Columbus, Ohio: then this contract is to be considered as rescinded; and in case of such rescinding the said party of the second part is to pay to the said Speed & Wade the sum of two thousand dollars as liquidated damages for the failure of said party of the second part, to perform this contract.

In witness whereof, the said Speed & Wade, on their part and a majority of the Executive Committee of the New York & Mississippi Valley Printing Telegraph Company, on the part of said Company, have hereunto subscribed their names respectively, the day and year first above written.

(Signed.)   J. J. SPEED, JR.
J. H. WADE.

Henry S. Potter,
Hiram Sibley,
Samuel L. Selden,   Executive Committee.
Freeman Clarke,

ASSIGNMENT,

Of J. J. Speed, J. H. Wade and I. R. Elwood, of the Morse Patent.

Know all men by these presents, that I John J. Speed, Jr., for and in consideration of the sum of four thousand dollars to me, in hand paid, have bargained and sold, and by the presents do bargain, sell, assign and convey unto Isaac R. Elwood, for the exclusive use and benefit of the New York & Mississippi Valley Printing Telegraph Company, all my rights and interests in and to any patent or patents heretofore issued to S. F. B. Morse, or his assigns, for any invention or improvement in the art of telegraphing, or in the electric telegraph, so far as the States of Ohio, Michigan, Indiana, Illinois, Wisconsin, Iowa and the Territory of Minnesota, are concerned, together with all his rights and interests in and to any re-issue, renewal or extension of such patent or patents in and for said States and Territory; such rights and interests having been acquired under and by virtue of two certain assignments or conveyances to said Speed, one from F. O. J. Smith, and the other proprietors of such patents executed by Henry O'Rielly, as their attorney, and bearing date December 25, 1852; the other from the said S. F. B. Morse and Alfred Vail, executed by Amos Kendall, as their attorney, and bearing date June 20, 1853; copies of which assignments are hereunto annexed; and I, the said Speed, do hereby undertake and agree, that this assignment does and shall convey all the rights conveyed to me by the said two assignments or conveyances, except so far as contracts may have been made by myself, or my legally authorized agents for the construction of lines within the said States or Territory, in good faith and prior to the date thereof.

Dated April 29, 1854.

JOHN J. SPEED, JR., (L.S.)

For and in consideration of the sum of one dollar to me in hand paid, I do hereby release and assign to Isaac R. Elwood, for the uses mentioned in the within deed, all my rights and interests, either legal or equitable, in and to the patent or patents, or in the re-issue, renewal or extension of the patent or patents mentioned and conveyed in and by said deed.

J. H. WADE.

For a good and valuable consideration, and for the purpose of carrying out the Sixth Article of a certain Agreement between the New York & Mississippi Valley Printing Telegraph Company, of the first part; Francis Morris, Hiram Sibley and Freeman M. Edson Trustees appointed to hold the undisposed of interests in House's Telegraph Patents, of the second part, and Henry S. Potter and other Stockholders in the said Telegraph Company, of the third part, bearing date April 29, 1854, I, Isaac R. Elwood, have bargained and sold, and by these presents do bargain, sell, assign and convey unto the above named Francis Morris, Hiram Sibley and Freeman M. Edson, as Trustees for the exclusive use and benefit of the said New York & Mississippi Valley Printing Telegraph Company, and for the purposes, and upon the terms specified in the aforesaid Article VI of said Agreement, all the rights and interests in and to any patent or patents heretofore issued to S. F. B. Morse, or his assigns, for any invention or improvement in the art of telegraphing, or in the electric telegraph, so far as the States of Ohio, Michigan, Indiana, Illinois, Wisconsin, Iowa, and the Territory of Minnesota are concerned, together with all rights and interests in and to said States and Territory, acquired by me, said Elwood, by, through or under and by virtue of a certain assignment or conveyance to me executed by John J. Speed, Jr., bearing date April 29, 1854, hereunto annexed, in as full and ample manner as the same were conveyed to me by the aforesaid assignment or conveyance.

In witness whereof, I have hereunto set my hand and seal this twentieth day of December, in the year one thousand eight hundred and fifty-four.

ISAAC R. ELWOOD, (L.S.)

(Source: O'Rielly Collection, Telegraph Pamphlets.)

APPENDIX 13

CONSOLIDATION AGREEMENT BETWEEN THE NEW YORK & MISSISSIPPI VALLEY PRINTING TELEGRAPH COMPANY AND THE ERIE & MICHIGAN TELEGRAPH COMPANY, OCTOBER 19-20, 1855.

Whereas, at a meeting of the Stockholders of the ERIE AND MICHIGAN TELEGRAPH COMPANY, held at the city of Detroit, in the State of Michigan, in pursuance of notice duly given on the eighth day of August, A.D. 1855, the said Stockholders passed a resolution, in the following words:

Resolved, That the proposal made to the Stockholders this day, by the NEW YORK & MISSISSIPPI VALLEY PRINTING TELEGRAPH COMPANY, through Messrs. Selden and Elwood, relative to a Consolidation of this Company

Resolution E. & M. Tel. Co.

with that, is considered favorably by the Stockholders of this Company.

That this Company are willing to enter into such a Consolidation upon the general terms, and embracing the property of the New York and Mississippi Valley Printing Telegraph Company, as set forth in said proposal; and that a committee of three Stockholders of this Company be appointed, with full powers and authority to carry said proposal into effect, by arranging and agreeing upon the necessary details, and reducing the same to a formal contract, to be executed by the Board of Directors of this Company, and by the Board of Directors or other authorized agents of the said first mentioned Company, to be executed in duplicate, and filed among the records and proceedings of this Company.

Capital,
$500,000

Provided, That the capital stock of the Company, as consolidated shall be Five Hundred Thousand Dollars. One Hundred and Fifty Thousand Dollars of which shall belong to the Stockholders of this Company, to be distributed and delivered to them according to the amount of stock which each holds in this Company, at the time the contract is to take effect. This proviso to be assented to by said first named Company. The committee appointed are Messrs. Ezra Cornell, D. S. Walbridge, and J. M. Howard. AND WHEREAS, The proposal referred to in said resolution, was in the following words, to wit:

"Proposals of the New York and Mississippi Valley Printing Telegraph Company, by the Committee; Capital Stock $342,000; represented by House Line, from Buffalo to Chicago, and from Cleveland to Louisville, about 930 miles; Lake Erie Line, from Buffalo to Detroit and from Cleveland to Pittsburgh, 600 miles; House Patent for the States of Ohio, Indiana, Illinois, Michigan, Wisconsin, Iowa, and territory of Minnesota. We owe about $90,000; represented by the following property; about fifteen sixteenths of the stock in the line along the Rail Road from Pittsburgh to Fort Wayne, from west line to Union, and from Mansfield to Sandusky, about 500 miles; making about $84,000 Stock. The Capital Stock in the Erie and Michigan Telegraph Company, $30,000. The Capital Stock in the Cleveland and Cincinnati Telegraph Company, $20,000. The Capital Stock in Cincinnati and St. Louis Telegraph Company, $15,000. Bonds against Cincinnati and St. Louis Telegraph Company, $2,500. A majority of the stock in the Sciota Line, $9,050. We are to have the stock which is to be represented in the said Line now building from Cincinnati to Vincennes, (88 miles now in operation,) when completed, about 190 miles, $19,000. The Morse Patent for the States and Territory above named. We also are to receive for the House Patent, $500 on the Illinois Central Rail Road Line, and an exclusive connection with it at Chicago and other points, where it may intersect Lines belonging to or controlled by this Company."

And Whereas, at a meeting of the said New York and Mississippi Valley Printing Telegraph Company, held at the office of the Secretary thereof, at Rochester, New York, on the thirteenth day of August, A.D. 1855, the said Company passed a resolution in the words following, to wit:

Resolved, That this Board hereby assent and agree on behalf of this

Company, to a consolidation with the Erie and Michigan Telegraph Company, substantially according to the resolution of the Stockholders of the last named Company, passed at a meeting thereof, held at Detroit, on the 8th day of August, 1855, by increasing the Capital Stock of this Company, to Five Hundred Thousand Dollars; of which one hundred and fifty thousand dollars shall belong to the Stockholders of the Erie and Michigan Telegraph Company, and be issued and distributed according to the foregoing resolution, and the remaining $350,000 of the said capital to belong to the present Stockholders of this Company; that Hiram Sibley, Samuel L. Selden, and Isaac Butts, be a committee on the part of the Company, to meet a like committee on the part of the Erie and Michigan Telegraph Company, to arrange and agree upon the necessary details, and reduce the same to a formal contract or agreement, and that the President and Secretary of this Board be, and they are hereby authorized to execute the said contract or agreement, on behalf of this Company, when the same shall be settled and agreed upon by the said committee. *Resolution N.Y. & M. V.P. Tel. Co.*

Now, in order to carry out said two resolutions, and to unite and consolidate said two companies, they, the said two companies, hereby enter into an agreement as follows, that is to say:

FIRST.—Said companies shall, for the purposes herein expressed, become consolidated, and shall be denominated "THE WESTERN UNION TELEGRAPH." But, until the incorporation of the said consolidated company shall be effected, as hereinafter proposed, the affairs and business of said consolidated company, shall be managed by and in the name of the New York and Mississippi Valley Printing Company, a body corporate, organized under the laws of the State of New York, subject, however, to the terms and provisions of this agreement. *Name of consolidated Co. By whom managed.*

SECOND.—From the date at which this contract shall take effect, all the property owned by either company, except cash on hand and debts owing to each company, respectively, shall, for the purpose of carrying out the business of telegraphing, which is the object of this agreement, belong to said consolidated company, and be liable for the payment of all debts contracted by said last mentioned company. But the property of the said Erie and Michigan Telegraph Company now owned by them, shall not be held liable for any debt now contracted by said New York and Mississippi Valley Printing Telegraph Company; nor shall the Stockholders of said Erie and Michigan Telegraph Company be under any personal liability for such debts. *Property to belong to consolidated Co.* *E. & M. property not liable for old debts.*

THIRD.—The earnings of said consolidated company together with all the avails of the property mentioned in said proposal above recited, shall be used and applied as follows: *Earnings how to be used.*

1. To the payment of all the current expenses of operating and sustaining the lines owned or worked by said two companies, including repairs, rents, and all incidental expenses connected with the operating of said lines. But this provision shall not be construed to authorize the said consolidated company to use said earnings for building new lines, or for rebuilding any part of the Cincinnati and St. Louis Line, which is now

down, without the consent of a majority of the Directors of the Erie and Michigan Telegraph Company.

Surplus earnings, how divided & used.

2. After payment of the current expenses, as aforesaid, seven-tenths of the net earnings shall be set apart, to be applied upon the indebtedness of the New York and Mississippi Valley Printing Telegraph Company, hereinbefore mentioned, and of any bonds which may be issued, as hereinafter provided. Of the remaining three-tenths of the said net earnings, five thousand dollars shall in like manner be applied to the payment of the said indebtedness; after which, a dividend may be made to the Stockholders of the Erie and Michigan Telegraph Company, not exceeding six per cent per annum, payable semi-annually; and the residue of such earnings, if any, shall be applied to the payment of the indebtedness aforesaid, until the same is fully discharged.

If the application, as aforesaid, of seven-tenths of the net earnings shall overpay that portion of the indebtedness which will belong to the New York and Mississippi Valley Printing Telegraph Company to pay, (it being understood each company is to pay in proportion to its share of stock,) the disposition of the remaining three-tenths, hereinbefore prescribed, shall continue until such excess, with annual interest, is repaid to the said New York and Mississippi Valley Printing Telegraph Company.

E. & M. Co. to pay its share of bonds.

3. Until the Erie and Michigan Telegraph Company has paid its share of the indebtedness and bonds, in the manner above provided, the stock of the consolidated company, belonging to the Erie and Michigan Telegraph Company, shall stand in the name of said last mentioned company, and shall not be assignable.

4. In case the consolidated company shall deem it advisable to issue any more of said bonds, for the purchase of any stock, or interests in other Telegraph Lines, or for extending its existing lines, such bonds shall be paid in the manner and in the proportions hereinbefore provided.

E. & M. Co. not dissolved.

FOURTH.—The organization of the Erie and Michigan Telegraph Company shall not be considered as dissolved by this agreement, but its Board of Directors and other officers, duly elected and appointed by said company, shall be considered as vested with full power to conduct all its affairs, subject, however, to this agreement; and it shall be the duty of said last mentioned company, its directors and officers to cause the same to be performed.

E. & M. Co. to vote at election.

FIFTH.—The said Board of Directors or any person or persons, by them or by the Stockholders, duly appointed for the purpose, shall have the right to represent said Erie and Michigan Telegraph Company, and to vote at all meetings of Stockholders of the said New York and Mississippi Valley Printing Telegraph Company, upon the one hundred and fifty thousand dollars of stock mentioned in the first recited resolution, hereby granted to said Erie and Michigan Telegraph Company, until a new incorporation shall be effected under the laws of New York, now contemplated, and which is to embrace both said companies and their property, so far as practicable, and until said $150,000 stock shall be distributed among the Stockholders of said Erie and Michigan Telegraph Company; but the person or persons voting on said stock of Erie and Michigan Telegraph Company, shall not be entitled to give more than three-tenths of the votes cast or given for Directors, or upon any other question voted upon at such meeting. It is understood that the consolidated company is to be incorporated under the general law of the State of New York, under the name of THE WESTERN UNION TELEGRAPH COMPANY, or the name of the New York and Mississippi Valley Printing Telegraph Company is to be changed to the name aforesaid, and its capital stock increased to the sum of five hundred thousand dollars, as required by this agreement. *To be incorporated or name chang'd.*

SIXTH.—It is further agreed, that the articles of agreement, bearing date the tenth day of April, A.D. 1855, by and between the said Erie and Michigan Telegraph Company by Ezra Cornell, their President, and the New York, Albany and Buffalo Electro-Magnetic Telegraph Company, shall be carried out and performed according to its spirit and intent, by said consolidated company, and by any incorporated company that may be formed in pursuance of this contract. *To fulfil contract with N.Y., A. & B. Tel. Co.*

SEVENTH.—It is further agreed, that the contract entered into by and between the Southern Michigan Telegraph Company, by Mr. Ezra Cornell, supposed to be dated some time in May, 1855, shall also be carried out and performed according to its spirit and intent, so far at least as to secure said Southern Michigan Telegraph Company, the same amount of business in the aggregate, as it would have had under said contract. But this provision is upon the condition that said company shall at all times keep up and maintain its lines in good working order, and shall continue to do its proper share of the business from Toledo to Chicago. In case of any disagreement as to the share of the Southern Michigan Telegraph Company, or as to the good working order of its line, it shall be referred to three persons, one to be chosen by the Southern Michigan Telegraph Company, and one by the consolidated company, and the two so selected, to choose a third, and the decision of the said three persons, or any two of them, shall be final on the subject of said disagreement. *Clauses as to S. M. Tel. Co.*

Reference.

EIGHTH.—It is further agreed, that the Patents owned by the consolidated company, shall not be used for the purpose of building a line or lines of Telegraph, which shall come in direct competition with, or where the principal object shall be, to get the business of places on the lines of the Illinois and Mississippi Telegraph Company; the Wisconsin State Telegraph Company, or the Ohio, Indiana, and Illinois Telegraph Company: *Provided*, That in case either of said companies shall neglect to keep and maintain, upon their respective routes, Lines of Telegraph, which shall work with reasonable regularity, then the said last mentioned company shall be no longer bound by this article, so far as the company, guilty of such neglect, is concerned; but this article shall not be construed so as to prevent the consolidated company from extending their present line to St. Louis from Louisville, and from Cincinnati. And provided further, that the said Illinois and Mississippi Telegraph Company, the Wisconsin State Telegraph Company, and the Ohio, Indiana, and Illinois Telegraph Com- *As to new lines.*

Ill. and Miss. Co. Wis. State Co. O., Ind., & Ill. Co.

May extend line to St. Louis.

*Exclusive
connection.*
pany, shall connect exclusively with said consolidated company, at all
points of intersection at their respective lines: Excepting so far as the
Ohio, Indiana and Illinois Line is bound by existing contract, to connect
with the National Line, which contract expires two years from next May,
and requires the Ohio, Indiana and Illinois Line to give all its business,
(except answers to messages from other lines,) originating at any of its
offices south of a line drawn from the city of New York to Quincy, in the
State of Illinois, to the National Line, to be forwarded in exchange for its
business, leaving the Ohio, Indiana and Illinois Line the right to send all
its business north of the aforesaid line from New York to Quincy, by the
lines along the Lakes, except answers to messages received from the National Line.

*Certain lines
entitled to
local
business.*
　　　It is further understood and agreed, that whenever the Ohio, Indiana
and Illinois Line shall be extended into the offices of the consolidated
company, at Cincinnati, Dayton and Chicago, and furnished with instruments, and operated in said offices, it shall be entitled to all the local business, between Chicago and Cincinnati, and intermediate places, whenever
said Ohio, Indiana and Illinois Line shall be in working condition; and
so long as the said Ohio, Indiana and Illinois Line remains in the offices
of the National Line, at Cincinnati and Dayton, it shall send at least an
equal share of its business, to be delivered from the offices of the consolidated company, at Dayton and Cincinnati. And whenever the said
Ohio, Indiana, and Illinois Line shall be extended into the office of the
consolidated company, at Toledo, and furnished with an instrument, and
operated in said office, it shall be entitled to all business between Toledo
and Vincennes, and intermediate places, whenever said line is in working
condition. And the business to and from Fort Wayne eastward, shall be
transmitted by the Ohio, Indiana and Illinois Line, by way of Toledo, and
by the line along the Ohio and Indiana Rail Road, as near as may be in
equal parts, when both said lines are in working order.

*Office
expenses,
how di-
vided.*
　　　It is also understood and agreed, that the Ohio, Indiana and Illinois
Line shall, from time to time, pay a just and fair share of the office expenses, at Chicago, Toledo, Dayton and Cincinnati, and at any other
place where the two lines shall occupy an office together; and in case the
companies cannot agree upon the share of the office expenses, which each
shall bear, it shall be referred, from time to time, to three persons, one to
be chosen by each company, and the two so selected shall choose a third,
and the decision of the said three persons, or any two of them, shall be
final.

*E. & M. Co.
entitled
to two
directors.*
　　　NINTH.—The said Erie and Michigan Telegraph Company, shall at all
times be entitled to at least two Directors in the Board of Directors, of
said New York and Mississippi Valley Printing Telegraph Company,
whether under this contract or the contemplated incorporation.

　　　TENTH.—This contract, after having been executed according to the two
above recited resolutions, shall take effect on and after the first day of
November, A.D. 1855.

Hiram Sibley, ⎫ Com. on part
Samuel L. Selden, ⎬ of the N. Y.
Isaac Butts, ⎭ & Miss. Val.
    Print. Tel. Co.

E. Cornell, ⎤ Com. on part of the
J. M. Howard, ⎦ E. & M. Tel. Co.

At a meeting of the Board of Directors of the Erie and Michigan Telegraph Company, held at the office of J. M. Howard, Esq., in the city of Detroit, on the 19th day of October, A.D. 1855—Present, Mr. Cornell, Pres't; Mr. Joslin, Mr. Wood, Mr. Sholes, Mr. Howard and Mr. Wendell, Directors—After reading and considering the foregoing contract, it was

Resolved, That this Board do hereby ratify and confirm the said contract: Provided, a duplicate thereof, shall, according to the first recited resolution, be executed by the above names New York and Mississippi Valley Printing Telegraph Company.

Witness our hands, at Detroit, the day and year last aforesaid.

E. Cornell,
C. Joslin,
M. B. Woods,   Directors of the
C. C. Sholes,   E. & M. Tel. Co.
J. M. Howard,
C. E. Wendell,

Attest

C. E. Wendell, Sec'y.

At a meeting of the Directors of the New York and Mississippi Valley Printing Telegraph Company, held at the office of the Secretary, on the 20th day of October, 1855, it was

Resolved, That this Board approves of the amended contract, between the New York and Mississippi Valley Printing Telegraph Company and the Erie and Michigan Telegraph Company, as agreed to and signed by Hiram Sibley, Samuel L. Selden, and Isaac Butts, the Committee on the part of this company, and do hereby ratify and adopt the same, and authorize and direct the President and Secretary to execute the same.

Now, therefore, in pursuance of the resolutions above recited, passed by the Board of Directors of the New York and Mississippi Valley Printing Telegraph Company, in witness of the foregoing agreement, on behalf the said last named company, the President and Secretary thereof, have hereunto subscribed their names and affixed the corporate seal of the said

{ L.S. } company, this twentieth day of October, in the year of our Lord one thousand eight hundred and fifty-five.

HENRY S. POTTER, Pres't,
of N. Y. & M. V. P. Tel. Co.

Isaac R. Elwood, Sec'y,
of N.Y. & M. V. P. Tel. Co.

(Source: O'Rielly Collection, Telegraph Pamphlets.)

APPENDIX 14

The Six Party Contract, or Treaty of the Six Nations

Articles of Agreement for the Union, Protection and Improvement of Certain Telegraph Lines in North America, August 10, 1857; and Certain Supplemental Agreements.

ARTICLES OF AGREEMENT in Six Parts, made and concluded this Tenth Day of August, in the year of our Lord, One Thousand Eight Hundred and Fifty-seven, by and between—

1st Part. The American Telegraph Company, of the *First* part;

2d Part.   The New York, Albany and Buffalo Electro-Magnetic Telegraph Company, of the *second* part;

3d Part.   The Atlantic and Ohio Telegraph Company and the Pennsylvania Telegraph Company, acting together under a contract of union, of the *Third* part;

4th Part. The Western Union Telegraph Company, of the *Fourth* part;

5th Part. The New Orleans and Ohio Telegraph Lessees, of the *Fifth* part;

6th Part. The Illinois and Mississippi Telegraph Company, and the Chicago and Mississippi Telegraph Company, of the *Sixth* part;

all said parties being corporations or associations, respectively acting under and by virtue of charters, granted by the Legislature of some State of the United States, or by articles of association:—Witnesseth,

Patent. ARTICLE I. That the *five* last named parties aforesaid, hereby covenant and agree to unite with the party of the *first* part, in the payment of the purchase of the *patented invention* of David E. Hughes, called "Hughes' Compound Magnetic and Vibrating Printing Instrument," as conveyed by said Hughes and David W. Brodnax to Peter Cooper and others by contract, dated November 1st, 1855, (and which contract was subsequently assigned by said Cooper and others to said party of the first part,) and *Amounts.* pay therefor the respective proportions hereinafter assigned to each, of the sum of *Fifty Thousand Dollars*, and a like *pro rata* of the sum of *Six Thousand Dollars*, to said party of the first part, for their net outlay and expenses in improving and perfecting said invention, it being hereby mutually agreed, that no party hereto shall be liable for the sums, or any part thereof, herein apportioned to any other party, nor for any other than its own percentage of said liabilities.

ART. II. Sec. 1. That the proportions of sums aforesaid, the parties hereto, hereby covenant and agree, shall be borne and paid by each, as follows, viz:—

Proportions. The party of the *first* part forty-five per cent.;

The party of the *second* part thirteen per cent.;

The party of the *third* part ten per cent.;

The party of the *fourth* part fifteen per cent.;

The party of the *fifth* part twelve per cent.; and

The party of the *sixth* part five per cent.;

Sec. 2. And the payments therefor shall be made in the proportions aforesaid, as follows, to wit:—There shall be paid in cash down;

(16,000) Sixteen Thousand Dollars.

(5,000) Five Thousand Dollars on the first day of February, 1858;

(10,000) Ten Thousand Dollars on the first day of August, 1858;

(5,000) Five Thousand Dollars on the first day of February, 1859;

(10,000) Ten Thousand Dollars on the first day of August, 1859; and

(10,000) Ten Thousand Dollars on the first day of February, 1860.

Payments.

$56,000

ART. III. Sec. 1. The parties hereto hereby mutually covenant and agree with each other that each party shall own the patent rights as aforesaid, *exclusively*, in the territory hereinafter assigned and allotted to each, except for patent rights for lines as hereinafter specified, that is to say:

Ownership of Patents.

Sec. 2. To said party of the *first* part, all of Newfoundland, Nova Scotia, New Brunswick, the New England States, Long Island, Staten Island, the States of New Jersey, Delaware, North Carolina, South Carolina, Georgia and Florida; also, the portion of New York north of the latitude of Troy and east of the Champlain Canal, including the towns on said Canal; also, the rights for lines along the general routes of the "New York and Harlem" and the "Western" Railroads from New York city to Troy; also, the rights for northern, eastern and southern lines which enter the cities of Troy, Albany and New York; also, the rights for lines from New York *via* Philadelphia and Baltimore to Washington; also, the portion of Maryland south-east of the line from Philadelphia *via* Baltimore to Washington; also, that part of the District of Columbia and of the State of Virginia south of the latitude of Washington; also, the portion of Alabama south of the latitude of Centreville, and also the rights for lines thence to New Orleans, but not the right to receive or transmit business to or from New Orleans on the one hand, and Philadelphia or points north of the latitude thereof on the other, nor to open offices for public business in the States of Mississippi or Louisiana, except at New Orleans.

American Telegraph Co.'s Territory, &c.

Sec. 3. To the party of the *second* part, all of New York west of the meridian of Buffalo and north of the latitude thereof, and all of New York east of said meridian and west of Lake Champlain and of the Champlain Canal, and west from, and including the cities of New York, Albany and Troy, and the routes of all the present lines of said party connecting said cities, with the exclusive right to the business between said cities; and the business of Albany and Troy for points south of New York, to be there given over to the party of the *first* part; and also, the rights to the patents on the present lines on the New York and Erie railroad, whenever said party of the *second* part shall purchase said lines or obtain the permanent control thereof, or build a line on said route; but in case any business shall be sent *via* Dunkirk, which should be sent *via* Buffalo, ac-

N.Y., Alb. & Buf. E. M. Co.'s Territory.

cording to the contract of February 15, 1856, with the party hereto of the *fourth* part, the same tariff shall be paid to them as if sent *via* Buffalo.

Sec. 4. To the party of the *third* part, all of Pennsylvania west of the meridian of Philadelphia and east of the meridian of Pittsburgh, except for lines from New York through Philadelphia to Baltimore; the portion of Maryland northwest of the line from Philadelphia *via* Baltimore to Washington; and the portion of Virginia north of the latitude of Washington, with the rights for a line across the western part of Pennsylvania, connecting Wheeling and Baltimore.

Sec. 5. To the party of the *fourth* part, all of the States of Ohio, Indiana and Michigan; the portion of New York south of the latitude of Buffalo and west of the meridian thereof; all of Pennsylvania west of the meridian of Pittsburgh, except for a line connecting Wheeling and Baltimore; the rights for lines in Illinois, on the following routes, viz:—on the Michigan Central railroad; on the Michigan Southern and Northern Indiana railroad; on the Pittsburgh, Fort Wayne and Chicago railroad; on the Railroad from Chicago to Milwaukee; on the route from Beloit and Freeport to Savannah on the Mississippi river, *via* the Racine and Mississippi railroad; on the Terre Haute, Alton and St. Louis railroad, and on the Ohio and Mississippi railroad; also all of Wisconsin, except the portion hereinafter assigned to the party of the *sixth* part; the rights for a line in the territory of Minnesota on so much of the route of the Chicago, Fon du Lac and St. Paul railroad as extends into the territory of Minnesota; the portion of Missouri south of the Missouri river; and also, the rights for their present lines to Louisville, Frankfort, Covington and Lexington, with the right to change said lines to routes substantially the same as the present, or on Railroads connecting the places last above named; and rights for their line or lines into Wheeling in the State of Virginia, excepting, however, the rights of the party of the *fifth* part for lines to Cincinnati, to Cairo and Mound City, as hereinafter provided.

Sec. 6. To the party of the *fifth* part, all of Kentucky, Tennessee, Arkansas, Mississippi and Louisiana, the portion of Alabama north of the latitude of Centerville; with the rights for their line to Cincinnati now under lease to the party of the *fourth* part, when the leases by which the latter party hold that line may be terminated, excepting, however, the rights of the party of the *fourth* part for their lines to Louisville, and the rights of the party of the *first* part for lines through Mississippi and Louisiana to New Orleans.

Sec. 7. To the party of the *sixth* part, all of the State of Iowa; all of Illinois, excepting the routes hereinbefore named, and the rights for lines which are reserved to the party of the *fourth* part; the rights for a line in Wisconsin on so much of the route of the Chicago, Fon du Lac and St. Paul Railroad, between Chicago and Janesville, as lies in Wisconsin; all of Minnesota, except the route hereinbefore named, and the rights for lines which are reserved to the party of the *fourth* part; all of the State of Missouri north of the Missouri river, with the right to cross said river below a point due west from St. Louis, and extend one or more lines therefrom to St. Louis, and open offices on said line or lines; and also with the right to cross the Mississippi river at and north of St. Louis, and to extend such lines to St. Louis.

ART. IV. Sec. 1. In all cases in this Agreement where a city or town shall *Dividing* be named to indicate a dividing line of territory between any two com-*line.* panies, parties hereto, each of the parties named shall have the right to extend its line or lines into any part of said city or town, and be entitled to the business thereof, which may be properly sent by such line; provided, however, this permission shall not authorize any party to establish here-after such line in competition with any then existing line of any other party hereto.

Sec. 2. And each of the parties hereto shall be entitled to the exclusive *Exclusive* enjoyment of all telegraph business within the territory in which the *rights.* patent right has been allotted to them respectively, in article *Third* of this agreement, subject only to the specific grants of rights for lines to parties *Exception.* therein named, and subject also to the provisions hereinafter made to prevent collision of interests by competition.

ART. V. Sec. 1. It is further mutually covenanted and agreed by and be-*Exclusive* tween the parties hereto, that each party shall be the exclusive owner of *owner on per-* the patent rights aforesaid, within the territory, and for the lines desig-*formance.* nated herein in article *Third*; and upon the performance of article *Second*, *Conveyances.* said party shall be entitled to proper conveyances of the same. And the party entitled to said exclusive rights of territory and for lines, shall at their own charge and risk protect and defend the same therein and *Defence of* thereon, at their option; and the patents in all other territory named in *Patent.* said contract with Peter Cooper and others, not hereinbefore set apart *Property in* and allotted to any party hereto, shall be owned in the proportions afore-*common.* said, and *in common*.

Sec. 2. A majority in interest may sell the patent rights for lines in *Majority may* any such territory, held in common, under such restrictions as will protect *sell rights &c.* the interests of the parties hereto in the territories respectively allotted to them; and the proceeds of any such sale or sales, or of any recovery for *Division* the use or violation of the patent therein, shall belong to the parties *of proceeds.* hereto, in the proportion which shall be paid by each therefor, as herein-before provided. But no sales shall be made of such rights without notice to all the parties hereto of the time and place of meeting to act upon that subject, and parties hereto shall have the privilege of purchase at the same *Notice of* price in preference to any other party. *Sales &c.*

ART. VI. Sec. 1. The parties hereto severally and collectively hereby cov-*Exclusive* enant and agree to enter, and they do by these presents enter, into an *connection.* *exclusive connection* with each other for all *telegraph* business which may hereafter pass over a portion of the lines of either, destined for points on or beyond those of the others, and which may be reached by means of them, excepting so much business as the party of the *first* part may be *Exceptions.* legally liable to give to the New England Union Telegraph Company at Boston; and excepting also so much business as the party of the *second* part may be legally liable to give to the New York and Washington

Printing Telegraph Company, under a contract between said party of the *second* part and the New York State Printing Telegraph Company, bearing date February 15th, 1856.

Exclusive enjoyment.

Sec. 2. And each of the parties hereto shall be entitled to the *exclusive enjoyment* of all Telegraph business within the territory in which the Hughes patent rights have been allotted to them, and upon such lines as specific grants of said rights have herein been made respectively to

Exceptions extended.

any of the parties hereto; *subject only* to the other provisions of this Agreement, if any of said provisions shall be found to conflict with the assignment or allotment or rights of territory, or grant of rights for lines, as hereinbefore described, that is to say:

Div. of business.

Am. Tel. Co.

ART. VII. Sec. 1. The business between New York and points northerly from Troy, east of or upon the Champlain Canal, or in Canada, east of the meridian of Belleville, or between Albany and Troy and all places east of or upon said Canal or in Canada, east of the meridian of Belleville, or in the New England States, or easterly therefrom, shall belong to the party herein of the *first* part.

N.Y., A. & B. Tel. Co.

Sec. 2. The business between the cities of New York, Albany and Troy, or between either of those cities, and all places in Canada, west of the meridian of Belleville, shall belong to the party herein of the *second* part.

Sec. 3. The business between Philadelphia, or points easterly and northerly therefrom, and New Orleans, or any point south of a dividing line from the city of New York to Quincy in the State of Illinois, agreed upon between the parties hereto of the *third* and *second* parts, and not in the territory allotted to the party of the *first* part shall be given to said party

At. & Ohio Tel. Com.

of the *third* part, at New York, so long as said party of the *first* part does not control a line from New York to Philadelphia. But when said party of the *first* part shall control a line from New York to Philadelphia, the said party of the *third* part shall receive the aforesaid business at Philadelphia, or deliver it to said party of the *first* part at Philadelphia, and shall not receive business in New York, nor send to New York except over the lines of said party of the *first* part; and if said party of the *third* part shall acquire the control of the existing line, or build a line between Washington, Baltimore and Wheeling, they shall have the exclusive right to the business between Washington and Baltimore on the one hand, and points in the territory allotted to the party herein or the *fourth* part, west of the States of New York or Pennsylvania, or in that allotted to the

Am. Tel. Co.

parties herein of the *fifth* and *sixth* parts, on the other hand, but they shall not receive New Orleans business at either of those cities after the party of the *first* part shall become the owners of or work a line to New Orleans.

Am. Tel. Co.

Sec. 4. The business to and from between New Orleans and Baltimore, and all places intermediate, in the territory allotted to the said party of the first part, and not elsewhere, and the local business between New York, Philadelphia, Baltimore and Washington, or between these points and all south of Washington and easterly from New Orleans, shall belong exclusively to such line as said party of the *first* part may own, work or control on that route, which shall not take any New Orleans business, except to and from points south of Philadelphia.

Sec. 5. The business of the party of the *second* part, and of the party of the *third* part, destined west or south, is to pass over the lines of the party of the *fourth* part, according to a geographical division indicated between said party of the *second* part and said party of the *third* part. *West. U. Tel. Com.*

Sec. 6. And all business on any portion of the lines of the parties of the *second, third, fourth* and *sixth* parts, destined for points on, or which may be reached by means of, the lines of the party of the *fifth* part, shall be given to them at Louisville, in the State of Kentucky. And the said party of the *fifth* part shall have the right to transmit business over the existing line to and from Cairo and Mound City, in the State of Illinois, and to purchase and maintain said line or build a new line to those points. *N.O. & Ohio Tel. Lessees.*

Sec. 7. All the business of Chicago and St. Louis, for New Orleans, and for all points in the territory of or which is to pass on the lines of the party of the *fifth* part, and all the business of St. Louis for Cleveland and southerly and easterly of a line from St. Louis to Cleveland; all the business of the territory of the party of the *sixth* part, or which may pass over their lines for New Orleans and for other points in the territory of the party of the *fifth* part, or which is to pass over their lines, to be given over at St. Louis or such other point as the party of the *fourth* part may direct, and the return business, to be given over at the same places; and all business of the state of Illinois taken at places therein, where the party of the *fourth* part has offices, for points in their territory and easterly thereof, except as hereinafter provided, shall belong to the party hereto of the *fourth* part. *West. U. Tel. Co.*

Sec. 8. All business between Chicago and St. Louis, shall belong to the party of the sixth part, and all business of St. Louis for points north and west of a line from St. Louis to Cleveland, and also for Terre Haute, but when the party of the *fourth* part shall have or work a line or lines from St. Louis to Terre Haute or Indianapolis, in Indiana, or Toledo in Ohio, then the latter shall have the St. Louis business for the points on said lines, and all points south of the line to Toledo, when the line to that place shall be completed; all the business of Alton, except for points in Illinois not reached by the lines of the party of the *sixth* part, but the latter is to furnish office room, operate the instruments and do the Telegraph business of the party of the *fourth* part, without charge, if required so to do. *Ill. & Miss. & Chic. & Miss. Tel. Co.*

Sec. 9. At all other points in Illinois where the parties of the *fourth* and sixth parts shall each have Telegraph offices, each shall be entitled to the business for points reached exclusively by their respective lines. *W.U. & Ill. and Miss. Cos.*

Sec. 10. All Texas business to be divided upon the basis provided herein relative to the New Orleans business. *Texas.*

ART. VIII. The Agreement, by and between the several Telegraph Companies, constituting the *six* several parties hereto, for the mutual exclusive interchange of business, as herein provided, binds each company to each other company, and each to all that may be affected by any failure *Desp. of business.*

of performance of the covenants and agreements herein contained: Wherefore the parties hereto, each for themselves, hereby further covenant and agree, with each and all the other parties, to transmit all business that may be delivered to them as herein agreed, with reasonable promptness, accuracy and dispatch, exercising all the diligence requisite to keep their lines in good, reliable, working condition. But in case a connecting line shall be down, the party having business to transmit, shall be at liberty during such disability, and it shall be their duty to send forward, if practicable, said business in some other way, without any violation of the provisions of this Agreement.

When lines down.

ART. IX. It is further hereby mutually covenanted and agreed by the parties hereto, that nothing in this Agreement shall supersede, modify or annul any part of any existing contract between any of the parties hereto, but no contract by any said parties with any one not a party to this agreement shall be binding upon any other party than the party making the same; nor shall either party hereto be entitled to raise its through *tariff* of charges to points reached over or by means of the lines of any other party hereto, without the consent of the party affected by such increase.

Con'ts binding only.

Tariff not to be raised.

ART. X. Sec. 1. And each party to this Agreement severally covenants and agrees to and with each other party hereto, not to build or in any manner encourage the building of new lines or the maintenance of old ones in opposition to or in competition with the lines of any party hereto; nor sell, lease, or in any way dispose of any line owned or controlled by such party to any person or company to be used or operated as a competing line to the lines of any party hereto, nor sell, lease or otherwise dispose of any telegraph patent or interest owned or controlled by such party to any person or company to use, or who shall propose to use, a telegraph line in competition with the lines of the parties hereto, or which shall divert any business from such line properly belonging thereto:—

Not to build comp. lines.

Nor sell rights therefor.

Sec. 2. And in any case any party hereto, shall sell, lease or otherwise dispose of any line, telegraph patent or interest to any person or company, the instrument of conveyance by which such sale, lease or transfer shall be affected [*sic*], shall contain a covenant binding the party taking the same, to each of the parties hereto, to perform and fulfil the conditions of this article, and said instrument shall also contain a clause, that a violation of such covenant shall render such sale, lease or other transfer of any line, telegraph patent, or interest, absolutely null and void. But nothing herein contained shall be construed to prevent any party hereto from extending, by such means as each may elect, the construction of new lines or the purchase or lease of old ones, within their respective limits, provided the same shall not affect prejudicially the interests of any other party hereto.

Covenant of protection.

ART. XI. It is hereby mutually covenanted and agreed by each and all the parties hereto, that patent rights for lines, from any point or points on the Mississippi river to the Pacific ocean, shall be and hereby are reserved as the common property of the parties hereto, out of the territory allotted to any of said parties respectively, but said rights are not to come

Pacific line reserved.

in conflict with the lines of said parties for the local business within their respective territories.

ART. XII. It is agreed that the parties of the *first* and *second* parts shall each have the right to establish as many offices in the City of New York as they may see fit, and to do city business. *Offices in New York.*

ART. XIII. Sec. 1. And it is hereby covenanted and agreed, that the Montreal Telegraph Company of Canada may be admitted to a participation in the provisions of this compact, on such terms and conditions as the parties hereto of the *first, second* and *fourth* parts shall agree upon, anything herein contained to the contrary notwithstanding; all the parties hereto having the same voice in the disposition of the common property as in other cases. *Montreal Tel. Co. to be admitted.*

Sec. 2. And any three of the parties hereto may hereafter agree to connect exclusively with any other existing line or lines, on such terms as they see fit, provided such agreement shall in no way be prejudicial to the interests of any one or more of the parties hereto; nor in violation of any of the provisions of this Agreement. But no agreement, in this article mentioned, shall be finally concluded and become binding, until fully thirty days after the same shall have been submitted to each of the other parties, to give them an opportunity to state their objections, if any they have, to such agreement. *Other connections how formed.* *Notice.*

ART. XIV. Sec. 1. It is further mutually covenanted and agreed, by each and all of the parties hereto, that, in case either of said parties shall desire to increase the through tariffs or charges and cannot agree with the other parties affected by such increase; or in case any two parties hereto shall disagree as to the amount of tariffs, for business passing over the lines of both, or the share of such tariff to be paid to each; or in case of any dispute between any two parties hereto, growing out of this Agreement, the same shall be referred to one person or more disinterested person or persons, to be mutually chosen by said disagreeing parties:—And upon such selection the person or persons so chosen shall, on request of either party notify the other party of the time and place of the hearing in the premises, and if either after due notice shall neglect or refuse, then and there to attend, said referee or referees may, at discretion, proceed *ex-parte* the decision of whom or a major part of whom, shall be binding and conclusive upon the parties; except that such decision in respect to *tariffs* shall not be binding for a longer period than two years:—after the expiration of that period and after three months notice, that question may be again revised by the proceedings herein provided. *Modes of settling controversies.* *Referees how chosen.* *Power.* *Effect.* *Exception.*

Sec. 2. But, if the parties in controversy cannot agree to choose a tribunal for the settlement of the controversies aforesaid, the subject of their disagreement may be referred to three disinterested persons, to be selected in the manner following, to wit: The President or other officer legally acting as such, of each of the companies, parties hereto, not interested in the controversy, shall each nominate two disinterested persons, and notify the disputing parties thereof, who shall each choose one from the persons so nominated, and the two so chosen as aforesaid, within thirty days after *If parties cannot agree.* *Proceedings.*

notice of said nomination, the other party may choose both as aforesaid, and the two so chosen shall choose the third:

Proviso.

Sec. 3. Provided, however, that no party shall be compelled to refer any question or dispute as above provided, until at least three of the Presidents or the Officers legally acting as such, of the companies, parties hereto, and not parties to the dispute, shall certify, in writing, that in their opinion, such question or dispute *ought*, if not settled between the parties themselves, *to be referred* to one or more disinterested persons, as hereinbefore provided.

Consequences of refusal.

Expulsion.

Sec. 4. And if, after the above proceedings shall be had, any party hereto, shall *then* neglect or refuse to enter into a reference, in one of the modes aforesaid, or, entering into the same, shall neglect or refuse to attend a hearing before the tribunal thus selected, or so attending, shall neglect or refuse to comply with, abide by, or perform the decision or award of said tribunal, then the party, so neglecting or refusing, may be expelled from all participation in the provisions of this compact, whereby said party, so expelled, shall be deprived and debarred of the enjoyment of any and all of the rights, privileges and benefits, resulting therefrom.

How effected.

Notice.

Effect.

Not to effect [sic] other parties.

Sec. 5. And, said expulsion shall be had in the manner following, to wit: All the parties hereto shall be notified, in writing, by the aggrieved party, of the proceedings had to settle the matter in dispute, and of the neglect or refusal of the party to comply with the provisions aforesaid:—*whereupon*, the parties hereto, not parties to the controversy, shall without delay, convene their respective boards of directors, or boards of control, who shall give reasonable notice to the party complained of, to show cause why such party should not be expelled from this association, and in case the party complained of shall neglect or refuse to appear before any of said boards, or fail to show sufficient cause, then such board shall proceed at once to act upon said question of expulsion; and if it shall be found that all of said parties, by a majority vote of their respective boards shall decide *in favor* of expulsion, the same shall be so certified to the disputing parties, and thenceforth said expelled party shall be deprived and debarred of all the rights, privileges and benefits of this Agreement: But such expulsion shall in no way affect, impair or discharge the rights or obligations, the duties or liabilities of the remaining parties thereto, but the same shall continue in full force and be as effectual and binding upon each and all of them, as if originally made by them only.

Reversionary interests. How disposed of.

Sec. 6. All reversion of the rights and privileges of the expelled party consequent upon such expulsion, shall belong to and become the property of the remaining parties in common, in the proportions as herein before provided and agreed, and may be disposed of in the same manner as herein provided, for the disposition of other common property.

Duration of this agreem't.

ART. XV. Sec. 1. It is finally hereby covenanted and agreed that this Agreement shall exist and continue in force for the term of *Thirty* years, and thereafter until twelve months notice shall have been given of the intention of any one of said parties to withdraw therefrom.

Sec. 2. And this agreement shall, in each and every covenant and agreement herein contained, as effectually bind the *successors* and *assigns* of each and all the parties hereto, as if those words had been particularly recited therein.

Successors and assigns.

ART. XVI. Sec. 1. It is recommended, as a matter of expediency rather than of contract, that a meeting annually—and as much oftener as any exigency may require—be held of the parties hereto, at such place as shall be designated at the prior meeting, to *consult* and *advise* upon all matters of interest to the parties to this compact, at which meetings delegates may be sent by the parties hereto, with instructions to present any matters for deliberation, or any subject for consideration; but there shall be no change of this Agreement either by addition, subtraction or revision, without the concurrence of *all* the parties hereto.

Meetings for advise [sic].

Sec. 2. The first annual meeting, as above recommended, shall be held in the city of New York, on the third Wednesday of October, 1858.

In witness Whereof, the parties hereto, by their respective and duly authorized officers or representatives, have subscribed their names to six several agreements, each a counterpart of this one, and affixed the seal of their respective Companies thereto, this tenth day of August, in the year of our Lord one thousand eight hundred and fifty-seven.

Signed and Sealed

in the presence of   [No name given in printed source]

AGREEMENT RELATING TO NEW ORLEANS BUSINESS, &C.

ARTICLES OF AGREEMENT made and entered into this 10th day of August, 1857, between the New Orleans and Ohio Telegraph Lessees of the first part, The Western Union Telegraph Company of the second part, and the Illinois and Mississippi Telegraph Company, and Chicago and Mississippi Telegraph Company of the third part; Witnesseth:

The party of the first part for and in consideration of the agreements herein contained, agrees to transmit over their lines between New Orleans and Louisville, all messages from or to New Orleans coming from or destined to any point on the lines of the party of the third part; excepting, all places situated upon the Mississippi River, and excepting also Chicago, where the party of the third part is not to take New Orleans business, for a tariff of one dollar and twenty-five cents on a message of ten words, excluding signature and address, and eight cents for every additional word.

The party of the second part, for and in consideration of the agreements herein contained, agrees to transmit over their lines between St. Louis and Louisville, or such other point of intersection on their lines at which such messages shall be exchanged, all messages from or to New Orleans, coming from or destined to any point on the lines of the party of the third part, excepting the places situated on the Mississippi River, at a tariff of thirty-five cents on a message of ten words, excluding signature and address, and three cents for every additional word.

It is also, for the considerations aforesaid, mutually agreed by and between the parties of the second and third parts, that the messages above mentioned, shall be registered at St. Louis, or other place of intersection, where the same shall be exchanged at the ordinary and usual tariffs to New Orleans, and at the end of each month, the party of the second part shall allow and account for to the party of the third part for the amount which the ordinary and usual tariff on the messages above specified, shall exceed the tariff above agreed upon.

It is further agreed by and between all the parties hereto, that the tariff on New Orleans business, as above specified, shall continue for two years from the first day of September next.

It is further agreed by and between all the parties hereto, that until the party of the first part shall build a line from the South to Cairo in Illinois, or obtain the control of the existing line from Cairo southward, known as the Montgomery Line, the party of the third part, shall have the right to take business at Cairo for New Orleans and other intermediate points South of Cairo, at such tariffs as may be deemed expedient to compete with the line referred to as the Montgomery Line, and the loss by any tariff below the ordinary rates to be equally divided between the parties hereto, and in case the parties hereto cannot agree as to the amount of such tariff, the same shall be referred to a disinterested party for adjustment, and whenever the party of the first part shall build and work a line from the South into Cairo, or obtain the control of, and work the existing line above mentioned, then this clause of this agreement is to cease, and the party of the first part is to be entitled to all the local business of Cairo for places south of the State of Missouri and west of the Mississippi River.

In witness Whereof, the parties hereto, by their respective and duly authorized officers, or representatives, have subscribed their names and affixed the seal of their respective companies hereto, this tenth day of August, 1857.

HIRAM SIBLEY, President of the
W. U. Tel. Co.
ISAAC R. ELWOOD, Secretary of the
W. U. Tel. Co.
N. GREEN, President
N. O. & O. Tel. Lessees.
GEO. L. DOUGLASS, Treasurer
N. O. & O. Tel. Lessees.
Illinois and Mississippi Telegraph Company, and
Chicago and Mississippi Telegraph Company, by
J. D. CATON, President.
THOMAS BASSNETT, Secretary
Ill. & Miss., and Chicago & Miss. Tel. Companies.

SUPPLEMENTAL AGREEMENT

THIS AGREEMENT between the Western Union Telegraph Company of the first part, and Illinois and Mississippi Telegraph Company, and the Chicago and Mississippi Telegraph Company, parties of the second part, which is supplemental to and in explanation of an agreement or covenant entered into in six parts between certain Telegraph Companies, of which, the said Western Union Telegraph Company is the party of the fourth part, and the said Illinois and Mississippi Telegraph Company, and the Chicago and Mississippi Telegraph Company are the parties of the sixth part, and which bears date the tenth day of August, 1857; Witnesseth:

That the seventh section of the seventh article of said agreement, shall not be so construed as to authorize the said party of the first part hereto, to require the said parties of the second part hereto, or either of them, to give over the business in the said section mentioned, at any other point than St. Louis, except at some point or points on any line owned or controlled by the party of the first part, from St. Louis in Missouri to Vincennes in Indiana, where the line or lines of the party of the second part may cross the said line from St. Louis to Vincennes.

In Witness Whereof, the parties hereto, by their respective and duly authorized officers or representatives, have subscribed their names, and affixed the seal of their respective Companies hereto, this twentieth day of August, 1857.

HIRAM SIBLEY, President of the
W. U. Tel. Co.

ISAAC R. ELWOOD, Secretary of the
W. U. Tel. Co.

Illinois and Mississippi Telegraph Company, and
Chicago and Mississippi Telegraph Company, by
J. D. CATON, President.

THOMAS BASSNETT, Secretary
Ill. & Miss., and Chicago & Miss. Tel. Companies.

(Source: O'Rielly Collection, Telegraph Pamphlets.)

APPENDIX 15

"AN ACT TO FACILITATE COMMUNICATION BETWEEN THE ATLANTIC AND PACIFIC STATES BY ELECTRIC TELEGRAPH," PASSED BY THE SENATE AND HOUSE OF REPRESENTATIVES OF THE UNITED STATES AND APPROVED BY THE PRESIDENT, JUNE 16, 1860.

Be it enacted by the Senate and House of Representatives of the United States of America in Congress assembled, That the Secretary of the Treasury, under the direction of the President of the United States, is hereby authorized and directed to advertise for sealed proposals, to be received for sixty days after the passage of this act, (and the fulfilment of which shall be guaranteed by responsible parties, as in the case of bids for mail contracts,) for the use by the government of a line or lines of magnetic telegraph, to be constructed within two years from the thirty-first day of July, eighteen hundred and sixty, from some point or points on the west

Proposals to be advertised for.

line of the State of Missouri, by any route or routes which the said contractors may select, (connecting at such point or points by telegraph with the cities of Washington, New Orleans, New York, Charleston, Philadelphia, Boston, and other cities in the Atlantic, Southern, and Western States, to the city of San Francisco, in the State of California, for a period of ten years, and shall award the contract to the lowest responsible bidder or bidders, provided such proffer does not require a larger amount per year from the United States than forty thousand dollars; and permission is hereby granted to the said parties to whom said contract may be awarded, or a majority of them, and their assigns, to use until the end of said term, such unoccupied public lands of the United States as may be necessary for the right of way and for the purpose of establishing stations for repairs along said line, not exceeding at any station one-quarter section of land, such stations not to exceed one in fifteen miles on an average of the whole distance, unless said lands shall be required by the government of the United States for railroad or other purposes, and provided that no right to preempt any of said lands under the laws of the United States shall inure to said company, their agents or servants, or to any other person or persons whatsoever: *Provided,* That no such contract shall be made until the said line shall be in actual operation, and payments thereunder shall cease whenever the contractors fail to comply with their contract; that the government shall at all times be entitled to priority in the use of the line or lines, and shall have the privilege, when authorized by law, of connecting said line or lines by telegraph with any military posts of the United States, and to use the same for government purposes: *And provided, also,* That said line or lines, except such as may be constructed by the government to connect said line or lines with the military posts of the United States, shall be open to the use of all citizens of the United States during the term of said contract, on payment of the regular charges for transmission of dispatches: *And provided, also,* That such charges shall not exceed three dollars for a single dispatch of ten words, with the usual proportionate reductions upon dispatches of greater length, provided that nothing herein contained shall confer upon the said parties any exclusive right to construct a telegraph to the Pacific, or debar the government of the United States from granting from time to time, similar franchises and privileges to other parties.

Sec. 2. *And be it further enacted,* That the said contractors, or their assigns, shall have the right to construct and maintain, through any of the territories of the United States, a branch line, so as to connect their said line or lines with Oregon; and that they shall have the permanent right of way for said line or lines, under, or over, any unappropriated public lands and waters in the said territories, by any route or routes which the said contractors may select, with the free use during the said term of such lands as may be necessary for the purpose of establishing stations for repairs along said line or lines, not exceeding, at any station, one quarter-section of land, such stations not to exceed one in fifteen miles or an average of the whole distance; but should any of said quarter-sections be

Marginal notes:

Contract to be given to lowest responsible bidder, etc.

Right of way, etc.

Contract not to be made until line is in operation, etc.

Lines to be open to the use of all citizens, on payment, etc.

Rate of charges.

Right granted not to be exclusive.

Branch line to Oregon. Right of way, etc.

deemed essential by the government, or any company acting under its authority, for railroad purposes, the said contractors shall relinquish the occupancy of so much as may be necessary for the railroad, receiving an equal amount of land for like use in its stead.

Sec. 3. *And be it further enacted,* That if, in any year during the continuance of the said contract, the business done for the government, as hereinbefore mentioned, by such contractors or their assigns, shall, at the ordinary rate of charges for private messages, exceed the price contracted to be paid as aforesaid, the Secretary of the Treasury shall, upon said accounts being duly authenticated, certify the amount of such excess to Congress: *Provided,* That the use of the line be given, at any time, free of cost, to the Coast Survey, the Smithsonian Institution, and the National Observatory, for scientific purposes: *And provided further,* That messages received from any individual, company, or corporation, or from any telegraph lines connecting with this line at either of its termini, shall be impartially transmitted in the order of their reception, excepting that the dispatches of the government shall have priority: *And provided further,* That Congress shall at any time have the right to alter or amend this act.

If government business, at usual rates, exceeds contract price, excess to be certified to Congress.

Use to be free for certain scientific purposes.

Telegrams to be impartially transmitted.

Congress may alter, etc. this act.

Approved, June 16, 1860.

(Source: U.S. Statutes at Large, 36 Cong., 1 Sess., Chapter 137.)

{ BIBLIOGRAPHY }

No attempt has been made to enumerate all the materials examined and referred to in the text and notes of this volume. Inasmuch as newspapers, periodicals, pamphlets, legal cases, government reports, and documents have already been given in full in the reference notes, they generally are not repeated here. An exception is made in the case of certain important articles. A selective list of sources follows.

MANUSCRIPT SOURCES

John Dean Caton Papers, Library of Congress. 25 boxes of miscellaneous letters and printed materials chronologically arranged from 1826-1895. These papers are invaluable for an insight into the telegraph wars of the 1850's and 1860's from which Western Union emerged as the nation's first great industrial monopoly.

Cooper-Hewitt Papers, Library of Congress. This collection of 31 boxes, 230 portfolios, and 212 volumes of account books concerns itself largely with the business correspondence of Peter Cooper and his son-in-law, Abram S. Hewitt from 1840-1900. It contains little of value on the history of the telegraph.

Ezra Cornell Papers, Cornell University Library. A dozen boxes of unorganized manuscript material dating from about 1844-1860. While the collection contains much helpful material on the early telegraph, its value has been decreased by numerous deletions made throughout.

J. S. H. Fogg Autograph Collection, Maine Historical Society Library. This collection contains a few miscellaneous letters dealing with the early years of the telegraph in New England.

Benjamin Brown French Papers, Library of Congress. 7 volumes of manuscript material ranging from 1826-1885. Scattered references are made to the telegraph, but the collection's chief value is the insight it provides into Washington society between 1830-1870.

John Horn, Old Time Telegraph History (Scrapbook), Cornell University Library. 7 volumes of portraits, autographs, letters, circulars, and newspaper clippings dealing with the early days of the telegraph.

Amos Kendall Papers, Library of Congress. 2 boxes of miscellaneous manuscripts ranging from 1835-1868. Only a small amount of material on his telegraph activities as agent for Morse.

Samuel F. B. Morse Papers, Library of Congress. This is a large and notable collection of manuscripts numbering some 60 volumes chronologically arranged from 1793-1877. Deals with the inception of the telegraph (1832-1850), and the innumerable patent controversies arising therefrom.

Henry O'Rielly Papers, New York Historical Society Library. This is the most important manuscript collection on the telegraph in existence.

Trained as a newspaperman, O'Rielly set out to make a documentary history of the telegraph "that the truth and the whole truth may be known . . . concerning the Origin and Progress of the American Telegraph System."* The collection comprises 60 volumes of letters and 40 volumes of pamphlets including such valuable material as Articles of Association, Annual Reports, Legal Cases, Newspaper Clippings, etc., for the period 1845-1870. There is also some O'Rielly manuscript material in both the Library of Congress and in the Library of the Rochester Historical Society, but these collections contribute little that is new after an examination of the material in the New York Historical Society Library.

H. R. and S. L. Selden Papers. A small collection of letters (1847-1849) in the possession of the family of Leonard Bacon of Rochester, New York.

Francis Ormond Jonathan Smith Papers, Maine Historical Society Library. This collection comprises 26 volumes of manuscripts in addition to a dozen bound volumes of telegraph pamphlets including such material as Articles of Association, Minutes of the Meetings, and Annual Reports of the New York & Boston Telegraph Company and other early telegraph companies with which Smith was associated. Especially good for the period 1840-1856. There is a small collection of Smith Papers in the New York Public Library; it consists largely of correspondence between Eliphalet Case and Smith on the building of telegraph lines in the Ohio Valley.

Alvah Strong Papers. A manuscript autobiography of Alvah Strong dated October 1881. Contains some interesting comments on the introduction of the magnetic telegraph. This autobiography along with a few other papers are in the possession of Alvah Griffin Strong of Rochester, New York.

D. T. Tillotson Scrapbook. Contains newspaper and magazine clippings pertaining to the early telegraph (1845-1860). Cornell University Library.

Alfred Vail Papers, Smithsonian Institution, Washington, D.C. This collection comprises 37 volumes of manuscripts in addition to a quantity of unbound material. Valuable chiefly for the early telegraph (1837-1847).

Jeptha H. Wade Papers, in possession of the Wade family, Cleveland, Ohio. A large collection of Wade manuscripts is in existence but not available to scholars. Limited use of biographical material was made through the courtesy of George Garretson Wade.

Charles V. Walker Scrapbook. Contains newspaper and magazine clippings, letters, etc., concerning the electric telegraph, chiefly relevant to the Southeastern Railroad Company, England, 1847-1876. New York Public Library.

* From O'Rielly's letter to the New York Historical Society upon presentation of his collection.

BOOKS AND ARTICLES

The American Annual Cyclopaedia and Register of Important Events of the Year. New York: D. Appleton, 1861-1874. 14 vols.

Babcock, F. Lawrence, *Spanning the Atlantic*. New York: A. Knopf, 1931.

Bancroft, Hubert Hower. *Chronicles of the Builders of the Commonwealth*. San Francisco: The History Company, 1891-1892. 7 vols.

Bates, Alice L. "The History of the Telegraph in California," *Southern California Historical Society Publication*, IX, No. 3 (1914), 181-187.

Bates, David Homer. *Lincoln in the Telegraph Office: Recollections of the U. S. Military Telegraph Corps during the Civil* War. New York: Century, 1907.

Bemis, Samuel Flagg. *A Diplomatic History of the United States*. New York: Henry Holt, 1936.

Bleyer, Willard G. *Main Currents in the History of American Journalism*. New York: Houghton Mifflin, 1927.

Bonner, William T. *New York, The World's Metropolis, 1623-1624, 1923-1924*. New York: R. L. Polk, 1924.

Brewer, A. R. *Western Union Telegraph Company. A Retrospect*. New York: James Kempster, Printer, 1901.

Brooks, Sidney. *American Communications: the position and problems of telephones, telegraphs and radio both at home and abroad and the necessity for adoption of a broad national policy regarding them; a report based on investigations and study of these questions over a period of years*, mimeographed, Washington, D. C., 1934.

Bryan, George S. *Edison the Man and his Work*. London and New York: A. Knopf, 1926.

Carnegie, Andrew. *Autobiography of Andrew Carnegie*. Boston and New York: Houghton Mifflin, 1920.

Chabrand, M. Ernest. "La Télégraphie à Travers Les Âges," *Bulletin de la Société Dauphinoise d'Ethnologie et d'Anthropologie*, Grenoble, 1909.

Chamberlain, Joseph Edgar. *The Boston Transcript: A History of Its First Hundred Years*. New York: Houghton Mifflin, 1930.

Channing, Edward. *A History of the United States*. New York: Macmillan, 1905-1925. 6 vols.

The Chronicles of America Series. Allen Johnson, ed., New Haven: Yale University Press, 1918-1921. 50 vols.

Clews, Henry. *Fifty Years in Wall Street*. New York: Irving Publishing Co., 1908.

Collins, Perry McD. *Overland Explorations in Siberia, Northern Asia, and the Great Amoor River Country: incidental notices of Manchooria, Mongolia, Kamschatka, and Japan with map and plan of an overland telegraph around the world, via Behring's Strait and Asiatic Russia to Europe*. New York: D. Appleton, 1864.

Commons, John R., *et al. History of Labor in the United States*. New York: Macmillan, 1926. 2 vols.

Coon, Horace. *American Tel. & Tel., The Story of a Great Monopoly*. New York: Longmans, Green, 1939.

[Cornell, Alonzo B.]. *True and Firm. Biography of Ezra Cornell, Founder of the Cornell University.* New York: A. S. Barnes, 1884.

Currier, Festus C. *Reminiscences of Festus C. Currier.* Fitchburg, Mass.: Fitchburg Historical Society, 1900.

Danielian, Noobar R. *A. T. & T.; the Story of Industrial Conquest.* New York: Vanguard Press, 1939.

Davis, E. H. *History of the New York Times, 1851-1921.* New York: *New York Times,* 1921.

Dictionary of American Biography. New York: Chas. Scribner's Sons, 1928-1936. 20 vols.

Duane, William. "Letter Duane to Thomas Jefferson, July 8, 1807," Massachusetts Historical Society, *Proceedings,* Second Series, xx, Boston, 1907.

Dyer, Frank L. and Martin, Thomas C. *Edison: His Life and Inventions.* New York: Harper Brothers, 1929. 2 vols.

Encyclopaedia of the Social Sciences. E. R. A. Seligman, ed. New York: Macmillan, 1935. 15 vols.

The Encyclopaedia Britannica, 14th ed. New York: Encyclopaedia Britannica Inc., 1936. 24 vols.

Fahie, J. J. *History of Electric Telegraph to 1837,* [n.p.]. London, 1884.

Fite, Emerson D. *The Presidential Campaign of 1860.* New York: Macmillan, 1911.

———. *Social and Industrial Conditions in the North During the Civil War.* New York: Macmillan, 1910.

Flick, Alexander C., ed. *History of the State of New York.* New York: Columbia University Press, 1933-1937. 10 vols.

Flint, Charles L., *et al. Eighty Years Progress of the United States.* Hartford: L. Stebbins, 1868. 2 vols.

Foreman, Edward F., ed. *Centennial History of Rochester, New York.* (Rochester Historical Society, Publication Fund Series, Vols. x-xiii), Rochester, New York, 1931-1934. 4 vols.

Glover, G. G. and Cornell, W. B., eds. *The Development of American Industries, Their Economic Significance.* New York: Prentice-Hall, 1932.

Grant, E. B. *Western Union Telegraph Company: Its Past, Present and Future.* New York: Hotchkiss, Burnham & Co., 1883.

———. *Report on the Western Union Telegraph Company.* New York: Sun Job Printing, 1869.

Grant, U. S. *Personal Memoirs of U. S. Grant.* New York: Charles L. Webster, 1885. 2 vols.

Greeley, Horace, Leon Case, Edward Howland, *et al. The Great Industries of the United States: Being an Historical Summary of the Origin, Growth, and Perfection of the Chief Industrial Arts of this Country.* Hartford: J. B. Burr and Hyde, 1873.

Greeley, Horace. *Recollections of a Busy Life.* New York: J. B. Ford, 1868.

Green, E. "Canada's First Electric Telegraph," Ontario Historical Society, *Papers and Records,* xxiv, Toronto, 1927.

Greene, Laurence. *America Goes to Press.* New York: Bobbs-Merrill, 1936.

Hallock, William. *Life of Gerard Hallock*. New York: Oakley Mason, 1869.

Haney, Lewis Henry. *A Congressional History of Railroads in the United States 1840-1887*. University of Wisconsin Bulletin no. 342, *Economics and Political Science Series*, VI, no. 1.

Harlow, Alvin F. *Old Wires and New Waves, The History of the Telegraph, Telephone and Wireless*. New York: D. Appleton-Century, 1936.

Harper's Cyclopedia of United States History. New York: Harpers, 1902. 10 vols.

Hayes, Carlton J. H. *A Political and Cultural History of Modern Europe*. New York: Macmillan, 1936. 2 vols.

Heaton, Herbert. *Economic History of Europe*. New York: Harpers, 1936.

Hendrick, Burton J. *Age of Big Business. A Chronicle of the Captains of Industry* (Vol. XXXIX in *Chronicles of America Series*). New Haven: Yale University Press, 1919.

Herring, J. M. and G. C. Gross, *Telecommunication. Economics and Regulation*. New York: McGraw-Hill, 1936.

Highton, Edward. *The Electric Telegraph: its History and Progress*. London: John Weale, 1852.

Hudson, Frederic. *Journalism in the United States from 1690 to 1872*. New York: Harpers, 1873.

Hungerford, Edward. *The Story of the Baltimore and Ohio Railroad, 1827-1927*. New York: G. P. Putnam's Sons, 1928.

———. *The Story of Public Utilities*. New York: G. P. Putnam's Sons, 1928.

Iles, George, *Leading American Inventors*. New York: Henry Holt, 1912.

Jones, Alexander. *Historical Sketch of the Electric Telegraph including its Rise and Progress in the United States*. New York: G. P. Putnam's Sons, 1852.

Josephson, Matthew. *The Robber Barons. The Great American Capitalists, 1861-1901*. New York: Harcourt Brace, 1934.

Kaempffert, Waldemar. *Modern Wonder Workers. A Popular History of American Invention*. New York: Chas. Scribner's Sons, 1924.

Kamm, S. R. "Thomas A. Scott and the Pennsylvania Railroad, 1850-1880" (examined in manuscript).

Kendall, Amos. *Autobiography*, edited by his son-in-law, Wm. Stickney. Boston: Lee & Shepard, 1872.

———. *Morse's Patent. Full Exposure of Dr. Chas. T. Jackson's Pretensions to the Invention of the American Electro-Magnetic Telegraph*. Washington: Jno T. Towers, 1852.

Kennan, George. *Tent Life in Siberia*. New York: G. P. Putnam's Sons, 1910.

Killikelly, Sarah. *The History of Pittsburgh, Its Rise and Progress*. Pittsburgh: B. C. & Gordon Montgomery Co., 1906.

Lamb's Biographical Dictionary of the United States. John H. Brown, ed. Boston: Federal Book Co., 1903. 7 vols.

Laut, Agnes C. *The Romance of the Rails*. New York: Robt. McBride, 1929. 2 vols.

Lee, Alfred McClung. *The Daily Newspaper in America*. New York: Macmillan, 1937.

Lee, James Melvin. *History of American Journalism*. New York: Houghton Mifflin, 1923.

Lefferts, Marshall. "The Electric Telegraph: its Influence and Geographical Distribution," American Geographical and Statistical Society, *Bulletin*, II, New York, 1857.

Macy, Jesse. *The Anti-Slavery Crusade* (Vol. XXVIII in *Chronicles of America Series*). New Haven: Yale University Press, 1919.

Memorial of Samuel Finley Breese Morse, including appropriate ceremonies of respect at the national capitol and elsewhere, published by order of the U.S. Cong., Government Printing Office, Washington, 1875.

Meyer, B. H., C. H. MacGill, *et al*, eds. *History of Transportation in the United States before 1860*. Carnegie Institution of Washington, Washington, 1917.

Moigno, François Napoléon. *Traite de Télégraphie Électrique*. Paris: A. Franck, 1852.

Moody, John. *Moody's Manual of Industrial and Miscellaneous Securities*. New York: Moody's Investor's Service, 1900, ff.

——. *Masters of Capital*. New Haven: Yale University Press, 1919.

——. *The Truth about the Trusts. A Description and Analysis of the American Trust Movement*. New York: Moody Pub. Co., 1904.

Morison, Samuel L. and Henry S. Commager. *The Growth of the American Republic*. New York: Oxford University Press, 1937. 2 vols.

Morse, Edward Lind, ed. *Samuel F. B. Morse, His Letters and Journals*. Boston: Houghton Mifflin, 1914. 2 vols.

——. "The District of Columbia's Part in the Early History of the Telegraph," Columbia Historical Society, *Records* III, Washington, 1900.

Mott, Edward Harold. *Between the Ocean and the Lakes; the Story of Erie*. New York: J. S. Collins, 1899.

Muzzey, D. S. *History of the United States*. Boston and New York: Ginn, 1933. 2 vols.

Myers, Gustavus. *History of the Great American Fortunes*. New York: The Modern Library, 1936.

McDonald, Phillip B. *A Saga of the Seas. The Story of Cyrus W. Field and the Laying of the First Atlantic Cable*. New York: Wilson-Erickson, 1937.

McMaster, John Bach. *History of the People of the United States*. New York: D. Appleton, 1883-1913. 8 vols.

The National Cyclopedia of American Biography. New York: James T. White, 1921. 28 vols. and current vols.

Nevins, Allan. *The Emergence of Modern America*. (Vol. VIII in *History of American Life Series*). New York: Macmillan, 1927.

——. *American Social History as Recorded by British Travelers*. New York: Henry Holt, 1931.

——. *The Evening Post. A Century of Journalism*. New York: Boni and Liveright, 1922.

Nevins, Allan. *Grover Cleveland. A Study in Courage.* New York: Dodd, Mead, 1932.

Oberholtzer, E. P. *A History of the United States Since the Civil War.* New York: Macmillan, 1917-1937. 5 vols.

O'Brien, Frank M. *The Story of the Sun.* New York: George H. Doran, 1918.

O'Brien, John Emmet. *Telegraphing in Battle; Reminiscences of the Civil War.* Scranton, Pa.: The Raeder Press, 1910.

Parker, Jane Marsh, "How the Men of Rochester Saved the Telegraph," Rochester Historical Society *Publication Fund Series,* v, Rochester, New York, 1926.

Parsons, Frank. *The Telegraph Monopoly.* (*Equity Series*). Philadelphia: C. F. Taylor, 1899.

Patten, J. Alexander. "Oliver H. Palmer," *Sketches of Men of Mark.* New York: New York & Hartford Pub. Co., 1871.

Plum, William R. *The Military Telegraph During the Civil War in the United States.* Chicago: Jansen, McClurg & Co., 1882. 2 vols.

Poor's Manual of Public Utilities. New York: Poor's Manual Co., 1912, 1917, 1937.

Pray, Isaac C. *Memoirs of James Gordon Bennett.* New York: Stringer & Townsend, 1855.

Prescott, George B. *Electricity and the Electric Telegraph,* 6th ed. New York: D. Appleton, 1885. 2 vols.

——. *History, Theory, and Practice of the Electric Telegraph.* Boston: Ticknor and Fields, 1860.

Prime, S. I. *The Life of Samuel F. B. Morse, Inventor of the Electro-Magnetic Recording Telegraph.* New York: D. Appleton, 1875.

Regan, John W. "The Inception of the Associated Press," Nova Scotia Historical Society, *Collections,* xix, 1918.

Reid, James D. *The Telegraph in America and Morse Memorial.* New York: Derby Bros., 1879. (This is edition referred to throughout unless specific reference is made to 1886 edition.)

——. *The Telegraph in America and Morse Memorial.* New York: John Polhemus, 1886.

Rhoads, C. S. *Telegraph and Telephony with Railroad Applications.* New York: Simmons-Boardman Pub. Co., 1924.

Richardson, James D. *A Compilation of the Messages and Papers of the Presidents, 1789-1897.* Washington: Government Printing Office, 1898. 10 vols.

Rochester Chamber of Commerce. *One Hundred Years. A Century of Commerce in Rochester, New York.* New York: Rochester, 1934.

Rohan, Jack. *Yankee Arms Maker. The Incredible Career of Samuel Colt.* New York: Harpers, 1935.

Rosewater, Victor. *History of Cooperative News-gathering in the United States.* New York: D. Appleton, 1930.

Sabine, Robert. *The History and Progress of the Electric Telegraph.* [n.p.], New York, 1869.

Seitz, Don C. *James Gordon Bennetts. Father and Son.* Indianapolis: Bobbs-Merrill, 1928.

Shaffner, Tal. P. *The Telegraph Manual; a Complete History and Description of the Semaphoric, Electric and Magnetic Telegraphs of Europe, Asia, Africa and America, Ancient and Modern.* New York: Pudney and Russell, 1859.

Sherman, W. T. *Memoirs of General William T. Sherman.* New York: D. Appleton, 1875. 2 vols.

Sibley, Hiram W. "Memories of Hiram Sibley," Rochester Historical Society *Publication Fund Series,* II, Rochester, New York, 1923.

Smith, Albert W. *Ezra Cornell, a Character Study.* Ithaca: W. A. Church, 1934.

Smith, Francis O. J. *The Secret Corresponding Vocabulary; Adapted for Use to Morse's Electro-magnetic Telegraph; and also in Conducting Written Correspondence Transmitted by the Mails or Otherwise.* Portland: Thurston, Ilsley & Co., 1845.

Sparks, E. E. *National Development.* (Vol. XXIII in the *American Nation Series*). New York: Harpers, 1907.

Swan, William Upham. "Early Visual Telegraphs in Massachusetts," in Bostonian Society *Proceedings,* Boston, 1933.

Taylor, William B. *An Historical Sketch of Henry's Contribution of the Electro-magnetic Telegraph; with an Account of the Origins and Development of Prof. Morse's Invention.* Washington: Government Printing Office, 1879.

Thompson, Holland. *The Age of Invention.* (Vol. XVIII in the *Chronicles of America Series*). New Haven: Yale University Press, 1921.

Thompson, Joseph P. *Memoir of David Hale.* [n.p.], New York, 1850.

Towers, Walter Kellogg, *Masters of Space: Morse and the Telegraph; Thompson and the Cable; Bell and the Telephone; Marconi and the Wireless Telegraph; Cortez and the Wireless Telephone.* New York: Harpers, 1917.

———, *From Beacon Fire to Radio. The Story of Long-Distance Communications.* New York: Harpers, 1924.

Turnbull, Lawrence. *The Electro-magnetic Telegraph with an historical account of its Rise, Progress and Present Condition.* Philadelphia: A. Hart, 1853.

Turner, Harry B. "Nantucket's Early Telegraph Service." Nantucket Historical Association, *Proceedings,* XXIII.

Vail, Alfred. *The American Electro-magnetic Telegraph: with the Reports of Congress, and a Description of All Telegraphs Known, Employing Electricity or Galvanism.* Philadelphia: Lea and Blanchard, 1845.

———. *Description of the American Electro-magnetic Telegraph now in operation between Washington and Baltimore.* Washington: J. & G. S. Gideon, 1847.

———, comp. *The Telegraph Register of the Electro-magnetic Telegraph Companies in the United States and Canada, using Prof. Morse's patent, containing the rates of charges for transmission of messages.* Washington: J. T. Towers, 1849.

Vail, J. Cummings, ed. *Early History of the Electro-magnetic Telegraph, from letters and journals of Alfred Vail,* arranged by his son, J. Cummings Vail. New York: Hine Bros., 1914.

Van Hise, Charles T. *Concentration and Control. A Solution of the Trust Problem in the United States.* New York: Macmillan, 1921.

Warren, Charles. *The Supreme Court in United States History.* Boston: Little, Brown, 1923. 3 vols.

Wells, David Ames. *The Relation of the Government to the Telegraph; or a Review of the two propositions now pending before Congress for changing the telegraphic service of the country.* [n.p.], New York, 1873.

Werner, Edgar A. *Civil List and Constitutional History of the Colony and State of New York.* Albany: Weed, Parsons & Co., 1884.

Western Union Telegraph Company. *Corporate History of the Western Union Company, History and organization of the company and of all the corporations which have been leased, consolidated, merged with or purchased by Western Union.* Excellent diagrammatic charts showing how the company grew to December 31, 1914. (Mimeograph copy in the Western Union library), 1915.

Weston, A. W. "Trial of Anthony Burns," Letter of Anne Warren Weston to family, Boston, May 30, 1854, in Mass. Historical Society *Proceedings,* Vol. XLIV, Boston, 1911.

White, Bouck. *The Book of Daniel Drew.* New York: Doubleday, Page, 1910.

White, Roy B. Address: "Railroad Telegraph Service," American Railway Association, Telegraph and Telephone Section, *Proceedings,* June 12-14, 1934.

Willets, Gilson, *et al. Workers of the Nation. An Encyclopedia of the Occupations of the American People and a Record of Business, Professional and Industrial Achievement at the Beginning of the Twentieth Century.* New York: P. F. Collier, 1903. 2 vols.

Wilson, William B. "The Early Telegraph," Lancaster County Historical Society *Historical Papers and Addresses,* 1, Lancaster, Pennsylvania, 1897.

———, *History of the Pennsylvania Railroad Company.* Philadelphia: Henry T. Coates, 1899. 2 vols.

INDEX

Abell, Arunah S., 218
Adams, Theodore, 357, 361, 402
Alaska: influence of telegraph on development of, 439
Albany Atlas, 71
Alden, Hiram O., 305, 310, 332, 336, 414
Allen, Sir Hugh, 253
Allen, J. L., 271n.
Allen, Oliver E., 345
Alling, William, 268n., 271n.
Allston, Washington, 6
Alta Telegraph Company, 347
Alvord, J. N., 259, 285
American Journal of Science, 9, 14
America (a Cunard steamship), 232
American Telegraph Company: background, 302-5; organization, 305; expansion along seaboard, 305-6; Atlantic cable project, 306; position in the industry (close of 1856), 307; friction with Magnetic Telegraph Co., 308-9; feared by rivals, 310-11; American Telegraph Convention, 311-12; Hughes patent controversy, 312-13; Six Party Contract, 313-17; further expansion along seaboard, 319-31; purchase of New York & Washington Printing Telegraph Co., 325; reorganization (Oct. 1859), 331, 331n.; purchase of branch lines in South, 331; absorption of Magnetic Telegraph Co., 331-32; absorption of New York & New England Union Telegraph Co., 332; dominant position along seaboard, 333; growing rivalry with Western Union, 334-35, 342; contest with New York Associated Press, 335-42; relation to transcontinental project, 351-52, 358-60; rent by Civil War, 373-75; southern lines reorganized as Southern or Confederate Telegraph Co., 374; Western Union pressure for consolidation, 400, 405; postwar position of the company in the industry, 407-8, 413-16; absorption of the Southwestern Telegraph Co. (Nov. 1865), 415; absorption of the Washington & New Orleans Telegraph Co., 415; continued rivalry with Western Union, 416, 423; consolidation with Western Union (June 1866), 424-25; *also* 287, 318, 384-85, 387, 418, 421, 427, 442
American Telegraph Confederation: or-
ganization, 260; weaknesses, 260-64, 285-88; *also* 293-94, 441
American Telegraph Convention: discussion, 259-60; organized on permanent basis as American Telegraph Confederation, 260
American Telegraph Magazine, 248
Ampère, André M., 4
Anderson, James, 235n.
Arago, François, 14
Arnold, A., 271n.
Arthur, Mr. (Illinois Central Railroad official), 403
Associated Press, 225
Atlantic cable: Shaffner's project, 299n., 321; Field's project, 299-301; Atlantic Telegraph Company organized, 306; failure of Field's first attempt, 319-20; Field's second attempt (1858), 323; North American Telegraph Association urged to support Field's project, 334-35; project halted by Civil War, 375, 383; rejuvenation of project, 414, 427; cable successfully laid (1866), 433-34; value to Western Union land lines, 434; *also* 307, 310, 312-13, 352, 429, 438
Atlantic, Lake & Mississippi Telegraph Company: original compact, 72; directors, 72n.; formal organization, 73; officers, 73; plan of development, 73-75; war against the Erie & Michigan, 87-89; meeting of the general council, 194; *also* 92, 98, 109, 110, 116, 135, 136, 151, 155, 158, 184, 199
Atlantic & Ohio Telegraph Company: opening, 98; capitalization, 98-99; Western Union attack on National Lines system, 285; sister company, Pittsburgh, Cincinnati & Louisville, leased by Western Union, 292-93; becomes satellite of Western Union following absorption of Pennsylvania Telegraph Co., 296; Six Party Contract, 313-17; leased to Western Union (April 1864), 397; *also* 84, 86n., 87, 88, 92, 100, 136, 137-38, 150, 155, 156, 162, 167, 199, 202, 246, 259, 261, 290, 329, 335
Atlantic Telegraph Company: organized to lay an Atlantic Cable, 306; *also* 321, 352
Auburn-Palmyra side line, 178
Audubon, John J., 45